BOOKS BY MAXWELL GEISMAR

Author

AMERICAN MODERNS

REBELS AND ANCESTORS

THE LAST OF THE PROVINCIALS

WRITERS IN CRISIS

Editor

THE RING LARDNER READER

JACK LONDON: SHORT STORIES

THE WALT WHITMAN READER

THE PORTABLE THOMAS WOLFE

THE RING LARDNER READER

The
RING LARDNER
Reader

Edited by *MAXWELL GEISMAR*

Charles Scribner's Sons   *New York*

818
L

COPYRIGHT © 1963 CHARLES SCRIBNER'S SONS

Copyright 1924, 1925, 1926, 1927 Charles Scribner's Sons; renewal copyright 1952, 1953, 1954, 1955 Ellis A. Lardner.
Copyright 1915, 1917, 1920, 1921, 1922 The Curtis Publishing Company; renewal copyright 1943, 1945, 1948, 1949, 1950 Ellis A. Lardner.
Copyright 1917 The Bobbs-Merrill Company; renewal copyright 1945 Ellis A. Lardner.
Copyright 1921, 1922, 1925, 1926, 1927, 1928 Ellis A. Lardner; renewal copyright 1949, 1950, 1953, 1954, 1955, 1956.
Copyright 1931 F-R Publishing Corp.; renewal copyright © 1959 Ellis A. Lardner.
Copyright 1923, 1924, 1926, 1927, 1928 International Magazines Company, Inc.; renewal copyright 1951, 1952, 1954, 1955, 1956 Ellis A. Lardner.
Copyright 1929 Harper's Bazaar; renewal copyright © 1957 Ellis A. Lardner.
Copyright 1922 Crowell Publishing Company; renewal copyright 1950 Ellis A. Lardner.
Copyright 1934 Ellis A. Lardner; renewal copyright © 1962 Ring Lardner, Jr.
Copyright 1925 Charles Scribner's Sons; renewal copyright 1953 Ellis A. Lardner.

THIS BOOK PUBLISHED SIMULTANEOUSLY IN THE UNITED STATES OF AMERICA AND IN CANADA—COPYRIGHT UNDER THE BERNE CONVENTION

ALL RIGHTS RESERVED. NO PART OF THIS BOOK MAY BE REPRODUCED IN ANY FORM WITHOUT THE PERMISSION OF CHARLES SCRIBNER'S SONS.

A-11.62 [H]

PRINTED IN THE UNITED STATES OF AMERICA

LIBRARY OF CONGRESS CATALOG CARD NUMBER 63-8675

Acknowledgment

To Harms, Inc. for two lines from "Night and Day" by Cole Porter. Copyright 1932 Harms, Inc. Reprinted by permission.

CONTENTS

Part Four: LITTLE TALES OF SUBURBIA

Part Five: THE POPULAR ARTS

Part Six: *NATIVE DADA*

INTRODUCTION
BY MAXWELL GEISMAR

Introduction

1

The present volume is a gathering-in of Ring Lardner's best work in the area of fiction and non-fiction; in prose, verse and drama; in mordant satire and hilarious comedy and brilliant nonsense. All of Lardner's famous stories are here (so the present editor believes), as well as many articles, essays, parodies and songs that are not so well known, and presented for an audience which knows Ring Lardner perhaps least well of all those celebrated talents of the nineteen twenties who are now familiar names in the capitals of the world.

To many of these readers Ring Lardner is still a popular sports writer of that period; at best a newspaper columnist or Broadway entertainer. To a smaller circle of intellectuals, Lardner is better known as one of the most savage and merciless satirists and social critics of his period who dissected Babbitt before Babbitt was born; who anticipated the despairing American critique of John Dos Passos's *U.S.A.* while Dos Passos was still a sophomore at Harvard; who created a new American language that made Hemingway's look like parlor conversation.

Well, both of these opposing views of Lardner are true in their way, and neither of them is quite true enough. Somewhere between them, this enigmatic artist and remarkable folk poet, Ring Lardner himself—this suffering, silent and dark spirit of the popular entertainment world—somewhere between these "theories" of his art, Lardner's spirit still hovers, ambiguous, ironic and sardonic. He had very little use for art as an abstraction; he must have secretly smiled at Scott Fitzgerald's youthful preachings to him. He wrote about the world he knew as truthfully and carefully as he could—and in his best things not a line can be changed.

But there are still some missing lines, too, and not even the solid body of personal information which Donald Elder's recent biography, *Ring Lardner,* presents to us, quite gives the answer as to the nature of Lardner's talent and his torment alike. He was born in

Niles, Michigan, as Ringgold Wilmer Lardner on March 5, 1885 —"of respectable colored parents," as Lardner once told a Southern gentleman. Actually the Lardners were eminently respectable, prosperous, cultivated middle-westerners of that earlier, old-fashioned, leisurely and graceful provincial culture whose true spokesman was the early Booth Tarkington. Ring was brought up with all these graces; these native good-manners; this code of decency, honor, loyalty within an affectionate and close family circle—and perhaps he never quite met this again in the later and very different American scene which he lived in and wrote about.

Until he was eleven he wore a brace for a deformed foot, which perhaps already had set him apart from the general. His mother, a charming creature with cultivated talents and cultural aspirations, also set her children apart from the town life, and even the public education of the period; though Ring's exuberant youthful spirit gravitated naturally to the first area, and avoided the second. He barely got through high school, while he already had a solid background of classical music and literature alike, and a pronounced talent for popular songs and satirical verse. He had the unique distinction, as he said, of entering Armour Institute in Chicago in January, and leaving in the spring—faster than any other student in the dean's memory. By 1902, the year of this debacle, the Lardner family fortune had collapsed, too, in the new epoch of land and mining speculation which was transforming our solid, older midwestern society.

Ring's earliest passions were baseball, music and the stage; and he already knew the friendly social life of the small-town bars, a haven for provincial rebels and outcasts. He went to work as a sports writer for the *South Bend Times* in 1905; he wrote for other newspapers in Chicago, St. Louis and Boston; he came back to the *Chicago Tribune* as a feature sports writer and then took over, in 1913, the daily column, "In the Wake of the News." Perhaps this dubious personal career (in his own mind), perhaps his family's disintegrating financial and social status, perhaps some yet deeper temperamental insecurity, contributed to the tone of the love letters to his future wife, the beautiful, charming, rich and college-educated Ellis Abbott of Goshen, Indiana. Lardner was in turn witty, affectionate, yearning in these letters; and curiously anxious, self-deprecatory and humble. Yet he was determined to marry this upper-class western girl, and to support her in the grand style to which she had been accustomed—the style perhaps of his own early youth, too, rather than of his present circumstances. It was he, again, rather than Ellis, who was determined to get to New York, for New York was "where the money was." It was his financial need, quite as much as his literary aspirations which impelled him to write the first Busher stories for *The Saturday Evening Post* in 1914.

2

You Know Me Al brought Lardner into the national consciousness. The ball-player Jack Keefe is still a remarkable figure of folk poetry—the figure who is the original matrix and source for all of Lardner's later portraits of the average American citizen, or Mr. USA.

The section I have used here is the Busher's first adventures in New York, and the whole point of this fabulous provincial is the tremendous Bush-League Ego which converts all outward experience —people as well as places—into his own ignorant, rigid and infantile fantasy of life: a "life" which is of course centered around his own needs and demands rather than concerned with any objective reality. This is the core of that American "individualism" which the later Lardner was to scourge with the relentless lash of his wit; but here it is viewed with more geniality, warmth and comedy simply because the Busher is not merely a four-flusher but a flop. New York itself— the "Enfabled Rock" of a Tom Wolfe's similar provincial pilgrimage —is simply another hick town to Jack Keefe where they charge him more for the same things. The Busher's universe is run by a kind of Hick God who has singled out Jack Keefe, rather than a useless sparrow, for His special care. In New York the Busher's stinginess is more evident and appalling, his ignorance more pronounced, his credibility and his prejudices more obvious. Since he has no idea of human relations—or of human beings outside of himself— he is perfectly capable of carrying on his double romances (by post cards) with only the regret that "I wish they was two of me" to take care of his two girls.

The girl he loses is worthless, obviously. The girl he wins is always worth two of the girl who has jilted him—which is about right. He has the gift of crushing repartee which renders his opponents speech-less; he always has a double—sometimes a triple—alibi for his own slight errors of judgment—his obvious boners. He is the small-town boy who makes good by the simple process of never admitting, never even recognizing, the large areas of life where he has made bad. But if a sublime ignorance, an immutable self-confidence, carry the Busher a long way, his "passion"—and that is to say, his passion for himself—eventually destroys him, as when he beans the ball-player who has stolen his girl (i.e., "gotten his goat") —with bases full. Keefe is a marvellous example of what some esoteric critics have called "primitive virtue," but which they never would recognize on a local baseball diamond. And the pages of *You Know Me Al* are filled with the glow of an earlier and rural American scene.

One almost hates to leave the Busher indeed, when Lardner, just like his aspiring provincial protagonist, must have had his own hopes and ambitions for the major leagues—the Big Town and the Dream of Success. If Jack Keefe is used in the present volume as a symbol, or a figurehead, of "Provincial Life," rather than of "Sports" or of the Lardnerian commentary on the other "Popular Arts," it is be-cause he transcends the narrow limits of baseball itself—just as Lardner's talent could make all these sports interesting to readers who might know little, and care less, about them. Wasn't the anonymous "Mr" of *Gullible's Travels,* in 1917, a partial extension of the Busher? He is the "Wise-Boob" from the sticks who is being taken for a ride by a social system whose primary aim was "mobility upwards"—which was converting all these ignorant or innocent farm boys (and small-town souls) into a "lower middle class"; which was elevating this social stratum, in turn, to a "middle class," and then—by the simple instrumentality of instant cash in the Teens and Twenties—into a new American and social "aristocracy." These were the omnipotent "Bourjoyces" of Sinclair Lewis's work; the American "booboisie" of Mencken's; the "high polloi" of Lardner's.

This bit of social history—or this seachange of the older American destiny whereby our provincial order—our mixed economy of farms, towns and cities—was transformed into a new American Empire, standardized, mechanized, conformist, urban and abstract—was im-plicit in Lardner's work as early as *Gullible's Travels* and *The Big Town* (1921). The "Mr. Gullible" of the second volume (for he is the same hero in effect, the same anonymous Mr. USA) is living on his deceased father-in-law's "quick returns"—his war profits. Unfortunately, however, this inheritance belongs to Gullible's wife and her sister Katie. These ambitious, grasping, vain and materialistic midwestern women never let Gullible forget where the real power (the money) is. Curiously enough, Lardner's pervasive and vitriolic scorn for the American woman as a type seems to stem from the fact that She—far more than his typical American man—was eager to accept all the lures and blandishments, the illusions and traps, of a society on the make. Or at least She had taken over enough of these new social values in the post-World-War-I period to make the American male miserable, when he is not odious.

Gullible, his wife and unmarried sister are out to "travel," to get "culture," to find "pleasure;" to establish themselves in what Lardner called the "cesspools of society." In the Big Town—Chicago, Miami, New York—the earlier Lardner hero, if he is that, goes along with all this "sophistication" as a reluctant, though sometimes a highly destructive spectator. Their gilded "vacations" are an inferno of social snobbery, boredom, and wasted money. There is no pleasure to be found in these "pleasure resorts," just as the idea of pleasure, or even comfort, is never visible in their home life; for what they are seeking so desperately is just what they are incapable of enjoying. Just so, the American landscape itself becomes a reflection of their inner aridity. "Speaking o' the scenery, it certainly was somethin' grand. First we'd pass a few pine trees with fuzz on 'em and then a couple o' acres o' yellow mud. Then they'd be more pine trees and more fuzz and then more yellow mud. And after a w'ile we'd come to some pine trees with fuzz on 'em and then, if we watched close, we'd see some yellow mud."

This is just as good as T. S. Eliot's magniloquent Waste Land, any day; and it is real, not lit'ry. The element of the Grand Dada was present in Lardner from the start (nor did he have to seek out Hemingway's exotic Spanish "Nada"), only here it is still funny, in this desolate native scene. But already the American husband of these volumes has found one steady source of solace, escape and oblivion: drinking. Just drinking; solitary drinking. There is no sexual pleasure ever hinted at in the lower middle class Lardnerian literary cosmos—I beg your pardon, the rising middle class!—just as there is no pleasure, period. When these American wives dissolve into tears (or hysterics) it is simply to get their own benighted, self-destructive way. The only defense of the Lardnerian husband is the wise-crack and the liquor bottle. The only cure for "true love," so this native American artist also suggested, was to allow the two lovers to get to know each, other—if they ever could. The only true human bond (as Henry James had also proclaimed, if more elegantly and voluminously) was the cash nexus. What really comes out, through all the elaborate, expensive southern vacation resorts in *Gullible's Travels* itself, is the high cost of torture. "After supper we said good-bye to the night clerk and twenty-two bucks."

But what beautiful sentences, with their lack of logic and their faithfulness to the human mind and tongue; what an original midwestern native language Lardner had already mastered here. There is Mr.'s fifty cent tip, "legal and tender." There is the young Floridian bathing queen: "one little girl, either fourteen or twenty-four." There are also the society acquaintances of these chronicles whose chief delight is to snub you or ignore you—but who, when you do get to know them, you wish you hadn't. There is the gay social life provided by these expensive hotel resorts. "We dance, but we don't never change partners." There is the notable sister-in-law of these tales who: "You couldn't look at her without a slight relapse. She had two complexions—A.M. and P.M." But of course Mr. USA hasn't much use for any in-laws. "You're bound to get tired of one person, no matter how much they sparkle." And his in-laws never sparkle much. Like Dreiser, Lardner used all the clichés of his culture, and all his culture's humorous clichés, but what he did with them was something altogether fresh.

At his best, the long-suffering Mr. Gullible develops an absolute frenzy to destroy, to obliterate the pillows o' society—or all the social climbing, social pretense, social snobbery which marked the American rising middle class in the big money profiteering and speculation of the 1920's. In the present volume, "Three Without, Doubled" is an absolutely savage and hilarious tale of a provincial lout amidst the "upper class" amenities. The society bridge club is called "Sans Souci." The hostess happens to own the building in which the hero pays too much rent; so that he takes every occasion to complain to his "landlady," who of course has nothing to do with such sordid matters. The other guests? Well, "my pardner was a strappin' big woman with a name somethin' like Rowley or Phillips." Who cares about names, or about personalities, in this fabulous new arena of our vaunted individualism, when the purpose of getting to "know" people is to be able to use them, and to rise above them—when it may not be convenient, or even wise socially, to know those people tomorrow whom you have just met today. In this story, Gullible is just about the world's worst guest. He has indeed almost a pathological fury to destroy not only the whole fashionable bridge-club society, but himself along with it. But his social companions, his upper class acquaintances, are the most terrible hosts in the world. At the conclusion, or the debacle of "Three Without, Doubled," Mr. USA goes home to his own inferior apartment quite triumphant. He has accomplished his own ruin. And: "The Missus was pleasant company, just like a bloodhound with the rabies."

3

Yes, I know that the "Categories," or Sub-titles for the different sections of this Lardner Reader are mainly for the sake of convenience in presenting the material itself. Some of these stories, articles, sketches and plays could be placed elsewhere. Some of them combine two or three of Lardner's dominant themes. But the section headings do have the merit of corresponding generally to Lardner's own career, and of describing the historical and social development of his period. Lardner could describe this period so accurately and so brilliantly—so purely in its own terms—just because he belonged so completely to it. Or at least part of him, the outward part, did, while he went through all the painful rituals and public ceremonies of the Twenties en route to becoming one of the most popular and highly paid "entertainers" of the period. The period was *all* entertainment, it seemed—and Lardner was leading that gay and fashionable upper class life, on wealthy, suburban Long Island, whose fundamental corruption of human values, whose triviality and emptiness, he had already seen through.

No wonder the young Scott Fitzgerald, who was just then climbing up the same chimerical ladder of popular "success," even though he possessed a broader intellectual horizon than Lardner (which he but imperfectly understood; while Lardner simply scorned it) , and had more serious literary values—no wonder Fitzgerald, drinking as heavily as Lardner, spending perhaps even more money for *his* Long Island estate which became a sort of hostelry for visiting guests and endless parties, may have appeared to the older man as a kind of precocious, enchanting child of the age whom Lardner admired, adored even—along with the fabulous Zelda—and yet could not take seriously.

What is curious, however, in the sequence of Lardner's career, is that despite all his aversion to the new-rich industrial-commercial-financial social scene of the Twenties, his stories of provincial life in the raw ("Haircut," "The Maysville Minstrel," "The Facts," "Anniversary") are hardly more flattering. Unlike a Sherwood Anderson, another small-town western writer who also distrusted what was happening to modern American life, Lardner had no sense of alternatives. He was a man caught between two worlds, who went along with "what was," rather like his own Mr. USA, complaining like crazy, but finding no recourse except in "liquid stimulus"—or perhaps for a while in that beautiful native language which at times seemed to be Lardner's only source of catharsis. Was Niles, Michigan, historically, like Sherwood Anderson's Winesburg, Ohio, or the early Sinclair Lewis's Gopher Prairie, Minnesota, the true capital of our older western agrarian culture? "There's only one place . . . New York City," says the Ella of *The Big Town*. "I've heard of it," says her sardonic husband—but he is going there, too; even though all these Lardnerian protagonists are already spending more money than they have, and their "great world" itself exists on the edge of bankruptcy.

They are buying new apartments, new cars, new furniture, new dresses, new parties, new vacations, in their desperate search for sensation and status. The Long Island hotel in "Lady Perkins" is one of Lardner's most brilliant evocations of this new American social scene, where "the men get up about eight o'clock and go down to New York to Business. They don't never go to work." And where: "Saturday nights everybody puts on their evening clothes like something was going to happen. But it don't"—while:

"Sunday mornings the husbands and bachelors gets up earlier than usual to go to their real business, which is golf. The women-folks are in full possession of the hotel till Sunday night supper and wives and husbands don't see one another all day long, but it don't seem as long as if they did. Most of them's approaching their golden-wedding jubilee and haven't nothing more to say to each other that you could call a novelty. The husband may make the remark, Sunday night, that he would of broke one hundred and twenty in the afternoon round if the caddy hadn't of handed him a spoon when he asked for a nut pick, and the wife'll probably reply that she's got to go in Town some day soon and see a chiropodist . . ."

In the same story there was another Lardner parody of a Broadway play and one of its typical songs—

> "But my most exclusive token
> Is a little hangnail broken
> Off the girl from Gussie's School for Manicures."

He was beginning to experiment more boldly in this vein for which he had always had a natural bent, and the volume called *First and Last* carried not only such classical pieces as "The Young Immigrunts" and "Symptoms of Being 35" (both of which had been written in the early Twenties) but other brilliant satires and sketches. In *What of It?* Hemingway's addiction to bullfighting was described in five pages of pure acid. "A Close-Up of Domba Splew" was a surrealist satire on literary fame and high-class poetry. The Lardnerian laughter was playing over the whole range of "make-believe" values in the great age of make-believe; and the upper ranges of "art" and thought in the Twenties were not to be excluded. What a great comic view Lardner took, at his best, of an epoch that was in itself a kind of deliberately artificial musical comedy—whose chief personages usually spoke, like the later characters in Sandy Wilson's *The Boy Friend,* to an imaginary audience rather than to each other. In a similar vein, in the sketch called " 'In Conference,' " Lardner showed the workings of big business. In all these areas the newly swollen American Ego was his main target; the "me-centered world" of all the big-shots who, ignorant, ambitious, avaricious, had become the "kings" of a brash, vulgar, boundless (so it seemed) and wholly commercial middle class empire.

Was there really any difference between Lardner's American boob, the Busher or Mr. Gullible, and these new Titans of Sports, Entertainment, Finance, not to mention the gambling and racketeering which flourished during the "Big Drought," or even, as Lardner believed, the high arts themselves? Any difference, that is, except that between failure and success on a purely materialistic level? In a series of classic tales written during this period—"Champion," "The Love Nest," "A Day with Conrad Green," "Mr. Frisbie,"— Lardner took them all off, while his own personal accent became increasingly sardonic, merciless and cold. If you want a picture of American womanhood, there are such tales as "I Can't Breathe" or "Zone of Quiet." If you want a picture of American children, there is "Old Folks' Christmas." If you want a picture of the most sacred of all American superstitions, a happy marriage which extends into lovable old age, there is "The Golden Honeymoon."

The ultimate paradise for all these typical Lardnerian figures was suburban life. They came from the sticks and the small western towns; they came to Chicago and New York to make their fortunes and get somewhere in "society;" to lead the dream-life of American success. What could be a better sign of their whole new status— financially insecure as it always was; a life above their means, always trembling on the edge of disaster, just as, indeed, the whole period finally collapsed into the abyss of the Depression—than the Connecticut or Long Island "mansion," the chauffeur, the governess, and the supporting cast of servants; and then the "big parties," as in Fitzgerald's *Gatsby,* which were simply intended to demonstrate that you could give big parties. Lardner made an ignominious inferno of this suburban life, too, in stories like "A Caddy's Diary" or "Liberty Hall" or "Ex Parte."

Most of these stories, written in the early or mid-twenties appeared in two famous volumes, *How to Write Short Stories* (1924) and *The Love Nest* (1926). But in the first of these books Lardner, as if reacting in some intensely personal way to the Big Ego of American success—and rather like Mark Twain who insisted on including himself in the "damned human race" which he, too, had scoured in a vain attempt to clean up its sins and frailties—Lardner also insisted on describing his own best work in curious terms of disparagement. "The Facts," for example, was a sample story of life in the Kentucky mountains—

"An English girl leaves her husband, an Omaha policeman, but neglects to obtain a divorce. She later meets the man she loves, a garbage inspector from Bordeaux, and goes with him 'without benefit of clergy.' This story was written on top of a Fifth Avenue bus, and some of the sheets blew away, which may account for the apparent scarcity of interesting situations."

"Some Like Them Cold," another hard-bitten tale of an ambitious young Broadway entertainer—not unlike the "Pal Joey" of the stage—was an example of a story written from a title—

"the title being a line from Tennyson's immortal 'Hot Cross Buns.' A country-bred youth, left a fortune, journeys to London 'to become a gentleman.' Adventures beset him, not the least of them being that he falls out of a toy balloon."

"The Golden Honeymoon" was "a story with sex appeal." "Champion" was an example of the mystery story. "The mystery is how it came to get printed." "My Roomy," one of Lardner's stories with the greatest psychological depth, where the "eccentric" becomes the perverse and the pathological, and the comic mood turns to cruelty and madness; this story, so Lardner said, took place in "a house party in a fashionable Third Avenue laundry." And: "The predicament of a hero who has posed as a famous elevator starter forms the background of this delightful tale of life in the Kiwanis Club." "A Frame-Up" was "a stirring romance of the Hundred Years' War, detailing the adventures in France and Castile of a pair of well-bred weasels. The story is an example of what can be done with a stub pen." "Harmony" was, according to the literary editor of the United Cigar Stores Premium Catalogue, "the love story, half earthly, half spiritual, of a beautiful snare drummer and a hospital interne; unique for its word pictures of the unpleasant after-effects of anaesthesia." "Horseshoes" was the kind of story "which the reader can take up at any point and lay down as soon as he feels like it. A trail of vengeance, ruthless and sinister, is uncovered to its hidden source by a flat-footed detective."

Well, this is great nonsense in itself, of course—and not altogether nonsense. But what writer except Lardner, and Lardner even more brutally than Twain, would direct this ridicule at his own best work? And that "flat-footed detective" had become a leading, a symbolic personage in Lardner's inner creative world. The second of these major collections of short stories, *The Love Nest*, omitted the "introductions" to his tales; but included a "preface" by Sarah E.

Spooldripper, who announced that "the Master is gone," and the next question was, who will succeed him. "Perhaps some writer still unborn. Perhaps one who will never be born. That is what I hope."

It almost appeared that this was what Ring Lardner hoped.

4

He was at the peak of his literary fame, both financial and intellectual. He was earning from $50,000 to $60,000 a year as a syndicated columnist, a short story writer who got away with murder in the slick magazines, a playwright on the edge of the Broadway hit which Lardner always yearned for, and, with the exception of *June Moon*, never achieved. He was the friend not only of Scott Fitzgerald and the glamorous Zelda; but of the Grantland Rices of F.P.A., Herbert Swope of the New York *World*, Paul Lannin the composer, Bert Williams, George Cohan, George Kaufman. He was an intimate of the Algonquin set; and, even more important, of the Broadway theatrical crowd.

The large house on East Shore Road, Great Neck, Long Island, had its own chauffeur, governess and other servants. The Lardner sons were in the best eastern preparatory schools and colleges. Ring had everything that the small-town boy from Niles, Michigan—with a great, a unique talent for entertainment—could have desired; what was wrong? He was a journalist meeting a deadline; his work had become all "copy" and no fun, so Scott Fitzgerald declared at least. He had resolved to speak "only a small portion of his mind," and "to withhold what was most deeply personal." "He felt vulnerable enough with self-revelation," so his recent biographer, Donald Elder, also tells us. But there were constant financial troubles, too. Lardner quit his syndicated column at last, in order to devote himself to "serious work" and the stage; he had to return to journalism shortly, on an even more strenuous schedule. He began to repeat the Busher stories less effectively; his mock "autobiography," *The Story of a Wonder Man,* was a tired, flat satire.

It is a horrible thing to be a professional "funny man," as Mark Twain declared; and Twain at least had freed himself from the daily ordeal of copy for copy's sake. Lardner, who always drank in order to sleep, now slept little and drank more. He was in the same trap of "Success" that Jack London had been in—as the highly paid fictioneer of the period just preceding Lardner—and he used the same opiates with the same sense of despair. By 1924, just when Lardner was publishing his best collections of short stories, and was being accepted at last as a serious literary figure, the trap had closed on him. At the peak of his success, he was beginning to disintegrate; and the rest, the last seven years of pain and torture, was as inevitable, as inexorable as a Greek tragedy, but with no *deus ex machina,* and no catharsis.

Like Eugene O'Neill, Lardner went out on those inexplicable binges, for hours, or for days, or sometimes weeks. Seeking what? Escape, oblivion, rather than any sort of pleasure. There were no women in these escapades; a woman might have saved him from the solitary, frozen, silent, desperate drinking bouts. But Lardner had always been puritanical (for a good writer) about sex. He thought there was too much of it in Hemingway and Dreiser; he was still shocked at the evening clothes—or lack of evening clothes—which eastern women wore to their parties. One of his last "crusades" in the columns of *The New Yorker* was waged against off-color songs, including "Tea for Two." Perhaps this odd strain of prurience in Lardner's temperament was responsible, as it was in the similar cases of William Dean Howells and Henry James, for his passionate yearning for the "stage" itself, as the very antithesis of puritanical inhibition. But in any case Lardner's dramatic career was almost as disastrous as James's was; and unlike O'Neill, Lardner could never return to the support and refuge which serious literary work always is for a serious writer—the solace as well as the bane of a writer's life; and his only durable reason for existing.

He had contracted an incipient tuberculosis which kept him away, in his concern and his fastidiousness, from his own children during these years. He took no real care of this disease except his periodic sojourns at the hospital. At his peak Lardner had contracted with the *Cosmopolitan* editor, Ray Long, for twelve short stories, one every forty-five days, at $3500 each—something few writers would dare to do to their own talent. And the real price for these jobs came out of his own temperament and health. Sleeping became even more difficult for him; drinking became easier; and after his jags the smell of paraldehyde would mark his return to reality—to work. (The story in the present volume called "Sun Cured" is a gruesome account of such drinking bouts.) At 41 Lardner was worn out, sick and defeated; and he had already anticipated this state in his "Symptoms of Being 35," which, marvellous comedy that it is, almost reads like the symptoms of being 65. Perhaps he, even more than Fitzgerald, had the "age complex," not only of a social period which was essentially adolescent in its values, but of some deeper inner sense of life's brevity, fragility. Perhaps even more than Fitzgerald, Lardner was the real, and doomed, *enfant terrible* of the Twenties.

June Moon, with Kaufman's professional stage sense, *was* a hit in 1929—and Lardner went on a three-month spree, ending up again in the hospital. During his recuperation, and his suicidal fantasies, he had decided, as he wrote to Fitzgerald, that the only crime was "not to keep on going." But it was too late; and the "going" was now mainly the sheer moral and physical determination of an exhausted organism. There were still those touching, if fragmentary, recurrences of Ring Lardner's warmth, affection, and humor. His wife Ellis, so he also wrote the Fitzgeralds, "had two babies this summer. They are both girls. . . ." Yet the self-depreciating strain in Lardner's work from the beginning—that strain which had in itself made him such an acute and merciless critic of a period which was so opulent, bloated and crass, and so full of vanity, selfishness and pride—had become a kind of self-loathing. Maybe he felt all the sins of the "damned race" in himself. Maybe, like Swift, he could no longer stand the smell of human beings; and he was one of them, one of the worst of them. Perhaps all he really cared about now was the life-insurance which would provide for the family which he had in fact taken care of so generously, at the expense of his own talent and health, but which in his secret heart he felt his own vices and weaknesses had betrayed.

He sometimes signed those late and touching letters to his sons and nephews as "A Cadaver." He deliberately classed himself with the second-rate American humorists such as Bill Nye, Artemus Ward, Finley Peter Dunne, George Ade, or even Will Rogers, whom he despised. He now had a heart ailment; his legs and feet were swollen. Yet he went back, through sheer need of money, and waning talent, and slackening prices for his material, to a daily letter for the Bell Syndicate; almost to his journalistic beginnings. The early Thirties were a nightmare for Ring Lardner, just as they were a nightmare—and a hangover—for the nation at large. It almost seemed that this writer was born for, and died with, the boom period which he entertained and despised. Back at the Doctors Hospital, he did still another Busher series for *The Saturday Evening Post;* he wrote a radio column and a sports column for *The New Yorker.* But he had lost interest, or belief, in sports too. After the Chicago White Sox scandal in 1919, he had written those lines—

> "I'm forever throwing ball games
> Pretty ball games in the air . . ."

Only now he was suspicious of the Fix in everything; of the gamblers, the racketeers, the syndicates; of the *professional* corruption in what had been the natural popular entertainment, the source of folk pleasure and legends, in the U.S.A. And wasn't he right in believing that a nation's sports (like an individual's humor) was the real key to its character?

Sick, weak, and sad, Lardner sometimes cried over his typewriter, and sometimes fell asleep over it. He alternated between morphine and caffeine; though nothing did much good. He borrowed money for a health trip to the Mojave Desert in 1933; as the end grew near he was still working on another play with Kaufman, on the theme of alcoholism. Despite all his guilt, the respectable midwestern characters in this play were obnoxious, according to Elder's *Ring Lardner,* while the sympathetic characters were still the drunks. And how true! And perhaps here, at least, Lardner linked himself with all those major figures in our native letters, from Melville to Whitman and Dreiser, who had always identified themselves with the outcasts and sinners of the New World; though he lacked their major range and their purpose as, if need be, *un*popular artists. On September 24th 1933, so gaunt that he was using a padded chair for a bridge game with his wife Ellis and the Grantland Rices, he had another heart attack and died at the age of 48.

5

A word on the last section of this Reader, which is called "Native Dada," and which sometimes, to the present editor, seems to be Lardner's most brilliant vein of humor. These weird sketches, articles, modern fairy tales and surrealistic plays were compared with André Breton's work in Lardner's own time; and today they appear to anticipate a Beckett, an Ionesco or an Edward Albee. Lardner would probably have laughed at such a pretentious listing of literary "trends," and he wrote these pieces simply for his own pleasure.

But isn't that really the point? After the early Twenties, his only real pleasure seemed to be in non-human or extra-human spheres, where again his marvellous gift of language went soaring into the "non-logical" realm of nonsense—which somehow becomes more human, or at least less painful, than his naturalistic or realistic chronicles of the American success story. If the real purpose of life is simply our pleasure in living—for without a minimum of this, no organism, except perhaps man, will survive—then this area of writing was Lardner's real life. "The Young Immigrunts" can be classified as an early example of surrealistic comedy, with its brilliant play of verbal ingenuity. "My parents are both married," says the young author of this sketch (who really is a young author), "and ½ of them are very good looking." Or again: "I was born in a hospittle in Chicago 4 years ago and liked it very much and had no idear we were going to move till 1 day last summer I heard my mother arsk our nurse did she think she could get along O.K. with myself and 3 brothers John Jimmie and David for 10 days wilst she and my old man went east to look for a costly home."

This was at the beginning of Ring Lardner's own provincial pilgrimage to the Big Town and the costly life; and what gaiety, what warmth, what laughter were in this little comic idyll. And what sentences, what phrases, were thrown off here in this free-wheeling burst of Lardner's original, exuberant, free talent! "The boat leaves Detroit every afternoon at 5 oclock and reachs Buffalo the next morning at 9 tho I would better exclaim to my readers that when it is 9 oclock in Buffalo it is only 8 oclock in Goshen for instants as Buffalo peaple are qeer." There is the "bride and glum going to Niagara Falls"—on the city of Detroit 3—and the immortal dialogue of these newlyweds. The whole piece is hilarious, poetic and beautiful; and Lardner on Long Island dogs is almost as good; and Lardner on Wives is perhaps even better. "Wives is people that always wants to go home when you don't and vice versa. . . . Wives is people that ain't never satisfied as they are always too fat or too thin. . . . Wives is people that asks you what time the 12:55 train gets to New York. 'At 1:37,' you tell them. 'How do you know?' they ask. . . . They are people that never have nothing that is fit to wear. They are people that think when the telephone bell rings it is against the law to not answer it. . . . They are people whose watch is always a ¼ of a hr. off either one way or the other."

There is his famous first rule on how to be a happy marriage. "The marital twain should ought to be opp. sex if possible and somewheres near the other one's age." Or the third rule: "The bride should ought to have at lease as much money as the groom and a salary of her own so as when she feels like she has got to buy something she don't want she will know that it's her money being throwed away." There is Rule 8. "Marred life is a job just the same as like a telegraph operator or a enbalmer. . . ." And Rule 10. "Finely, try and forget once in a wile that you are marred and go out somewheres together for a good time." There are the Lardnerian variations on the theme of Cole Porter's "Night and Day"—

"Night and day under the rind of me
There's an Oh, such a zeal for spooning ru'ning the mind of me."

Or:

"Night and day under the bark of me
There's an Oh, such a mob of microbes making a park of me."

Or:

"Night and day under the fleece of me
There's an Oh, such a flaming furneth burneth the grease of me."

Or:

"Night and day under my dermis, dear,
There's a spot just as hot as coffee kept in a thermos, dear."

Or:

"Night and day under my cuticle
There's a love for you so true it never would do to kill."

Or:

"Night and day under my tegument
There's a voice telling me I'm he, the good little egg you meant."

This was the earlier or simpler period of Lardner's native Dada. With the surrealist plays, we reach an even more exotic and brilliant realm of verbal comedy.

In "Clemo Uti—'The Water Lilies,'" the characters include Padre, a Priest; Sethso and Gethso, both twins; a shepherd's boy named Wayshatten, and two capitalists who don't appear in the show. The scene is the outskirts of a parchesi board, where people are wondering what has become of the discs. There is a Lardner song on this theme, while Wama Tammisch—"her daughter," but whose? Well, hers—enters from an exclusive waffle parlor, and exits as if she had waffles. Acts II and III were thrown out of the play "because nothing seemed to happen"—a procedure that could be recommended to more Broadway plays. Wayshatten, the shepherd's boy, cries plaintively: "Why wasn't you out there this morning to help me look after my sheep? A chorus of assistant Shepherds echoes his complaint:

> "Why did you lay there asleep
> When you should of looked after his sheep?
> Why did you send telegrams
> When you should of looked after his lambs?
> Why did you sleep there, so old
> When you should of looked after his fold?

And Sethso cries: "Who is our father?"

Who is, indeed? What we are getting here, underneath the merriment, and just as in "The Young Immigrunts," and perhaps as in all of Lardner's most personal humor, is the play of that unfettered fantasy of childhood which, as Ernest Schactel has pointed out in his admirable study called *Metamorphosis,* is the natural state of the human spirit before it is curbed, inhibited, repressed by the codes of civilization. Gethso's rejoinder to the universal lament of Sethso is: "What of it? We're twins, ain't we?" and Wama adds: "Hush, clemo uti *(the Water Lilies)*" in a closing benediction (almost) of brotherhood and human grace which this artist never discovered elsewhere in the grasping and striving American scene of his own maturity.

Almost; but not quite; for even in the childhood utopia of "Clemo

Uti," this Edenite garden of innocent mirth, the play's *real* conclusion is the entrance of "two queels . . . overcome with water lilies:

"They both make fools of themselves. They don't seem to have any self-control. They quiver. They want to play the show over again, but it looks useless."

And this was the surrealistic description of Lardner's own deepest feeling about maturity and society alike—about life. There was no point in playing the show over again; it was useless.

The same note of innocent infancy always betrayed is evident in "I. Gaspiri" or "The Upholsterers"—that childlike innocence indeed which lay hidden, still, in Lardner's deepest psyche; which lies beneath the surface in all major artists, and which may be the distinguishing element that makes an artist what he is. (Though the essential thing here is to what *use* a writer puts this kind of innocence; how he adapts it to the realities of maturity; just as Lardner's own savage satires on the sporting, business, social and entertainment world of the American Twenties were simply the obverse form of his earlier trust and belief and pleasure in life.) The scene of the second play was a public street in a bathroom. "Where was you born?" inquires the First Stranger. "Out of wedlock," says the Second Stranger. "That's a mighty pretty country around there," is the First Stranger's comment—but who are all these "Strangers" amidst the plaintive accents of infancy?

"Quadroon" is "a play in four pelts which may all be attended in one day or missed in a group." It was a take-off on Eugene O'Neill's massive trilogy, *Mourning Becomes Electra,* in which Lardner simply listed the dinner menus that became increasingly important as you watched the plays. "Dinner Bridge," one of the best of these surrealistic parodies, again dealt with food and the very noble, gentlemanly, leisure-class American workmen who were forever repairing, or maybe obstructing, the Fifty-Ninth Street Bridge in New York. "I was beginning to like you, Mr. Amorosi," says the character called Llanuza. "You get that right out of your mind, Mr. Barrows," says Amorosi: "I'm married; been married twice. My first wife died." "How long were you married to her?" says Hansen. "Right up to the time she died," says Amorosi. In "Cora, or Fun at a Spa," the curtain is lowered and raised to see if it will work, while two milch cows sit at a mixed grill playing draughts. "Don't you feel a draught?" says the First Milch Cow. In "Abend Di Anni Nouveau," the waiter tethers his mount and lies down on the hors d'oeuvres. "The curtain is lowered and partially destroyed to denote the passage of four days." Acts 3, 4, and 5 take place in "a one-way street in Jeopardy."

There again, as in all these "nonsense" sketches, essays and plays of Ring Lardner, was the underlying, the recurrent refrain and contrast between "childlike play"—play for the sake of play, pleasure for the sake of pleasure, life for the sake of life—and that adult world which for Lardner himself, at least, was surely close to a one-way street in Jeopardy. Mighty pretty country around there too, but a disappointment, and dangerous; in short, a blind alley, a *cul-de-sac*. But in the concluding note to the Lardner Reader, why do I find myself stressing this specific vein of his general talent? Well, maybe, once you start to quote from Lardner's purest vein of comedy, it is difficult to stop. It is just very funny. But also, I suppose, there is the fact, when you watch the free play of his fancy, so exuberant, so inherently poetic, that the contrast between this natural gaiety and the later years of his tormented and desperate commercial career becomes so marked and so melancholy.

Now we might agree with those critics who acclaim Ring Lardner precisely because he was working in the popular arts; who almost say, indeed, that he could only have worked within this medium. But to take this view is also to minimize the real nature of Lardner's talent, to diminish the importance of his durable work in the national letters rather than in the entertainment field; and to miss the tragedy of such a uniquely free spirit which was bound down—or which insisted upon binding itself down—by the most repressive conventions of maturity. In his case it was a gilded, lavish and bitter maturity; but when Ring Lardner had learned this, it was too late.

—*Maxwell Geismar*

Harrison, New York.
April, 1962.

THE RING LARDNER READER

PART ONE
Provincial Life

You Know Me Al

A Busher's Letters

New York, New York, September 16.

FRIEND AL: I opened the serious here and beat them easy but I know
you must of saw about it in the Chi papers. At that they don't give
me no fair show in the Chi papers. One of the boys bought one here
and I seen in it where I was lucky to win that game in Cleveland. If
I knowed which one of them reporters wrote that I would punch his
jaw.

Al I told you Boston was some town but this is the real one. I
never seen nothing like it and I been going some since we got here.
I walked down Broadway the Main Street last night and I run into
a couple of the ball players and they took me to what they call the
Garden but it ain't like the gardens at home because this one is
indoors. We sat down to a table and had several drinks. Pretty soon
one of the boys asked me if I was broke and I says No, why? He says
You better get some lubricateing oil and loosen up. I don't know
what he meant but pretty soon when we had had a lot of drinks the
waiter brings a check and hands it to me. It was for one dollar. I
says Oh I ain't paying for all of them. The waiter says This is just
for that last drink.

I thought the other boys would make a holler but they didn't say
nothing. So I give him a dollar bill and even then he didn't act
satisfied so I asked him what he was waiting for and he said Oh
nothing, kind of sassy. I was going to bust him but the boys give me
the sign to shut up and not to say nothing. I excused myself pretty
soon because I wanted to get some air. I give my check for my hat to
a boy and he brought my hat and I started going and he says Haven't
you forgot something? I guess he must of thought I was wearing a
overcoat.

Then I went down the Main Street again and some man stopped
me and asked me did I want to go to the show. He said he had a

3

ticket. I asked him what show and he said the Follies. I never heard of it but I told him I would go if he had a ticket to spare. He says I will spare you this one for three dollars. I says You must take me for some boob. He says No I wouldn't insult no boob. So I walks on but if he had of insulted me I would of busted him.

I went back to the hotel then and run into Kid Gleason. He asked me to take a walk with him so out I go again. We went to the corner and he bought me a beer. He don't drink nothing but pop himself. The two drinks was only ten cents so I says This is the place for me. He says Where have you been? and I told him about paying one dollar for three drinks. He says I see I will have to take charge of you. Don't go round with them ball players no more. When you want to go out and see the sights come to me and I will stear you. So to-night he is going to stear me. I will write to you from Philadelphia.

Your pal,   JACK.

Philadelphia, Pa., September 19.

FRIEND AL: They won't be no game here to-day because it is raining. We all been loafing round the hotel all day and I am glad of it because I got all tired out over in New York City. I and Kid Gleason went round together the last couple of nights over there and he wouldn't let me spend no money. I seen a lot of girls that I would of liked to of got acquainted with but he wouldn't even let me answer them when they spoke to me. We run in to a couple of peaches last night and they had us spotted too. One of them says I'll bet you're a couple of ball players. But Kid says You lose your bet. I am a bell-hop and the big rube with me is nothing but a pitcher.

One of them says What are you trying to do kid somebody? He says Go home and get some soap and remove your disguise from your face. I didn't think he ought to talk like that to them and I called him about it and said maybe they was lonesome and it wouldn't hurt none if we treated them to a soda or something. But he says Lonesome. If I don't get you away from here they will steal everything you got. They won't even leave you your fast ball. So we left them and he took me to a picture show. It was some California pictures and they made me think of Hazel so when I got back to the hotel I sent her three postcards.

Gleason made me go to my room at ten o'clock both nights but I was pretty tired anyway because he had walked me all over town. I guess we must of saw twenty shows. He says I would take you to the grand opera only it would be throwing money away because we can hear Ed Walsh for nothing. Walsh has got some voice Al a loud high tenor.

To-morrow is Sunday and we have a double header Monday on account of the rain to-day. I thought sure I would get another chance to beat the Athaletics and I asked Callahan if he was going to pitch me here but he said he thought he would save me to work against Johnson in Washington. So you see Al he must figure I am about the best he has got. I'll beat him Al if they get a couple of runs behind me.

Yours truly,   JACK.

P.S. They was a letter here from Violet and it pretty near made me feel like crying. I wish they was two of me so both them girls could be happy.

Washington, D. C., September 22.

DEAR OLD AL: Well Al here I am in the capital of the old United States. We got in last night and I been walking round town all morning. But I didn't tire myself out because I am going to pitch against Johnson this afternoon.

This is the prettiest town I ever seen but I believe they is more colored people here than they is in Evansville or Chi. I seen the White House and the Monumunt. They say that Bill Sullivan and Gabby St. once catched a baseball that was threw off of the top of the Monumunt but I bet they couldn't catch it if I throwed it.

I was in to breakfast this morning with Gleason and Bodie and Weaver and Fournier. Gleason says I'm supprised that you ain't sick in bed to-day. I says Why?

He says Most of our pitchers gets sick when Cal tells them they are going to work against Johnson. He says Here's these other fellows all feeling pretty sick this morning and they ain't even pitchers. All they have to do is hit against him but it looks like as if Cal would have to send substitutes in for them. Bodie is complaining of a sore arm which he must of strained drawing to two card flushes. Fournier and Weaver have strained their legs doing the tango dance. Nothing could cure them except to hear that big Walter had got throwed out of his machine and wouldn't be able to pitch against us in this serious.

I says I feel O. K. and I ain't afraid to pitch against Johnson and I ain't afraid to hit against him neither. Then Weaver says Have you ever saw him work? Yes, I says, I seen him in Chi. Then Weaver says Well if you have saw him work and ain't afraid to hit against him I'll bet you would go down to Wall Street and holler Hurrah for Roosevelt. I says No I wouldn't do that but I ain't afraid of no pitcher and what is more if you get me a couple of runs I'll beat him. Then Fournier says Oh we will get you a couple of runs all right. He says That's just as easy as catching whales with a angle-worm.

Well Al I must close and go in and get some lunch. My arm feels great and they will have to go some to beat me Johnson or no Johnson.

Your pal,   JACK.

Washington, D. C., September 22.

FRIEND AL: Well I guess you know by this time that they didn't get no two runs for me, only one, but I beat him just the same. I beat him one to nothing and Callahan was so pleased that he give me a ticket to the theater. I just got back from there and it is pretty late and I already have wrote you one letter to-day but I am going to sit up and tell you about it.

It was cloudy before the game started and when I was warming up I made the remark to Callahan that the dark day ought to make my speed good. He says Yes and of course it will handicap Johnson.

While Washington was takeing their practice their two coachers Schaefer and Altrock got out on the infield and cut up and I pretty near busted laughing at them. They certainly is funny Al. Callahan asked me what was I laughing at and I told him and he says That's the first time I ever seen a pitcher laugh when he was going to work against Johnson. He says Griffith is a pretty good fellow to give us something to laugh at before he shoots that guy at us.

I warmed up good and told Schalk not to ask me for my spitter much because my fast one looked faster than I ever seen it. He says it won't make much difference what you pitch to-day. I says Oh, yes,

it will because Callahan thinks enough of me to work me against
Johnson and I want to show him he didn't make no mistake. Then
Gleason says No he didn't make no mistake. Wasteing Cicotte or
Scotty would of been a mistake in this game.

Well, Johnson whiffs Weaver and Chase and makes Lord pop out
in the first inning. I walked their first guy but I didn't give Milan
nothing to bunt and finally he flied out. And then I whiffed the next
two. On the bench Callahan says That's the way, boy. Keep that up
and we got a chance.

Johnson had fanned four of us when I come up with two out in
the third inning and he whiffed me to. I fouled one though that if
I had ever got a good hold of I would of knocked out of the park.
In the first seven innings we didn't have a hit off of him. They had
got five or six lucky ones off of me and I had walked two or three,
but I cut loose with all I had when they was men on and they
couldn't do nothing with me. The only reason I walked so many was
because my fast one was jumping so. Honest Al it was so fast that
Evans the umpire couldn't see it half the time and he called a lot of
balls that was right over the heart.

Well I come up in the eighth with two out and the score still
nothing and nothing. I had whiffed the second time as well as the
first but it was account of Evans missing one on me. The eighth
started with Shanks muffing a fly ball off of Bodie. It was way out by
the fence so he got two bases on it and he went to third while they
was throwing Berger out. Then Schalk whiffed.

Callahan says Go up and try to meet one Jack. It might as well be
you as anybody else. But your old pal didn't whiff this time Al. He
gets two strikes on me with fast ones and then I passed up two bad
ones. I took my healthy at the next one and slapped it over first base.
I guess I could of made two bases on it but I didn't want to tire
myself out. Anyway Bodie scored and I had them beat. And my hit
was the only one we got off of him so I guess he is a pretty good
pitcher after all Al.

They filled up the bases on me with one out in the ninth but it
was pretty dark then and I made McBride and their catcher look like
suckers with my speed.

I felt so good after the game that I drunk one of them pink cocktails. I don't know what their name is. And then I sent a postcard to

poor little Violet. I don't care nothing about her but it don't hurt me none to try and cheer her up once in a while. We leave here Thursday night for home and they had ought to be two or three letters there for me from Hazel because I haven't heard from her lately. She must of lost my road addresses.

Your pal,   JACK.

P. S. I forgot to tell you what Callahan said after the game. He said I was a real pitcher now and he is going to use me in the city serious. If he does Al we will beat them Cubs sure.

Chicago, Illinois, September 27.

FRIEND AL: They wasn't no letter here at all from Hazel and I guess she must of been sick. Or maybe she didn't think it was worth while writeing as long as she is comeing next week.

I want to ask you to do me a favor Al and that is to see if you can find me a house down there. I will want to move in with Mrs. Keefe, don't that sound funny Al? sometime in the week of October twelfth. Old man Cutting's house or that yellow house across from you would be O. K. I would rather have the yellow one so as to be near you. Find out how much rent they want Al and if it is not no more than twelve dollars a month get it for me. We will buy our furniture here in Chi when Hazel comes.

We have a couple of days off now Al and then we play St. Louis two games here. Then Detroit comes to finish the season the third and fourth of October.

Your pal,   JACK.

Chicago, Illinois, October 3.

DEAR OLD AL: Thanks Al for getting the house. The one-year lease is O. K. You and Bertha and me and Hazel can have all sorts of good times together. I guess the walk needs repairs but I can fix that up when I come. We can stay at the hotel when we first get there.

I wish you could of came up for the city serious Al but anyway I want you and Bertha to be sure and come up for our wedding. I will let you know the date as soon as Hazel gets here.

The serious starts Tuesday and this town is wild over it. The Cubs finished second in their league and we was fifth in ours but that don't scare me none. We would of finished right on top if I had of been here all season.

Callahan pitched one of the bushers against Detroit this afternoon and they beat him bad. Callahan is saveing up Scott and Allen and Russell and Cicotte and I for the big show. Walsh isn't in no shape and neither is Benz. It looks like I would have a good deal to do because most of them others can't work no more than once in four days and Allen ain't no good at all.

We have a day to rest after to-morrow's game with the Tigers and then we go at them Cubs.

Your pal,   JACK.

P. S. I have got it figured that Hazel is fixing to surprise me by dropping in on me because I haven't heard nothing yet.

Chicago, Illinois, October 7.

FRIEND AL: Well Al you know by this time that they beat me to-day and tied up the serious. But I have still got plenty of time Al and I will get them before it is over. My arm wasn't feeling good Al and my fast ball didn't hop like it had ought to. But it was the rotten support I got that beat me. That lucky stiff Zimmerman was the only guy that got a real hit off of me and he must of shut his eyes and throwed his bat because the ball he hit was a foot over his head. And if they hadn't been makeing all them errors behind me they wouldn't of been nobody on bases when Zimmerman got that lucky scratch. The serious now stands one and one Al and it is a cinch we will beat them even if they are a bunch of lucky stiffs. They has been great big crowds at both games and it looks like as if we should ought to get over eight hundred dollars a peace if we win and we will win sure because I will beat them three straight if necessary.

But Al I have got bigger news than that for you and I am the happyest man in the world. I told you I had not heard from Hazel for a long time. To-night when I got back to my room they was a letter waiting for me from her.

Al she is married. Maybe you don't know why that makes me happy but I will tell you. She is married to Kid Levy the middle weight. I guess my thirty dollars is gone because in her letter she called me a cheap skate and she inclosed one one-cent stamp and two twos and said she was paying me for the glass of beer I once bought her. I bought her more than that Al but I won't make no holler. She all so said not for me to never come near her or her husband would bust my jaw. I ain't afraid of him or no one else Al but they ain't no danger of me ever bothering them. She was no good and I was sorry the minute I agreed to marry her.

But I was going to tell you why I am happy or maybe you can guess. Now I can make Violet my wife and she's got Hazel beat forty ways. She ain't nowheres near as big as Hazel but she's classier Al and she will make me a good wife. She ain't never asked me for no money.

I wrote her a letter the minute I got the good news and told her to come on over here at once at my expense. We will be married right after the serious is over and I want you and Bertha to be sure and stand up with us. I will wire you at my own expence the exact date.

It all seems like a dream now about Violet and I haveing our mis-understanding Al and I don't see how I ever could of accused her of sending me that postcard. You and Bertha will be just as crazy about her as I am when you see her Al. Just think Al I will be married inside of a week and to the only girl I ever could of been happy with instead of the woman I never really cared for except as a passing fancy. My happyness would be complete Al if I had not of let that woman steal thirty dollars off of me.

Your happy pal,   JACK.

P. S. Hazel probibly would of insisted on us takeing a trip to Niagara falls or somewheres but I know Violet will be perfectly satis-fied if I take her right down to Bedford. Oh you little yellow house.

Chicago, Illinois, October 9.

FRIEND AL: Well Al we have got them beat three games to one now and will wind up the serious to-morrow sure. Callahan sent me in to save poor Allen yesterday and I stopped them dead. But I don't care now Al. I have lost all interest in the game and I don't care if Callahan pitches me to-morrow or not. My heart is just about broke Al and I wouldn't be able to do myself justice feeling the way I do.

I have lost Violet Al and just when I was figureing on being the happyest man in the world. We will get the big money but it won't do me no good. They can keep my share because I won't have no little girl to spend it on.

Her answer to my letter was waiting for me at home to-night. She is engaged to be married to Joe Hill the big lefthander Jennings got from Providence. Honest Al I don't see how he gets by. He ain't got no more curve ball than a rabbit and his fast one floats up there like a big balloon. He beat us the last game of the regular season here but it was because Callahan had a lot of bushers in the game.

I wish I had knew then that he was stealing my girl and I would of made Callahan pitch me against him. And when he come up to bat I would of beaned him. But I don't suppose you could hurt him by hitting him in the head. The big stiff. Their wedding ain't going to come off till next summer and by that time he will be pitching in the Southwestern Texas League for about fifty dollars a month.

Violet wrote that she wished me all the luck and happyness in the world but it is too late for me to be happy Al and I don't care what kind of luck I have now.

Al you will have to get rid of that lease for me. Fix it up the best way you can. Tell the old man I have changed my plans. I don't know just yet what I will do but maybe I will go to Australia with Mike Donlin's team. If I do I won't care if the boat goes down or not. I don't believe I will even come back to Bedford this winter. It would drive me wild to go past that little house every day and think how happy I might of been.

Maybe I will pitch to-morrow Al and if I do the serious will be over to-morrow night. I can beat them Cubs if I get any kind of decent support. But I don't care now Al.

Yours truly,   JACK.

Chicago, Illinois, October 12.

AL: Your letter received. If the old man won't call it off I guess I will have to try and rent the house to some one else. Do you know of any couple that wants one Al? It looks like I would have to come down there myself and fix things up someway. He is just mean enough to stick me with the house on my hands when I won't have no use for it.

They beat us the day before yesterday as you probibly know and it rained yesterday and to-day. The papers says it will be all O. K.

to-morrow and Callahan tells me I am going to work. The Cub pitchers was all shot to peaces and the bad weather is just nuts for them because it will give Cheney a good rest. But I will beat him Al if they don't kick it away behind me.

I must close because I promised Allen the little lefthander that I would come over to his flat and play cards a while to-night and I must wash up and change my collar. Allen's wife's sister is visiting them again and I would give anything not to have to go over there. I am through with girls and don't want nothing to do with them.

I guess it is maybe a good thing it rained to-day because I dreamt about Violet last night and went out and got a couple of high balls before breakfast this morning. I hadn't never drank nothing before breakfast before and it made me kind of sick. But I am all O.K. now.

Your pal,   JACK.

Chicago, Illinois, October 13.

DEAR OLD AL: The serious is all over Al. We are the champions and I done it. I may be home the day after to-morrow or I may not come for a couple of days. I want to see Comiskey before I leave and fix up about my contract for next year. I won't sign for no less than five thousand and if he hands me a contract for less than that I will leave the White Sox flat on their back. I have got over fourteen hundred dollars now Al with the city serious money which was $814.30 and I don't have to worry.

Them reporters will have to give me a square deal this time Al. I had everything and the Cubs done well to score a run. I whiffed Zimmerman three times. Some of the boys say he ain't no hitter but he is a hitter and a good one Al only he could not touch the stuff I got. The umps give them their run because in the fourth inning I had Leach flatfooted off of second base and Weaver tagged him O. K. but the umps wouldn't call it. Then Schulte the lucky stiff happened to get a hold of one and pulled it past first base. I guess Chase must of been asleep. Anyway they scored but I don't care because we piled up six runs on Cheney and I drove in one of them myself with one of the prettiest singles you ever see. It was a spitter and I hit it like a shot. If I had hit it square it would of went out of the park.

Comiskey ought to feel pretty good about me winning and I guess he will give me a contract for anything I want. He will have to or I will go to the Federal League.

We are all invited to a show to-night and I am going with Allen and his wife and her sister Florence. She is O. K. Al and I guess she thinks the same about me. She must because she was out to the game to-day and seen me hand it to them. She maybe ain't as pretty as Violet and Hazel but as they say beauty isn't only so deep.

Well Al tell the boys I will be with them soon. I have gave up the idea of going to Australia because I would have to buy a evening full-dress suit and they tell me they cost pretty near fifty dollars. dollars.   Your truly,   JACK.

Chicago, Illinois, October 14.

FRIEND AL: Never mind about that lease. I want the house after all Al and I have got the supprise of your life for you.

When I come home to Bedford I will bring my wife with me. I and Florence fixed things all up after the show last night and we are going to be married to-morrow morning. I am a busy man to-day Al because I have got to get the license and look round for furniture. And I have also got to buy some new cloths but they are haveing a sale on Cottage Grove Avenue at Clark's store and I know one of the clerks there.

I am the happyest man in the world Al. You and Bertha and I and Florence will have all kinds of good times together this winter because I know Bertha and Florence will like each other. Florence looks something like Bertha at that. I am glad I didn't get tied up with Violet or Hazel even if they was a little bit prettier than Florence.

Florence knows a lot about baseball for a girl and you would be supprised to hear her talk. She says I am the best pitcher in the league and she has saw them all. She all so says I am the best looking ball player she ever seen but you know how girls will kid a guy Al. You will like her O. K. I fell for her the first time I seen her.

Your old pal,   JACK.

P. S. I signed up for next year. Comiskey slapped me on the back when I went in to see him and told me I would be a star next year if I took good care of myself. I guess I am a star without waiting for next year Al. My contract calls for twenty-eight hundred a year which is a thousand more than I was getting. And it is pretty near a cinch that I will be in on the World Serious money next season.

P. S. I certainly am relieved about that lease. It would of been fierce to of had that place on my hands all winter and not getting any use out of it. Everything is all O. K. now. Oh you little yellow house.

THE BUSHER'S HONEYMOON

Chicago, Illinois, October, 17.

FRIEND AL: Well Al it looks as if I would not be writeing so much to you now that I am a married man. Yes Al I and Florrie was married the day before yesterday just like I told you we was going to be and Al I am the happyest man in the world though I have spent $30 in the last 3 days incluseive. You was wise Al to get married in Bedford where not nothing is nearly half so dear. My expenses was as follows:

License	$ 2.00
Preist	3.50
Haircut and shave	.35
Shine	.05
Carfair	.45
New suit	14.50
Show tickets	3.00
Flowers	.50
Candy	.30
Hotel	4.50
Tobacco both kinds	.25

You see Al it costs a hole lot of money to get married here. The sum of what I have wrote down is $29.40 but as I told you I have spent $30 and I do not know what I have did with that other $0.60. My new brother-in-law Allen told me I should ought to give the preist $5 and I thought it should be about $2 the same as the license so I split the difference and give him $3.50. I never seen him before and probily won't never see him again so why should I give him anything at all when it is his business to marry couples? But I like to do the right thing. You know me Al.

I thought we would be in Bedford by this time but Florrie wants to stay here a few more days because she says she wants to be with her sister. Allen and his wife is thinking about takeing a flat for the winter instead of going down to Waco Texas where they live. I don't see no sense in that when it costs so much to live here but it is none of my business if they want to throw their money away. But I am glad I got a wife with some sense though she kicked because I did not get no room with a bath which would cost me $2 a day instead of $1.50. I says I guess the clubhouse is still open yet and if I want a bath I can go over there and take the shower. She says Yes and I suppose I can go and jump in the lake. But she would not do that Al because the lake here is cold at this time of the year.

When I told you about my expenses I did not include in it the meals because we would be eating them if I was getting married or not getting married only I have to pay for six meals a day now instead of three and I didn't used to eat no lunch in the playing season except once in a while when I knowed I was not going to work that afternoon. I had a meal ticket which had not quite ran out over to a resturunt on Indiana Ave and we eat there for the first day except at night when I took Allen and his wife to the show with us and then he took us to a chop suye resturunt. I guess you have not never had no chop suye Al and I am here to tell you you have not missed nothing but when Allen was going to buy the supper what could I say? I could not say nothing.

Well yesterday and to-day we been eating at a resturunt on Cottage Grove Ave near the hotel and at the resturunt on Indiana that I had the meal ticket at only I do not like to buy no new meal ticket when I am not going to be round here no more than a few days. Well Al I guess the meals has cost me all together about $1.50 and I have eat very little myself. Florrie always wants desert ice cream or something and that runs up into money faster than regular stuff like stake and ham and eggs.

Well Al Florrie says it is time for me to keep my promise and take her to the moveing pictures which is $0.20 more because the one she likes round here costs a dime apeace. So I must close for this time and will see you soon.

Your pal,   JACK.

Chicago, Illinois, October 22.

AL: Just a note Al to tell you why I have not yet came to Bedford yet where I expected I would be long before this time. Allen and his wife have took a furnished flat for the winter and Allen's wife wants

Florrie to stay here untill they get settled. Meentime it is costing me a hole lot of money at the hotel and for meals besides I am paying $10 a month rent for the house you got for me and what good am I getting out of it? But Florrie wants to help her sister and what can I say? Though I did make her promise she would not stay no longer than next Saturday at least. So I guess Al we will be home on the evening train Saturday and then may be I can save some money.

I know Al that you and Bertha will like Florrie when you get acquainted with her spesially Bertha though Florrie dresses pretty swell and spends a hole lot of time fusing with her face and her hair.

She says to me to-night Who are you writeing to and I told her Al Blanchard who I have told you about a good many times. She says I bet you are writeing to some girl and acted like as though she was kind of jealous. So I thought I would tease her a little and I says I don't know no girls except you and Violet and Hazel. Who is Violet and Hazel? she says. I kind of laughed and says Oh I guess I better not tell you and then she says I guess you will tell me. That made me kind of mad because no girl can't tell me what to do. She says Are you going to tell me? and I says No.

Then she says If you don't tell me I will go over to Marie's that is her sister Allen's wife and stay all night. I says Go on and she went downstairs but I guess she probily went to get a soda because she has some money of her own that I give her. This was about two hours ago and she is probily down in the hotel lobby now trying to scare me by makeing me believe she has went to her sister's. But she can't fool me Al and I am now going out to mail this letter and get a beer. I won't never tell her about Violet and Hazel if she is going to act like that.

Yours truly,   JACK.

Chicago, Illinois, October 24.

FRIEND AL: I guess I told you Al that we would be home Saturday evening. I have changed my mind. Allen and his wife has a spair bedroom and wants us to come there and stay a week or two. It won't cost nothing except they will probily want to go out to the moveing pictures nights and we will probily have to go along with them and I am a man Al that wants to pay his share and not be cheap.

I and Florrie had our first quarrle the other night. I guess I told you the start of it but I don't remember. I made some crack about Violet and Hazel just to tease Florrie and she wanted to know who they was and I would not tell her. So she gets sore and goes over to Marie's to stay all night. I was just kidding Al and was willing to tell her about them two poor girls whatever she wanted to know except that I don't like to brag about girls being stuck on me. So I goes over to Marie's after her and tells her all about them except that I turned them down cold at the last minute to marry her because I did not want her to get all swelled up. She made me sware that I did not never care nothing about them and that was easy because it was the truth. So she come back to the hotel with me just like I knowed she would when I ordered her to.

They must not be no mistake about who is the boss in my house. Some men lets their wife run all over them but I am not that kind. You know me Al.

I must get busy and pack my suitcase if I am going to move over to Allen's. I sent three collars and a shirt to the laundrey this morning so even if we go over there to-night I will have to take another trip back this way in a day or two. I won't mind Al because they sell my kind of beer down to the corner and I never seen it sold nowheres else in Chi. You know the kind it is, eh Al? I wish I was lifting a few with you to-night.

Your pal,   J<small>ACK</small>.

D<small>EAR</small> O<small>LD</small> A<small>L</small>: Florrie and Marie has went downtown shopping because Florrie thinks she has got to have a new dress though she has got two changes of cloths now and I don't know what she can do with another one. I hope she don't find none to suit her though it would not hurt none if she got something for next spring at a reduckshon. I guess she must think I am Charles A. Comiskey or somebody. Allen has went to a colledge football game. One of the reporters give him a pass. I don't see nothing in football except a lot of scrapping between little slobs that I could lick the whole bunch of them so I did not care to go. The reporter is one of the guys that travled round with our club all summer. He called up and said he hadn't only the one pass but he was not hurting my feelings none because I would not go to no rotten football game if they payed me.

The flat across the hall from this here one is for rent furnished.

They want $40 a month for it and I guess they think they must be lots of suckers running round loose. Marie was talking about it and says Why don't you and Florrie take it and then we can be right together all winter long and have some big times? Florrie says It would be all right with me. What about it Jack? I says What do you think I am? I don't have to live in no high price flat when I got a home in Bedford where they ain't no people trying to hold every-body up all the time. So they did not say no more about it when they seen I was in ernest. Nobody cannot tell me where I am going to live sister-in-law or no sister-in-law. If I was to rent the rotten old flat I would be paying $50 a month rent includeing the house down in Bedford. Fine chance Al.

Well Al I am lonesome and thirsty so more later.

Your pal,   JACK.

Chicago, Illinois, November 2.

FRIEND AL: Well Al I got some big news for you. I am not come-ing to Bedford this winter after all except to make a visit which I guess will be round Xmas. I changed my mind about that flat across the hall from the Allens and decided to take it after all. The people who was in it and owns the furniture says they would let us have it till the 1 of May if we would pay $42.50 a month which is only $2.50 a month more than they would of let us have it for for a short time. So you see we got a bargain because it is all furnished and every-thing and we won't have to blow no money on furniture besides the club goes to California the middle of Febuery so Florrie would not have no place to stay while I am away.

The Allens only subleased their flat from some other people till the 2 of Febuery and when I and Allen goes West Marie can come over and stay with Florrie so you see it is best all round. If we should of boughten furniture it would cost us in the neighborhood of $100 even without no piano and they is a piano in this here flat which makes it nice because Florrie plays pretty good with one hand and we can have lots of good times at home without it costing us nothing except just the bear liveing expenses. I consider myself lucky to of found out about this before it was too late and somebody else had of gotten the tip.

Now Al old pal I want to ask a great favor of you Al. I all ready have payed one month rent $10 on the house in Bedford and I want you to see the old man and see if he won't call off that lease. Why should I be paying $10 a month rent down there and $42.50 up here when the house down there is not no good to me because I am liveing up here all winter? See Al? Tell him I will gladly give him another month rent to call off the lease but don't tell him that if you don't have to. I want to be fare with him.

If you will do this favor for me, Al (I won't never forget it. Give my kindest to Bertha and tell her I am sorry I and Florrie won't see her right away but you see how it is Al.   Yours,   JACK.

Chicago, Illinois, November 30.

FRIEND AL: I have not wrote for a long time have I Al but I have been very busy. They was not enough furniture in the flat and we have been buying some more. They was enough for some people may be but I and Florrie is the kind that won't have nothing but the best. The furniture them people had in the liveing room was oak but they had a bookcase bilt in in the flat that was mohoggeny and Florrie would not stand for no joke combination like that so she moved the oak chairs and table in to the spair bedroom and we went downtown to buy some mohoggeny. But it costs too much Al and we was feeling pretty bad about it when we seen some Sir Cashion walnut that was prettier even than the mohoggeny and not near so expensive. It is not no real Sir Cashion walnut but it is just as good and we got it reasonable. Then we got some mission chairs for the dining room because the old ones was just straw and was no good and we got a big lether couch for $9 that somebody can sleep on if we get to much company.

I hope you and Bertha can come up for the holidays and see how comfertible we are fixed. That is all the new furniture we have boughten but Florrie set her heart on some old Rose drapes and a red table lamp that is the biggest you ever seen Al and I did not have the heart to say no. The hole thing cost me in the neighborhood of $110 which is very little for what we got and then it will always be ourn even when we move away from this flat though we will have to leave the furniture that belongs to the other people but their part of it is not no good anyway.

I guess I told you Al how much money I had when the season

ended. It was $1400 all told includeing the city serious money. Well Al I got in the neighborhood of $800 left because I give $200 to Florrie to send down to Texas to her other sister who had a bad egg for a husband that managed a club in the Texas Oklahoma League and this was the money she had to pay to get the divorce. I am glad Al that I was lucky enough to marry happy and get a good girl for my wife that has got some sense and besides if I have got $800 left I should not worry as they say.   Your pal,   JACK.

Chicago, Illinois, December 7.

DEAR OLD AL: No I was in ernest Al when I says that I wanted you and Bertha to come up here for the holidays. I know I told you that I might come to Bedford for the holidays but that is all off. I have gave up the idea of comeing to Bedford for the holidays and I want you to be sure and come up her for the holidays and I will show you a good time. I would love to have Bertha come to and she can come if she wants to only Florrie don't know if she would have a good time or not and thinks maybe she would rather stay in Bedford and you come alone. But be sure and have Bertha come if she wants to come but maybe she would not injoy it. You know best Al.

I don't think the old man give me no square deal on that lease but if he wants to stick me all right. I am grateful to you Al for trying to fix it up but maybe you could of did better if you had of went at it in a different way. I am not finding no fault with my old pal though. Don't think that. When I have a pal I am the man to stick to him threw thick and thin. If the old man is going to hold me to that lease I guess I will have to stand it and I guess I won't starv to death for no $10 a month because I am going to get $2800 next year besides the city serious money and maybe we will get into the World Serious too. I know we will if Callahan will pitch me every 3d day like I wanted him to last season. But if you had of approached the old man in a different way maybe you could of fixed it up. I wish you would try it again Al if it is not no trouble.

We had Allen and his wife here for thanksgiveing dinner and the dinner cost me better than $5. I thought we had enough to eat to last a week but about six o'clock at night Florrie and Marie said they was hungry and we went downtown and had dinner all over again and I payed for it and it cost me $5 more. Allen was all ready to pay for it when Florrie said No this day's treat is on us so I had to pay for it but I don't see why she did not wait and let me do the talking. I was going to pay for it any way.

Be sure and come and visit us for the holidays Al and of coarse if Bertha wants to come bring her along. We will be glad to see you both. I won't never go back on a friend and pal. You know me Al.

Your old pal,   JACK.

Chicago, Illinois, December 20.

FRIEND AL: I don't see what can be the matter with Bertha because you know Al we would not care how she dressed and would not make no kick if she come up here in a night gown. She did not have no license to say we was to swell for her because we did not never think of nothing like that. I wish you would talk to her again Al and tell her she need not get sore on me and that both her and you is welcome at my house any time I ask you to come. See if you can't make her change her mind Al because I feel like as if she must of took offense at something I may of wrote you. I am sorry you and her are not comeing but I suppose you know best. Only we was getting all ready for you and Florrie said only the other day that she wished the holidays was over but that was before she knowed you was not comeing. I hope you can come Al.

Well Al I guess there is not no use talking to the old man no more. You have did the best you could but I wish I could of came down there and talked to him. I will pay him his rotten old $10 a month and the next time I come to Bedford and meet him on the street I will bust his jaw. I know he is a old man Al but I don't like to see nobody get the best of me and I am sorry I ever asked him to let me off. Some of them old skinflints has no heart Al but why should I fight with a old man over chicken feed like $10? Florrie says a star pitcher like I should not ought never to scrap about little things and I guess she is right Al so I will pay the old man his $10 a month if I have to.

Florrie says she is jealous of me writing to you so much and she says she would like to meet this great old pal of mine. I would like to have her meet you to Al and I would like to have you change your mind and come and visit us and I am sorry you can't come Al.

Your truly,   JACK.

Chicago, Illinois, December 27.

OLD PAL: I guess all these lefthanders is alike though I thought this Allen had some sense. I thought he was different from the most and was not no rummy but they are all alike Al and they are all lucky that somebody don't hit them over the head with a ax and kill them but I guess at that you could not hurt no lefthanders by hitting them over the head. We was all down on State St. the day before Xmas and the girls was all tired out and ready to go home but Allen says No I guess we better stick down a while because now the crowds is out and it will be fun to watch them. So we walked up and down State St. about a hour longer and finally we come in front of a big jewlry store window and in it was a swell dimond ring that was marked $100. It was a ladie's ring so Marie says to Allen Why don't you buy that for me? And Allen says Do you really want it? And she says she did.

So we tells the girls to wait and we goes over to a salloon where Allen has got a friend and gets a check cashed and we come back and he bought the ring. Then Florrie looks like as though she was getting all ready to cry and I asked her what was the matter and she says I had not boughten her no ring not even when we was engaged. So I and Allen goes back to the salloon and I gets a check cashed and we come back and bought another ring but I did not think the ring Allen had boughten was worth no $100 so I gets one for $75. Now Al you know I am not makeing no kick on spending a little money for a present for my own wife but I had allready boughten her a rist watch for $15 and a rist watch was just what she had wanted. I was willing to give her the ring if she had not of wanted the rist watch more than the ring but when I give her the ring I kept the rist watch and did not tell her nothing about it.

Well I come downtown alone the day after Xmas and they would not take the rist watch back in the store where I got it. So I am going to give it to her for a New Year's present and I guess that will make Allen feel like a dirty doose. But I guess you cannot hurt no lefthander's feelings at that. They are all alike. But Allen has not got nothing but a dinky curve ball and a fast ball that looks like my slow one. If Comiskey was not good hearted he would of sold him long ago.

I sent you and Bertha a cut glass dish Al which was the best I could get for the money and it was pretty high pricet at that. We was glad to get the pretty pincushions from you and Bertha and Florrie says to tell you that we are well supplied with pincushions now because the ones you sent makes a even half dozen. Thanks Al for remembering us and thank Bertha too though I guess you paid for them.   Your pal,   JACK.

Chicago, Illinois, Januery 3.

OLD PAL: Al I been pretty sick ever since New Year's eve. We had a table at 1 of the swell resturunts downtown and I never seen so much wine drank in my life. I would rather of had beer but they would not sell us none so I found out that they was a certain kind that you can get for $1 a bottle and it is just as good as the kind that has got all them fancy names but this lefthander starts ordering some other kind about 11 oclock and it was $5 a bottle and the girls both says they liked it better. I could not see a hole lot of difference myself and I would of gave $0.20 for a big stine of my kind of beer. You know me Al. Well Al you know they is not nobody that can drink more than your old pal and I was all O. K. at one oclock but I seen the girls was getting kind of sleepy so I says we better go home.

Then Marie says Oh, shut up and don't be no quiter. I says You better shut up yourself and not be telling me to shut up, and she says What will you do if I don't shut up? And I says I would bust her in the jaw. But you know Al I would not think of busting no girl. Then Florrie says You better not start nothing because you had to much to drink or you would not be talking about busting girls in the jaw. Then I says I don't care if it is a girl I bust or a lefthander. I did not mean nothing at all Al but Marie says I had insulted Allen and he gets up and slaps my face. Well Al I am not going to stand that from nobody not even if he is my brother-in-law and a lefthander that has not got enough speed to brake a pain of glass.

So I give him a good beating and the waiters butts in and puts us all out for fighting and I and Florrie comes home in a taxi and Allen and his wife don't get in till about 5 oclock so I guess she must of had to of took him to a doctor to get fixed up. I been in bed ever since till just this morning kind of sick to my stumach. I guess I must of eat something that did not agree with me. Allen come over after breakfast this morning and asked me was I all right so I guess he is not sore over the beating I give him or else he wants to make friends because he has saw that I am a bad guy to monkey with.

Florrie tells me a little while ago that she paid the hole bill at the resturunt with my money because Allen was broke so you see what kind of a cheap skate he is Al and some day I am going to bust his jaw. She won't tell me how much the bill was and I won't ask her to no more because we had a good time outside of the fight and what do I care if we spent a little money?

Yours truly,   JACK.

Chicago, Illinois, January 20.

FRIEND AL: Allen and his wife have gave up the flat across the hall from us and come over to live with us because we got a spair bedroom and why should they not have the bennifit of it? But it is pretty hard for the girls to have to cook and do the work when they is four of us so I have a hired girl who does it all for $7 a week. It is great stuff Al because now we can go round as we please and don't have to wait for no dishes to be washed or nothing. We generally almost always has dinner downtown in the evening so it is pretty soft for the girl too. She don't generally have no more than one meal to get because we generally run round downtown till late and don't get up till about noon.

That sounds funny don't it Al, when I used to get up at 5 every morning down home. Well Al I can tell you something else that may sound funny and that is that I lost my taste for beer. I don't seem to care for it no more and I found I can stand allmost as many drinks of other stuff as I could of beer. I guess Al they is not nobody ever lived can drink more and stand up better under it than me. I make the girls and Allen quit every night.

I only got just time to write you this short note because Florrie and Marie is giving a big party to-night and I and Allen have got to beat it out of the house and stay out of the way till they get things ready. It is Marie's berthday and she says she is 22 but say Al if she is 22 Kid Gleason is 30. Well Al the girls says we must blow so I will run out and mail this letter.   Yours truly,   JACK.

Chicago, Illinois, January 31.

AL: Allen is going to take Marie with him on the training trip to California and of course Florrie has been at me to take her along. I told her postivly that she can't go. I can't afford no stunt like that but still I am up against it to know what to do with her while we are on the trip because Marie won't be here to stay with her. I don't like to leave her here all alone but they is nothing to it Al I can't afford to take her along. She says I don't see why you can't take me if Allen takes Marie. And I says That stuff is all O. K. for Allen because him and Marie has been grafting off of us all winter. And then she gets mad and tells me I should not ought to say her sister was no grafter. I did not mean nothing like that Al but you don't never know when a woman is going to take offense.

If our furniture was down in Bedford everything would be all O. K. because I could leave her there and I would feel all O. K. because I would know that you and Bertha would see that she was getting along O. K. But they would not be no sense in sending her down to a house that has not no furniture in it. I wish I knowed somewheres where she could visit Al. I would be willing to pay her bord even.

Well Al enough for this time.   Your old pal,   JACK.

Chicago, Illinois, Febuery 4.

FRIEND AL: You are a real old pal Al and I certainly am greatful to you for the invatation. I have not told Florrie about it yet but I am sure she will be tickled to death and it is certainly kind of you old pal. I did not never dream of nothing like that. I note what you say Al about not excepting no bord but I think it would be better and I would feel better if you would take something say about $2 a week.

I know Bertha will like Florrie and that they will get along O. K. together because Florrie can learn her how to make her cloths look good and fix her hair and fix up her face. I feel like as if you had took a big load off of me Al and I won't never forget it.

If you don't think I should pay no bord for Florrie all right. Suit yourself about that old pal.

We are leaveing here the 20 of Febuery and if you don't mind I will bring Florrie down to you about the 18. I would like to see the old bunch again and spesially you and Bertha.

Yours,   JACK.

P. S. We will only be away till April 14 and that is just a nice visit. I wish we did not have no flat on our hands.

Chicago, Illinois, Febuery 9.

OLD PAL: I want to thank you for asking Florrie to come down there and visit you Al but I find she can't get away. I did not know she had no engagements but she says she may go down to her folks in Texas and she don't want to say that she will come to visit you when it is so indefanate. So thank you just the same Al and thank Bertha too.

Florrie is still at me to take her along to California but honest Al I can't do it. I am right down to my last $50 and I have not payed no rent for this month. I owe the hired girl 2 weeks' salery and both I and Florrie needs some new cloths.

Florrie has just came in since I started writeing this letter and we have been talking some more about California and she says maybe if I would ask Comiskey he would take her along as the club's guest. I had not never thought of that Al and maybe he would because he is a pretty good scout and I guess I will go and see him about it. The league has its skedule meeting here to-morrow and may be I can see him down to the hotel where they meet at. I am so worried Al that I can't write no more but I will tell you how I come out with Comiskey.   Your pal,   JACK.

Chicago, Illinois, Febuery 11.

FRIEND AL: I am up against it right Al and I don't know where I am going to head in at. I went down to the hotel where the league was holding its skedule meeting at and I seen Comiskey and got some money off of the club but I owe all the money I got off of them and I am still wondering what to do about Florrie.

Comiskey was busy in the meeting when I went down there and they was not no chance to see him for a while so I and Allen and some of the boys hung round and had a few drinks and fanned. This here Joe Hill the busher that Detroit has got that Violet is hooked up to was round the hotel. I don't know what for but I felt like busting his jaw only the boys told me I had better not do nothing because I might kill him and any way he probily won't be in the league much longer. Well finally Comiskey got threw the meeting and I seen him and he says Hello Young man what can I do for you? And I says I would like to get $100 advance money. He says Have you been takeing care of yourself down in Bedford? And I told him I had been liveing here all winter and it did not seem to make no hit with him though I don't see what business it is of hisn where I live.

So I says I had been takeing good care of myself. And I have Al. You know that. So he says I should come to the ball park the next day which is to-day and he would have the secretary take care of me but I says I could not wait and so he give me $100 out of his pocket and says he would have it charged against my salery. I was just going to brace him about the California trip when he got away and went back to the meeting.

Well Al I hung round with the bunch waiting for him to get threw again and we had some more drinks and finally Comiskey was threw again and I braced him in the lobby and asked him if it was all right to take my wife along to California. He says Sure they would be glad to have her along. And then I says Would the club pay her fair? He says I guess you must of spent that $100 buying some nerve. He says Have you not got no sisters that would like to go along to? He says Does your wife insist on the drawing room or will she take a lower berth? He says Is my special train good enough for her?

Then he turns away from me and I guess some of the boys must of heard the stuff he pulled because they was laughing when he went away but I did not see nothing to laugh at. But I guess he ment that I would have to pay her fair if she goes along and that is out of the question Al. I am up against it and I don't know where I am going to head in at.   Your pal,   JACK.

Chicago, Illinois, Febuery 12.

DEAR OLD AL: I guess everything will be all O. K. now at least I am hopeing it will. When I told Florrie about how I come out with Comiskey she bawled her head off and I thought for a while I was going to have to call a doctor or something but pretty soon she cut it out and we sat there a while without saying nothing. Then she says If you could get your salery razed a couple of hundred dollars a year would you borrow the money ahead somewheres and take me along to California? I says Yes I would if I could get a couple hundred dollars more salery but how could I do that when I had signed a contract for $2800 last fall allready? She says Don't you think you are worth more than $2800? And I says Yes of coarse I was worth more than $2800. She says Well if you will go and talk the right way to Comiskey I believe he will give you $3000 but you must be sure you go at it the right way and don't go and ball it all up.

Well we argue about it a while because I don't want to hold nobody up Al but finally I says I would. It would not be holding nobody up anyway because I am worth $3000 to the club if I am worth a nichol. The papers is all saying that the club has got a good chance to win the pennant this year and talking about the pitching staff and I guess they would not be no pitching staff much if it was not for I and one or two others—about one other I guess.

So it looks like as if everything will be all O. K. now Al. I am going to the office over to the park to see him the first thing in the morning and I am pretty sure that I will get what I am after because if I do not he will see that I am going to quit and then he will see what he is up against and not let me get away.

I will let you know how I come out.

Your pal,   JACK.

Chicago, Illinois, Febuery 14.

FRIEND AL: Al old pal I have got a big supprise for you. I am going to the Federal League. I had a run in with Comiskey yesterday and I guess I told him a thing or 2. I guess he would of been glad to sign me at my own figure before I got threw but I was so mad I would not give him no chance to offer me another contract.

I got out to the park at 9 oclock yesterday morning and it was a hour before he showed up and then he kept me waiting another hour so I was pretty sore when I finally went in to see him. He says Well young man what can I do for you? I says I come to see about my contract. He says Do you want to sign up for next year all ready? I says No I am talking about this year. He says I thought I and you talked business last fall. And I says Yes but now I think I am worth more money and I want to sign a contract for $3000. He says If you behave yourself and work good this year I will see that you are took care of. But I says That won't do because I have got to be sure I am going to get $3000.

Then he says I am not sure you are going to get anything. I says What do you mean? And he says I have gave you a very fare contract and if you don't want to live up to it that is your own business. So I give him a awful call Al and told him I would jump to the Federal League. He says Oh, I would not do that if I was you. They are haveing a hard enough time as it is. So I says something back to him and he did not say nothing to me and I beat it out of the office.

I have not told Florrie about the Federal League business yet as I am going to give her a big supprise. I bet they will take her along with me on the training trip and pay her fair but even if they don't I should not worry because I will make them give me a contract for $4000 a year and then I can afford to take her with me on all the trips.

I will go down and see Tinker to-morrow morning and I will write you to-morrow night Al how such salery they are going to give me. But I won't sign for no less than $4000. You know me Al.

Yours,   JACK.

Chicago, Illinois, Febuery 15.

OLD PAL: It is pretty near midnight Al but I been to bed a couple of times and I can't get no sleep. I am worried to death Al and I don't know where I am going to head in at. Maybe I will go out and buy a gun Al and end it all and I guess it would be better for everybody. But I cannot do that Al because I have not got the money to buy a gun with.

I went down to see Tinker about signing up with the Federal League and he was busy in the office when I come in. Pretty soon Buck Perry the pitcher that was with Boston last year come out and seen me and as Tinker was still busy we went out and had a drink together. Buck shows me a contract for $5000 a year and Tinker had allso gave him a $500 bonus. So pretty soon I went up to the office and pretty soon Tinker seen me and called me into his private office and asked what did I want. I says I was ready to jump for $4000 and a bonus. He says I thought you was signed up with the White

Sox. I says Yes I was but I was not satisfied. He says That does not make no difference to me if you are satisfied or not. You ought to of came to me before you signed a contract. I says I did not know enough but I know better now. He says Well it is to late now. We cannot have nothing to do with you because you have went and signed a contract with the White Sox. I argude with him a while and asked him to come out and have a drink so we could talk it over but he said he was busy so they was nothing for me to do but blow.

So I am not going to the Federal League Al and I will not go with the White Sox because I have got a raw deal. Comiskey will be sorry for what he done when his team starts the season and is up against it for good pitchers and then he will probily be willing to give me anything I ask for but that don't do no good now Al. I am way in debt and no chance to get no money from nobody. I wish I had of stayed with Terre Haute Al and never saw this league.

Your pal,   JACK.

Chicago, Illinois, Febuery 17.
FRIEND AL: Al don't never let nobody tell you that these here lefthanders is right. This Allen my own brother-in-law who married sisters has been grafting and spongeing on me all winter Al. Look what he done to me now Al. You know how hard I been up against it for money and I know he has got plenty of it because I seen it on him. Well Al I was scared to tell Florrie I was cleaned out and so I went to Allen yesterday and says I had to have $100 right away because I owed the rent and owed the hired girl's salery and could not even pay no grocery bill. And he says No he could not let me have none because he has got to save all his money to take his wife on the trip to California. And here he has been liveing on me all winter and maybe I could of took my wife to California if I had not of spent all my money takeing care of this no good lefthander and his wife. And Al honest he has not got a thing and ought not to be in the league. He gets by with a dinky curve ball and has not got no more smoke than a rabbit or something.

Well Al I felt like busting him in the jaw but then I thought No I might kill him and then I would have Marie and Florrie both to take care of and God knows one of them is enough besides paying his funeral expenses. So I walked away from him without takeing a crack at him and went into the other room where Florrie and Marie was at. I says to Marie I says Marie I wish you would go in the other room a minute because I want to talk to Florrie. So Marie beats it into the other room and then I tells Florrie all about what Comiskey and the Federal League done to me. She bawled something awful and then she says I was no good and she wished she had not never married me. I says I wisht it too and then she says Do you mean that and starts to cry.

I told her I was sorry I says that because they is not no use fusing with girls Al specially when they is your wife. She says No California trip for me and then she says What are you going to do? And I says I did not know. She says Well if I was a man I would do something. So then I got mad and I says I will do something. So I went down to the corner salloon and started in to get good and drunk but I could not do it Al because I did not have the money.

Well old pal I am going to ask you a big favor and it is this I want you to send me $100 Al for just a few days till I can get on my feet. I do not know when I can pay it back Al but I guess you know the money is good and I know you have got it. Who would not have it when they live in Bedford? And besides I let you take $20 in June 4 years ago Al and give it back but I would not have said nothing to you if you had of kept it. Let me hear from you right away old pal.   Yours truly,   JACK.

                    Chicago, Illinois, Febuery 19.
AL: I am certainly greatful to you Al for the $100 which come just a little while ago. I will pay the rent with it and part of the grocery bill and I guess the hired girl will have to wait a while for hern but she is sure to get it because I don't never forget my debts. I have changed my mind about the White Sox and I am going to go on the trip and take Florrie along because I don't think it would not be right to leave her here alone in Chi when her sister and all of us is going.

I am going over to the ball park and up in the office pretty soon to see about it. I will tell Comiskey I changed my mind and he will be glad to get me back because the club has not got no chance to finish nowheres without me. But I won't go on no trip or give the

club my services without them giveing me some more advance money
so as I can take Florrie along with me because Al I would not go
without her.

Maybe Comiskey will make my salery $3000 like I wanted him to
when he sees I am willing to be a good fellow and go along with
him and when he knows that the Federal League would of gladly
gave me $4000 if I had not of signed no contract with the White Sox.

I think I will ask him for $200 advance money Al and if I get it
may be I can send part of your $100 back to you but I know you
cannot be in no hurry Al though you says you wanted it back as
soon as possible. You could not be very hard up Al because it don't
cost near so much to live in Bedford as it does up here.

Anyway I will let you know how I come out with Comiskey and
I will write you as soon as I get out to Paso Robles if I don't get no
time to write you before I leave.   Your pal,   JACK.

P. S. I have took good care of myself all winter Al and I guess I
ought to have a great season.

P. S. Florrie is tickled to death about going along and her and I
will have some time together out there on the Coast if I can get
some money somewheres.

Chicago, Illinois, Febuery 21.

FRIEND AL: I have not got the heart to write this letter to you Al.
I am up here in my $42.50 a month flat and the club has went to
California and Florrie has went too. I am flat broke Al and all I am
asking you is to send me enough money to pay my fair to Bedford
and they and all their leagues can go to hell Al.

I was out to the ball park early yesterday morning and some of
the boys was there allready fanning and kidding each other. They
tried to kid me to when I come in but I guess I give them as good
as they give me. I was not in no mind for kidding Al because I was
there on business and I wanted to see Comiskey and get it done with.

Well the secretary come in finally and I went up to him and says
I wanted to see Comiskey right away. He says The boss was busy and
what did I want to see him about and I says I wanted to get some
advance money because I was going to take my wife on the trip. He
says This would be a fine time to be telling us about it even if you
was going on the trip.

And I says What do you mean? And he says You are not going on no trip with us because we have got wavers on you and you are sold to Milwaukee.

Honest Al I thought he was kidding at first and I was waiting for him to laugh but he did not laugh and finally I says What do you mean? And he says Cannot you understand no English? You are sold to Milwaukee. Then I says I want to see the boss. He says It won't do you no good to see the boss and he is to busy to see you. I says I want to get some money. And he says You cannot get no money from this club and all you get is your fair to Milwaukee. I says I am not going to no Milwaukee anyway and he says I should not worry about that. Suit yourself.

Well Al I told some of the boys about it and they was pretty sore and says I ought to bust the secretary in the jaw and I was going to do it when I thought No I better not because he is a little guy and I might kill him.

I looked all over for Kid Gleason but he was not nowheres round and they told me he would not get into town till late in the afternoon. If I could of saw him Al he would of fixed me all up. I asked 3 or 4 of the boys for some money but they says they was all broke.

But I have not told you the worst of it yet Al. When I come back to the flat Allen and Marie and Florrie was busy packing up and they asked me how I come out. I told them and Allen just stood there stareing like a big rummy but Marie and Florrie both begin to cry and I almost felt like as if I would like to cry to only I am not no baby Al.

Well Al I told Florrie she might just as well quit packing and make up her mind that she was not going nowheres till I got money enough to go to Bedford where I belong. She kept right on crying and it got so I could not stand it no more so I went out to get a drink because I still had just about a dollar left yet.

It was about 2 oclock when I left the flat and pretty near 5 when I come back because I had ran in to some fans that knowed who I was and would not let me get away and besides I did not want to see no more of Allen and Marie till they was out of the house and on their way.

But when I come in Al they was nobody there. They was not nothing except the furniture and a few of my things scattered round.

I sit down for a few minutes because I guess I must of had to much to drink but finally I seen a note on the table addressed to me and I seen it was Florrie's writeing.

I do not remember just what was there in the note Al because I tore it up the minute I read it but it was something about I could not support no wife and Allen had gave her enough money to go back to Texas and she was going on the 6 oclock train and it would not do me no good to try and stop her.

Well Al they was not no danger of my trying to stop her. She was not no good Al and I wisht I had not of never saw either she or her sister or my brother-in-law.

For a minute I thought I would follow Allen and his wife down to the deepo where the special train was to pull out of and wait till I see him and punch his jaw but I seen that would not get me nothing.

So here I am all alone Al and I will have to stay here till you send me the money to come home. You better send me $25 because I have got a few little debts I should ought to pay before I leave town. I am not going to Milwaukee Al because I did not get no decent deal and nobody cannot make no sucker out of me.

Please hurry up with the $25 Al old friend because I am sick and tired of Chi and want to get back there with my old pal.

Yours,   JACK.

P. S. Al I wish I had of took poor little Violet when she was so stuck on me.

Gullible's Travels

I

I promised the Wife that if anybody ast me what kind of a time did I have at Palm Beach I'd say I had a swell time. And if they ast me who did we meet I'd tell 'em everybody that was worth meetin'. And if they ast me didn't the trip cost a lot I'd say Yes; but it was worth the money. I promised her I wouldn't spill none o' the real details.

But if you can't break a promise you made to your own wife what kind of a promise can you break? Answer me that, Edgar.

I'm not one o' these kind o' people that'd keep a joke to themself just because the joke was on them. But they's plenty of our friends that I wouldn't have 'em hear about it for the world. I wouldn't tell you, only I know you're not the village gossip and won't crack it to anybody. Not even to your own Missus, see? I don't trust no women.

It was along last January when I and the Wife was both hit by the *society bacillus*. I think it was at the opera. You remember me tellin' you about us and the Hatches goin' to *Carmen* and then me takin' my Missus and her sister, Bess, and four of one suit named Bishop to see *The Three Kings?* Well, I'll own up that I enjoyed wearin' the soup and fish and minglin' amongst the *high polloi* and pretendin' we really was somebody. And I know my wife enjoyed it, too, though they was nothin' said between us at the time.

The next stage was where our friends wasn't good enough for us no more. We used to be tickled to death to spend an evenin' playin' rummy with the Hatches. But all of a sudden they didn't seem to be no fun in it and when Hatch'd call up we'd stall out of it. From the number o' times I told him that I or the Missus was tired out and goin' right to bed, he must of thought we'd got jobs as telephone linemen.

We quit attendin' pitcher shows because the rest o' the audience wasn't the kind o' people you'd care to mix with. We didn't go over to Ben's and dance because they wasn't no class to the crowd there. About once a week we'd beat it to one o' the good hotels down-town, all dressed up like a horse, and have our dinner with the rest o' the E-light. They wasn't nobody talked to us only the waiters, but we could look as much as we liked and it was sport tryin' to guess the names o' the gang at the next table.

Then we took to readin' the society news at breakfast. It used to be that I didn't waste time on nothin' but the market and sportin' pages, but now I pass 'em up and listen w'ile the Missus rattled off what was doin' on the Lake Shore Drive.

Every little w'ile we'd see where So-and-So was at Palm Beach or just goin' there or just comin' back. We got to kiddin' about it.

"Well," I'd say, "we'd better be startin' pretty soon or we'll miss the best part o' the season."

"Yes," the Wife'd say back, "we'd go right now if it wasn't for all them engagements next week."

We kidded and kidded till finally, one night, she forgot we was just kiddin'.

"You didn't take no vacation last summer," she says.

"No," says I. "They wasn't no chance to get away."

"But you promised me," she says, "that you'd take one this winter to make up for it."

"I know I did," I says; "but it'd be a sucker play to take a vacation in weather like this."

"The weather ain't like this everywheres," she says.

"You must of been goin' to night school," I says.

"Another thing you promised me," says she, "was that when you could afford it you'd take me on a real honeymoon trip to make up for the dinky one we had."

"That still goes," I says, "when I can afford it."

"You can afford it now," says she. "We don't owe nothin' and we got money in the bank."

"Yes," I says. "Pretty close to three hundred bucks."

"You forgot somethin," she says. "You forgot them war babies."

Did I tell you about that? Last fall I done a little dabblin' in Crucial Steel and at this time I'm tellin' you about I still had a hold of it, but stood to pull down six hundred. Not bad, eh?

"It'd be a mistake to let loose now," I says.

"All right," she says. "Hold on, and I hope you lose every cent. You never did care nothin' for me."

Then we done a little spoonin' and then I ast her what was the big idear.

"We ain't swelled on ourself," she says; "but I know and you know that the friends we been associatin' with ain't in our class. They don't know how to dress and they can't talk about nothin' but their goldfish and their meat bills. They don't try to get nowheres, but all they do is play rummy and take in the Majestic. I and you like nice people and good music and things that's worth w'ile. It's a crime for us to be wastin' our time with riff and raff that'd run round barefooted if it wasn't for the police."

"I wouldn't say we'd wasted much time on 'em lately," I says.

"No," says she, "and I've had a better time these last three weeks than I ever had in my life."

"And you can keep right on havin' it," I says.

"I could have a whole lot better time, and you could, too," she says, "if we could get acquainted with some congenial people to go round with; people that's tastes is the same as ourn."

"If any o' them people calls up on the phone," I says, "I'll be as pleasant to 'em as I can."

"You're always too smart," says the Wife. "You don't never pay attention to no schemes o' mine."

"What's the scheme now?"

"You'll find fault with it because I thought it up," she says. "If it was your scheme you'd think it was grand."

"If it really was good you wouldn't be scared to spring it," I says.

"Will you promise to go through with it?" says she.

"If it ain't too ridic'lous," I told her.

"See! I knowed that'd be the way," she says.

"Don't talk crazy," I says. "Where'd we be if we'd went through with every plan you ever sprang?"

"Will you promise to listen to my side of it without actin' cute?" she says.

So I didn't see no harm in goin' that far.

"I want you to take me to Palm Beach," says she. "I want you to take a vacation, and that's where we'll spend it."

"And that ain't all we'd spend," I says.

"Remember your promise," says she.

So I shut up and listened.

The dope she give me was along these lines: We could get special round-trip rate on any o' the railroads and that part of it wouldn't cost nowheres near as much as a man'd naturally think. The hotel rates was pretty steep, but the meals was throwed in, and just imagine what them meals would be! And we'd be stayin' under the same roof with the Vanderbilts and Goulds, and eatin' at the same table, and probably, before we was there a week, callin' 'em Steve and Gus. They was dancin' every night and all the guests danced with each other, and how would it feel fox-trottin' with the president o' the B. & O., or the Delmonico girls from New York! And all

Chicago society was down there, and when we met 'em we'd know 'em for life and have some real friends amongst 'em when we got back home.

That's how she had it figured and she must of been practisin' her speech, because it certainly did sound good to me. To make it short, I fell, and dated her up to meet me down-town the next day and call on the railroad bandits. The first one we seen admitted that his was the best route and that he wouldn't only soak us one hundred and forty-seven dollars and seventy cents to and from Palm Beach and back, includin' an apartment from here to Jacksonville and as many stop-overs as we wanted to make. He told us we wouldn't have to write for no hotel accommodations because the hotels had an agent right over on Madison Street that'd be glad to do everything to us.

So we says we'd be back later and then we beat it over to the Florida East Coast's local studio.

"How much for a double room by the week?" I ast the man.

"They ain't no weekly rates," he says. "By the day it'd be twelve dollars and up for two at the Breakers, and fourteen dollars and up at the Poinciana."

"I like the Breakers better," says I.

"You can't get in there," he says. "They're full for the season."

"That's a long spree," I says.

"Can we get in the other hotel?" ast the Wife.

"I can find out," says the man.

"We want a room with bath," says she.

"That'd be more," says he. "That'd be fifteen dollars or sixteen dollars and up."

"What do we want of a bath," I says, "with the whole Atlantic Ocean in the front yard?"

"I'm afraid you'd have trouble gettin' a bath," says the man. "The hotels is both o' them pretty well filled up on account o' the war in Europe."

"What's that got to do with it?" I ast him.

"A whole lot," he says. "The people that usually goes abroad is all down to Palm Beach this winter."

"I don't see why," I says. "If one o' them U-boats hit 'em they'd at least be gettin' their bath for nothin'."

We left him with the understandin' that he was to wire down

there and find out what was the best they could give us. We called him up in a couple o' days and he told us we could have a double room, without no bath, at the Poinciana, beginnin' the fifteenth o' February. He didn't know just what the price would be.

Well, I fixed it up to take my vacation startin' the tenth, and sold out my Crucial Steel, and divided the spoils with the railroad company. We decided we'd stop off in St. Augustine two days, because the Missus found out somewheres that they might be two or three o' the Four Hundred lingerin' there, and we didn't want to miss nobody.

"Now," I says, "all we got to do is set round and wait for the tenth o' the month."

"Is that so!" says the Wife. "I suppose you're perfectly satisfied with your clo'es."

"I've got to be," I says, "unless the Salvation Army has somethin' that'll fit me."

"What's the matter with our charge account?" she says.

"I don't like to charge nothin'," I says, "when I know they ain't no chance of ever payin' for it."

"All right," she says, "then we're not goin' to Palm Beach. I'd rather stay home than go down there lookin' like general housework."

"Do you need clo'es yourself?" I ast her.

"I certainly do," she says. "About two hundred dollars' worth. But I got one hundred and fifty dollars o' my own."

"All right," I says. "I'll stand for the other fifty and then we're all set."

"No, we're not," she says. "That just fixes me. But I want you to look as good as I do."

"Nature'll see to that," I says.

But they was no arguin' with her. Our trip, she says, was an investment; it was goin' to get us in right with people worth w'ile. And we wouldn't have a chance in the world unless we looked the part.

So before the tenth come round, we was long two new evenin' gowns, two female sport suits, four or five pairs o' shoes, all colors, one Tuxedo dinner coat, three dress shirts, half a dozen other kinds o' shirts, two pairs o' transparent white trousers, one new business suit and Lord knows how much underwear and how many hats and stockin's. And I had till the fifteenth o' March to pay off the mortgage on the old homestead.

Just as we was gettin' ready to leave for the train the phone rung. It was Mrs. Hatch and she wanted us to come over for a little rummy. I was shavin' and the Missus done the talkin'.

"What did you tell her?" I ast.

"I told her we was goin' away," says the Wife.

"I bet you forgot to mention where we was goin'," I says.

"Pay me," says she.

II

I thought we was in Venice when we woke up next mornin', but the porter says it was just Cairo, Illinois. The river'd went crazy and I bet they wasn't a room without a bath in that old burg.

As we set down in the diner for breakfast the train was goin' acrost the longest bridge I ever seen, and it looked like we was so near the water that you could reach right out and grab a handful. The Wife was a little wabbly.

"I wonder if it's really safe," she says.

"If the bridge stays up we're all right," says I.

"But the question is, Will it stay up?" she says.

"I wouldn't bet a nickel either way on a bridge," I says. "They're treacherous little devils. They'd cross you as quick as they'd cross this river."

"The trainmen must be nervous," she says. "Just see how we're draggin' along."

"They're givin' the fish a chance to get offen the track," I says. "It's against the law to spear fish with a cowcatcher this time o' year."

Well, the Wife was so nervous she couldn't eat nothin' but toast and coffee, so I figured I was justified in goin' to the prunes and steak and eggs.

After breakfast we went out in what they call the sun parlor. It was a glassed-in room on the tail-end o' the rear coach and it must of been a pleasant place to set and watch the scenery. But they was a gang o' missionaries or somethin' had all the seats and they never budged out o' them all day. Every time they'd come to a crossroads they'd toss a stack o' Bible studies out o' the back window for the southern heathen to pick up and read. I suppose they thought they was doin' a lot o' good for their fellow men, but their fellow passengers meanw'ile was gettin' the worst of it.

Speakin' o' the scenery, it certainly was somethin' grand. First we'd pass a few pine trees with fuzz on 'em and then a couple o' acres o' yellow mud. Then they'd be more pine trees and more fuzz and then more yellow mud. And after a w'ile we'd come to some pine trees with fuzz on 'em and then, if we watched close, we'd see some yellow mud.

Every few minutes the train'd stop and then start up again on low. That meant the engineer suspected he was comin' to a station and was scared that if he run too fast he wouldn't see it, and if he run past it without stoppin' the inhabitants wouldn't never forgive him. You see, they's a regular schedule o' duties that's followed out by the more prominent citizens down those parts. After their wife's attended to the chores and got the breakfast they roll out o' bed and put on their overalls and eat. Then they get on their horse or mule or cow or dog and ride down to the station and wait for the next train. When it comes they have a contest to see which can count the passengers first. The losers has to promise to work one day the followin' month. If one fella loses three times in the same month he generally always kills himself.

All the towns has got five or six private residences and seven or eight two-apartment buildin's and a grocery and a post-office. They told me that somebody in one o' them burgs, I forget which one, got a letter the day before we come through. It was misdirected, I guess.

The two-apartment buildin's is constructed on the ground floor, with a porch to divide one flat from the other. One's the housekeepin' side and the other's just a place for the husband and father to lay round in so's they won't be disturbed by watchin' the women work.

It was a blessin' to them boys when their states went dry. Just think what a strain it must of been to keep liftin' glasses and huntin' in their overalls for a dime!

In the afternoon the Missus went into our apartment and took a nap and I moseyed into the readin'-room and looked over some o' the comical magazines. They was a fat guy come in and set next to me. I'd heard him, in at lunch, tellin' the dinin'-car conductor what

Wilson should of done, so I wasn't su'prised when he opened up
on me.   ●

"Tiresome trip," he says.

I didn't think it was worth w'ile arguin' with him.

"Must of been a lot o' rain through here," he says.

"Either that," says I, "or else the sprinklin' wagon run shy o'
streets."

He laughed as much as it was worth.

"Where do you come from?" he ast me.

"Dear old Chicago," I says.

"I'm from St. Louis," he says.

"You're frank," says I.

"I'm really as much at home one place as another," he says. "The
Wife likes to travel and why shouldn't I humor her?"

"I don't know," I says. "I haven't the pleasure."

"Seems like we're goin' all the w'ile," says he. "It's Hot Springs or
New Orleans or Florida or Atlantic City or California or somewheres."

"Do you get passes?" I ast him.

"I guess I could if I wanted to," he says. "Some o' my best friends
is way up in the railroad business."

"I got one like that," I says. "He generally stands on the fourth or
fifth car behind the engine."

"Do you travel much?" he ast me.

"I don't live in St. Louis," says I.

"Is this your first trip south?" he ast.

"Oh, no," I says. "I live on Sixty-fifth Street."

"I meant, have you ever been down this way before?"

"Oh, yes," says I. "I come down every winter."

"Where do you go?" he ast.

That's what I was layin' for.

"Palm Beach," says I.

"I used to go there," he says. "But I've cut it out. It ain't like it
used to be. They leave everybody in now."

"Yes," I says; "but a man don't have to mix up with 'em."

"You can't just ignore people that comes up and talks to you,"
he says.

"Are you bothered that way much?" I ast.

"It's what drove me away from Palm Beach," he says.

"How long since you been there?" I ast him.

"How long you been goin' there?" he says.

"Me?" says I. "Five years."

"We just missed each other," says he. "I quit six years ago this winter."

"Then it couldn't of been there I seen you," says I. "But I know I seen you somewheres before."

"It might of been most anywheres," he says. "They's few places I haven't been at."

"Maybe it was acrost the pond," says I.

"Very likely," he says. "But not since the war started. I been steerin' clear of Europe for two years."

"So have I, for longer'n that," I says.

"It's certainly an awful thing, this war," says he.

"I believe you're right," says I; "but I haven't heard nobody express it just that way before."

"I only hope," he says, "that we succeed in keepin' out of it."

"If we got in, would you go?" I ast him.

"Yes, sir," he says.

"You wouldn't beat me," says I. "I bet I'd reach Brazil as quick as you."

"Oh, I don't think they'd be any action in South America," he says. "We'd fight defensive at first and most of it would be along the Atlantic Coast."

"Then maybe we could get accommodations in Yellowstone Park," says I.

"They's no sense in this country gettin' involved," he says. "Wilson hasn't handled it right. He either ought to of went stronger or not so strong. He's wrote too many notes."

"You certainly get right to the root of a thing," says I. "You must of thought a good deal about it."

"I know the conditions pretty well," he says. "I know how far you can go with them people over there. I been amongst 'em a good part o' the time."

"I suppose," says I, "that a fella just naturally don't like to butt in. But if I was you I'd consider it my duty to romp down to Washington and give 'em all the information I had."

"Wilson picked his own advisers," says he. "Let him learn his lesson."

"That ain't hardly fair," I says. "Maybe you was out o' town, or your phone was busy or somethin'."

"I don't know Wilson nor he don't know me," he says.

"That oughtn't to stop you from helpin' him out," says I. "If you seen a man drownin' would you wait for some friend o' the both o' you to come along and make the introduction?"

"They ain't no comparison in them two cases," he says. "Wilson ain't never called on me for help."

"You don't know if he has or not," I says. "You don't stick in one place long enough for a man to reach you."

"My office in St. Louis always knows where I'm at," says he. "My stenographer can reach me any time within ten to twelve hours."

"I don't think it's right to have this country's whole future dependin' on a St. Louis stenographer," I says.

"That's nonsense!" says he. "I ain't makin' no claim that I could save or not save this country. But if I and Wilson was acquainted I might tell him some facts that'd help him out in his foreign policy."

"Well, then," I says, "it's up to you to get acquainted. I'd introduce you myself only I don't know your name."

"My name's Gould," says he; "but you're not acquainted with Wilson."

"I could be, easy," says I. "I could get on a train he was goin' somewheres on and then go and set beside him and begin to talk. Lots o' people make friends that way."

It was gettin' along to'rd supper-time, so I excused myself and went back to the apartment. The Missus had woke up and wasn't feelin' good.

"What's the matter?" I ast her.

"This old train," she says. "I'll die if it don't stop goin' round them curves."

"As long as the track curves, the best thing the train can do is curve with it," I says. "You may die if it keeps curvin', but you'd die a whole lot sooner if it left the rails and went straight ahead."

"What you been doin'?" she ast me.

"Just talkin' to one o' the Goulds," I says.

"Gould!" she says. "What Gould?"

"Well," I says, "I didn't ask him his first name, but he's from St. Louis, so I suppose it's Ludwig or Heinie."

"Oh," she says, disgusted. "I thought you meant one o' the real ones."

"He's a real one, all right," says I. "He's so classy that he's passed up Palm Beach. He says it's gettin' too common."

"I don't believe it," says the Wife. "And besides, we don't have to mix up with everybody."

"He says they butt right in on you," I told her.

"They'll get a cold reception from me," she says.

But between the curves and the fear o' Palm Beach not bein' so exclusive as it used to be, she couldn't eat no supper, and I had another big meal.

The next mornin' we landed in Jacksonville three hours behind time and narrowly missed connections for St. Augustine by over an hour and a half. They wasn't another train till one-thirty in the afternoon, so we had some time to kill. I went shoppin' and bought a shave and five or six rickeys. The Wife helped herself to a chair in the writin'-room of one o' the hotels and told pretty near everybody in Chicago that she wished they was along with us, accompanied by a pitcher o' the Elks' Home or the Germania Club, or Trout Fishin' at Atlantic Beach.

W'ile I was gettin' my dime's worth in the tonsorial parlors, I happened to look up at a calendar on the wall, and noticed it was the twelfth o' February.

"How does it come that everything's open here to-day?" I says to the barber. "Don't you-all know it's Lincoln's birthday?"

"Is that so?" he says. "How old is he?"

III

We'd wired ahead for rooms at the Alcazar, and when we landed in St. Augustine they was a motor-bus from the hotel to meet us at the station.

"Southern hospitality," I says to the Wife, and we was both pleased till they relieved us o' four bits apiece for the ride.

Well, they hadn't neither one of us slept good the night before, w'ile we was joltin' through Georgia; so when I suggested a nap they wasn't no argument.

"But our clo'es ought to be pressed," says the Missus. "Call up the valet and have it done w'ile we sleep."

So I called up the valet, and sure enough, he come.

"Hello, George!" I says. "You see, we're goin' to lay down and take a nap, and we was wonderin' if you could crease up these two suits and have 'em back here by the time we want 'em."

"Certainly, sir," says he.

"And how much will it cost?" I ast him.

"One dollar a suit," he says.

"Are you on parole or haven't you never been caught?" says I.

"Yes, sir," he says, and smiled like it was a joke.

"Let's talk business, George," I says. "The tailor we go to on Sixty-third walks two blocks to get our clo'es, and two blocks to take 'em to his joint, and two blocks to bring 'em back, and he only soaks us thirty-five cents a suit."

"He gets poor pay and he does poor work," says the burglar. "When I press clo'es I press 'em right."

"Well," I says, "the tailor on Sixty-third satisfies us. Suppose you don't do your best this time, but just give us seventy cents' worth."

But they wasn't no chance for a bargain. He'd been in the business so long he'd become hardened and lost all regard for his fellow men.

The Missus slept, but I didn't. Instead, I done a few problems in arithmetic. Outside o' what she'd gave up for postcards and stamps in Jacksonville, I'd spent two bucks for our lunch, about two more for my shave and my refreshments, one for a rough ride in a bus, one more for gettin' our trunk and grips carried round, two for havin' the clo'es pressed, and about half a buck in tips to people that I wouldn't never see again. Somewheres near nine dollars a day, not countin' no hotel bill, and over two weeks of it yet to come!

Oh, you rummy game at home, at half a cent a point!

When our clo'es come back I woke her up and give her the figures.

"But to-day's an exception," she says. "After this our meals will be included in the hotel bill and we won't need to get our suits pressed only once a week and you'll be shavin' yourself and they won't be no bus fare when we're stayin' in one place. Besides, we can practise economy all spring and all summer."

"I guess we need the practise," I says.

"And if you're goin' to crab all the time about expenses," says she, "I'll wish we had of stayed home."

"That'll make it unanimous," says I.

Then she begin sobbin' about how I'd spoiled the trip and I had to promise I wouldn't think no more o' what we were spendin'. I might just as well of promised to not worry when the White Sox lost or when I'd forgot to come home to supper.

We went in the dinin'-room about six-thirty and was showed to a table where they was another couple settin'. They was husband and wife, I guess, but I don't know which was which. She was wieldin' the pencil and writin' down their order.

"I guess I'll have clams," he says.

"They disagreed with you last night," says she.

"All right," he says. "I won't try 'em. Give me cream-o'-tomato soup."

"You don't like tomatoes," she says.

"Well, I won't have no soup," says he. "A little o' the blue-fish."

"The blue-fish wasn't no good at noon," she says. "You better try the bass."

"All right, make it bass," he says. "And them sweet-breads and a little roast beef and sweet potatoes and peas and vanilla ice-cream and coffee."

"You wouldn't touch sweet-breads at home," says she, "and you can't tell what they'll be in a hotel."

"All right, cut out the sweet-breads," he says.

"I should think you'd have the stewed chicken," she says, "and leave out the roast beef."

"Stewed chicken it is," says he.

"Stewed chicken and mashed potatoes and string beans and buttered toast and coffee. Will that suit you?"

"Sure!" he says, and she give the slip to the waiter.

George looked at it long enough to of read it three times if he could of read it once and then went out in the kitchen and got a trayful o' whatever was handy.

But the poor guy didn't get more'n a taste of anything. She was watchin' him like a hawk, and no sooner would he delve into one victual than she'd yank the dish away from him and tell him to remember that health was more important than temporary happiness. I felt so sorry for him that I couldn't enjoy my own repast and I told the Wife that we'd have our breakfast apart from that stricken soul if I had to carry the case to old Al Cazar himself.

In the evenin' we strolled acrost the street to the Ponce—that's supposed to be even sweller yet than where we were stoppin' at. We walked all over the place without recognizin' nobody from our set. I finally warned the Missus that if we didn't duck back to our room I'd probably have a heart attack from excitement; but she'd read in her Florida guide that the decorations and pitchers was worth goin' miles to see, so we had to stand in front o' them for a couple hours and try to keep awake. Four or five o' them was thrillers, at that. Their names was Adventure, Discovery, Contest, and so on, but what they all should of been called was Lady Who Had Mislaid Her Clo'es.

The hotel's named after the fella that built it. He come from Spain and they say he was huntin' for some water that if he'd drunk it he'd feel young. I don't see myself how you could expect to feel young on water. But, anyway, he'd heard that this here kind o' water could be found in St. Augustine, and when he couldn't find it he went into the hotel business and got even with the United States by chargin' five dollars a day and up for a room.

Sunday mornin' we went in to breakfast early and I ast the head waiter if we could set at another table where they wasn't no convalescent and his mate. At the same time I give the said head waiter somethin' that spoke louder than words. We was showed to a place way acrost the room from where we'd been the night before. It was a table for six, but the other four didn't come into our life till that night at supper.

Meanw'ile we went sight-seein'. We visited Fort Marion, that'd be a great protection against the Germans, provided they fought with paper wads. We seen the city gate and the cathedral and the slave market, and then we took the boat over to Anastasia Island, that the ocean's on the other side of it. This trip made me homesick, because the people that was along with us on the boat looked just like the ones we'd often went with to Michigan City on the Fourth o' July. The boat landed on the bay side o' the island and from there we was drug over to the ocean side on a horse car, the horse walkin' to one side o' the car instead of in front, so's he wouldn't get ran over.

We stuck on the beach till dinner-time and then took the chariot back to the pavilion on the bay side, where a whole family served the meal and their pigs put on a cabaret. It was the best meal I had in dear old Dixie—fresh oysters and chicken and mashed potatoes and gravy and fish and pie. And they charged two bits a plate.

"Goodness gracious!" says the Missus, when I told her the price. "This is certainly reasonable. I wonder how it happens."

"Well," I says, "the family was probably washed up here by the tide and don't know they're in Florida."

When we got back to the hotel they was only just time to clean up and go down to supper. We hadn't no sooner got seated when our table companions breezed in. It was a man about forty-five, that looked like he'd made his money in express and general haulin', and he had his wife along and both their mother-in-laws. The shirt he had on was the one he'd started from home with, if he lived in Yokohama. His womenfolks wore mournin' with a touch o' gravy here and there.

"You order for us, Jake," says one o' the ladies.

So Jake grabbed the bill o' fare and his wife took the slip and pencil and waited for the dictation.

"Let's see," he says. "How about oyster cocktail?"

"Yes," says the three Mrs. Black.

"Four oyster cocktails, then," says Jake, "and four orders o' blue-points."

"The oysters is nice, too," says I.

They all give me a cordial smile and the ice was broke.

"Everything's good here," says Jake.

"I bet you know," I says.

He seemed pleased at the compliment and went on dictatin'.

"Four chicken soups with rice," he says, "and four o' the blue-fish and four veal chops breaded and four roast chicken and four boiled potatoes—"

But it seemed his wife would rather have sweet potatoes.

"All right," says Jake; "four boiled potatoes and four sweets. And chicken salad and some o' that tapioca puddin' and ice-cream and tea. Is that satisfactory?"

"Fine!" says one o' the mother-in-laws.

"Are you goin' to stay long?" says Mrs. Jake to my Missus.

The party addressed didn't look very clubby, but she was too polite to pull the cut direct.

"We leave to-morrow night," she says.

Nobody ast her where we was goin'.

"We leave for Palm Beach," she says.

"That's a nice place, I guess," says one o' the old ones. "More people goes there than comes here. It ain't so expensive there, I guess."

"You're some guesser," says the Missus and freezes up.

I ast Jake if he'd been to Florida before.

"No," he says; "this is our first trip, but we're makin' up for lost time. We're seein' all they is to see and havin' everything the best."

"You're havin' everything, all right," I says, "but I don't know if it's the best or not. How long have you been here?"

"A week to-morrow," says he. "And we stay another week and then go to Ormond."

"Are you standin' the trip O. K.?" I ast him.

"Well," he says, "I don't feel quite as good as when we first come."

"Kind o' logy?" I says.

"Yes; kind o' heavy," says Jake.

"I know what you ought to do," says I. "You ought to go to a European plan hotel."

"Not w'ile this war's on," he says, "and besides, my mother's a poor sailor."

"Yes," says his mother; "I'm a very poor sailor."

"Jake's mother can't stand the water," says Mrs. Jake.

So I begun to believe that Jake's wife's mother-in-law was a total failure as a jolly tar.

Social intercourse was put an end to when the waiter staggered in with their order and our'n. The Missus seemed to of lost her appetite and just set there lookin' grouchy and tappin' her fingers on the table-cloth and actin' like she was in a hurry to get away. I didn't eat much, neither. It was more fun watchin'.

"Well," I says, when we was out in the lobby, "we finally got acquainted with some real people."

"Real people!" says the Missus, curlin' her lip. "What did you talk to 'em for?"

"I couldn't resist," I says. "Anybody that'd order four oyster cocktails and four rounds o' blue-points is worth knowin'."

"Well," she says, "if they're there when we go in to-morrow

mornin' we'll get our table changed again or you can eat with 'em alone."

But they was absent from the breakfast board.

"They're probably stayin' in bed to-day to get their clo'es washed," says the Missus.

"Or maybe they're sick," I says. "A change of oysters affects some people."

I was for goin' over to the island again and gettin' another o' them quarter banquets, but the program was for us to walk round town all mornin' and take a ride in the afternoon.

First, we went to St. George Street and visited the oldest house in the United States. Then we went to Hospital Street and seen the oldest house in the United States. Then we turned the corner and went down St. Francis Street and inspected the oldest house in the United States. Then we dropped into a soda fountain and I had an egg phosphate, made from the oldest egg in the Western Hemisphere. We passed up lunch and got into a carriage drawn by the oldest horse in Florida, and we rode through the country all afternoon and the driver told us some o' the oldest jokes in the book. He felt it was only fair to give his customers a good time when he was chargin' a dollar an hour, and he had his gags rehearsed so's he could tell the same one a thousand times and never change a word. And the horse knowed where the point come in every one and stopped to laugh.

We done our packin' before supper, and by the time we got to our table Jake and the mourners was through and gone. We didn't have to ask the waiter if they'd been there. He was perspirin' like an evangelist.

After supper we said good-by to the night clerk and twenty-two bucks. Then we bought ourself another ride in the motor-bus and landed at the station ten minutes before train-time; so we only had an hour to wait for the train.

Say, I don't know how many stations they is between New York and San Francisco, but they's twice as many between St. Augustine and Palm Beach. And our train stopped twice and started twice at every one. I give up tryin' to sleep and looked out the window, amusin' myself by readin' the names o' the different stops. The only one that expressed my sentiments was Eau Gallie. We was an hour and a half late pullin' out o' that joint and I figured we'd be two hours to the bad gettin' into our destination. But the guy that made out the time-table must of had the engineer down pat, because when we went acrost the bridge over Lake Worth and landed at the Poinciana depot, we was ten minutes ahead o' time.

They was about two dozen uniformed Ephs on the job to meet us. And when I seen 'em all grab for our baggage with one hand and hold the other out, face up, I knowed why they called it Palm Beach.

IV

The Poinciana station's a couple hundred yards from one end o' the hotel, and that means it's close to five miles from the clerk's desk. By the time we'd registered and been gave our key and marathoned another five miles or so to where our room was located at, I was about ready for the inquest. But the Missus was full o' pep and wild to get down to breakfast and look over our stable mates. She says we would eat without changin' our clo'es; people'd forgive us for not dressin' up on account o' just gettin' there. W'ile she was lookin' out the window at the royal palms and buzzards, I moseyed round the room inspectin' where the different doors led to. Pretty near the first one I opened went into a private bath.

"Here," I says; "they've give us the wrong room."

Then my wife seen it and begin to squeal.

"Goody!" she says. "We've got a bath! We've got a bath!"

"But," says I, "they promised we wouldn't have none. It must be a mistake."

"Never you mind about a mistake," she says. "This is our room and they can't chase us out of it."

"We'll chase ourself out," says I. "Rooms with a bath is fifteen and sixteen dollars and up. Rooms without no bath is bad enough."

"We'll keep this room or I won't stay here," she says.

"All right, you win," I says; but I didn't mean it.

I made her set in the lobby down-stairs w'ile I went to the clerk pretendin' that I had to see about our trunk.

"Say," I says to him, "you've made a bad mistake. You told your man in Chicago that we couldn't have no room with a bath, and now you've give us one."

"You're lucky," he says. "A party who had a bath ordered for these two weeks canceled their reservation and now you've got it."

"Lucky, am I?" I says. "And how much is the luck goin' to cost me?"

"It'll be seventeen dollars per day for that room," he says, and turned away to hide a blush.

I went back to the Wife.

"Do you know what we're payin' for that room?" I says. "We're payin' seventeen dollars."

"Well," she says, "our meals is throwed in."

"Yes," says I, "and the hotel furnishes a key."

"You promised in St. Augustine," she says, "that you wouldn't worry no more about expenses."

Well, rather than make a scene in front o' the bellhops and the few millionaires that was able to be about at that hour o' the mornin', I just says "All right!" and led her into the dinin'-room.

The head waiter met us at the door and turned us over to his assistant. Then some more assistants took hold of us one at a time and we was relayed to a beautiful spot next door to the kitchen and bounded on all sides by posts and pillars. It was all right for me, but a whole lot too private for the Missus; so I had to call the fella that had been our pacemaker on the last lap.

"We don't like this table," I says.

"It's the only one I can give you," he says.

I slipped him half a buck.

"Come to think of it," he says, "I believe they's one I forgot all about."

And he moved us way up near the middle o' the place.

Say, you ought to seen that dinin'-room! From one end of it to the other is a toll call, and if a man that was settin' at the table farthest from the kitchen ordered roast lamb he'd get mutton. At that, they was crowded for fair and it kept the head waiters hustlin' to find trough space for one and all.

It was round nine o'clock when we put in our modest order for orange juice, oatmeal, liver and bacon, and cakes and coffee, and a quarter to ten or so when our waiter returned from the nearest orange grove with Exhibit A. We amused ourself meanw'ile by givin' our neighbors the once over and wonderin' which o' them was goin' to pal with us. As far as I could tell from the glances we received, they wasn't no immediate danger of us bein' annoyed by attentions.

They was only a few womenfolks on deck and they was dressed pretty quiet; so quiet that the Missus was scared she'd shock 'em with the sport skirt she'd bought in Chi. Later on in the day, when the girls come out for their dress parade, the Missus' costume made about as much noise as eatin' marshmallows in a foundry.

After breakfast we went to the room for a change o' raiment. I put on my white trousers and wished to heaven that the sun'd go under a cloud till I got used to tellin' people without words just where my linen began and I left off. The rest o' my outfit was white shoes that hurt, and white sox, and a two-dollar silk shirt that showed up a zebra, and a red tie and a soft collar and a blue coat. The Missus wore a sport suit that I won't try and describe—you'll probably see it on her sometime in the next five years.

We went down-stairs again and out on the porch, where some o' the old birds was takin' a sun bath.

"Where now?" I says.

"The beach, o' course," says the Missus.

"Where is it at?" I ast her.

"I suppose," she says, "that we'll find it somewheres near the ocean."

"I don't believe you can stand this climate," says I.

"The ocean," she says, "must be down at the end o' that avenue, where most everybody seems to be headed."

"Havin' went to our room and back twice, I don't feel like another five-mile hike," I says.

"It ain't no five miles," she says; "but let's ride, anyway."

"Come on," says I, pointin' to a street-car that was standin' in the middle o' the avenue.

"Oh, no," she says. "I've watched and found out that the real people takes them funny-lookin' wheel chairs."

I was wonderin' what she meant when one o' them pretty near run over us. It was part bicycle, part go-cart and part African. In the one we dodged they was room for one passenger, but some o' them carried two.

"I wonder what they'd soak us for the trip," I says.

"Not more'n a dime, I don't believe," says the Missus.

But when we'd hired one and been w'isked down under the palms and past the golf field to the bath-house, we was obliged to part with fifty cents legal and tender.

"I feel much refreshed," I says. "I believe when it comes time to go back I'll be able to walk."

The bath-house is acrost the street from the other hotel, the Breakers, that the man had told us was full for the season. Both buildin's fronts on the ocean; and, boy, it's some ocean! I bet they's fish in there that never seen each other!

"Oh, let's go bathin' right away!" says the Missus.

"Our suits is up to the other beanery," says I, and I was glad of it. They wasn't nothin' temptin' to me about them man-eatin' waves.

But the Wife's a persistent cuss.

"We won't go to-day," she says, "but we'll go in the bath-house and get some rooms for to-morrow."

The bath-house porch was a ringer for the *Follies*. Here and down on the beach was where you seen the costumes at this time o' day. I was so busy rubbcrin' that I passed the entrance door three times without noticin' it. From the top o' their heads to the bottom o' their feet the girls was a mess o' colors. They wasn't no two dressed alike and if any one o' them had of walked down State Street we'd of had an epidemic o' stiff neck to contend with in Chi. Finally the Missus grabbed me and hauled me into the office.

"Two private rooms," she says to the clerk. "One lady and one gent."

"Five dollars a week apiece," he says. "But we're all filled up."

"You ought to be all locked up!" I says.

"Will you have anything open to-morrow?" ast the Missus.

"I think I can fix you then," he says.

"What do we get for the five?" I ast him.

"Private room and we take care o' your bathin' suit," says he.

"How much if you don't take care o' the suit?" I ast him. "My suit's been gettin' along fine with very little care."

"Five dollars a week apiece," he says, "and if you want the rooms you better take 'em, because they're in big demand."

By the time we'd closed this grand bargain, everybody'd moved offen the porch and down to the water, where a couple dozen o' them went in for a swim and the rest set and watched. They was a long row o' chairs on the beach for spectators and we was just goin' to flop into two o' them when another bandit come up and told us it'd cost a dime apiece per hour.

"We're goin' to be her two weeks," I says. "Will you sell us two chairs?"

He wasn't in no comical mood, so we sunk down on the sand and seen the show from there. We had plenty o' company that preferred these kind o' seats free to the chairs at ten cents a whack.

Besides the people that was in the water gettin' knocked down by the waves and pretendin' like they enjoyed it, about half o' the gang on the sand was wearin' bathin' suits just to be clubby. You could tell by lookin' at the suits that they hadn't never been wet and wasn't intended for no such ridic'lous purpose. I wisht I could describe 'em to you, but it'd take a female to do it right.

One little girl, either fourteen or twenty-four, had white silk slippers and sox that come pretty near up to her ankles, and from there to her knees it was just plain Nature. Northbound from her knees was pair o' bicycle trousers that disappeared when they come to the bottom of her Mother Hubbard. This here garment was a thing without no neck or sleeves that begin bulgin' at the top and spread out gradual all the way down, like a croquette. To top her off, she had a jockey cap; and—believe me—I'd of played her mount acrost the board. They was plenty o' class in the field with her, but nothin' that approached her speed. Later on I seen her several times round the hotel, wearin' somethin' near the same outfit, without the jockey cap and with longer croquettes.

We set there in the sand till people begun to get up and leave. Then we trailed along back o' them to the Breakers' porch, where they was music to dance and stuff to inhale.

"We'll grab a table," I says to the Missus. "I'm dyin' o' thirst."

But I was allowed to keep on dyin'.

"I can serve you somethin' soft," says the waiter.

"I'll bet you can't!" I says.

"You ain't got no locker here?" he says.

"What do you mean—locker?" I ast him.

"It's the locker liquor law," he says. "We can serve you a drink if you own your own bottles."

"I'd just as soon own a bottle," I says. "I'll become the proprietor of a bottle o' beer."

"It'll take three or four hours to get it for you," he says, "and
you'd have to order it through the order desk. If you're stoppin' at
one o' the hotels and want a drink once in a w'ile, you better get
busy and put in an order."

So I had to watch the Missus put away a glass of orange juice that
cost forty cents and was just the same size as they give us for breakfast free for nothin'. And, not havin' had nothin' to make me forget
that my feet hurt, I was obliged to pay another four bits for an
Afromobile to cart us back to our own boardin' house.

"Well," says the Missus when we got there, "it's time to wash up
and go to lunch."

"Wash up and go to lunch, then," I says; "but I'm goin' to investigate this here locker liquor or liquor locker law."

So she got her key and beat it, and I limped to the bar.

"I want a highball," I says to the boy.

"What's your number?" says he.

"It varies," I says. "Sometimes I can hold twenty and sometimes
four or five makes me sing."

"I mean, have you got a locker here?" he says.

"No; but I want to get one," says I.

"The gent over there to the desk will fix you," says he.

So over to the desk I went and ast for a locker.

"What do you drink?" ast the gent.

"I'm from Chicago," I says. "I drink bourbon."

"What's your name and room number?" he says, and I told him.

Then he ast me how often did I shave and what did I think o' the
Kaiser and what my name was before I got married, and if I had any
intentions of ever running an elevator. Finally he says I was all
right.

"I'll order you some bourbon," he says. "Anything else?"

I was goin' to say no, but I happened to remember that the Wife
generally always wants a bronix before dinner. So I had to also put
in a bid for a bottle o' gin and bottles o' the Vermouth brothers,
Tony and Pierre. It wasn't till later that I appreciated what a grand
law this here law was. When I got my drinks I paid ten cents apiece
for 'em for service, besides payin' for the bottles o' stuff to drink.
And, besides that, about every third highball or bronix I ordered,
the waiter'd bring back word that I was just out of ingredients and

then they'd be another delay w'ile they sent to the garage for more. If they had that law all over the country they'd soon be an end o' drinkin', because everybody'd get so mad they'd kill each other.

My cross-examination had took quite a long time, but when I got to my room the Wife wasn't back from lunch yet and I had to cover the Marathon route all over again and look her up. We only had the one key to the room, and o' course couldn't expect no more'n that at the price.

The Missus had bought one o' the daily programs they get out and she knowed just what we had to do the rest o' the day.

"For the next couple hours," she says, "we can suit ourself."

"All right," says I. "It suits me to take off my shoes and lay down."

"I'll rest, too," she says; "but at half past four we have to be in the Cocoanut Grove for tea and dancin'. And then we come back to the room and dress for dinner. Then we eat and then we set around till the evenin' dance starts. Then we dance till we're ready for bed."

"Who do we dance all these dances with?" I ast her.

"With whoever we get acquainted with," she says.

"All right," says I; "but let's be careful."

Well, we took our nap and then we followed schedule and had our tea in the Cocoanut Grove. You know how I love tea! My feet was still achin' and the Missus couldn't talk me into no dance.

When we'd set there an hour and was saturated with tea, the Wife says it was time to go up and change into our Tuxedos. I was all in when we reached the room and willin' to even pass up supper and nestle in the hay, but I was informed that the biggest part o' the day's doin's was yet to come. So from six o'clock till after seven I wrestled with studs, and hooks and eyes that didn't act like they'd ever met before and wasn't anxious to get acquainted, and then down we went again to the dinin'-room.

"How about a little bronix before the feed?" I says.

"It would taste good," says the Missus.

So I called Eph and give him the order. In somethin' less than half an hour he come back empty-handed.

"You ain't got no cocktail stuff," he says.

"I certainly have," says I. "I ordered it early this afternoon."

"Where at?" he ast me.

"Over in the bar," I says.

"Oh, the regular bar!" he says. "That don't count. You got to have stuff at the service bar to get it served in here."

"I ain't as thirsty as I thought I was," says I.

"Me, neither," says the Missus.

So we went ahead and ordered our meal, and w'ile we was waitin' for it a young couple come and took the other two chairs at our table. They didn't have to announce through a megaphone that they was honeymooners. It was wrote all over 'em. They was reachin' under the table for each other's hand every other minute, and when they wasn't doin' that they was smilin' at each other or gigglin' at nothin'. You couldn't feel that good and be payin' seventeen dollars a day for room and board unless you was just married or somethin'.

I thought at first their company'd be fun, but after a few meals it got like the southern cookin' and begun to undermine the health.

The conversation between they and us was what you could call limited. It took place the next day at lunch. The young husband thought he was about to take a bite o' the entry, which happened to be roast mutton with sirup; but he couldn't help from lookin' at her at the same time and his empty fork started for his face prongs up.

"Look out for your eye," I says.

He dropped the fork and they both blushed till you could see it right through the sunburn. Then they give me a Mexican look and our acquaintance was at an end.

This first night, when we was through eatin', we wandered out in the lobby and took seats where we could watch the passin' show. The men was all dressed like me, except I was up to date and had on a mushroom shirt, w'ile they was sportin' the old-fashioned concrete bosom. The women's dresses begun at the top with a belt, and some o' them stopped at the mezzanine floor, w'ile others went clear down to the basement and helped keep the rugs clean. They was one that must of thought it was the Fourth o' July. From the top of her head to where the top of her bathin' suit had left off, she was a red, red rose. From there to the top of her gown was white, and her gown, what they was of it—was blue.

"My!" says the Missus. "What stunnin' gowns!"

"Yes," I says; "and you could have one just like 'em if you'd take the shade offen the piano lamp at home and cut it down to the right size."

Round ten o'clock we wandered in the Palm Garden, where the dancin' had been renewed. The Wife wanted to plunge right in the mazes o' the foxy trot.

"I'll take some courage first," says I. And then was when I found out that it cost you ten cents extra besides the tip to pay for a drink that you already owned in fee simple.

Well, I guess we must of danced about six dances together and had that many quarrels before she was ready to go to bed. And oh, how grand that old hay-pile felt when I finally bounced into it!

The next day we went to the ocean at the legal hour—half past eleven. I never had so much fun in my life. The surf was runnin' high, I heard 'em say; and I don't know which I'd rather do, go bathin' in the ocean at Palm Beach when the surf is runnin' high, or have a dentist get one o' my molars ready for a big inlay at a big outlay. Once in a w'ile I managed to not get throwed on my head when a wave hit me. As for swimmin', you had just as much chance as if you was at State and Madison at the noon hour. And before I'd been in a minute they was enough salt in my different features to keep the Blackstone hotel runnin' all through the onion season.

The Missus enjoyed it just as much as me. She tried to pretend at first, and when she got floored she'd give a squeal that was supposed to mean heavenly bliss. But after she'd been bruised from head to feet and her hair looked and felt like spinach with French dressin', and she'd drank all she could hold o' the Gulf Stream, she didn't resist none when I drug her in to shore and staggered with her up to our private rooms at five a week per each.

Without consultin' her, I went to the desk at the Casino and told 'em they could have them rooms back.

"All right," says the clerk, and turned our keys over to the next in line.

"How about a refund?" I ast him; but he was waitin' on somebody else.

After that we done our bathin' in the tub. But we was down to the beach every morning at eleven-thirty to watch the rest o' them get batted round.

And at half past twelve every day we'd follow the crowd to the Breakers' porch and dance together, the Missus and I. Then it'd be back to the other hostelry, sometimes limpin' and sometimes in an

Afromobile, and a drink or two in the Palm Garden before lunch. And after lunch we'd lay down; or we'd pay some Eph two or three dollars to pedal us through the windin' jungle trail, that was every bit as wild as the Art Institute; or we'd ferry acrost Lake Worth to West Palm Beach and take in a movie, or we'd stand in front o' the portable Fifth Avenue stores w'ile the Missus wished she could have this dress or that hat, or somethin' else that she wouldn't of looked at if she'd been home and in her right mind. But always at half past four we had to live up to the rules and be in the Cocoanut Grove for tea and some more foxy trottin'. And then it was dress for dinner, eat dinner, watch the parade and wind up the glorious day with more dancin'.

I bet you any amount you name that the Castles in their whole life haven't danced together as much as I and the Missus did at Palm Beach. I'd of gave five dollars if even one o' the waiters had took her offen my hands for one dance. But I knowed that if I made the offer public they'd of been a really serious quarrel between us instead o' just the minor brawls occasioned by steppin' on each other's feet.

She made a discovery one night. She found out that they was a place called the Beach Club where most o' the real people disappeared to every evenin' after dinner. She says we would have to go there too.

"But I ain't a member," I says.

"Then find out how you get to be one," she says.

So to the Beach Club I went and made inquiries.

"You'll have to be introduced by a guy that already belongs," says the man at the door.

"Who belongs?" I ast him.

"Hundreds o' people," he says. "Who do you know?"

"Two waiters, two barkeepers and one elevator boy," I says.

He laughed, but his laugh didn't get me no membership card and I had to dance three or four extra times the next day to square myself with the Missus.

She made another discovery and it cost me six bucks. She found out that, though the meals in the regular dinin'-room was included in the triflin' rates per day, the real people had at least two o' their meals in the garden grill and paid extra for 'em. We tried it for one meal and I must say I enjoyed it—all but the check.

"We can't keep up that clip," I says to her.

"We could," says she, "if you wasn't spendin' so much on your locker."

"The locker's a matter o' life and death," I says. "They ain't no man in the world that could dance as much with their own wife as I do and live without liquid stimulus."

When we'd been there four days she got to be on speakin' terms with the ladies' maid that hung round the lobby and helped put the costumes back on when they slipped off. From this here maid the Missus learned who was who, and the information was relayed to me as soon as they was a chance. We'd be settin' on the porch when I'd feel an elbow in my ribs all of a sudden. I'd look up at who was passin' and then try and pretend I was excited.

"Who is it?" I'd whisper.

"That's Mrs. Vandeventer," the Wife'd say. "Her husband's the biggest street-car conductor in Philadelphia."

Or somebody'd set beside us at the beach or in the Palm Garden and my ribs would be all battered up before the Missus was calm enough to tip me off.

"The Vincents," she'd say; "the canned prune people."

It was a little bit thrillin' at first to be rubbin' elbows with all them celeb's; but it got so finally that I could walk out o' the dinin'-room right behind Scotti, the opera singer, without forgettin' that my feet hurt.

The Washington's Birthday Ball brought 'em all together at once, and the Missus pointed out eight and nine at a time and got me so mixed up that I didn't know Pat Vanderbilt from Maggie Rockefeller. The only one you couldn't make no mistake about was a Russian count that you couldn't pronounce. He was buyin' bay mules or somethin' for the Russian government, and he was in ambush.

"They say he can't hardly speak a word of English," says the Missus.

"If I knowed the word for barber shop in Russia," says I, "I'd tell him they was one in this hotel."

V

In our mail box the next mornin' they was a notice that our first week was up and all we owed was one hundred and forty-six dollars and fifty cents. The bill for room and meals was one hundred and nineteen dollars. The rest was for gettin' clo'es pressed and keepin' the locker damp.

I didn't have no appetite for breakfast. I told the Wife I'd wait up in the room and for her to come when she got through. When she blew in I had my speech prepared.

"Look here," I says; "this is our eighth day in Palm Beach society. You're on speakin' terms with a maid and I've got acquainted with half a dozen o' the male hired help. It's cost us about a hundred and sixty-five dollars, includin' them private rooms down to the Casino and our Afromobile trips, and this and that. You know a whole lot o' swell people by sight, but you can't talk to 'em. It'd be just as much satisfaction and hundreds o' dollars cheaper to look up their names in the telephone directory at home; then phone to 'em and, when you got 'em, tell 'em it was the wrong number. That way, you'd get 'em to speak to you at least.

"As for sport," I says, "we don't play golf and we don't play tennis and we don't swim. We go through the same program o' doin' nothin' every day. We dance, but we don't never change partners. For twelve dollars I could buy a phonograph up home and I and you could trot round the livin'-room all evenin' without no danger o' havin' some o' them fancy birds cave our shins in. And we could have twice as much liquid refreshments up there at about a twentieth the cost.

"That Gould I met on the train comin' down," I says, "was a even bigger liar than I give him credit for. He says that when he was here people pestered him to death by comin' up and speakin' to him. We ain't had to dodge nobody or hide behind a cocoanut tree to remain exclusive. He says Palm Beach was too common for him. What he should of said was that it was too lonesome. If they was just one white man here that'd listen to my stuff I wouldn't have no kick. But it ain't no pleasure tellin' stories to the Ephs. They laugh whether it's good or not, and then want a dime for laughin'.

"As for our clo'es," I says, "they would be all right for a couple o' days' stay. But the dames round here, and the men, too, has some-thin' different to put on for every mornin', afternoon and night. You've wore your two evenin' gowns so much that I just have to snap my finger at the hooks and they go and grab the right eyes.

"The meals would be grand," I says, "if the cook didn't keep gettin' mixed up and puttin' puddin' sauce on the meat and gravy on the pie.

"I'm glad we've been to Palm Beach," I says. "I wouldn't of missed it for nothin'. But the ocean won't be no different to-morrow than it was yesterday, and the same for the daily program. It don't even rain here, to give us a little variety.

"Now what do you say," I says, "to us just settlin' this bill, and whatever we owe since then, and beatin' it out o' here just as fast as we can go?"

The Missus didn't say nothin' for a w'ile. She was too busy cryin'. She knowed that what I'd said was the truth, but she wouldn't give up without a struggle.

"Just three more days," she says finally. "If we don't meet some-body worth meetin' in the next three days I'll go wherever you want to take me."

"All right," I says; "three more days it is. What's a little matter o' sixty dollars?"

Well, in them next two days and a half she done some desperate flirtin', but as it was all with women I didn't get jealous. She picked out some o' the E-light o' Chicago and tried every trick she could think up. She told 'em their noses was shiny and offered 'em her powder. She stepped on their white shoes just so's to get a chance to beg their pardon. She told 'em their clo'es was unhooked, and then unhooked 'em so's she could hook 'em up again. She tried to loan 'em her finger-nail tools. When she seen one fannin' herself she'd say: "Excuse me, Mrs. So-and-So; but we got the coolest room in the hotel, and I'd be glad to have you go up there and quit perspirin'." But not a rise did she get.

Not till the afternoon o' the third day o' grace. And I don't know if I ought to tell you this or not—only I'm sure you won't spill it nowheres.

We'd went up in our room after lunch. I was tired out and she was discouraged. We'd set round for over an hour, not sayin' or doin' nothin'.

I wanted to talk about the chance of us gettin' away the next mornin', but I didn't dast bring up the subject.

The Missus complained of it bein' hot and opened the door to leave the breeze go through. She was settin' in a chair near the doorway, pretendin' to read the *Palm Beach News*. All of a sudden she jumped up and kind o' hissed at me.

"What's the matter?" I says, springin' from the lounge.

"Come here!" she says, and went out the door into the hall.

I got there as fast as I could, thinkin' it was a rat or a fire. But the Missus just pointed to a lady walkin' away from us, six or seven doors down.

"It's Mrs. Potter," she says; "*the* Mrs. Potter from Chicago!"

"Oh!" I says, puttin' all the excitement I could into my voice.

And I was just startin' back into the room when I seen Mrs. Potter stop and turn round and come to'rd us. She stopped again maybe twenty feet from where the Missus was standin'.

"Are you on this floor?" she says.

The Missus shook like a leaf.

"Yes," says she, so low you couldn't hardly hear her.

"Please see that they's some towels put in 559," says *the* Mrs. Potter from Chicago.

VI

About five o'clock the Wife quieted down and I thought it was safe to talk to her. "I've been readin' in the guide about a pretty river trip," I says. "We can start from here on the boat to-morrow mornin'. They run to Fort Pierce to-morrow and stay there to-morrow night. The next day they go from Fort Pierce to Rockledge, and the day after that from Rockledge to Daytona. The fare's only five dollars apiece. And we can catch a north-bound train at Daytona."

"All right, I don't care," says the Missus.

So I left her and went down-stairs and acrost the street to ask Mr. Foster. Ask Mr. Foster happened to be a girl. She sold me the boat tickets and promised she would reserve a room with bath for us at Fort Pierce, where we was to spend the followin' night. I bet she knowed all the w'ile that rooms with a bath in Fort Pierce is scarcer than toes on a sturgeon.

I went back to the room and helped with the packin' in an advisory capacity. Neither one of us had the heart to dress for dinner. We ordered somethin' sent up and got soaked an extra dollar for service. But we was past carin' for a little thing like that.

At nine o'clock next mornin' the good ship *Constitution* stopped at the Poinciana dock w'ile we piled aboard. One bellhop was down to see us off and it cost me a quarter to get that much attention. Mrs. Potter must of overslept herself.

The boat was loaded to the guards and I ain't braggin' when I say that we was the best-lookin' people aboard. And as for manners, why, say, old Bill Sykes could of passed off for Henry Chesterfield in that gang! Each one o' them occupied three o' the deck chairs and sprayed orange juice all over their neighbors. We could of talked to plenty o' people here, all right; they were as clubby a gang as I ever seen. But I was afraid if I said somethin' they'd have to answer; and, with their mouths as full o' citrus fruit as they was, the results might of been fatal to my light suit.

We went up the lake to a canal and then through it to Indian River. The boat run aground every few minutes and had to be pried loose. About twelve o'clock a cullud gemman come up on deck and told us lunch was ready. At half past one he served it at a long family table in the cabin. As far as I was concerned, he might as well of left it on the stove. Even if you could of bit into the food, a glimpse of your fellow diners would of strangled your appetite.

After the repast I called the Missus aside.

"Somethin' tells me we're not goin' to live through three days o' this," I says. "What about takin' the train from Fort Pierce and beatin' it for Jacksonville, and then home?"

"But that'd get us to Chicago too quick," says she. "We told people how long we was goin' to be gone and if we got back ahead o' time they'd think they was somethin' queer."

"They's too much queer on this boat," I says. "But you're goin' to have your own way from now on."

We landed in Fort Pierce about six. It was only two or three blocks to the hotel, but when they laid out that part o' town they overlooked some o' the modern conveniences, includin' sidewalks. We staggered through the sand with our grips and sure had worked up a hunger by the time we reached Ye Inn.

"Got reservations for us here?" I ast the clerk.

"Yes," he says, and led us to 'em in person.

The room he showed us didn't have no bath, or even a chair that you could set on w'ile you pulled off your socks.

"Where's the bath?" I ast him.

"This way," he says, and I followed him down the hall, outdoors and up an alley.

Finally we come to a bathroom complete in all details, except that it didn't have no door. I went back to the room, got the Missus and went down to supper. Well, sir, I wish you could of been present at that supper. The choice o' meats was calves' liver and onions or calves' liver and onions. And I bet if them calves had of been still livin' yet they could of gave us some personal reminiscences about Garfield.

The Missus give the banquet one look and then laughed for the first time in several days.

"The guy that named this burg got the capitals mixed," I says. "It should of been Port Fierce."

And she laughed still heartier. Takin' advantage, I says:

"How about the train from here to Jacksonville?"

"You win!" says she. "We can't get home too soon to suit me."

VII

The mornin' we landed in Chicago it was about eight above and a wind was comin' offen the Lake a mile a minute. But it didn't feaze us.

"Lord!" says the Missus. "Ain't it grand to be home!"

"You said somethin'," says I. "But wouldn't it of been grander if we hadn't never left?"

"I don't know about that," she says. "I think we both of us learned a lesson."

"Yes," I says; "and the tuition wasn't only a matter o' close to seven hundred bucks!"

"Oh," says she, "we'll get that back easy!"

"How?" I ast her. "Do you expect some tips on the market from Mrs. Potter and the rest o' your new friends?"

"No," she says. "We'll win it. We'll win it in the rummy game with the Hatches."

Haircut

I got another barber that comes over from Carterville and helps me out Saturdays, but the rest of the time I can get along all right alone. You can see for yourself that this ain't no New York City and besides that, the most of the boys works all day and don't have no leisure to drop in here and get themselves prettied up.

You're a newcomer, ain't you? I thought I hadn't seen you round before. I hope you like it good enough to stay. As I say, we ain't no New York City or Chicago, but we have pretty good times. Not as good, though, since Jim Kendall got killed. When he was alive, him and Hod Meyers used to keep this town in an uproar. I bet they was more laughin' done here than any town its size in America.

Jim was comical, and Hod was pretty near a match for him. Since Jim's gone, Hod tries to hold his end up just the same as ever, but it's tough goin' when you ain't got nobody to kind of work with.

They used to be plenty fun in here Saturdays. This place is jam-packed Saturdays, from four o'clock on. Jim and Hod would show up right after their supper, round six o'clock. Jim would set himself down in that big chair, nearest the blue spittoon. Whoever had been settin' in that chair, why they'd get up when Jim come in and give it to him.

You'd of thought it was a reserved seat like they have sometimes in a theayter. Hod would generally always stand or walk up and down, or some Saturdays, of course, he'd be settin' in this chair part of the time, gettin' a haircut.

Well, Jim would set there a w'ile without openin' his mouth only to spit, and then finally he'd say to me, "Whitey,"—my right name, that is, my right first name, is Dick, but everybody round here calls me Whitey—Jim would say, "Whitey, your nose looks like a rosebud tonight. You must of been drinkin' some of your aw de cologne."

So I'd say, "No, Jim, but you look like you'd been drinkin' somethin' of that kind or somethin' worse."

Jim would have to laugh at that, but then he'd speak up and say, "No, I ain't had nothin' to drink, but that ain't sayin' I wouldn't like somethin'. I wouldn't even mind if it was wood alcohol."

Then Hod Meyers would say, "Neither would your wife." That would set everybody to laughin' because Jim and his wife wasn't on very good terms. She'd of divorced him only they wasn't no chance to get alimony and she didn't have no way to take care of herself and the kids. She couldn't never understand Jim. He *was* kind of rough, but a good fella at heart.

Him and Hod had all kinds of sport with Milt Sheppard. I don't suppose you've seen Milt. Well, he's got an Adam's apple that looks more like a mushmelon. So I'd be shavin' Milt and when I'd start to shave down here on his neck, Hod would holler, "Hey, Whitey, wait a minute! Before you cut into it, let's make up a pool and see who can guess closest to the number of seeds."

And Jim would say, "If Milt hadn't of been so hoggish, he'd of ordered a half a cantaloupe instead of a whole one and it might not of stuck in his throat."

All the boys would roar at this and Milt himself would force a smile, though the joke was on him. Jim certainly was a card!

There's his shavin' mug, settin' on the shelf, right next to Charley Vail's. "Charles M. Vail." That's the druggist. He comes in regular for his shave, three times a week. And Jim's is the cup next to Charley's. "James H. Kendall." Jim won't need no shavin' mug no more, but I'll leave it there just the same for old time's sake. Jim certainly was a character!

Years ago, Jim used to travel for a canned goods concern over in Carterville. They sold canned goods. Jim had the whole northern half of the State and was on the road five days out of every week. He'd drop in here Saturdays and tell his experiences for that week. It was rich.

I guess he paid more attention to playin' jokes than makin' sales. Finally the concern let him out and he come right home here and told everybody he'd been fired instead of sayin' he'd resigned like most fellas would of.

It was a Saturday and the shop was full and Jim got up out of that chair and says, "Gentlemen, I got an important announcement to make. I been fired from my job."

Well, they asked him if he was in earnest and he said he was and nobody could think of nothin' to say till Jim finally broke the ice himself. He says, "I been sellin' canned goods and now I'm canned goods myself."

You see, the concern he'd been workin' for was a factory that made canned goods. Over in Carterville. And now Jim said he was canned himself. He was certainly a card!

Jim had a great trick that he used to play w'ile he was travelin'. For instance, he'd be ridin' on a train and they'd come to some little town like, well, like, we'll say, like Benton. Jim would look out the train window and read the signs on the stores.

For instance, they'd be a sign, "Henry Smith, Dry Goods." Well, Jim would write down the name and the name of the town and when he got to wherever he was goin' he'd mail back a postal card to Henry Smith at Benton and not sign no name to it, but he'd write on the card, well, somethin' like "Ask your wife about that book agent that spent the afternoon last week," or "Ask your Missus who kept her from gettin' lonesome the last time you was in Carterville." And he'd sign the card, "A Friend."

Of course, he never knew what really come of none of these jokes, but he could picture what *probably* happened and that was enough.

Jim didn't work very steady after he lost his position with the Carterville people. What he did earn, doin' odd jobs round town, why he spent pretty near all of it on gin and his family might of starved if the stores hadn't of carried them along. Jim's wife tried her hand at dressmakin', but they ain't nobody goin' to get rich makin' dresses in this town.

As I say, she'd of divorced Jim, only she seen that she couldn't support herself and the kids and she was always hopin' that some day Jim would cut out his habits and give her more than two or three dollars a week.

They was a time when she would go to whoever he was workin' for and ask them to give her his wages, but after she done this once or twice, he beat her to it by borrowin' most of his pay in advance. He told it all round town, how he had outfoxed his Missus. He certainly was a caution!

But he wasn't satisfied with just outwittin' her. He was sore the way she had acted, tryin' to grab off his pay. And he made up his

mind he'd get even. Well, he waited till Evans's Circus was advertised to come to town. Then he told his wife and two kiddies that
he was goin' to take them to the circus. The day of the circus, he told
them he would get the tickets and meet them outside the entrance
to the tent.

Well, he didn't have no intentions of bein' there or buyin' tickets
or nothin'. He got full of gin and laid round Wright's poolroom all
day. His wife and the kids waited and waited and of course he didn't
show up. His wife didn't have a dime with her, or nowhere else, I
guess. So she finally had to tell the kids it was all off and they cried
like they wasn't never goin' to stop.

Well, it seems, w'ile they was cryin', Doc Stair came along and he
asked what was the matter, but Mrs. Kendall was stubborn and
wouldn't tell him, but the kids told him and he insisted on takin'
them and their mother in the show. Jim found this out afterwards
and it was one reason why he had it in for Doc Stair.

Doc Stair come here about a year and a half ago. He's a mighty
handsome young fella and his clothes always look like he has them
made to order. He goes to Detroit two or three times a year and w'ile
he's there he must have a tailor take his measure and then make him
a suit to order. They cost pretty near twice as much, but they fit a
whole lot better than if you just bought them in a store.

For a w'ile everybody was wonderin' why a young doctor like Doc
Stair should come to a town like this where we already got old Doc
Gamble and Doc Foote that's both been here for years and all the
practice in town was always divided between the two of them.

Then they was a story got round that Doc Stair's gal had throwed
him over, a gal up in the Northern Peninsula somewheres, and the
reason he come here was to hide himself away and forget it. He said
himself that he thought they wasn't nothin' like general practice in
a place like ours to fit a man to be a good all round doctor. And
that's why he'd came.

Anyways, it wasn't long before he was makin' enough to live on,
though they tell me that he never dunned nobody for what they
owed him, and the folks here certainly has got the owin' habit, even
in my business. If I had all that was comin' to me for just shaves
alone, I could go to Carterville and put up at the Mercer for a week

and see a different picture every night. For instance, they's old George Purdy—but I guess I shouldn't ought to be gossipin'.

Well, last year, our coroner died, died of the flu. Ken Beatty, that was his name. He was the coroner. So they had to choose another man to be coroner in his place and they picked Doc Stair. He laughed at first and said he didn't want it, but they made him take it. It ain't no job that anybody would fight for and what a man makes out of it in a year would just about buy seeds for their garden. Doc's the kind, though, that can't say no to nothin' if you keep at him long enough.

But I was goin' to tell you about a poor boy we got here in town— Paul Dickson. He fell out of a tree when he was about ten years old. Lit on his head and it done somethin' to him and he ain't never been right. No harm in him, but just silly. Jim Kendall used to call him cuckoo; that's a name Jim had for anybody that was off their head, only he called people's head their bean. That was another of his gags, callin' head bean and callin' crazy people cuckoo. Only poor Paul ain't crazy, but just silly.

You can imagine that Jim used to have all kinds of fun with Paul. He'd send him to the White Front Garage for a left-handed monkey wrench. Of course they ain't no such a thing as a left-handed monkey wrench.

And once we had a kind of a fair here and they was a baseball game between the fats and the leans and before the game started Jim called Paul over and sent him way down to Schrader's hardware store to get a key for the pitcher's box.

They wasn't nothin' in the way of gags that Jim couldn't think up, when he put his mind to it.

Poor Paul was always kind of suspicious of people, maybe on account of how Jim had kept foolin' him. Paul wouldn't have much to do with anybody only his own mother and Doc Stair and a girl here in town named Julie Gregg. That is, she ain't a girl no more, but pretty near thirty or over.

When Doc first come to town, Paul seemed to feel like here was a real friend and he hung round Doc's office most of the w'ile; the only time he wasn't there was when he'd go home to eat or sleep or when he seen Julie Gregg doin' her shoppin'.

When he looked out Doc's window and seen her, he'd run downstairs and join her and tag along with her to the different stores. The poor boy was crazy about Julie and she always treated him mighty nice and made him feel like he was welcome, though of course it wasn't nothin' but pity on her side.

Doc done all he could to improve Paul's mind and he told me once that he really thought the boy was gettin' better, that they was times when he was as bright and sensible as anybody else.

But I was goin' to tell you about Julie Gregg. Old Man Gregg was in the lumber business, but got to drinkin' and lost the most of his money and when he died, he didn't leave nothin' but the house and just enough insurance for the girl to skimp along on.

Her mother was a kind of a half invalid and didn't hardly ever leave the house. Julie wanted to sell the place and move somewheres else after the old man died, but the mother said she was born here and would die here. It was tough on Julie, as the young people round this town—well, she's too good for them.

She's been away to school and Chicago and New York and different places and they ain't no subject she can't talk on, where you take the rest of the young folks here and you mention anything to them outside of Gloria Swanson or Tommy Meighan and they think you're delirious. Did you see Gloria in Wages of Virtue? You missed somethin'!

Well, Doc Stair hadn't been here more than a week when he come in one day to get shaved and I recognized who he was as he had been pointed out to me, so I told him about my old lady. She's been ailin' for a couple years and either Doc Gamble or Doc Foote, neither one, seemed to be helpin' her. So he said he would come out and see her, but if she was able to get out herself, it would be better to bring her to his office where he could make a completer examination.

So I took her to his office and w'ile I was waitin' for her in the reception room, in come Julie Gregg. When somebody comes in Doc Stair's office, they's a bell that rings in his inside office so as he can tell they's somebody to see him.

So he left my old lady inside and come out to the front office and that's the first time him and Julie met and I guess it was what they call love at first sight. But it wasn't fifty-fifty. This young fella was the slickest lookin' fella she'd ever seen in this town and she went wild over him. To him she was just a young lady that wanted to see the doctor.

She'd came on about the same business I had. Her mother had

been doctorin' for years with Doc Gamble and Doc Foote and without no results. So she'd heard they was a new doc in town and decided to give him a try. He promised to call and see her mother that same day.

I said a minute ago that it was love at first sight on her part. I'm not only judgin' by how she acted afterwards but how she looked at him that first day in his office. I ain't no mind reader, but it was wrote all over her face that she was gone.

Now Jim Kendall, besides bein' a jokesmith and a pretty good drinker, well, Jim was quite a lady-killer. I guess he run pretty wild durin' the time he was on the road for them Carterville people, and besides that, he'd had a couple little affairs of the heart right here in town. As I say, his wife could of divorced him, only she couldn't.

But Jim was like the majority of men, and women, too, I guess. He wanted what he couldn't get. He wanted Julie Gregg and worked his head off tryin' to land her. Only he'd of said bean instead of head.

Well, Jim's habits and his jokes didn't appeal to Julie and of course he was a married man, so he didn't have no more chance than, well, than a rabbit. That's an expression of Jim's himself. When somebody didn't have no chance to get elected or somethin', Jim would always say they didn't have no more chance than a rabbit.

He didn't make no bones about how he felt. Right in here, more than once, in front of the whole crowd, he said he was stuck on Julie and anybody that could get her for him was welcome to his house and his wife and kids included. But she wouldn't have nothin' to do with him; wouldn't even speak to him on the street. He finally seen he wasn't gettin' nowheres with his usual line so he decided to try the rough stuff. He went right up to her house one evenin' and when she opened the door he forced his way in and grabbed her. But she broke loose and before he could stop her, she run in the next room and locked the door and phoned to Joe Barnes. Joe's the marshal. Jim could hear who she was phonin' to and he beat it before Joe got there.

Joe was an old friend of Julie's pa. Joe went to Jim the next day and told him what would happen if he ever done it again.

I don't know how the news of this little affair leaked out. Chances is that Joe Barnes told his wife and she told somebody else's wife and they told their husband. Anyways, it did leak out and Hod Meyers had the nerve to kid Jim about it, right here in this shop. Jim didn't deny nothin' and kind of laughed it off and said for us all to wait; that lots of people had tried to make a monkey out of him, but he always got even.

Meanw'ile everybody in town was wise to Julie's bein' wild mad over the Doc. I don't suppose she had any idear how her face changed when him and her was together; of course she couldn't of, or she'd of kept away from him. And she didn't know that we was all noticin' how many times she made excuses to go up to his office or pass it on the other side of the street and look up in his window to see if he was there. I felt sorry for her and so did most other people.

Hod Meyers kept rubbin' it into Jim about how the Doc had cut him out. Jim didn't pay no attention to the kiddin' and you could see he was plannin' one of his jokes.

One trick Jim had was the knack of changin' his voice. He could make you think he was a girl talkin' and he could mimic any man's voice. To show you how good he was along this line, I'll tell you the joke he played on me once.

You know, in most towns of any size, when a man is dead and needs a shave, why the barber that shaves him soaks him five dollars for the job; that is, he don't soak *him,* but whoever ordered the shave. I just charge three dollars because personally I don't mind much shavin' a dead person. They lay a whole lot stiller than live customers. The only thing is that you don't feel like talkin' to them and you get kind of lonesome.

Well, about the coldest day we ever had here, two years ago last winter, the phone rung at the house w'ile I was home to dinner and I answered the phone and it was a woman's voice and she said she was Mrs. John Scott and her husband was dead and would I come out and shave him.

Old John had always been a good customer of mine. But they live seven miles out in the country, on the Streeter road. Still I didn't see how I could say no.

So I said I would be there, but would have to come in a jitney and it might cost three or four dollars besides the price of the shave. So she, or the voice, it said that was all right, so I got Frank Abbott to drive me out to the place and when I got there, who should open the door but old John himself! He wasn't no more dead than, well, than a rabbit.

It didn't take no private detective to figure out who had played me this little joke. Nobody could of thought it up but Jim Kendall. He certainly was a card!

I tell you this incident just to show you how he could disguise his voice and make you believe it was somebody else talkin'. I'd of swore it was Mrs. Scott had called me. Anyways, some woman.

Well, Jim waited till he had Doc Stair's voice down pat; then he went after revenge.

He called Julie up on a night when he knew Doc was over in Carterville. She never questioned but what it was Doc's voice. Jim said he must see her that night; he couldn't wait no longer to tell her somethin'. She was all excited and told him to come to the house. But he said he was expectin' an important long distance call and wouldn't she please forget her manners for once and come to his office. He said they couldn't nothin' hurt her and nobody would see her and he just *must* talk to her a little w'ile. Well, poor Julie fell for it.

Doc always keeps a night light in his office, so it looked to Julie like they was somebody there.

Meanw'ile Jim Kendall had went to Wright's poolroom, where they was a whole gang amusin' themselves. The most of them had drank plenty of gin, and they was a rough bunch even when sober. They was always strong for Jim's jokes and when he told them to come with him and see some fun they give up their card games and pool games and followed along.

Doc's office is on the second floor. Right outside his door they's a flight of stairs leadin' to the floor above. Jim and his gang hid in the dark behind these stairs.

Well, Julie come up to Doc's door and rung the bell and they was nothin' doin'. She rung it again and she rung it seven or eight times. Then she tried the door and found it locked. Then Jim made some kind of a noise and she heard it and waited a minute, and then she says, "Is that you, Ralph?" Ralph is Doc's first name.

They was no answer and it must of came to her all of a sudden that she'd been bunked. She pretty near fell downstairs and the whole gang after her. They chased her all the way home, hollerin', "Is that you, Ralph?" and "Oh, Ralphie, dear, is that you?" Jim says he couldn't holler it himself, as he was laughin' too hard.

Poor Julie! She didn't show up here on Main Street for a long, long time afterward.

And of course Jim and his gang told everybody in town, everybody but Doc Stair. They was scared to tell him, and he might of never knowed only for Paul Dickson. The poor cuckoo, as Jim called him, he was here in the shop one night when Jim was still gloatin' yet over what he'd done to Julie. And Paul took in as much of it as he could understand and he run to Doc with the story.

It's a cinch Doc went up in the air and swore he'd make Jim suffer. But it was a kind of a delicate thing, because if it got out that he had beat Jim up, Julie was bound to hear of it and then she'd know that Doc knew and of course knowin' that he knew would make it worse for her than ever. He was goin' to do somethin', but it took a lot of figurin'.

Well, it was a couple days later when Jim was here in the shop again, and so was the cuckoo. Jim was goin' duck-shootin' the next day and had come in lookin' for Hod Meyers to go with him. I happened to know that Hod had went over to Carterville and wouldn't be home till the end of the week. So Jim said he hated to go alone and he guessed he would call it off. Then poor Paul spoke up and said if Jim would take him he would go along. Jim thought a w'ile and then he said, well, he guessed a half-wit was better than nothin'.

I suppose he was plottin' to get Paul out in the boat and play some joke on him, like pushin' him in the water. Anyways, he said Paul could go. He asked him had he ever shot a duck and Paul said no, he'd never even had a gun in his hands. So Jim said he could set in the boat and watch him and if he behaved himself, he might lend him his gun for a couple of shots. They made a date to meet in the mornin' and that's the last I seen of Jim alive.

Next mornin', I hadn't been open more than ten minutes when Doc Stair come in. He looked kind of nervous. He asked me had I seen Paul Dickson. I said no, but I knew where he was, out duck-shootin' with Jim Kendall. So Doc says that's what he had heard, and he couldn't understand it because Paul had told him he wouldn't never have no more to do with Jim as long as he lived.

He said Paul had told him about the joke Jim had played on Julie. He said Paul had asked him what he thought of the joke and the Doc had told him that anybody that would do a thing like that ought not to be let live.

I said it had been a kind of a raw thing, but Jim just couldn't resist no kind of a joke, no matter how raw. I said I thought he was all right at heart, but just bubblin' over with mischief. Doc turned and walked out.

At noon he got a phone call from old John Scott. The lake where Jim and Paul had went shootin' is on John's place. Paul had came runnin' up to the house a few minutes before and said they'd been an accident. Jim had shot a few ducks and then give the gun to Paul and told him to try his luck. Paul hadn't never handled a gun and he was nervous. He was shakin' so hard that he couldn't control the gun. He let fire and Jim sunk back in the boat, dead.

Doc Stair, bein' the coroner, jumped in Frank Abbott's flivver and rushed out to Scott's farm. Paul and old John was down on the shore of the lake. Paul had rowed the boat to shore, but they'd left the body in it, waitin' for Doc to come.

Doc examined the body and said they might as well fetch it back to town. They was no use leavin' it there or callin' a jury, as it was a plain case of accidental shootin'.

Personally I wouldn't never leave a person shoot a gun in the same boat I was in unless I was sure they knew somethin' about guns. Jim was a sucker to leave a new beginner have his gun, let alone a half-wit. It probably served Jim right, what he got. But still we miss him round here. He certainly was a card!

Comb it wet or dry?

The Maysville Minstrel

Maysville was a town of five thousand inhabitants and its gas company served eight hundred homes, offices and stores.

The company's office force consisted of two men—Ed Hunter,

trouble shooter and reader of meters, and Stephen Gale, whose title was bookkeeper, but whose job was a lot harder than that sounds.

From the first to the tenth of the month, Stephen stayed in the office, accepted checks and money from the few thrifty customers who wanted their discount of five percent, soft-soaped and argued with the many customers who thought they were being robbed, and tried to sell new stoves, plates and lamps to customers who were constantly complaining of defects in the stoves, plates and lamps they had bought fifteen or twenty years ago.

After the tenth, he kept the front door locked and went all over town calling on delinquents, many of whom were a year or more behind and had no intention of trying to catch up. This tiring, futile task usually lasted until the twenty-seventh, when Hunter started reading meters and Stephen copied the readings and made out the bills.

On the twenty-ninth, Hunter usually got drunk and Stephen had to hustle out and read the unread meters and hustle back and make out the rest of the bills.

When Townsend, the Old Man, who owned the business and five other gas businesses in larger towns, paid his semimonthly visit to Maysville, Stephen had to take a severe bawling out for failing to squeeze blood from Maysville's turnips and allowing Hunter to get drunk.

All in all, Stephen earned the $22.50 per week which he had been getting the eight years he had worked for the gas company.

He was now thirty-one. At twelve, he had been obliged to quit school and go to work as a Western Union messenger boy. His father was dead and his mother, who established herself, without much profit, as a dressmaker, easily could use the few dollars Stephen drew from the telegraph company. Later on he had jobs as driver of a grocery wagon, soda clerk in a drug store and freight wrestler at the Lackawanna depot.

The $22.50 offer from the gas office was manna from somewhere; it topped his highest previous salary by seven dollars and a half.

Stephen's mother died and Stephen married Stella Nichols, to whom lack of money was no novelty. But they had a couple of children and soon fell into debt, which made Stephen less efficient than ever as a collector of the company's back bills. He couldn't

blame other people for not settling when he was stalling off credi-
tors himself.

All he could do was wish to heaven that the Old Man would come
across with a substantial raise, and he knew there was as much
chance of that as of Stella's swimming the English Channel with a
kid under each arm.

The Gales were too poor to go to picture shows; besides, there was
no one to leave the children with. So Stephen and Stella stayed at
home evenings and read books from the town library. The books
Stephen read were books of poetry.

And often, after Stella had gone to bed, he wrote poetry of his
own.

He wrote a poem to Stella and gave it to her on one of her birth-
days and she said it was great and he ought to quit the darn old gas
company and write poetry for a living.

He laughed that off, remarking that he was as poor now as he
cared to be.

He didn't show Stella his other poems—poems about Nature,
flowers, the Lackawanna Railroad, the beauties of Maysville, et
cetera—but kept them locked in a drawer of his desk at the gas office.

There was a man named Charley Roberts who traveled out of
New York for an instantaneous water-heater concern. For years he
had been trying to sell old Townsend, but old Townsend said the
heater ate up too much gas and would make the customers squawk.
They squawked enough as it was. Roberts was a determined young
man and kept after Townsend in spite of the latter's discouraging
attitude.

Roberts was also a wise-cracking, kidding New Yorker, who, when
at home, lunched where his heroes lunched, just to be near them,
look at them and overhear some of their wise-cracks which he could
repeat to his fellow drummers on the road. These heroes of his were
comic-strip artists, playwrights and editors of humorous columns in
the metropolitan press.

His favorite column was the one conducted by George Balch in
the Standard and when he was in the small towns, he frequently
clipped silly items from the local papers and sent them to George,
who substituted his own captions for Charley's and pasted them up.

Charley had a tip that Old Man Townsend would be in Maysville on a certain day, and as he was in the neighborhood, he took an interurban car thither and called at the gas office. Stephen had just got back from a fruitless tour among the deadheads and was in the shop, behind the office, telling Ed Hunter that Mrs. Harper's pilot-light wouldn't stay lighted.

Roberts, alone in the office, looked idly at Stephen's desk and saw a book.

It was a volume of poems by Amy Lowell. A moment later Stephen reentered from the shop.

"Hello there, Gale," said Roberts.

"How are you, Mr. Roberts?" said Stephen.

"I heard the Old Man was here," said Roberts.

"You've missed him," said Stephen. "He was here yesterday afternoon and left for Haines City last night."

"Will he be here tomorrow?"

"I couldn't tell you. He's hard to keep track of."

"He's hard to sell, too. But I'll run over there and take a chance. I notice you've been reading highbrow poetry."

"I got this from the library."

"How do you like it?"

"I'm not strong for poetry that don't rhyme," said Stephen.

"I guess it's easier to write," said Roberts.

"I don't believe so. It isn't much trouble rhyming if you've got it in you. Look at Edgar Guest."

"How do you know he doesn't have trouble?"

"His works don't read like it," said Stephen, and after a pause: "Besides, I've tried it myself."

"Oh, so you're a poet, are you?" asked Roberts.

"I wouldn't exactly claim that, but I've written a few verses and it was more like fun than work. Maybe other people would think they were rotten, but I get pleasure writing them just the same."

"I'd like to read them, Gale," said Roberts eagerly.

"I don't know if I'd like you to or not. And I don't know if I've saved any. I wrote a poem to my wife on her birthday three years ago. She thought it was pretty good. I might let you read that, only I don't know if I've got a copy of it around here."

He knew very well he had a copy of it around there.

"See if you can find it," said Roberts.

Stephen looked in two or three drawers before he unlocked the one that contained his manuscripts.

"It's just a little thing I wrote for my wife on her birthday. You'll probably think it's rotten. It's called 'To Stella.' That's my wife's first name."

Charley Roberts read the poem:

> Stella you today are twenty-three years old
> And yet your hair is still pure gold.
> Stella they tell me your name in Latin means a star
> And to me that is what you are
> With your eyes and your hair so yellow
> I rate myself a lucky fellow Stella.
> You know I cannot afford a costly gift
> As you know it costs us all I make to live
> And as you know we are already in debt,
> But if you will stay well and healthy
> Until I am rich and wealthy
> Maybe I will be more able then to give you a present
> Better than I can at present.
> So now Stella good-by for the present
> And I hope next year I can make things more pleasant.
> May you live to be old and ripe and mellow
> Is my kind birthday wish for you Stella.

"Do you mean to tell me," said Roberts, "that it was no trouble to write that?"

"It only took me less than a half-hour," said Stephen.

"Listen," said Roberts. "Let me have it."

"What do you want with it?"

"I can get it published for you."

"Where at?"

"In the New York Standard. I've got a friend, George Balch, who would run it in his column. He doesn't pay anything, but if this was printed and your name signed to it, it might attract attention from people who do pay for poetry. Then you could make a lot of money on the side."

"How much do they pay?"

"Well, some of the big magazines pay as high as a dollar a line."

"I forget how many lines there is in that."

Roberts counted them.

"Seventeen," he said. "And from what I've seen of old Townsend, I bet he doesn't pay you much more a week."

"And it only took me less than a half-hour to write," said Stephen.

"Will you let me send it to Balch?"

"I don't know if I've got another copy."

"Your wife must have a copy."

"I guess maybe she has."

He wasn't just guessing.

"I'll mail this to Balch tonight, along with a note. If he prints it, I'll send you the paper."

"I've got one that's even longer than that," said Stephen.

"Well, let's have it."

"No, I guess I'd better hang onto it—if your friend don't pay for them."

"You're absolutely right. A man's a sucker to work for nothing. You keep your other stuff till this is published and you hear from some magazine editor, as I'm sure you will. Then you can sell what you've already written, and write more, till you're making so much dough that you can buy the Maysville Gas Company from that old skinflint."

"I don't want any gas company. I want to get out of it. I just want to write."

"Why shouldn't you!"

"I've got to be sure of a living."

"Living! If you can make seventeen dollars in half an hour, that's thirty-four dollars an hour, or——— How many hours do you put in here?"

"Ten."

"Three hundred and forty dollars a day! If that isn't a living, I'm selling manicure sets to fish."

"I couldn't keep up no such a pace. I have to wait for inspiration," said Stephen.

"A dollar a line would be enough inspiration for me. But the times when you didn't feel like doing it yourself, you could hire somebody to do it for you."

"That wouldn't be square, and people would know the difference anyway. It's hard to imitate another man's style. I tried once to write like Edgar Guest, but it wouldn't have fooled people that was familiar with his works."

"Nobody can write like Guest. And you don't need to. Your own style is just as good as his and maybe better. And speaking of Guest, do you think he's starving to death? He gives away dimes to the Fords."

Stephen was wild to tell Stella what had happened, but he was afraid this Balch might not like the poem as well as Roberts had; might not think it worth publishing, and she would be disappointed.

He would wait until he actually had it in print, if ever, and then show it to her.

He didn't have to wait long. In less than a week he received by mail from New York a copy of the Standard, and in George Balch's column was his verse with his name signed to it and a caption reading "To Stella—A Maysville Minstrel Gives His Mrs. a Birthday Treat."

For the first time in his career at the gas office, Stephen quit five minutes early and almost ran home. His wife was as excited as he had hoped she would be.

"But why does he call you a minstrel?" she asked. "He must have heard some way about that night at the Elks."

Stephen told her the rest of the story—how Roberts had predicted that the poem would attract the attention of magazine editors and create a demand for his verses at a dollar a line. And he confessed that he had other poems all ready to send when the call came.

He had brought two of them home from the office and he read them aloud for her approval:

"1. The Lackawanna Railroad.

"The Lackawanna Railroad where does it go?
It goes from Jersey City to Buffalo.
Some of the trains stop at Maysville but they are few
Most of them go right through
Except the 8:22
Going west but the 10:12 bound for Jersey City
That is the train we like the best
As it takes you to Jersey City
Where you can take a ferry or tube for New York City.
The Lackawanna runs many freights

Sometimes they run late
But that does not make so much difference with a freight
Except the people who have to wait for their freight.
Maysville people patronize the Interurban a specially the farmers
So the Interurban cuts into the business of the Lackawanna,
But if you are going to New York City or Buffalo
The Lackawanna is the way to go.
Will say in conclusion that we consider it an honor
That the City of Maysville is on the Lackawanna.

"2. The Gas Business.

"The Maysville Gas Co. has eight hundred meters
The biggest consumer in town is Mrs. Arnold Peters
Who owns the big house on Taylor Hill
And is always giving parties come who will.
Our collections amount to about $2600.00 per month
Five per cent discount if paid before the tenth of the month.
Mr. Townsend the owner considers people a fool
Who do not at least use gas for fuel.
As for lighting he claims it beats electricity
As electric storms often cut off the electricity
And when you have no light at night
And have to burn candles all night.
This is hardly right
A specially if you have company
Who will ask you what is the matter with the electricity.
So patronize the Gas Company which storms do not effect
And your friends will have no reason to object."

Stella raved over both the poems, but made a very practical suggestion.

"You are cheating yourself, dear," she said. "The poem about the railroad, for instance, the way you have got it, it is nineteen lines, or nineteen dollars if they really pay a dollar a line. But it would be almost double the amount if you would fix the lines different."

"How do you mean?"

She got a pencil and piece of paper and showed him:

> The Lackawanna Railroad
> Where does it go?
> It goes from Jersey City
> To Buffalo.

"You see," she said, "you could cut most of the lines in half and make thirty-eight dollars instead of nineteen."

But Stephen, with one eye on profit and the other on Art, could only increase the lines of "The Lackawanna" from nineteen to thirty and those of "The Gas Business" from seventeen to twenty-one.

Three days later a special delivery came for Stephen.

It said:

Dear Mr. Gale:

On September second there was a poem entitled "To Stella" in the New York Standard. The poem was signed by you. It impressed me greatly and if you have written or will write others as good, our magazine will be glad to buy them, paying you one dollar a line.

Please let me hear from you and send along any poems you may have on hand.

> Sincerely,
> Wallace James,
> Editor, "James's Weekly,"
> New York City.

Stephen had never heard of "James's Weekly" and did not notice that the letter was postmarked Philadelphia and written on the stationery of a Philadelphia hotel.

He rushed to his house, addressed and mailed the railroad and gas verses, and after a brief and excited conference with Stella, decided to resign his job.

Old Man Townsend, dropping into Maysville the following morning, heard the decision and was not a bit pleased. He realized he never could get anyone else to do Stephen's work at Stephen's salary.

"I'll raise you to twenty-four dollars," he said.

"I'm not asking for a raise. I've got to quit so I can devote all my time to my poetry."

"Your poetry!"

"Yes, sir."

"Do you mean to say you're going to write poetry for a living?" asked the Old Man.

"Yes, sir."

"You'll starve to death."

"Edgar Guest is still alive."

"I don't care if he is or not," said the Old Man. "It's the twelfth of the month and Hunter can tend to his job and yours both for a couple of weeks. If you want to come back at the end of that time, I'll raise you to twenty-three dollars."

It was Stephen's intention to polish up some of his older poems and write one or two fresh ones so his supply would be ready for "James's" demand.

But he found it next to impossible to write while the fate of the two verses he had sent in was uncertain and, deciding to leave the old manuscripts as they were, he was able to make only a feeble start on a new one:

The Delaware River.

Not a great many miles from Maysville is the Delaware River
But there is no fish in this part of the River.
The upper part of the River is narrow and shallow
But they claim it is much wider near Philadelphia.

On the twentieth the envelope containing "The Lackawanna Railroad" and "The Gas Business" was returned from New York. There were several inscriptions stamped and written on it, such as "Not Found" and "Not in Directory."

And it dawned on Stephen that he was the victim of quite a joke.

To the accompaniment of Stella's sobs, he proceeded to tear up all his manuscripts save "To Stella," which she had hidden away where he couldn't find it.

"Mr. Townsend came in on the eight-thirty interurban," he said. "I'll have to go see him."

"All right," said the Old Man when Stephen walked into the office. "I'll take you back at your old salary, but don't let's have no more foolishness. Get out now and try and coax a little money out of that Harper woman. She ain't paid a nickel for eight months."

"I wanted to speak to you about those instantaneous water-heaters," said Stephen.

"What about them?"

"I was going to advise you not to buy them. They eat up too much gas."

"Thanks for your advice, but I ordered some from Roberts in Haines City. I told him to send half a dozen of them here," said the Old Man.

"Will he be here to demonstrate them?" asked Stephen grimly.

"He said he would."

"I hope he will."

But even as he spoke, Stephen realized there was nothing he could do about it.

Travelogue

They met for the first time at luncheon in the diner of the west-bound limited that had left Chicago the night before. The girls, it turned out, were Hazel Dignan and her friend Mildred Orr. The man was Dan Chapman.

He it was who broke the ice by asking if they minded riding backwards. It was Hazel who answered. She was a seasoned traveler and knew how to talk to strangers. Mildred had been hardly anywhere and had little to say, even when she knew people.

"Not at all," was Hazel's reply to his polite query. "I'm so used to trains that I believe I could ride on top of them and not be uncomfortable."

"Imagine," put in Mildred, "riding on top of a train!"

"Many's the time I've done it!" said their new acquaintance. "Freight-trains, though; not passenger-trains. And it was when I was a kid."

"I don't see how you dared," said Mildred.

"I guess I was a kind of a reckless, wild kid," he said. "It's a wonder I didn't get killed, the chances I took. Some kids takes lots of chances; that is, boys."

"Girls do, too," said Hazel quickly. "Girls take just as many chances as boys."

"Oh, no, Hazel!" remonstrated her friend, and received an approving look from the male.

"Where are you headed for?" he asked.

"Frisco first and then Los Angeles," Hazel replied.

"Listen—let me give you a tip. Don't say 'Frisco' in front of them native sons. They don't like that nickname."

"I should worry what they like and don't like!" said Hazel, rather snootily, Mildred thought.

"This your first trip out there?" Chapman inquired.

"No," Hazel answered to Mildred's surprise, for the purpose of the journey, she had been led to believe, was to give Hazel a glimpse of one of the few parts of America that she had never visited.

"How long since you was out there last?" asked Chapman.

"Let's see," said Hazel. "It's been——" She was embarrassed by Mildred's wondering look. "I don't know exactly. I've forgotten."

"This is about my fiftieth trip," said Chapman. "If you haven't been——"

"I like Florida better," interrupted Hazel. "I generally go there in the winter."

" 'Generally!' " thought Mildred, who had reliable information that the previous winter had been her friend's first in the South.

"I used to go to Palm Beach every year," said Chapman, "but that was before it got common. It seems to be that the people that goes to Florida now, well, they're just riffraff."

"The people that go to Tampa aren't riffraff," said Hazel. "I met some lovely people there last winter, especially one couple, the Babcocks. From Racine. They were perfectly lovely to me. We played Mah Jongg nearly every evening. They wanted me to come up and visit them in Racine this last summer, but something happened. Oh, yes; Sis's nurse got married. She was a Swedish girl. Just perfect! And Sis had absolute confidence in her.

"I always say that when a Swede is good, they're *good!* Now she's got a young girl about nineteen that's wild about movie actors and so absent-minded that Sis is scared to death she'll give Junior coffee and drink his milk herself. Just crazy! Jennie, her name is. So I didn't get up to Racine."

"Ever been out to Yellowstone?"

"Oh, isn't it wonderful!" responded Hazel. "Isn't 'Old Faithful' just fascinating! You see," she explained to Mildred, "It's one of the geysers and they call it 'Old Faithful' because it spouts every hour and ten minutes or something, just as regular as clockwork. Wonderful! And the different falls and canyons! Wonderful! And what a wonderful view from Inspiration Point!"

"Ever been to the Thousand Islands?" asked Chapman.

"Wonderful! And I was going up there again last summer with a girl friend of mine, Bess Eldridge. She was engaged to a man named Harley Bateman. A wonderful fellow when he wasn't drinking, but when he'd had a few drinks, he was just terrible. So Bess and I were in Chicago and we went to a show; Eddie Cantor. It was the first time I ever saw him when he wasn't blacked up. Well, we were walking out of the theater that night and who should we run into but Harley Bateman, terribly boiled, and a girl from Elkhart, Joan Killian. So Bess broke off her engagement and last fall she married a man named Wannop who's interested in flour-mills or something up in Minneapolis. So I didn't get to the Thousand Islands after all. That is, a second time.

"But I always think that if a person hasn't taken that trip, they haven't seen anything. And Bess would have certainly enjoyed it. She used to bite her finger-nails till she didn't have any left. But she married this man from Minneapolis."

After luncheon the three moved to the observation-car and made a brave effort to be interested in what passes for scenery in Nebraska.

For no possible reason, it reminded Chapman of Northern Michigan.

"Have you ever been up in Northern Michigan?"

"Yes, indeed," said Hazel. "I visited a week once in Petoskey. Some friends of mine named Gilbert. They had their own launch. Ina Gilbert—that's Mrs. Gilbert—her hair used to be the loveliest thing in the world and she had typhoid or something and lost nearly all of it. So we played Mah Jongg every afternoon and evening."

"I mean 'way up," said Chapman. "Mackinac Island and the Upper Peninsula, the Copper Country."

"Oh, wonderful!" said Hazel. "Calumet and Houghton and Hancock! Wonderful! And the boat trip is wonderful! Though I guess I was about the only one that thought so. Everybody else was sick. The captain said it was the roughest trip he'd ever been on, and he had lived on the Great Lakes for forty years. And another time I went across from Chicago to St. Joseph. But that wasn't so rough. We visited the House of David in Benton Harbor. They wear long beards. We were almost in hysterics, Marjorie Trumbull and I. But the time I went to Petoskey, I went alone."

"You see a lot of Finns up in that Nothern Peninsula," remarked Chapman.

"Yes, and Sis had a Finnish maid once. She couldn't hardly understand a word of English. She was a Finn. Sis finally had to let her go. Now she has an Irish girl for a maid and Jennie takes care of the kiddies. Poor little Dickie, my nephew, he's nearly seven and of course he's lost all his front teeth. He looks terrible! Teeth do make such a difference! My friends always say they envy me my teeth."

"Talking about teeth," said Chapman, "you see this?" He opened his mouth and pointed to a large, dark vacancy where once had dwelt a molar. "I had that one pulled in Milwaukee the day before yesterday. The fella said I better take gas, but I said no. So he said, 'Well, you must be pretty game.' I said I faced German shell-fire for sixteen months and I guess I ain't going to be a-scared of a little forceps. Well, he said afterwards that it was one of the toughest teeth he ever pulled. The roots were the size of your little finger. And the tooth itself was full of——"

"I only had one tooth pulled in my life," said Hazel. "I'd been suffering from rheumatism and somebody suggested that it might be from a tooth, but I couldn't believe it at first because my teeth are so perfect. But I hadn't slept in months on account of these pains in my arms and limbs. So finally, just to make sure, I went to a dentist, old Doctor Platt, and he pulled this tooth"—she showed him where it had been—"and my rheumatism disappeared just like that. It was terrible not to be able to sleep because I generally sleep like a log. And I do now, since I got my tooth pulled."

"I don't sleep very good on trains," said Chapman.

"Oh, I do. Probably on account of being so used to it. I slept just beautifully last night. Mildred here insisted on taking the upper. She said if she was where she could look out the window, she never would go to sleep. Personally, I'd just as lief have the upper. I don't mind it a bit. I like it really better. But this is Mildred's first long trip and I thought she ought to have her choice. We tried to get a compartment or drawing-room, but they were all gone. Sis and I had a compartment the time we went to New Orleans. I slept in the upper."

Mildred wished she had gone places so she could take part in the conversation. Mr. Chapman must think she was terribly dumb.

She had nothing to talk about that people would care to hear, and it was kind of hard to keep awake when you weren't talking yourself, even with such interesting, traveled people to listen to as Mr. Chapman and Hazel. Mr. Chapman was a dandy-looking man and it was terrible to have to appear dumb in front of him.

But after all, she *was* dumb and Hazel's erudition made her seem all the dumber. No wonder their new acquaintance had scarcely looked at her since luncheon.

"Have you ever been to San Antone?" Chapman asked his companions.

"Isn't it wonderful!" Hazel exclaimed. "The Alamo! Wonderful! And those dirty Mexicans! And Salt Lake City is wonderful, too! That temple! And swimming in the lake itself is one of the most fascinating experiences! You know, Mildred, the water is so salt that you can't sink in it. You just lie right on top of it like it was a floor. You can't sink. And another wonderful place is Lake Placid. I was going back there last summer with Bess Eldridge, but she was engaged at the time to Harley Bateman, an awfully nice boy when he wasn't drinking, but perfectly terrible when he'd had a few drinks. He went to college with my brother, to Michigan. Harley tried for the football nine, but the coach hated him. His father was a druggist and owned the first automobile in Berrien County. So we didn't go to Placid last summer, but I'm going next summer sure. And it's wonderful in winter, too!"

"It feels funny, where that tooth was," said Chapman.

"Outside of one experience," said Hazel, "I've never had any trouble with my teeth. I'd been suffering from rheumatism and somebody suggested it might be a bad tooth, but I couldn't believe it because my teeth are perfect——"

"This was all shot to pieces," said Chapman.

"But my friends always say they envy me my teeth; my teeth and my complexion. I try to keep my mouth clean and my face clean, and I guess that's the answer. But it's hard to keep clean on a train."

"Where are you going? Out to the coast?"

"Yes. Frisco and then Los Angeles."

"Don't call it Frisco in front of them Californians. They don't like their city to be called Frisco. Is this your first trip out there?"

"No. I was there a good many years ago."

She turned to Mildred.

"You didn't know that, did you?" she said. But Mildred was asleep. "Poor Mildred! She's worn out. She isn't used to traveling. She's quite a pretty girl, don't you think so?"

"Very pretty!"

"Maybe not exactly pretty," said her friend, "but kind of sweet-looking, like a baby. You'd think all the men would be crazy about her, but they aren't. Lots of people don't even think she's pretty and I suppose you can't be really pretty unless you have more expression in your face than she's got. Poor Mildred hasn't had many advantages."

"At this time of year, I'd rather be in Atlantic City than San Francisco."

"Oh, isn't Atlantic City wonderful! There's only one Atlantic City! And I really like it better in the winter. Nobody but nice people go there in the winter. In the summer-time it's different. I'm no snob, but I don't mind saying that I hate to mix up with some people a person has to meet at these resort places. Terrible! Two years ago I went to Atlantic City with Bess Eldridge. Like a fool I left it to her to make the reservations and she wired the Traymore, she says, but they didn't have anything for us. We tried the Ritz and the Ambassador and everywhere else, but we couldn't get in anywhere, that is, anywhere a person would want to stay. Bess was engaged to Harley Bateman at the time. Now she's married a man named Wannop from Minneapolis. But this time I speak of, we went to Philadelphia and stayed all night with my aunt and we had scrapple and liver and bacon for breakfast. Harley was a dandy boy when he wasn't drinking. But give me Atlantic City any time of the year!"

"I've got to send a telegram at Grand Island."

"Oh, if I sent one from there, when would it get to Elkhart?"

"Tonight or tomorrow morning."

"I want to wire my sister."

"Well, wire her from Grand Island."

"I think I'll wait and wire her from Frisco."

"But we won't be in San Francisco for over two days yet."

"But we change time before then, don't we?"

"Yes, we change at North Platte."

"Then I think I'll wire her from Grand Island."

"Your sister, you say?"

"Yes. My sister Lucy. She married Jack Kingston, the Kingston tire people."

"It certainly feels empty, where that tooth was," said Chapman.

As the train pulled out of North Platte, later in the afternoon, Chapman rejoined the two girls in the observation-car.

"Now, girls," he said, "you can set your watches back an hour. We change time here. We were Central time and now we're Mountain time."

"Mountain time," repeated Mildred. "I suppose that's where the expression started, 'it's high time'."

Hazel and Chapman looked blank and Mildred blushed. She felt she had made a mistake saying anything at all. She opened her book, "Carlyle on Cromwell and Others," which Rev. N. L. Veach had given her for Christmas.

"Have you ever been to Washington?" Chapman asked Hazel.

"Oh, isn't it beautiful! 'The City of Magnificent Distances.' Wonderful! I was there two years ago with Bess Eldridge. We were going to meet the President, but something happened. Oh, yes; Bess got a wire from Harley Bateman that he was going to get in that afternoon. And he never came at all. He was awfully nice when he wasn't drinking, and just terrible when he drank. Bess broke off her engagement to him and married a man named Wannop, who owned some flour-mills in Minneapolis. She was a dandy girl, but bit her fingernails just terribly. So we didn't get to see the President, but we sat through two or three sessions of the Senate and House. Do you see how they ever get anything done? And we went to Rock Creek Park and Mount Vernon and Arlington Cemetery and Keith's.

"Moran and Mack were there; you know, the black-face comedians. Moran, or maybe it's Mack, whichever is the little one, he says to the other—I've forgotten just how it went, but they were simply screaming and I thought Bess and I would be put out. We just howled. And the last night we were there we saw Thomas Meighan in 'Old Home Week.' Wonderful! Harley Bateman knows Thomas Meighan personally. He's got a beautiful home out on Long Island. He invited Harley out there to dinner one night, but something happened. Oh, yes; Harley lost a front tooth once and he had a false one put in and this day he ate some caramels and the tooth came out——"

"Look here," said Chapman, opening his mouth and pointing in it. "I got that one pulled in Milwaukee——"

"Harley was a perfect peach when he was sober, but terrible when——"

It occurred to Mildred that her presence might be embarrassing. Here were evidently kindred spirits, two people who had been everywhere and seen everything. But of course they couldn't talk anything but geography and dentistry before her.

"I think I'll go to our car and take a little nap," she said.

"Oh, don't——" began Chapman surprisingly, but stopped there. She was gone and the kindred spirits were alone.

"I suppose," said Chapman, "you've been to Lake Louise."

"Wonderful!" Hazel responded. "Did you ever see anything as pretty in your life? They talk about the lakes of Ireland and Scotland and Switzerland, but I don't believe they can compare with Lake Louise. I was there with Bess Eldridge just before she got engaged to Harley Bateman. He was——"

"Your friend's a mighty pretty girl."

"I suppose some people would think her pretty. It's a matter of individual taste."

"Very quiet, isn't she?"

"Poor Mildred hasn't much to say. You see, she's never had any advantages and there's really nothing she can talk about. But what was I saying? Oh, yes; about Harley Bateman——"

"I think that's a good idea, taking a little nap. I believe I'll try it, too."

Hazel and Chapman lunched alone next day.

"I'm afraid Mildred is a little train sick," said Hazel. "She says she is all right but just isn't hungry. I guess the trip has been a little too much for her. You see, this is the first time she's ever been anywhere at all."

The fact was that Mildred did not like to be stared at and Chapman had stared at her all through dinner the night before, stared at her, she thought, as if she were a curiosity, as if he doubted that one so dumb could be real. She liked him, too, and it would have been so nice if she had been more like Hazel, never at a loss for something to say and able to interest him in her conversation.

"We'll be in Ogden in half an hour," said Chapman. "We stay there twenty-five minutes. That ought to give your friend a chance to get over whatever ails her. She should get out and walk around and get some air."

"You seem quite interested in Mildred," Hazel said.

"She's a mighty attractive girl," he replied. "And besides, I feel sorry for anybody that——"

"Men don't usually find her attractive. She's pretty in a way, but it's a kind of a babyish face."

"I don't think so at all——"

"We change time here again, don't we?"

"Yes. Another hour back. We've been on Mountain time and now we go to Pacific time. Some people say it's bad for a watch to turn it backwards, but it never seemed to hurt mine any. This watch——"

"I bought this watch of mine in New York," said Hazel. "It was about two years ago, the last time Bess Eldridge and I went East. Let's see; was that before or after she broke her engagement to Harley Bateman? It was before. But Harley said he knew the manager of the Belmont and he would wire him and get us a good room. Well, of course, he forgot to wire, so we finally got into the Pennsylvania, Room 1012. No, Room 1014. It was some people from Pittsburgh, a Mr. and Mrs. Bradbury, in 1012. He was lame. Bess wanted to see Jeanne Eagles in 'Rain' and we tried to get tickets at the newsstand, but they said fifteenth row. We finally went to the Palace that night. Ina Claire was on the bill. So the next morning we came down to breakfast and who should we run into but Dave Homan! We'd met him at French Lick in the spring. Isn't French Lick wonderful!

"Well, Dave insisted on 'showing' us New York, like we didn't know it backwards. But we did have a dandy time. Dave kept us in hysterics. I remember he took us to the Aquarium and of course a lot of other people were in there and Dave gave one of the attendants a quarter to page Mr. Fish. I thought they'd put us out, we screamed so! Dave asked me to marry him once, just jokingly, and I told him I wouldn't think of it because I had heard it made people fat to laugh and if I lived with him I would soon have to buy my clothes from a tent-maker. Dave said we would make a great pair as we both have such a keen sense of humor. Honestly, I wouldn't give up my sense of humor for all the money in the world. I don't see how people can live without a sense of humor. Mildred, for instance; she never sees the funny side of things unless you make her a diagram and even then she looks at you like she thought you were deranged.

"But I was telling you about Dave Homan. We were talking along about one thing and another and I happened to mention Harley Bateman and Dave said, 'Harley Bateman! Do you know Harley Bateman?' and Bess and I smiled at each other and I said I guessed we did. Well, it seems that Dave and Harley had been at Atlantic City together at a Lion's convention or something and they had some drinks and Dave had a terrible time keeping a policeman from locking Harley up. He's just as different when he's drinking as day and night. Dave got him out of it all right and they met again later on, in Chicago. Or was it Duluth? So the next day was Wednesday and Dave asked Bess and I to go to the matinée of 'Rain,' but Bess had an engagement with a dentist——"

"Do you see this?" interrupted Chapman, opening his mouth wide.

"So Dave took me alone and he said he had been hoping for that chance right along. He said three was a crowd. I believe if I had given him any encouragement—— But the man I marry must be something more than clever and witty. I like men that have been around and seen things and studied human nature and have a background. Of course they must see the funny side, too. That's the trouble with Dave Homan—he can't be serious. Harley Bateman is twice as much of a man if he wouldn't drink. It's like two different people when he drinks. He's terrible! Bess Eldridge was engaged to him, but she broke it off after we happened to see him in Chicago one time with Joan Killian, from Elkhart. Bess is married now, to a man named Wannop, a flour man from Minneapolis. So after the matinée we met Bess. She'd been to the dentist——"

"Three days ago, in Milwaukee——" began Chapman.

"So the next afternoon we were taking the boat for Boston. I'd been to Boston before, of course, but never by boat. Harley Bateman told us it was a dandy trip, so we decided to try it. Well, we left New York at five o'clock and Bess and I were up on deck when somebody came up behind us and put their hands over my eyes and said, 'Guess who it is?' Well, I couldn't have guessed in a hundred years. It was Clint Poole from South Bend. Imagine! Harley Bateman's brother-in-law!"

"Here's Ogden," said Chapman as the train slowed down.

"Oh, and I've got to send Sis a telegram! My sister Lucy Kingston."

"I think I'll get out and get some air," said Chapman, but he went first to the car where Mildred sat reading.

"Miss Mildred," he said, "suppose you have breakfast with me early tomorrow morning. I'd like to show you the snow-sheds."

"That would be wonderful!" said Mildred. "I'll tell Hazel."

"No," said Chapman. "Please don't tell Hazel. I'd like to show them to you alone."

Well, even if Mildred had been used to trains, that remark would have interfered seriously with her night's sleep.

Mildred found Chapman awaiting her in the diner next morning, an hour west of Truckee.

"Are those the snow-sheds you spoke of?"

"Yes," he replied, "but we'll talk about them later. First I want to ask you a few questions."

"Ask *me* questions!" said Mildred. "Well, they'll have to be simple ones or I won't be able to answer them."

"They're simple enough," said Chapman. "The first one is, do you know Harley Bateman?"

"I know *of* him, but I don't know him."

"Do you know Bess Eldridge?"

"Just to speak to; that's all."

"What other trips have you taken besides this?"

"None at all. This is really the first time I've ever been anywhere."

"Has your friend ever been engaged?"

"Yes; twice. It was broken off both times."

"I bet I know why. There was no place to take her on a honeymoon."

"What do you mean?"

"Oh, nothing. Say, did I tell you about getting my tooth pulled in Milwaukee?"

"I don't believe so," said Mildred.

"Well, I had a terrible toothache. It was four days ago. And I thought there was no use fooling with it, so I went to a dentist and told him to pull it. He said I'd better take gas, but I wouldn't. So he pulled it and it pretty near killed me, but I never batted an eye. He said it was one of the toughest teeth he'd ever seen; roots as big as your little finger. And the tooth itself full of poison."

"How terrible! You must be awfully brave!"

"Look here, at the hole," said Chapman, opening his mouth.

"Why, Mr. Chapman, it must have hurt horribly!"

"Call me Dan."

"Oh, I couldn't."

"Well, listen—are you going to be with Miss Hazel all the time you're in San Francisco?"

"Why, no," said Mildred. "Hazel is going to visit her aunt in Berkeley part of the time. And I'm going to stop at the Fairmont."

"When is she going to Berkeley?"

"Next Tuesday, I think."

"Can I phone you next Wednesday?"

"But Hazel will be gone then."

"Yes, I know," said Chapman, "but if you don't mind, I'll phone you just the same. Now about these snow-sheds——"

The Facts

I

The engagement was broken off before it was announced. So only a thousand or so of the intimate friends and relatives of the parties knew anything about it. What they knew was that there had been an engagement and that there was one no longer. The cause of the breach they merely guessed, and most of the guesses were, in most particulars, wrong.

Each intimate and relative had a fragment of the truth. It remained for me to piece the fragments together. It was a difficult job, but I did it. Part of my evidence is hearsay; the major portion is fully corroborated. And not one of my witnesses had anything to gain through perjury.

So I am positive that I have at my tongue's end the facts, and I believe that in justice to everybody concerned I should make them public.

Ellen McDonald had lived on the North Side of Chicago for twenty-one years. Billy Bowen had been a South-Sider for seven years longer. But neither knew of the other's existence until they met in New York, the night before the Army-Navy game.

Billy, sitting with a business acquaintance at a neighboring table in Tonio's, was spotted by a male member of Ellen's party, a Chicagoan, too. He was urged to come on over. He did, and was introduced. The business acquaintance was also urged, came, was introduced and forgotten; forgotten, that is, by every one but the waiter, who observed that he danced not nor told stories, and figured that his function must be to pay. The business acquaintance had been Billy's guest. Now he became host, and without seeking the office.

It was not that Billy and Miss McDonald's male friends were niggards. But unfortunately for the b. a., the checks always happened to arrive when everybody else was dancing or so hysterical over Billy's repartee as to be potentially insolvent.

Billy was somewhere between his fourteenth and twenty-first highball; in other words, at his best, from the audience's standpoint. His dialogue was simply screaming and his dancing just heavenly. He was Frank Tinney doubling as Vernon Castle. On the floor he tried and accomplished twinkles that would have spelled catastrophe if attempted under the fourteen mark, or over the twenty-one. And he said the cutest things—one right after the other.

II

You can be charmed by a man's dancing, but you can't fall in love with his funniness. If you're going to fall in love with him at all, you'll do it when you catch him in a serious mood.

Miss McDonald caught Billy Bowen in one at the game next day. Entirely by accident or a decree of fate, her party and his sat in adjoining boxes. Not by accident, Miss McDonald sat in the chair that was nearest Billy's. She sat there first to be amused; she stayed to be conquered.

Here was a different Billy from the Billy of Tonio's. Here was a Billy who trained his gun on your heart and let your risibles alone. Here was a dreamy Billy, a Billy of romance.

How calm he remained through the excitement! How indifferent to the thrills of the game! There was depth to him. He was a man. Her escort and the others round her were children, screaming with delight at the puerile deeds of pseudo heroes. Football was a great sport, but a sport. It wasn't Life. Would the world be better or worse for that nine-yard gain that Elephant or Oliphant, or whatever his name was, had just made? She knew it wouldn't. Billy knew, too, for Billy was deep. He was thinking man's thoughts. She could tell by his silence, by his inattention to the scene before him. She scarcely could believe that here was the same person who, last night, had kept his own, yes, and the neighboring tables, roaring with laughter. What a complex character his!

In sooth, Mr. Bowen was thinking man's thoughts. He was thinking that if this pretty Miss McDowell, or Donnelly, were elsewhere, he could go to sleep. And that if he could remember which team he had bet on and could tell which team was which, he would have a better idea of whether he was likely to win or lose.

When, after the game, they parted, Billy rallied to the extent of asking permission to call. Ellen, it seemed, would be very glad to have him, but she couldn't tell exactly when she would have to be back in Chicago; she still had three more places to visit in the East. Could she possibly let him know when she did get back? Yes, she could and would; if he really wanted her to, she would drop him a note. He certainly wanted her to.

This, thought Billy, was the best possible arrangement. Her note would tell him her name and address, and save him the trouble of 'phoning to all the McConnells, McDowells, and Donnellys on the North Side. He did want to see her again; she was pretty, and, judging from last night, full of pep. And she had fallen for him; he knew it from that look.

He watched her until she was lost in the crowd. Then he hunted round for his pals and the car that had brought them up. At length he gave up the search and wearily climbed the elevated stairs. His hotel was on Broadway, near Forty-fourth. He left the train at Forty-second, the third time it stopped there.

"I guess you've rode far enough," said the guard. "Fifteen cents' worth for a nickel. I guess we ought to have a Pullman on these here trains."

"I guess," said Billy, "I guess——"

But the repartee well was dry. He stumbled down-stairs and hurried toward Broadway to replenish it.

III

Ellen McDonald's three more places to visit in the East must have been deadly dull. Anyway, on the sixth of December, scarcely more than a week after his parting with her in New York, Billy Bowen received the promised note. It informed him merely that her name was Ellen McDonald, that she lived at so-and-so Walton Place, and that she was back in Chicago.

That day, if you'll remember, was Monday. Miss McDonald's parents had tickets for the opera. But Ellen was honestly just worn out, and would they be mad at her if she stayed home and went to bed? They wouldn't. They would take Aunt Mary in her place.

On Tuesday morning, Paul Potter called up and wanted to know if she would go with him that night to "The Follies." She was horribly sorry, but she'd made an engagement. The engagement, evidently, was to study, and the subject was harmony, with Berlin, Kern, and Van Alstyne as instructors. She sat on the piano-bench from half-past seven till quarter after nine, and then went to her room vowing that she would accept any and all invitations for the following evening.

Fortunately, no invitations arrived, for at a quarter of nine Wednesday night, Mr. Bowen did. And in a brand-new mood. He was a bit shy and listened more than he talked. But when he talked, he talked well, though the sparkling wit of the night at Tonio's was lacking. Lacking, too, was the preoccupied air of the day at the football game. There was no problem to keep his mind busy, but even if the Army and Navy had been playing football in this very room, he could have told at a glance which was which. Vision and brain were perfectly clear. And he had been getting his old eight hours, and, like the railroad hen, sometimes nine and sometimes ten, every night since his arrival home from Gotham, N. Y. Mr. Bowen was on the wagon.

They talked of the East, of Tonio's, of the game (this was where

Billy did most of his listening), of the war, of theatres, of books, of college, of automobiles, of the market. They talked, too, of their immediate families. Billy's, consisting of one married sister in South Bend, was soon exhausted. He had two cousins here in town whom he saw frequently, two cousins and their wives, but they were people who simply couldn't stay home nights. As for himself, he preferred his rooms and a good book to the so-called gay life. Ellen should think that a man who danced so well would want to be doing it all the time. It was nice of her to say that he danced well, but really he didn't, you know. Oh, yes, he did. She guessed she could tell. Well, anyway, the giddy whirl made no appeal to him, unless, of course, he was in particularly charming company. His avowed love for home and quiet surprised Ellen a little. It surprised Mr. Bowen a great deal. Only last night, he remembered, he had been driven almost desperate by that quiet of which he was now so fond; he had been on the point of busting loose, but had checked himself in time. He had played Canfield till ten, though the book-shelves were groaning with their load.

Ellen's family kept them busy for an hour and a half. It was a dear family and she wished he could meet it. Mother and father were out playing bridge somewhere to-night. Aunt Mary had gone to bed. Aunts Louise and Harriet lived in the next block. Sisters Edith and Wilma would be home from Northampton for the holidays about the twentieth. Brother Bob and his wife had built the cutest house; in Evanston. Her younger brother, Walter, was a case! He was away to-night, had gone out right after dinner. He'd better be in before mother and father came. He had a new love-affair every week, and sixteen years old last August. Mother and father really didn't care how many girls he was interested in, so long as they kept him too busy to run round with those crazy schoolmates of his. The latter were older than he; just at the age when it seems smart to drink beer and play cards for money. Father said if he ever found out that Walter was doing those things, he'd take him out of school and lock him up somewhere.

Aunts Louise and Mary and Harriet did a lot of settlement work. They met all sorts of queer people, people you'd never believe existed. The three aunts were unmarried.

Brother Bob's wife was dear, but absolutely without a sense of

humor. Bob was full of fun, but they got along just beautifully together. You never saw a couple so much in love.

Edith was on the basket-ball team at college and terribly popular.
Wilma was horribly clever and everybody said she'd make Phi Beta
Kappa.

Ellen, so she averred, had been just nothing in school; not bright;
not athletic, and, of course, not popular.

"Oh, of course not," said Billy, smiling.

"Honestly," fibbed Ellen.

"You never could make me believe it," said Billy.

Whereat Ellen blushed, and Billy's unbelief strengthened.

At this crisis, the Case burst into the room with his hat on. He
removed it at sight of the caller and awkwardly advanced to be
introduced.

"I'm going to bed," he announced, after the formality.

"I hoped," said Ellen, "you'd tell us about the latest. Who is it
now? Beth?"

"Beth nothing!" scoffed the Case. "We split up the day of the
Keewatin game."

"What was the matter?" asked his sister.

"I'm going to bed," said the Case. "It's pretty near midnight."

"By George, it is!" exclaimed Billy. "I didn't dream it was that
late!"

"No," said Walter. "That's what I tell dad—the clock goes along
some when you're having a good time."

Billy and Ellen looked shyly at each other, and then laughed;
laughed harder, it seemed to Walter, than the joke warranted. In
fact, he hadn't thought of it as a joke. If it was that good, he'd spring
it on Kathryn to-morrow night. It would just about clinch her.

The Case, carrying out his repeated threat, went to bed and
dreamed of Kathryn. Fifteen minutes later Ellen retired to dream of
Billy. And an hour later than that, Billy was dreaming of Ellen, who
had become suddenly popular with him, even if she hadn't been so
at Northampton, which he didn't believe.

IV

They saw "The Follies" Friday night. A criticism of the show by
either would have been the greatest folly of all. It is doubtful that

they could have told what theatre they'd been to ten minutes after they'd left it. From wherever it was, they walked to a dancing place and danced. Ellen was so far gone that she failed to note the change in Billy's trotting. Foxes would have blushed for shame at its awkwardness and lack of variety. If Billy was a splendid dancer, he certainly did not prove it this night. All he knew or cared to know was that he was with the girl he wanted. And she knew only that she was with Billy, and happy.

On the drive home, the usual superfluous words were spoken. They were repeated inside the storm-door at Ellen's father's house, while the taxi driver, waiting, wondered audibly why them suckers of explorers beat it to the Pole to freeze when the North Side was so damn handy.

Ellen's father was out of town. So in the morning she broke the news to mother and Aunt Mary, and then sat down and wrote it to Edith and Wilma. Next she called up Bob's wife in Evanston, and after that she hurried to the next block and sprang it on Aunts Louise and Harriet. It was decided that Walter had better not be told. He didn't know how to keep a secret. Walter, therefore, was in ignorance till he got home from school. The only person he confided in the same evening was Kathryn, who was the only person he saw.

Bob and his wife and Aunts Louise and Harriet came to Sunday dinner, but were chased home early in the afternoon. Mr. McDonald was back and Billy was coming to talk to him. It would embarrass Billy to death to find such a crowd in the house. They'd all meet him soon, never fear, and when they met him, they'd be crazy about him. Bob and Aunt Mary and mother would like him because he was so bright and said such screaming things, and the rest would like him because he was so well-read and sensible, and so horribly good-looking.

Billy, I said, was coming to talk to Mr. McDonald. When he came, he did very little of the talking. He stated the purpose of his visit, told what business he was in and affirmed his ability to support a wife. Then he assumed the rôle of audience while Ellen's father delivered an hour's lecture. The speaker did not express his opinion of Tyrus Cobb or the Kaiser, but they were the only subjects he overlooked. Sobriety and industry were words frequently used.

"I don't care," he prevaricated, in conclusion, "how much money a man is making if he is sober and industrious. You attended college, and I presume you did all the fool things college boys do. Some men recover from their college education, others don't. I hope you're one of the former."

The Sunday-night supper, just cold scraps you might say, was partaken of by the happy but embarrassed pair, the trying-to-look happy but unembarrassed parents, and Aunt Mary. Walter, the Case, was out. He had stayed home the previous evening.

"He'll be here to-morrow night and the rest of the week, or I'll know the reason why," said Mr. McDonald.

"He won't, and I'll tell you the reason why," said Ellen.

"He's a real boy, Sam," put in the real boy's mother. "You can't expect him to stay home every minute."

"I can't expect anything of him," said the father. "You and the girls and Mary here have let him have his own way so long that he's past managing. When I was his age, I was in my bed at nine o'clock."

"Morning or night?" asked Ellen.

Her father scowled. It was evident he could not take a joke, not even a good one.

After the cold scraps had been ruined, Mr. McDonald drew Billy into the smoking-room and offered him a cigar. The prospective son-in-law was about to refuse and express a preference for cigarettes when something told him not to. A moment later he was deeply grateful to the something.

"I smoke three cigars a day," said the oracle, "one after each meal. That amount of smoking will hurt nobody. More than that is too much. I used to smoke to excess, four or five cigars per day, and maybe a pipe or two. I found it was affecting my health, and I cut down. Thank heaven, no one in my family ever got the cigarette habit; disease, rather. How any sane, clean-minded man can start on those things is beyond me."

"Me, too," agreed Billy, taking the proffered cigar with one hand and making sure with the other that his silver pill-case was as deep down in his pocket as it would go.

"Cigarettes, gambling, and drinking go hand in hand," continued the man of the house. "I couldn't trust a cigarette fiend with a nickel."

"There are only two or three kinds he could get for that," said Billy.

"What say?" demanded Mr. McDonald, but before Billy was obliged to wriggle out of it, Aunt Mary came in and reminded her brother-in-law that it was nearly church time.

Mr. McDonald and Aunt Mary went to church. Mrs. McDonald, pleading weariness, stayed home with "the children." She wanted a chance to get acquainted with this pleasant-faced boy who was going to rob her of one of her five dearest treasures.

The three were no sooner settled in front of the fireplace than Ellen adroitly brought up the subject of auction bridge, knowing that it would relieve Billy of the conversational burden.

"Mother is really quite a shark, aren't you, mother?" she said.

"I don't fancy being called a fish," said the mother.

"She's written two books on it, and she and father have won so many prizes that they may have to lease a warehouse. If they'd only play for money, just think how rich we'd all be!"

"The game is fascinating enough without adding to it the excitements and evils of gambling," said Mrs. McDonald.

"It is a fascinating game," agreed Billy.

"It is," said Mrs. McDonald, and away she went.

Before father and Aunt Mary got home from church, Mr. Bowen was a strong disciple of conservativeness in bidding and thoroughly convinced that all the rules that had been taught were dead wrong. He saw the shark's points so quickly and agreed so whole-heartedly with her arguments that he impressed her as one of the most intelligent young men she had ever talked to. It was too bad it was Sunday night, but some evening soon he must come over for a game.

"I'd like awfully well to read your books," said Billy.

"The first one's usefulness died with the changes in the rules," replied Mrs. McDonald. "But I think I have one of the new ones in the house, and I'll be glad to have you take it."

"I don't like to have you give me your only copy."

"Oh, I believe we have two."

She knew perfectly well she had two dozen.

Aunt Mary announced that Walter had been seen in church with Kathryn. He had made it his business to be seen. He and the lady had come early and had manœuvred into the third row from the

back, on the aisle leading to the McDonald family pew. He had
nudged his aunt as she passed on the way to her seat, and she had
turned and spoken to him. She could not know that he and Kathryn
had "ducked" before the end of the processional.

After reporting favorably on the Case, Aunt Mary launched into
a description of the service. About seventy had turned out. The
music had been good, but not quite as good as in the morning. Mr.
Pratt had sung "Fear Ye Not, O Israel!" for the offertory. Dr. Gish
was still sick and a lay reader had served. She had heard from Allie
French that Dr. Gish expected to be out by the middle of the week
and certainly would be able to preach next Sunday morning. The
church had been cold at first, but very comfortable finally.

Ellen rose and said she and Billy would go out in the kitchen and
make some fudge.

"I was afraid Aunt Mary would bore you to death," she told Billy,
when they had kissed for the first time since five o'clock. "She just
lives for the church and can talk on no other subject."

"I wouldn't hold that against her," said Billy charitably.

The fudge was a failure, as it was bound to be. But the Case, who
came in just as it was being passed round, was the only one rude
enough to say so.

"Is this a new stunt?" he inquired, when he had tested it.

"Is what a new stunt?" asked Ellen.

"Using cheese instead of chocolate."

"That will do, Walter," said his father. "You can go to bed."

Walter got up and started for the hall. At the threshold he
stopped.

"I don't suppose there'll be any of that fudge left," he said. "But
if there should be, you'd better put it in the mouse trap."

Billy called a taxi and departed soon after Walter's exit. When he
got out at his South Side abode, the floor of the tonneau was littered
with recent cigarettes.

And that night he dreamed that he was president of the anti-
cigarette league; that Dr. Gish was vice-president, and that the motto
of the organization was "No trump."

Billy Bowen's business took him out of town the second week in
December, and it was not until the twentieth that he returned. He
had been East and had ridden home from Buffalo on the same train

with Wilma and Edith McDonald. But he didn't know it and neither did they. They could not be expected to recognize him from Ellen's description—that he was horribly good-looking. The dining-car conductor was all of that.

Ellen had further written them that he (not the dining-car conductor) was a man of many moods; that sometimes he was just nice and deep, and sometimes he was screamingly funny, and sometimes so serious and silent that she was almost afraid of him.

They were wild to see him and the journey through Ohio and Indiana would not have been half so long in his company. Edith, the athletic, would have revelled in his wit. Wilma would gleefully have fathomed his depths. They would both have been proud to flaunt his looks before the hundreds of their kind aboard the train. Their loss was greater than Billy's, for he, smoking cigarettes as fast as he could light them and playing bridge that would have brought tears of compassion to the shark's eyes, enjoyed the trip, every minute of it.

Ellen and her father were at the station to meet the girls. His arrival on this train had not been heralded, and it added greatly to the hysterics of the occasion.

Wilma and Edith upbraided him for not knowing by instinct who they were. He accused them of recognizing him and purposely avoiding him. Much more of it was pulled in the same light vein, pro . and con.

He was permitted at length to depart for his office. On the way he congratulated himself on the improbability of his ever being obliged to play basket-ball versus Edith. She must be a whizz in condition. Chances were she'd train down to a hundred and ninety-five before the big games. The other one, Wilma, was a splinter if he ever saw one. You had to keep your eyes peeled or you'd miss her entirely. But suppose you did miss her; what then! If she won her Phi Beta Kappa pin, he thought, it would make her a dandy belt.

These two, he thought, were a misdeal. They should be reshuffled and cut nearer the middle of the deck. Lots of other funny things he thought about these two.

Just before he had left Chicago on this trip, his stenographer had quit him to marry an elevator-starter named Felix Bond. He had 'phoned one of his cousins and asked him to be on the lookout for a live stenographer who wasn't likely to take the eye of an elevator-starter. The cousin had had one in mind.

Here was her card on Billy's desk when he reached the office. It was not a business-card visiting-card, at $3 per hundred. "Miss Violet Moore," the engraved part said. Above was written: "Mr. Bowen—Call me up any night after seven. Calumet 2678."

Billy stowed the card in his pocket and plunged into a pile of uninteresting letters.

On the night of the twenty-second there was a family dinner at McDonald's, and Billy was in on it. At the function he met the rest of them—Bob and his wife, and Aunt Harriet and Aunt Louise.

Bob and his wife, despite the former's alleged sense of humor, spooned every time they were contiguous. That they were in love with each other, as Ellen had said, was easy to see. The wherefore was more of a puzzle.

Bob's hirsute adornment having been disturbed by his spouse's digits during one of the orgies, he went up-stairs ten minutes before dinner time to effect repairs. Mrs. Bob was left alone on the davenport. In performance of his social duties, Billy went over and sat down beside her. She was not, like Miss Muffet, frightened away, but terror or some other fiend rendered her temporarily dumb. The game Mr. Bowen was making his fifth attempt to pry open a conversation when Bob came back.

To the impartial observer the scene on the davenport appeared heartless enough. There was a generous neutral zone between Billy and Flo, that being an abbreviation of Mrs. Bob's given name, which, as a few may suspect, was Florence. Billy was working hard and his face was flushed with the effort. The flush may have aroused Bob's suspicions. At any rate, he strode across the room, scowling almost audibly, shot a glance at Billy that would have made the Kaiser wince, halted magnificently in front of his wife, and commanded her to accompany him to the hall.

Billy's flush became ace high. He was about to get up and break a chair when a look from Ellen stopped him. She was at his side before the pair of Bobs had skidded out of the room.

"Please don't mind," she begged. "He's crazy. I forgot to tell you that he's insanely jealous."

"Did I understand you to say he had a sense of humor?"

"It doesn't work where Flo's concerned. If he sees her talking to a man he goes wild."

"With astonishment, probably," said Billy.

"You're a nice boy," said Ellen irrelevantly.

Dinner was announced and Mr. Bowen was glad to observe that Flo's terrestrial body was still intact. He was glad, too, to note that Bob was no longer frothing. He learned for the first time that the Case and Kathryn were of the party. Mrs. McDonald had wanted to make sure of Walter's presence; hence the presence of his crush.

Kathryn giggled when she was presented to Billy. It made him uncomfortable and he thought for a moment that a couple of studs had fallen out. He soon discovered, however, that the giggle was permanent, just as much a part of Kathryn as her fraction of a nose. He looked forward with new interest to the soup course, but was disappointed to find that she could negotiate it without disturbing the giggle or the linen.

He next centred his attention on Wilma and Edith. Another disappointment was in store. There were as many and as large oysters in Wilma's soup as in any one's. She ate them all, and, so far as appearances went, was the same Wilma. He had expected that Edith would either diet or plunge. But Edith was as prosaic in her consumption of victuals as Ellen, for instance, or Aunt Louise.

He must content himself for the present with Aunt Louise. She was sitting directly opposite and he had an unobstructed view of the widest part he had ever seen in woman's hair.

"Ogden Avenue," he said to himself.

Aunt Louise was telling about her experiences and Aunt Harriet's among the heathen of Peoria Street.

"You never would dream there were such people!" said she.

"I suppose most of them are foreign born," supposed her brother, who was Mr. McDonald.

"Practically all of them," said Aunt Louise.

Billy wanted to ask her whether she had ever missionaried among the Indians. He thought possibly an attempt to scalp her had failed by a narrow margin.

Between courses Edith worked hard to draw out his predicated comicality and Wilma worked as hard to make him sound his **low** notes. Their labors were in vain. He was not sleepy enough to be deep, and he was fourteen highballs shy of comedy.

In disgust, perhaps, at her failure to be amused, the major portion of the misdeal capsized her cocoa just before the close of the meal and drew a frown from her father, whom she could have thrown in ten minutes, straight falls, any style.

"She'll never miss that ounce," thought Billy.

When they got up from the table and started for the living-room, Mr. Bowen found himself walking beside Aunt Harriet, who had been so silent during dinner that he had all but forgotten her.

"Well, Miss McDonald," he said, "it's certainly a big family, isn't it?"

"Well, young man," said Aunt Harriet, "it ain't no small family, that's sure."

"I should say not," repeated Billy.

Walter and his giggling crush intercepted him.

"What do you think of Aunt Harriet's grammar?" demanded Walter.

"I didn't notice it," lied Billy.

"No, I s'pose not. 'Ain't no small family.' I s'pose you didn't notice it. She isn't a real aunt like Aunt Louise and Aunt Mary. She's just an adopted aunt. She kept house for dad and Aunt Louise after their mother died, and when dad got married, she just kept on living with Aunt Louise."

"Oh," was Billy's fresh comment, and it brought forth a fresh supply of giggles from Kathryn.

Ellen had already been made aware of Billy's disgusting plans. He had to catch a night train for St. Louis, and he would be there all day to-morrow, and he'd be back Friday, but he wouldn't have time to see her, and he'd surely call her up. And Friday afternoon he was going to South Bend to spend Christmas Day with his married sister, because it was probably the last Christmas he'd be able to spend with her.

"But I'll hustle home from South Bend Sunday morning," he said, "And don't you dare make any engagement for the afternoon."

"I do wish you could be with us Christmas Eve. The tree won't be a bit of fun without you."

"You know I wish I could. But you see how it is."

"I think your sister's mean."

Billy didn't deny it.

"Who's going to be here Christmas Eve?"

"Just the people we had to-night, except Kathryn and you. Why?"

"Oh, nothing," said Billy.

"Look here, sir," said his betrothed. "Don't you do anything foolish. You're not supposed to buy presents for the whole family. Just a little, tiny one for me, if you want to, but you mustn't spend much on it. And if you get anything for any one else in this house, I'll be mad."

"I'd like to see you mad," said Billy.

"You'd wish you hadn't," Ellen retorted.

When Billy had gone, Ellen returned to the living-room and faced the assembled company.

"Well," she said, "now that you've all seen him, what's the verdict?"

The verdict seemed to be unanimously in his favor.

"But," said Bob, "I thought you said he was so screamingly funny."

"Yes," said Edith, "you told me that, too."

"Give him a chance," said Ellen. "Wait till he's in a funny mood. You'll simply die laughing!"

V

It is a compound fracture of the rules to have so important a character as Tommy Richards appear in only one chapter. But remember, this isn't a regular story, but a simple statement of what occurred when it occurred. During Chapter Four, Tommy had been on his way home from the Pacific Coast, where business had kept him all fall. His business out there and what he said en route to Chicago are collateral.

Tommy had been Billy's pal at college. Tommy's home was in Minnesota, and Billy was his most intimate, practically his only friend in the so-called metropolis of the Middle West. So Tommy, not knowing that Billy had gone to St. Louis, looked forward to a few pleasant hours with him between the time of the coast train's arrival and the Minnesota train's departure.

The coast train reached Chicago about noon. It was Thursday

noon, the twenty-third. Tommy hustled from the station to Billy's office, and there learned of the St. Louis trip. Disappointed, he roamed the streets a while and at length dropped into the downtown ticket office of his favorite Minnesota road. He was told that everything for the night was sold out. Big Christmas business. Tommy pondered.

The coast train reached Chicago about noon. It was Thursday noon, the twenty-third.

"How about to-morrow night?" he inquired.

"I can give you a lower to-morrow night on the six-thirty," replied Leslie Painter, that being the clerk's name.

"I'll take it," said Tommy.

He did so, and the clerk took $10.05.

"I'll see old Bill after all," said Tommy.

Leslie Painter made no reply.

In the afternoon Tommy sat through a vaudeville show, and at night he looped the loop. He retired early, for the next day promised to be a big one.

Billy got in from St. Louis at seven Friday morning and had been in his office an hour when Tommy appeared. I have no details of the meeting.

At half-past eight Tommy suggested that they'd better go out and h'ist one.

"Still on it, eh?" said Billy.

"What do you mean?"

"I mean that I'm off of it."

"Good Lord! For how long?"

"The last day of November."

"Too long! You look sick already."

"I feel great," averred Billy.

"Well, I don't. So come along and bathe in vichy."

On the way "along" Billy told Tommy about Ellen. Tommy's congratulations were physical and jarred Billy from head to heels.

"Good stuff!" cried Tommy so loudly that three pedestrians jumped sideways. "Old Bill hooked! And do you think you're going to celebrate this occasion with water?"

"I think I am," was Billy's firm reply.

"You think you are! What odds?"

"A good lunch against a red hot."

"You're on!" said Tommy. "And I'm going to be mighty hungry at one o'clock."

"You'll be hungry and alone."

"What's the idea? If you've got a lunch date with the future, I'm in on it."

"I haven't," said Billy. "But I'm going to South Bend on the one-forty, and between now and then I have nothing to do but clean up my mail and buy a dozen Christmas presents."

They turned in somewhere.

"Don't you see the girl at all to-day?" asked Tommy.

"Not to-day. All I do is call her up."

"Well, then, if you get outside of a couple, who'll be hurt? Just for old time's sake."

"If you need lunch money, I'll give it to you."

"No, no. That bet's off."

"It's not off. I won't call it off."

"Suit yourself," said Tommy graciously.

At half-past nine, it was officially decided that Billy had lost the bet. At half-past twelve, Billy said it was time to pay it.

"I'm not hungry enough," said Tommy.

"Hungry or no hungry," said Billy, "I buy your lunch now or I don't buy it. See? Hungry or no hungry."

"What's the hurry?" asked Tommy.

"I guess you know what's the hurry. Me for South Bend on the one-forty, and I got to go to the office first. Hurry or no hurry."

"Listen to reason, Bill. How are you going to eat lunch, go to the office, buy a dozen Christmas presents and catch the one-forty?"

"Christmas presents! I forgot 'em! What do you think of that? I forgot 'em. Good night!"

"What are you going to do?"

"Do! What can I do? You got me into this mess. Get me out!"

"Sure, I'll get you out if you'll listen to reason!" said Tommy. "Has this one-forty train got anything on you? Are you under obligations to it? Is the engineer your girl's uncle?"

"I guess you know better than that. I guess you know I'm not engaged to a girl who's got an uncle for an engineer."

"Well, then, what's the next train?"

"That's the boy, Tommy! That fixes it! I'll go on the next train."

"You're sure there is one?" asked Tommy.

"Is one! Say, where do you think South Bend is? In Europe?"

"I wouldn't mind," said Tommy.

"South Bend's only a two-hour run. Where did you think it was? Europe?"

"I don't care where it is. The question is, what's the next train after one-forty?"

"Maybe you think I don't know," said Billy. He called the gentleman with the apron. "What do you know about this, Charley? Here's an old pal of mine who thinks I don't know the time-table to South Bend."

"He's mistaken, isn't he?" said Charley.

"Is he mistaken? Say, Charley, if you knew as much as I do about the time-table to South Bend, you wouldn't be here."

"No, sir," said Charley. "I'd be an announcer over in the station."

"There!" said Billy triumphantly. "How's that, Tommy? Do I know the time-table or don't I?"

"I guess you do," said Tommy. "But I don't think you ought to have secrets from an old friend."

"There's no secrets about it, Charley."

"My name is Tommy," corrected his friend.

"I know that. I know your name as well as my own, better'n my own. I know your name as well as I know the time-table."

"If you'd just tell me the time of that train, we'd all be better off."

"I'll tell you, Tommy. I wouldn't hold out anything on you, old boy. It's five twenty-five."

"You're sure?"

"Sure! Say, I've taken it a hundred times if I've taken it once."

"All right," said Tommy. "That fixes it. We'll go in and have lunch and be through by half-past one. That'll give you four hours to do your shopping, get to your office and make your train."

"Where you going while I shop?"

"Don't bother about me."

"You go along with me."

"Nothing doing."

"Yes, you do."

"No, I don't."

But this argument was won by Mr. Bowen. At ten minutes of three, when they at last called for the check, Mr. Richards looked on the shopping expedition in an entirely different light. Two hours before, it had not appealed to him at all. Now he could think of nothing that would afford more real entertainment. Mr. Richards was at a stage corresponding to Billy's twenty-one. Billy was far past it.

"What we better do," said Tommy, "is write down a list of all the people so we won't forget anybody."

"That's the stuff!" said Billy. "I'll name 'em, you write 'em."

So Tommy produced a pencil and took dictation on the back of a menu-card.

"First, girl's father, Sam'l McDonald."

"Samuel McDonald," repeated Tommy. "Maybe you'd better give me some dope on each one, so if we're shy of time, we can both be buying at once."

"All right," said Billy. "First, Sam'l McDonal'. He's an ol' crab. Raves about cig'rettes."

"Like 'em?"

"No. Hates 'em."

"Sam'l McDonald, cigarettes," wrote Tommy. "Old crab," he added.

When the important preliminary arrangement had at last been completed, the two old college chums went out into the air.

"Where do we shop?" asked Tommy.

"Marsh's," said Billy. " 'S only place I got charge account."

"Maybe we better take a taxi and save time," suggested Tommy.

So they waited five minutes for a taxi and were driven to Marsh's, two blocks away.

"We'll start on the first floor and work up," said Tommy, who had evidently appointed himself captain.

They found themselves among the jewelry and silverware.

"You might get something for the girl here," suggested Tommy.

"Don't worry 'bout her," said Billy. "Leave her till las'."

"What's the limit on the others?"

"I don't care," said Billy. "Dollar, two dollars, three dollars."

"Well, come on," said Tommy. "We got to make it snappy."

But Billy hung back.

"Say, ol' boy," he wheedled. "You're my ol'st frien'. Is that right?"

"That's right," agreed Tommy.

"Well, say, ol' frien', I'm pretty near all in."

"Go home, then, if you want to. I can pull this all right alone."

"Nothin' doin'. But if I could jus' li'l nap, ten, fifteen minutes—you could get couple things here on fir'-floor and then come get me."

"Where?"

"Third floor waitin'-room."

"Go ahead. But wait a minute. Give me some of your cards. And will I have any trouble charging things?"

"Not a bit. Tell 'em you're me."

It was thus that Tommy Richards was left alone in a large store, with Billy Bowen's charge account, Billy Bowen's list, and Billy Bowen's cards.

He glanced at the list.

" 'Samuel McDonald, cigarettes. Old crab,' " he read.

He approached a floor-walker.

"Say, old pal," he said. "I'm doing some shopping and I'm in a big hurry. Where'd I find something for an old cigarette fiend?"

"Cigarette-cases, two aisles down and an aisle to your left," said Old Pal.

Tommy raised the limit on the cigarette-case he picked out for Samuel McDonald. It was $3.75.

"I'll cut down somewhere else," he thought. "The father-in-law ought to be favored a little."

"Charge," he said in response to a query. "William Bowen, Bowen and Company, 18 South La Salle. And here's a card for it. That go out to-night sure?"

He looked again at the list.

"Mrs. Samuel McDonald, bridge bug. Miss Harriet McDonald, reverse English. Miss Louise McDonald, thin hair. Miss Mary Carey, church stuff. Bob and Wife, 'The Man Who Married a Dumb Wife' and gets mysteriously jealous. Walter McDonald, real kid. Edith, fat lady. Wilma, a splinter."

He consulted Old Pal once more. Old Pal's advice was to go to the third floor and look over the books. The advice proved sound. On the third floor Tommy found for Mother "The First Principles of Auction Bridge," and for Aunt Harriet an English grammar. He also bumped into a counter laden with hymnals, chant books, and Books of Common Prayer.

"Aunt Mary!" he exclaimed. And to the clerk: "How much are your medium prayer-books?"

"What denomination?" asked the clerk, whose name was Freda Swanson.

"One or two dollars," said Tommy.

"What church, I mean?" inquired Freda.

"How would I know?" said Tommy. "Are there different books for different churches?"

"Sure. Catholic, Presbyterian, Episcopal, Lutheran——"

"Let's see. McDonald, Carey. How much are the Catholic ones?"

"Here's one at a dollar and a half. In Latin, too."

"That's it. That'll give her something to work on."

Tommy figured on the back of his list.

"Good work, Tommy!" he thought. "Four and a half under the top limit for those three. Walter's next."

He plunged on Walter. A nice poker set, discovered on the fourth floor, came to five even. Tommy wished he could keep it for himself. He also wished constantly that the women shoppers had taken a course in dodging. He was almost as badly battered as the day he played guard against the Indians.

"Three left besides the queen herself," he observed. "Lord, no. I forgot Bob and his missus."

He moved down-stairs again to the books.

"Have you got 'The Man Who Married a Dumb Wife'?" he queried.

Anna Henderson looked, but could not find it.

"Never mind!" said Tommy. "Here's one that'll do."

And he ordered "The Green-Eyed Monster" for the cooing doves in Evanston.

"Now," he figured, "there's just Wilma and Edith and Aunt Louise." Once more he started away from the books, but a title caught his eye: "Eat and Grow Thin."

"Great!" exclaimed Tommy. "It'll do for Edith. By George! It'll do for both of them. 'Eat' for Wilma, and the 'Grow Thin' for Edith. I guess that's doubling up some! And now for Aunt Louise."

The nearest floor-walker told him, in response to his query, that switches would be found on the second floor.

"I ought to have a switch-engine to take me round," said Tommy, who never had felt better in his life. But the floor-walker did not laugh, possibly because he was tired.

"Have you anything to match it with?" asked the lady in the switch-yard.

"No, I haven't."

"Can you give me an idea of the color?"

"What colors have you got?" demanded Tommy.

"Everything there is. I'll show them all to you, if you've got the time."

"Never mind," said Tommy. "What's your favorite color in hair?"

The girl laughed.

"Golden," she said.

"You're satisfied, aren't you?" said Tommy, for the girl had chosen the shade of her own shaggy mane. "All right, make it golden. And a merry Christmas to you."

He forgot to ask the price of switches. He added up the rest and found that the total was $16.25.

"About seventy-five cents for the hair," he guessed. "That will make it seventeen even. I'm some shopper. And all done in an hour and thirteen minutes."

He discovered Billy asleep in the waiting-room and it took him three precious minutes to bring him to.

"Everybody's fixed but the girl herself," he boasted. "I got books for most of 'em."

"Where you been?" asked Billy. "What time is it?"

"You've got about thirty-three minutes to get a present for your lady love and grab your train. You'll have to pass up the office."

"What time is it? Where you been?"

"Don't bother about that. Come on."

On the ride down, Billy begged every one in the elevator to tell him the time, but no one seemed to know. Tommy hurried him out of the store and into a taxi.

"There's a flock of stores round the station," said Tommy. "You can find something there for the dame."

But the progress of the cab through the packed down-town streets was painfully slow and the station clock, when at last they got in sight of it, registered 5.17.

"You can't wait!" said Tommy. "Give me some money and tell me what to get."

Billy fumbled clumsily in seven pockets before he located his pocketbook. In it were two fives and a ten.

"I gotta have a feevee," he said.

"All right. I'll get something for fifteen. What'll it be?"

"Make it a wrist-watch."

"Sure she has none?"

"She's got one. That's for other wris'."

"I used your last card. Have you got another?"

"Pocketbook," said Billy.

Tommy hastily searched and found a card. He pushed Billy toward the station entrance.

"Good-by and merry Christmas," said Tommy.

"Goo'-by and God bless you!" said Billy, but he was talking to a large policeman.

"Where are you trying to go?" asked the latter.

"Souse Ben'," said Billy.

"Hurry up, then. You've only got a minute."

The minute and six more were spent in the purchase of a ticket. And when Billy reached the gate, the 5.25 had gone and the 5.30 was about to chase it.

"Where to?" inquired the gateman.

"Souse Ben'," said Billy.

"Run then," said the gateman.

Billy ran. He ran to the first open vestibule of the Rock Island train, bound for St. Joe, Missouri.

"Where to?" asked a porter.

"Souse," said Billy.

"Ah can see that," said the porter. "But where you goin'?"

The train began to move and Billy, one foot dragging on the station platform, moved with it. The porter dexterously pulled him aboard. And he was allowed to ride to Englewood.

Walking down Van Buren Street, it suddenly occurred to the genial Mr. Richards that he would have to go some himself to get his baggage and catch the 6.30 for the northwest. He thought of it in front of a Van Buren jewelry shop. He stopped and went in.

Three-quarters of an hour later, a messenger-boy delivered a particularly ugly and frankly inexpensive wrist-watch at the McDonald home. The parcel was addressed to Miss McDonald and the accompanying card read:

"Mr. Bowen: Call me up any night after seven. Calumet 2678. Miss Violet Moore."

There was no good-will toward men in the McDonald home this Christmas. Ellen spent the day in bed and the orders were that she must not be disturbed.

Down-stairs, one person smiled. It was Walter. He smiled in spite of the fact that his father had tossed his brand-new five-dollar poker set into the open fireplace. He smiled in spite of the fact that he was not allowed to leave the house, not even to take Kathryn to church.

"Gee!" he thought, between smiles, "Billy sure had nerve!"

Bob walked round among his relatives seeking to dispel the gloom with a remark that he thought apt and nifty:

"Be grateful," was the remark, "that he had one of his screamingly funny moods before it was too late."

But no one but Bob seemed to think much of the remark, and no one seemed grateful.

Those are the facts, and it was quite a job to dig them up. But I did it.

Anniversary

Mrs. Taylor shuffled a worn pack of cards and began her evening session at solitaire. She would play probably forty games before she went to bed, and she would win thirty of them. What harm if she cheated a little? Russian Bank was more fun, but it cannot be played alone, and her husband was bored by it. He had been unable to learn bridge in spite of the patient and more or less expert teaching of the Hammonds, who lived three blocks away.

The thirty-four-dollar synthetic radio had done nothing but croak since the day following its installation. The cheap piano's D and G above middle C were mute. The town's Carnegie Library acquired very few "hot" books and the few were nearly always out. Picture plays hurt Louis' eyes and he would not let her go out nights by herself, though he had no scruples against leaving her at home from eight to eleven Wednesdays, when he attended lodge and bowled.

So Mrs. Taylor shuffled her cards and tried to listen when Louis read aloud from the Milton Daily Star or the Milton Weekly Democrat, or recounted stories she had heard six times before and would hear six times again.

She had awakened this morning to the realization that it was the twelfth day of November, the ninth anniversary of her marriage. Louis had remembered that date for the first six years of their life together; for the last three years it had been to him just November the twelfth.

Nine years ago the Star and the Democrat had called her one of Milton's most charming and beautiful young women, and they had been right. They had referred to Louis as a model young man, sober, industrious and "solid"; a young man whom any girl should be proud and glad to have as a husband. They were right again.

Now Mrs. Taylor, at thirty-three, was good-looking, but in a cold, indifferent sort of way. She no longer bothered to embellish her natural attractiveness and she lacked the warmth and vivacity which had won the adoration of most of Milton's male youth, notably Walter Frayne, Jim Satterly and Louis Taylor himself.

Louis was still a model young man, sober, industrious and "solid." When you thought of the precarious existence of the women who had married his chief rivals, you couldn't help feeling that wisdom and good luck had been on Mrs. Taylor's side when she made her choice.

Walter had attended college for one semester, at the end of which he came home with a perfect record of studies, 4; Flunks, 4. He had run amuck in Milton and ultimately, turned down by the girl he really cared for, had married an orphan whose parents had left her $150,000—but not for long. After this tidy sum had been poured away Walter was almost continuously unemployed and people wondered how he and his wife lived. And why.

There was nothing of the gay dog about Jim Satterly. He had graduated from high school and gone into the Milton Gas Company's office as bookkeeper at eight dollars per week. He was now thirty-five years old and still with the gas company, but his salary had been steadily increased until it was twenty-two dollars. His wife gave weekly piano lessons to a class of four pupils at fifty cents a half-hour each. She had borne Jim three children, or kiddies. The Satterlys seemed to enjoy their kiddies and an occasional picture show, but no magazine editor had ever sent a staff man to get a success story out of Jim.

Louis Taylor was secretary to the town's only wealthy man, old Thomas Parvis, who owned a controlling interest in the Interurban Railway. Louis worked long hours and was paid four thousand a year, big money in Milton. It was enough to keep the childless Taylors in comfort; in comparative luxury, even. Couples with smaller incomes owned cars, took trips to near-by lake resorts and to Harper City, where a stock company presented worth-while plays. But Louis was saving for a rainy day and his wife had long ago given up praying for rain.

Mrs. Taylor was winning her fourth successive victory over solitaire by the simple expedient of pretending that a black queen was red.

"It says here," stated her husband, "that there are 27,650,267 automobiles in the world, according to a census just completed."

It was Mrs. Taylor's own fault that Louis had contracted the habit of reciting interesting tidbits from the paper. Back in May, 1924, he had asked her whether she would like to hear the news of the Loeb-Leopold case. She had already read it, but she said yes, thinking it would be more thrilling, even in repetition, than one of Louis' own experiences, also in repetition. Since then, she had listened every evening—except Wednesday, when Louis went out, and Sundays, when there was no paper—to excerpts from the Star, consisting principally of what is known in newspaper offices as filler—incontrovertible statistics about men and things in all parts of the world, facts that seemed to smite her husband like a bolt from the blue.

"Think of it!" he said. "Nearly twenty-eight million automobiles!"

"Heavens!" said Mrs. Taylor.

"And speaking of automobiles: 'Storms have made roads so bad in parts of Chile that drivers have not dared to go into the rural districts.' That's the trouble with owning a car. If you don't stay right on the paved streets or paved roads, you're liable to get stuck and maybe walk home. Besides that, you've got to be a mechanic yourself or else, when there's something wrong, you have to take it to a garage and lay it up a week till they consent to look at it and find out what's the matter, and then they don't know themselves nine times out of ten. But they charge you just the same and they charge you plenty. Did I tell you about Walter Trumbull's trip to Harper City?"

"Yes," said Mrs. Taylor.

"I don't believe I did. It was only last Friday night; no, Thursday night, the night after the Spartans beat us by one pin, when I had a chance to get a 202 and hit the head pin just a little too full and they split on me. That was the night Berger showed up so drunk he couldn't bowl and we had to use Tommy and he shot 123.

"So it was the night after that when Walter and Marjorie started over to the City to see the 'Seventh Heaven,' and about five miles the other side of Two Oaks the engine died and Walter couldn't get it going again. His flash-light wouldn't work and Marjorie wouldn't let him strike matches with the hood up to see what the trouble was. As it turned out, it wouldn't have done him any good anyway.

"Finally he left poor Marjorie in the car and walked way back to Two Oaks, but the garage was closed up for the night and the whole town was asleep, so he went back to the car and by that time of course it was too late to see the show. He hailed three or four cars coming from the other way, trying to get a ride home, but it wasn't till after ten o'clock that he could get a car to stop and pick them up. The next morning he sent Charlie Thomas out to fix up the car so it would run or else tow it in, and Charlie found out there was nothing the matter with it except it was out of gas. When Walter told me about it, I said that was what he deserved for not patronizing the Interurban."

"We don't patronize it ourselves."

"I hear enough about it in the daytime without riding on it at night."

Mrs. Taylor shuffled the cards and Louis resumed perusal of the Star.

"The old U. S. is a pretty good country after all," he said presently. "Listen to this: 'The Netherlands' unemployed now include 26,000 skilled and 24,000 unskilled workers.' And listen: 'A large proportion of Belgium's population still wear wooden shoes.' You wouldn't think that was possible in this day and age!"

"I imagine," said Mrs. Taylor, "that there are some places in the United States where people don't wear any shoes at all."

"Oh, sure, but not a large proportion; probably a few of those backwoods Tennessee mountaineers. And of course the colored people in the small towns in Georgia and South Carolina. You see lots of them, passing through on the train, that never had a shoe on in their life. I remember a place named Jesup, Georgia, a kind of junction. There was—— No, that wasn't Jesup; it was some other place, some place the boss and I went through on the way to Daytona that time. I guess I told you about it."

"Yes," said Mrs. Taylor.

"You wouldn't believe the way some of those people live. Not all colored people, either; white people, too. Poor white trash, they call them. Or rather, 'po' white trash.' Families of four and five in one room. Mr. Parvis said it was a crime and kept wishing he could do something for them."

"Why didn't he?"

"Well, he's hardly got money enough to house and clothe the whole South and it wouldn't do any good to just pick out some one town and try and better conditions there."

"Why not?"

"It would be a drop in the bucket, and besides, other towns would hear about it and pester the life out of him. I reminded him he was taking the trip to get away from care and worry for a while and he ought not to fret himself about other people's business. Then, too, if he was going to practise some of his philanthrophy down there, I'd probably be put in charge of it. We might have even had to live there a year or two. I guess you wouldn't like that, would you?"

"It wouldn't make any difference to me," said Mrs. Taylor.

"What! Live in one of those God-forsaken holes, without any friends or anybody you'd want to make friends with! Nothing to do all day and all night but eat and sleep and——"

"Play solitaire," suggested Mrs. Taylor.

"You may think you wouldn't mind it, but that's because you've never seen it. Those Georgia villages are an interesting study, but as for making your home in one of them, you'd die of loneliness. Of course there's some spots in Florida that are pretty close to heaven. Take Daytona, for instance. But I've told you what it's like."

"Yes."

"They've got a beach that's so hard and smooth that they have automobile races on it. It's beautiful. And it's right close to Ormond, where Rockefeller spends his winters. Mr. Parvis and I saw him playing golf on the Ormond course. I can't see anything in golf myself, but maybe I would if I had a chance to get interested in it. When I'm as old as he is, I'll try it out, providing I've got as much time and one-millionth as much money."

"There's no reason why you shouldn't have fully as much money."

"I know what you mean by that. You're digging at my thriftiness, though I suppose you call it stinginess. You'll look at it differently when we're old."

"I hope I won't be here to look at it at all."

"No, you don't. But what was I saying? Oh, yes. Daytona is where I'd like to live in winter, if I had the means. I must have told you about running into Harry Riker down there."

"You did."

"It certainly was a funny thing, running into him! We hadn't seen each other for twenty-two years and he recognized me the minute he set eyes on me. I wouldn't have known him from Adam's off ox.

"It sure did take me back, running into Harry. He recalled one time, just before I left Shelbyville, when his father and mother were away on a visit somewhere. Harry's aunt, Mr. Riker's sister, was supposed to be taking care of Harry while his father and mother was away, but she was kind of old and she used to go to sleep right after supper.

"Well, there were a couple of girls, sisters, named Lindsay. They lived out in the country, but came in town to school. Harry and I thought we were stuck on them, so one night after supper, when Harry's aunt had gone to sleep, we hitched up Mr. Riker's horse and buggy and drove seven miles out in the country to call on the Lindsay girls. When we got out there it was raining, so we unhitched the horse and put him in the barn and——"

"He got loose, didn't he? And ran all the way home?"

"Yes, but that comes later. We put him in Lindsay's barn and we thought we had him tied all right, and Harry and I went in the house and sat around with the girls. Mrs. Lindsay stayed right in the room with us and did most of the talking——"

"You're sure of that?"

"I certainly am! She was one of these women that talk all the time. She never stopped. So about half past nine she said the girls would have to go to bed, and that was telling us to get out. Well, to make a long story short, the horse wasn't in the barn and Harry and I walked home seven miles in the pouring rain. We found the horse in his own stall and Harry had to ride him out to Lindsay's next day and get the buggy. That was the last time we ever called on the Lindsay girls."

"Kind of hard on them," said Mrs. Taylor.

"Oh, we were all just kids and there wasn't anything serious between us. Harry's in the insurance business now in Indianapolis, doing fine, he told me."

Louis was almost, but not quite, through with his paper.

"Here's a funny thing," he said. "Although Edinburgh, Scotland, had only 237 ice-cream parlors last season, the number was fifty more than were in the city a year ago."

"I should think that was enough ice-cream parlors."

"Not for the size of the town. Let's see. How big is Edinburgh? I'll have to look it up."

He was on his way to the bookcase when the door-bell rang. He went to the door and admitted Florence Hammond.

"Hello, Louis. Hello, Bess. This isn't a social call. We're out here with a flat tire and Perce wants to borrow your flash."

"There's automobiles for you!" said Louis. "More trouble than they're worth."

"I tried to persuade Perce to take it to the garage and have them fix it, but he's afraid driving it even that far would ruin the rim or the shoe or whatever you call it."

"I'll get the flash and see if I can help him," said Louis.

"And you sit down, Florence, and keep me company," said Mrs. Taylor. "I haven't been out of the house for three days and I'm dying to hear what's going on in Milton."

"You take the Star, don't you?"

"I'm afraid we do, but it hasn't been very thrilling lately."

"You can't blame the paper for that," said Mrs. Hammond. "Nothing exciting has happened; that is, in Milton."

"Has anything happened anywhere?"

"Yes. In Clyde."

"Clyde. That's where your sister lives, isn't it?"

"If you call it living. I'd rather be dead! Honestly, Bess, you and I ought to thank the Lord that we married men who are at least sane and normal. Louis and Perce may not be as good-looking or 'brilliant' as Ed, but anyway we always know where they are and what to expect of them."

"That's true," said Mrs. Taylor.

"I wrote Grace a letter today and told her she was simply crazy not to leave him, especially after this last mess. But she won't give him up. I believe he's got her hypnotized. And she still loves him. She admits his faults and excuses him and expects everybody to do the same. If she didn't, she'd keep her troubles to herself and not write me all the details. I realize everybody has their weakness, but it seems to me there are some things I couldn't forgive. And one of them is a punch in the eye."

"You don't mean——"

"Yes, I do. And Grace took it and accepted his apology when he made one. When I think of it, I simply boil!"

"What was the occasion?"

"No special occasion. Just Saturday night. Everybody in Clyde goes to the Yacht Club Saturday nights. There's no river or lake and no yachts, but they have a sunset gun, so I suppose they're entitled to call it a yacht club. Grace hated it at first and let Ed go alone, but that only made him drink more and get home later Sunday mornings. Besides, she's always been a little jealous, and probably with reason. So she decided to go with him and try to enjoy herself. Grace loves to dance and there are some awfully good dancers in Clyde; that is, early in the evening, before they begin to flounder and reel.

"Of course nobody can say Ed married her under false pretenses. She went into it with her eyes wide open. She saw him for the first time at one of those parties and she fell in love with him when he got mad at a man and knocked him down for cutting in on a dance. The man was about half Ed's size and Ed hit him when he wasn't looking. That didn't make any difference to Grace. And it didn't seem to make any difference to the Yacht Club. Anybody else would have been expelled, but Ed begged everyone's pardon and wasn't even scolded.

"That first night he asked Grace to let him drive her home. She was visiting Helen Morse, and Helen advised her not to take the chance. Ed didn't seem to be in very good driving condition. But Grace was so crazy about him that she told him yes. And then he forgot all about it, went home with another girl and left Grace at the club with some people she hardly knew. She had to call up the Morses and get them to come back after her.

"Well, they met again the next week and Grace thought she would put him in his place by ignoring him entirely, but that didn't work because he didn't remember having seen her before. He was comparatively sober this time and awfully nice and attentive. I'll admit Ed can be nice when he wants to. After that they played tennis together two or three times and then Ed proposed and Grace accepted him and he said he couldn't wait for a big wedding and she agreed to marry him secretly at Colby, a town about thirty miles from Clyde. She was to be in front of the Clyde post-office at twelve o'clock on a certain day and he was to pick her up in his car and drive to Colby and be married.

"The day came and she waited for him an hour and then went back to the Morses'. That evening he telephoned that he had made a mistake in the day and had just discovered it, and would she please forgive him and meet him the next day at the same place. I blush to say she succumbed, though she suspected what she found out later to be true—Ed had been on a bat and was sleeping it off at the time he was supposed to do his eloping.

"They were married and Ed behaved beautifully on the honeymoon. They spent two weeks in New York and went to the theatre every night and sightseeing in the mornings and afternoons. He had men friends of his to dinner once or twice and gave them all they wanted to drink, but wouldn't touch anything himself.

"When they got back to Clyde, Ed bought a lovely house already furnished, and the furniture was just what Grace would have picked out. Grace was so happy it seemed as if it couldn't last, and it didn't.

"They had been in Clyde a week when Ed announced that he had to go away on a trip. He didn't trouble to say where or why or

how long. He just went, stayed away five days and came home looking as if he had had five or six operations. Grace tried to get him to
tell her where he had been, but he just laughed and said it was a
secret.

"And that's the way things have gone on ever since. Ed's got
plenty of money and he gives Grace all she can possibly spend, besides buying her presents that are always lovely and terribly expensive. He'll be as good as pie for weeks and weeks—except for the
Saturday night carousal—and then he'll disappear for a few days, and
she won't know where he is or when to expect him home. Her life is
one surprise after another. But when he suddenly hits her in the eye,
it's more than a surprise. It's a kind of a shock. At least it would be
to me."

"When did it happen?" asked Mrs. Taylor.

"A week ago Saturday," said Mrs. Hammond. "There was the
usual party at the Yacht Club and Ed took more than his usual
amount to drink. Along about midnight he disappeared, and so did
a girl named Eva Grayson.

"Finally Grace went home, but she sat up and waited for Ed. He
came in about four o'clock, pie-eyed. He walked right to where
Grace was sitting and without saying anything at all, he hit her, not
hard enough to knock her out of her chair but with enough force to
really hurt. Then, still not saying anything, he went to bed without
taking the time to undress.

"In the morning, or whenever he woke up, he noticed that Grace's
eye was discolored and asked her what had happened. She told him
and he made no attempt to deny it. All he said was, 'Dearest, I can't
tell you how sorry I am. You must believe me when I say I had no
idea it was you. I thought it was Eva Grayson. And she deserved to
be hit.'

"Can you imagine forgiving a man for a thing like that? Can you
imagine continuing to live with him and love him? I'd kill myself
before I'd stand it! And Grace excuses him and writes me the full
details, just as if it were something she was proud of. I tell you,
Bess, you and I can consider ourselves lucky——"

The front door opened and Louis came in with his flash-light.

"You're all set, Florence," said he. "I asked Perce in, but he thinks
it's time to drive on."

"I know it is," said Mrs. Hammond. "We're going to play bridge out at the Cobbs' and we're terribly late. I ought to have phoned them, but I guess they'll sit up for us. Good night, Bess. I hope I didn't bore you with my long monolog."

"You didn't," said Mrs. Taylor.

Louis sat down to finish the Star. Mrs. Taylor shuffled her cards and started a new game, but in the middle of it she rose from the table and went close to her husband's chair.

"Do you know what day this is?" she said.

"Why, yes," Louis replied. "It's Tuesday."

"It's Tuesday, November twelfth. Our anniversary."

"Gosh! That's right! I wish I'd remembered it. I'd have bought you some flowers. Will it do tomorrow?"

"I don't want any flowers. But there is something I would like you to give me. And you don't have to wait till tomorrow."

"What is it?"

"A punch in the eye," said Mrs. Taylor.

"You're feeling kind of funny, aren't you? Did Florence have a shot of their home-made gin in her bag?"

"No. And I'm not feeling funny. I'm just sleepy. I think I'll go to bed."

Louis was reading again.

"It says: 'Experiments in the raising of sisal are being made in Haiti.' I don't suppose you happen to know what sisal is."

But Mrs. Taylor was on her way up-stairs.

PART TWO

On the Make

Quick Returns

This is just a clipping from one of the New York papers; a little kidding piece that they had in about me two years ago. It says:

HOOSIER CLEANS UP IN WALL STREET

Employees of the brokerage firm of H. L. Krause & Co. are authority for the statement that a wealthy Indiana speculator made one of the biggest killings of the year in the Street yesterday afternoon. No very definite information was obtainable, as the Westerner's name was known to only one of the firm's employees, Francis Griffin, and he was unable to recall it last night.

You'd think I was a millionaire and that I'd made a sucker out or Morgan or something, but it's only a kid, see? If they'd of printed the true story they wouldn't of had no room left for that day's selections at Pimlico, and God knows that would of been fatal.

But if you want to hear about it, I'll tell you.

Well, the war wound up in the fall of 1918. The only member of my family that was killed in it was my wife's stepfather. He died of grief when it ended with him two hundred thousand dollars ahead. I immediately had a black bandage sewed round my left funny bone, but when they read us the will I felt all right again and tore it off. Our share was seventy-five thousand dollars. This was after we had paid for the inheritance tax and the amusement stamps on a horse-less funeral.

My young sister-in-law, Katie, dragged down another seventy-five thousand dollars and the rest went to the old bird that had been foreman in papa's factory. This old geezer had been starving to death for twenty years on the wages my stepfather-in-law give him, and the rest of us didn't make no holler when his name was read off for a small chunk, especially as he didn't have no teeth to enjoy it with.

I could have had this old foreman's share, maybe, if I'd of took advantage of the offer "father" made me just before his daughter and I was married. I was over in Niles, Michigan, where they lived, and he insisted on me seeing his factory, which meant smelling it too. At that time I was knocking out about eighteen hundred dollars per annum selling cigars out of South Bend, and the old man said he would start me in with him at only about a fifty percent. cut, but we would also have the privilege of living with him and my wife's kid sister.

"They's a lot to be learnt about this business," he says, "but if you would put your mind on it you might work up to manager. Who knows?"

"My nose knows," I said, and that ended it.

The old man had lost some jack and went into debt a good many years ago, and for a long wile before the war begin about all as he was able to do was support himself and the two gals and pay off a part of what he owed. When the war broke loose and leather went up to hell and gone I and my wife thought he would get prosperous, but before this country went in his business went on about the same as usual.

"I don't know how they do it," he would say. "Other leather men is getting rich on contracts with the Allies, but I can't land a one."

I guess he was trying to sell razor strops to Russia.

Even after we got into it and he begin to clean up, with the factory running day and night, all as we knew was that he had contracts with the U. S. Government, but he never confided in us what special stuff he was turning out. For all as we knew, it may of been medals for the ground navy.

Anyway, he must of been hitting a fast clip when the armistice come and ended the war for everybody but Congress! It's a cinch he wasn't amongst those arrested for celebrating too loud on the night of November 11. On the contrary they tell me that when the big news hit Niles the old bird had a stroke that he didn't never recover from, and though my wife and Katie hung round the bedside day after day in the hopes he would tell how much he was going to leave he was keeping his fiscal secrets for Oliver Lodge or somebody, and it wasn't till we seen the will that we knew we wouldn't have to work no more, which is pretty fair consolation even for the loss of a stepfather-in-law that ran a perfume mill.

"Just think," said my wife, "after all his financial troubles, papa died a rich man!"

"Yes," I said to myself, "and a patriot. His only regret was that he just had one year to sell leather to his country."

If the old codger had of only been half as fast a salesman as his two daughters this clipping would of been right when it called me a wealthy Hoosier. It wasn't two weeks after we seen the will when the gals had disposed of the odor factory and the old home in Niles, Michigan. Katie, it seemed, had to come over to South Bend and live with us. That was agreeable to me, as I figured that if two could live on eighteen hundred dollars a year three could struggle along some way on the income off one hundred and fifty thousand dollars.

Only for me, though, Ella and Sister Kate would of shot the whole wad into a checking account so as the bank could enjoy it wile it lasted. I argued and fought and finally persuaded them to keep five thousand apiece for pin money and stick the rest into bonds.

The next thing they done was run over to Chi and buy all the party dresses that was vacant. Then they come back to South Bend and wished somebody would give a party. But between you and I the people we'd always ran round with was birds that was ready for bed as soon as they got home from the first show, and even though it had been printed in the News-Times that we had fell heir to a lot of jack we didn't have to hire no extra clerical help to tend to invitations received from the demi-Monday.

Finally Ella said we would start something ourselves. So she got a lot of invitations printed and sent them to all our friends that could read and hired a cater and a three-piece orchestra and everything, and made me buy a dress suit.

Well, the big night arrived and everybody come that had somebody to leave their baby with. The hosts wore evening clothes and the rest of the merrymakers prepared for the occasion with a shine or a clean collar. At first the cat had everybody's tongue, but when we sat down to eat some of the men folks begun to get comical. For instance, they would say to my wife or Katie, "Ain't you afraid you'll catch cold?" And they'd say to me, "I didn't know you was a waiter at the Oliver." Before the fish course everybody was in a fair way to get the giggles.

After supper the musicians come and hid behind a geranium and played a jazz. The entire party set out the first dance. The second was a solo between Katie and I, and I had the third with my wife. Then Kate and the Mrs. had one together, wile I tried holds with a lady named Mrs. Eckhart, who seemed to think that somebody had ast her to stand for a time exposure. The men folks had all drifted over behind the plant to watch the drummer, but after the stalemate between Mrs. Eckhart and I I grabbed her husband and took him out in the kitchen and showed him a bottle of bourbon that I'd been saving for myself, in the hopes it would loosen him up. I told him it was my last bottle, but he must of thought I said it was the last bottle in the world. Anyway, when he got through they was international prohibition.

We went back in the ballroom and sure enough he ast Katie to dance. But he hadn't no sooner than win one fall when his wife challenged him to take her home and that started the epidemic that emptied the house of everybody but the orchestra and us. The orchestra had been hired to stay till midnight, which was still two hours and a half distance, so I invited both of the gals to dance with me at once, but it seems like they was surfeited with that sport and wanted to cry a little. Well, the musicians had ran out of blues, so I chased them home.

"Some party!" I said, and the two girls give me a dirty look like it was my fault or something. So we all went to bed and the ladies beat me to it on account of being so near ready.

Well, they wasn't no return engagements even hinted at and the only other times all winter when the gals had a chance to dress up was when some second-hand company would come to town with a show and I'd have to buy a box. We couldn't ask nobody to go with us on account of not having no friends that you could depend on to not come in their stocking feet.

Finally it was summer and the Mrs. said she wanted to get out of town.

"We've got to be fair to Kate," she said.

"We don't know no young unmarried people in South Bend and it's no fun for a girl to run round with her sister and brother-in-law. Maybe if we'd go to some resort somewheres we might get acquainted with people that could show her a good time."

So I hired us rooms in a hotel down to Wawasee Lake and we stayed there from the last of June till the middle of September. During that time I caught a couple of bass and Kate caught a couple of carp from Fort Wayne. She was getting pretty friendly with one of them when along come a wife that he hadn't thought was worth mentioning. The other bird was making a fight against the gambling fever, but one night it got the best of him and he dropped forty-five cents in the nickel machine and had to go home and make a new start.

About a week before we was due to leave I made the remark that it would seem good to be back in South Bend and get some home cooking.

"Listen!" says my wife. "I been wanting for a long wile to have a serious talk with you and now's as good a time as any. Here are I and Sis and you with an income of over eight thousand dollars a year and having pretty near as good a time as a bird with habitual boils. What's more, we can't never have a good time in South Bend, but have got to move somewheres where we are unknown."

"South Bend is certainly all of that," I said.

"No, it isn't," said the Mrs. "We're acquainted there with the kind of people that makes it impossible for us to get acquainted with the other kind. Kate could live there twenty years and never meet a decent man. She's a mighty attractive girl, and if she had a chance they's nobody she couldn't marry. But she won't never have a chance in South Bend. And they's no use of you saying 'Let her move,' because I'm going to keep her under my eye till she's married and settled down. So in other words, I want us to pack up and leave South Bend for good and all and move somewheres where we'll get something for our money."

"For instance, where?" I ast her.

"They's only one place," she said; "New York City."

"I've heard of it," said I, "but I never heard that people who couldn't enjoy themselves on eight thousand a year in South Bend could go to New York and tear it wide open."

"I'm not planning to make no big splurge," she says. "I just want to be where they's Life and fun; where we can meet real live people. And as for not living there on eight thousand, think of the families that's already living there on half of that and less!"

"And think of the Life and fun they're having!" I says.

"But when you talk about eight thousand a year," said the Mrs., "why do we have to hold ourselves to that? We can sell some of those bonds and spend a little of our principal. It will just be taking money out of one investment and putting it in another."

"What other?" I ast her.

"Kate," said the wife. "You let me take her to New York and manage her and I'll get her a husband that'll think our eight thousand a year fell out of his vest."

"Do you mean," I said, "that you'd let a sister of yours marry for money?"

"Well," she says, "I know a sister of hers that wouldn't mind if she had."

So I argued and tried to compromise on somewheres in America, but it was New York or nothing with her. You see, she hadn't never been here, and all as she knew about it she'd read in books and magazines, and for some reason another when authors starts in on that subject it ain't very long till they've got a weeping jag. Besides, what chance did I have when she kept reminding me that it was her stepfather, not mine, that had croaked and made us all rich?

When I had give up she called Kate in and told her, and Kate squealed and kissed us both, though God knows I didn't deserve no remuneration or ask for none.

Ella had things all planned out. We was to sell our furniture and take a furnished apartment here, but we would stay in some hotel till we found a furnished apartment that was within reason.

"Our stay in some hotel will be lifelong," I said.

The furniture, when we come to sell it, wasn't worth nothing, and that's what we got. We didn't have nothing to ship, as Ella found room for our books in my collar box. I got two lowers and an upper in spite of the Government, and with two taxi drivers and the baggageman thronging the station platform we pulled out of South Bend and set forth to see Life.

The first four miles of the journey was marked by considerable sniveling on the part of the heiresses.

"If it's so painful to leave the Bend let's go back," I said.

"It isn't leaving the Bend," said the Mrs., "but it makes a person sad to leave any place."

"Then we're going to have a muggy trip," said I. "This train stops pretty near everywheres to either discharge passengers or employees."

They were still sobbing when we left Mishawaka and I had to pull some of my comical stuff to get their minds off. My wife's mighty easy to look at when she hasn't got those watery blues, but I never did see a gal that knocked you for a goal when her nose was in full bloom.

Katie had brought a flock of magazines and started in on one of them at Elkhart, but it's pretty tough trying to read with the Northern Indiana mountains to look out at, to say nothing about the birds of prey that kept prowling up and down the aisle in search of a little encouragement or a game of rhum.

I noticed a couple of them that would of give a lady an answer if she'd approached them in a nice way, but I've done some traveling myself and I know what kind of men it is that allows themselves to be drawed into a flirtation on trains. Most of them has made the mistake of getting married some time, but they don't tell you that. They tell you that you and a gal they use to be stuck on is as much alike as a pair of corsets, and if you ever come to Toledo to give them a ring, and they hand you a telephone number that's even harder to get than the ones there are; and they ask you your name and address and write it down, and the next time they're up at the Elks they show it to a couple of the brothers and tell what they'd of done if they'd only been going all the way through.

"Say, I hate to talk about myself! But say!"

Well, I didn't see no sense in letting Katie waste her time on those kind of guys, so every time one of them looked our way I give him the fish eye and the non-stop signal. But this was my first long trip since the Government started to play train, and I didn't know the new rules in regards to getting fed; otherwise I wouldn't of never cleaned up in Wall Street.

In the old days we use to wait till the boy come through and announced that dinner was now being served in the dining car forward; then we'd saunter into the washroom and wash our hands if necessary, and ramble into the diner and set right down and enjoy as big a meal as we could afford. But the Government wants to be economical, so they've cut down the number of trains, to say nothing about the victuals; and they's two or three times as many people traveling, because they can't throw their money away fast enough at home. So the result is that the wise guys keeps an eye on their watch and when it's about twenty minutes to dinner time they race to the diner and park against the door and get quick action; and after they've eat the first time they go out and stand in the vestibule and wait till it's their turn again, as one Federal meal don't do nothing to your appetite only whet it, you might say.

Well, anyway, I was playing the old rules and by the time I and the two gals started for the diner we run up against the outskirts of a crowd pretty near as big as the ones that waits outside restaurant windows to watch a pancake turn turtle. About eight o'clock we got to where we could see the wealthy dining car conductor in the distance, but it was only about once every quarter of an hour that he raised a hand, and then he seemed to of had all but one of his fingers shot off.

I have often heard it said that the way to a man's heart is through his stomach, but every time I ever seen men and women keep waiting for their eats it was always the frail sex that give the first yelp, and personally I've often wondered what would of happened in the trenches Over There if ladies had of been occupying them when the rations failed to show up. I guess the bombs bursting round would of sounded like Sweet and Low sang by a quextette of deef mutes.

Anyway, my two charges was like wild animals, and when the con finally held up two fingers I didn't have no more chance or desire to stop them than as if they was the Center College Football Club right after opening prayer.

The pair of them was ushered to a table for four where they already was a couple of guys making the best of it, and it wasn't more than ten minutes later when one of these birds dipped his bill in the finger bowl and staggered out, but by the time I took his place the other gent and my two gals was talking like barbers.

The guy was Francis Griffin that's in the clipping. But when Ella introduced us all as she said was, "This is my husband," without mentioning his name, which she didn't know at that time, or mine, which had probably slipped her memory.

Griffin looked at me like I was a side dish that he hadn't ordered.

Well, I don't mind snubs except when I get them, so I ast him if he wasn't from Sioux City—you could tell he was from New York by his blue collar.

"From Sioux City!" he says. "I should hope not!"

"I beg your pardon," I said. "You look just like a photographer I used to know out there."

"I'm a New Yorker," he said, "and I can't get home too soon."

"Not on this train, you can't," I said.

"I missed the Century," he says.

"Well," I says with a polite smile, "the Century's loss is our gain."

"Your wife's been telling me," he says, "that you're moving to the Big Town. Have you ever been there?"

"Only for a few hours," I says.

"Well," he said, "when you've been there a few weeks you'll wonder why you ever lived anywhere else. When I'm away from old Broadway I always feel like I'm only camping out."

Both the gals smiled their appreciation, so I says: "That certainly expresses it. You'd ought to remember that line and give it to Georgie Cohan."

"Old Georgie!" he says. "I'd give him anything I got and welcome. But listen! Your wife mentioned something about a good hotel to stop at wile you're looking for a home. Take my advice and pick out one that's near the center of things; you'll more than make up the difference in taxi bills. I lived up in the Hundreds one winter and it averaged me ten dollars a day in cab fares."

"You must of had a pleasant home life," I says.

"Me!" he said. "I'm an old bachelor."

"Old!" says Kate, and her and the Mrs. both giggled.

"But seriously," he says, "if I was you I would go right to the Baldwin, where you can get a room for twelve dollars a day for the three of you; and you're walking distance from the theaters or shops or cafés or anywheres you want to go."

"That sounds grand!" said Ella.

"As far as I'm concerned," I said, "I'd just as lief be overseas from any of the places you've mentioned. What I'm looking for is a home with a couple of beds and a cookstove in the kitchen, and maybe a bath."

"But we want to see New York first," said Katie, "and we can do that better without no household cares."

"That's the idear!" says Griffin. "Eat, drink and be merry; to-morrow we may die."

"I guess we won't drink ourselves to death," I said, "not if the Big Town's like where we been living."

"Oh, say!" says our new friend. "Do you think little old New York is going to stand for Prohibition? Why, listen! I can take you to thirty places to-morrow night where you can get all you want in any one of them."

"Let's pass up the other twenty-nine," I says.

"But that isn't the idear," he said. "What makes we New Yorkers sore is to think they should try and wish a law like that on Us. Isn't this supposed to be a government of the people, for the people and by the people?"

"People!" I said. "Who and the hell voted for Prohibition if it wasn't the people?"

"The people of where?" he says. "A lot of small-time hicks that couldn't buy a drink if they wanted it."

"Including the hicks," I says, "that's in the New York State legislature."

"But not the people of New York City," he said. "And you can't tell me it's fair to spring a thing like this without warning on men that's got their fortunes tied up in liquor that they can't never get rid of now, only at a sacrifice."

"You're right," I said. "They ought to give them some warning. Instead of that they was never even a hint of what was coming off till Maine went dry seventy years ago."

"Maine?" he said. "What the hell is Maine?"

"I don't know," I said. "Only they was a ship or a boat or some-thing named after it once, and the Spaniards sunk it and we sued them for libel or something."

"You're a smart Aleck," he said. "But speaking about war, where was you?"

"In the shipyards at South Bend painting a duck boat," I says. "And where was you?"

"I'd of been in there in a few more weeks," he says. "They wasn't no slackers in the Big Town."

"No," said I, "and America will never forget New York for coming in on our side."

By this time the gals was both giving me dirty looks, and we'd eat all we could get, so we paid our checks and went back in our car and I felt kind of apologetic, so I dug down in the old grip and got out a bottle of bourbon that a South Bend pal of mine, George Hull, had give me the day before; and Griffin and I went in the wash-room with it and before the evening was over we was pretty near ready to forget national boundaries and kiss.

The old bourb' helped me save money the next morning, as I didn't care for no breakfast. Ella and Kate went in with Griffin and you could of knocked me over with a coupling pin when the Mrs. come back and reported that he'd insisted on paying the check. "He told us all about himself," she said. "His name is Francis Griffin and he's in Wall Street. Last year he cleared twenty thousand dollars in commissions and everything."

"He's a piker," I says. "Most of them never even think under six figures."

"There you go!" said the Mrs. "You never believe nothing. Why shouldn't he be telling the truth? Didn't he buy our breakfast?"

"I been buying your breakfast for five years," I said, "but that don't prove that I'm knocking out twenty thousand per annum in Wall Street."

Francis and Katie was setting together four or five seats ahead of us.

"You ought to of seen the way he looked at her in the diner," said the Mrs. "He looked like he wanted to eat her up."

"Everybody gets desperate in a diner these days," I said. "Did you and Kate go fifty-fifty with him? Did you tell him how much money we got?"

"I should say not!" says Ella. "But I guess we did say that you wasn't doing nothing just now and that we was going to New York to see Life, after being cooped up in a small town all these years. And Sis told him you'd made us put pretty near everything in bonds, so all we can spend is eight thousand a year. He said that wouldn't go very far in the Big Town."

"I doubt if it ever gets as far as the Big Town," I said. "It won't if he makes up his mind to take it away from us."

"Oh, shut up!" said the Mrs. "He's all right and I'm for him, and I hope Sis is too. They'd make a stunning couple. I wished I knew what they're talking about."

"Well," I said, "they're both so reserved that I suppose they're telling each other how they're affected by cucumbers."

When they come back and joined us Ella said: "We was just remarking how well you two young things seemed to be getting along. We was wondering what you found to say to one another all this time."

"Well," said Francis, "just now I think we were discussing you. Your sister said you'd been married five years and I pretty near felt like calling her a fibber. I told her you looked like you was just out of high school."

"I've heard about you New Yorkers before," said the Mrs. "You're always trying to flatter somebody."

"Not me," said Francis. "I never say nothing without meaning it."

"But sometimes," says I, "you'd ought to go on and explain the meaning."

Along about Schenectady my appetite begin to come back. I'd made it a point this time to find out when the diner was going to open, and then when it did our party fell in with the door.

"The wife tells me you're on the stock exchange," I says to Francis when we'd give our order.

"Just in a small way," he said. "But they been pretty good to me down there. I knocked out twenty thousand last year."

"That's what he told us this morning," said Ella.

"Well," said I, "they's no reason for a man to forget that kind of money between Rochester and Albany, even if this is a slow train."

"Twenty thousand isn't a whole lot in the Big Town," said Francis, "but still and all, I manage to get along and enjoy myself a little on the side."

"I suppose it's enough to keep one person," I said.

"Well," says Francis, "they say two can live as cheap as one."

Then him and Kate and Ella all giggled, and the waiter brought in a part of what he thought we'd ordered and we eat what we could and ast for the check. Francis said he wanted it and I was going to give in to him after a long hard struggle, but the gals reminded him that he'd paid for breakfast, so he said all right, but we'd all have to take dinner with him some night.

I and Francis set a wile in the wash-room and smoked, and then he went to entertain the gals, but I figured the wife would go right to sleep like she always does when they's any scenery to look out at, so I stuck where I was and listened to what a couple of toothpick salesmen from Omsk would of done with the League of Nations if Wilson had of had sense enough to leave it to them.

Pulling into the Grand Central Station, Francis apologized for not being able to steer us over to the Baldwin and see us settled, but said he had to rush right downtown and report on his Chicago trip before the office closed. To see him when he parted with the gals you'd of thought he was going clear to Siberia to compete in the Olympic Games, or whatever it is we're in over there.

Well, I took the heiresses to the Baldwin and got a regular Big Town welcome. Ella and Kate set against a pillar wile I tried different tricks to make an oil-haired clerk look at me. New York hotel clerks always seem to of just dropped something and can't take their eyes of the floor. Finally I started to pick up the register and the guy give me the fish eye and ast what he could do for me.

"Well," I said, "when I come to a hotel I don't usually want to buy a straw hat."

He ast me if I had a reservation and I told him no.

"Can't do nothing for you then," he says. "Not till to-morrow morning anyway."

So I went back to the ladies.

"We'll have to go somewheres else," I said. "This joint's a joint. They won't give us nothing till to-morrow."

"But we can't go nowheres else," said the Mrs. "What would Mr. Griffin think, after recommending us to come here?"

"Well," I said, "if you think I'm going to park myself in a four-post chair all night just because we got a tip on a hotel from Wall Street you're Queen of the Cuckoos."

"Are you sure they haven't anything at all?" she says.

"Go ask them yourself!" I told her.

Well, she did, and in about ten minutes she come back and said everything was fixed.

"They'll give us a single room with bath and a double room with bath for fifteen dollars a day," she said.

" 'Give us' is good!" said I.

"I told him we'd wired for reservations and it wasn't our fault if the wire didn't get here," she said. "He was awfully nice."

Our rooms was right close to each other on the twenty-first floor. On the way up we decided by two votes to one that we'd dress for dinner. I was still monkeying with my tie when Katie come in for Ella to look her over. She had on the riskiest dress she'd bought in Chi.

"It's a pretty dress," she said, "but I'm afraid maybe it's too daring for just a hotel dining room."

Say, we hadn't no sooner than set down in the hotel dining room when two other gals come in that made my team look like they was dressed for a sleigh ride with Doc Cook.

"I guess you don't feel so daring now," I said. "Compared to that baby in black you're wearing Jess Willard's ulster."

"Do you know what that black gown cost?" said Ella. "Not a cent under seven hundred dollars."

"That would make the material twenty-one hundred dollars a yard," I says.

"I'd like to know where she got it," said Katie.

"Maybe she cut up an old stocking," said I.

"I wished now," said the Mrs., "that we'd waited till we got here before we bought our clothes."

"You can bet one thing," says Katie. "Before we're ast out any-wheres on a real party we'll have something to wear that isn't a year old."

"First thing to-morrow morning," says the Mrs., "we'll go over on Fifth Avenue and see what we can see."

"They'll only be two on that excursion," I says.

"Oh, we don't want you along," said Ella. "But I do wished you'd go to some first-class men's store and get some ties and shirts and things that don't look like an embalmer."

Well, after a wile one of the waiters got it in his head that maybe we hadn't came in to take a bath, so he fetched over a couple of programs.

"Never mind them," I says. "What's ready? We're in a hurry."

"The Long Island Duckling's very nice," he said. "And how about some nice au gratin potatoes and some nice lettuce and tomato salad with Thousand Island dressing, and maybe some nice French pastry?"

"Everything seems to be nice here," I said. "But wait a minute. How about something to drink?"

He give me a mysterious smile.

"Well," he said, "they're watching us pretty close here, but we serve something we call a cup. It comes from the bar and we're not supposed to know what the bartender puts in it."

"We'll try and find out," I said. "And rush this order through, as we're starved."

So he frisked out and was back again in less than an hour with another guy to help carry the stuff, though Lord knows he could of parked the three ducklings on one eyelid and the whole meal on the back of his hand. As for the cup, when you tasted it they wasn't no big mystery about what the bartender had put in it—a bottle of seltzer and a prune and a cherry and an orange peel, and maybe his finger. The check come to eighteen dollars and Ella made me tip him the rest of a twenty.

Before dinner the gals had been all for staying up a wile and looking the crowd over, but when we was through they both owned up that they hadn't slept much on the train and was ready for bed.

Ella and Kate was up early in the morning. They had their breakfast without me and went over to stun Fifth Avenue. About ten o'clock Francis phoned to say he'd call round for us that evening and take us to dinner. The gals didn't get back till late in the afternoon, but from one o'clock on I was too busy signing for packages to get lonesome. Ella finally staggered in with some more and I told her about our invitation.

"Yes, I know," she said.

"How do you know?" I ast her.

"He told us," she said. "We had to call him up to get a check cashed."

"You got plenty nerve!" I said. "How does he know your checks is good?"

"Well, he likes us," she said. "You'll like us too when you see us in some of the gowns we bought."

"Some!" I said.

"Why, yes," said the Mrs. "You don't think a girl can go round in New York with one evening dress!"

"How much money did you spend to-day?" I ast her.

"Well," she said, "things are terribly high—that is, nice things. And then, of course, there's suits and hats and things besides the gowns. But remember, it's our money. And as I told you, it's an investment. When young Mister Wall Street sees Kate to-night it'll be all off."

"I didn't call on you for no speech," I says. "I ast you how much you spent."

"Not quite sixteen hundred dollars."

I was still out on my feet when the phone rung. Ella answered it and then told me it was all right about the tickets.

"What tickets?" I said.

"Why, you see," she says, "after young Griffin fixing us up with that check and inviting us to dinner and everything we thought it would be nice to take him to a show to-night. Kate wanted to see Ups and Downs, but the girl said she couldn't get us seats for it. So I ast that nice clerk that took care of us yesterday and he's fixed it."

"All right," I said, "but when young Griffin starts a party, why and the hell not let him finish it?"

"I suppose he would of took us somewheres after dinner," says the Mrs., "but I couldn't be sure. And between you and I, I'm positive that if he and Kate is throwed together a whole evening, and her looking like she'll look to-night, we'll get mighty quick returns on our investment."

Well, to make a short story out of it, the gals finally got what they called dressed, and I wished Niles, Michigan, or South Bend could of seen them. If boxers wore bathing skirts I'd of thought I was in the ring with a couple of bantams.

"Listen!" I said. "What did them two girdles cost?"

"Mine was three hundred and Kate's three hundred and fifty," said the Mrs.

"Well," I says, "don't you know that you could of went to any cut-rate drug store and wrapped yourself up just as warm in thirty-two cents' worth of adhesive tape? Listen!" I said. "What's the use of me paying a burglar for tickets to a show like Ups and Downs when I could set round here and look at you for nothing?"

Then Griffin rung up to say that he was waiting and we went downstairs. Francis took us in the same dining room we'd been in the night before, but this time the waiters all fought each other to get to us first.

I don't know what we eat, as Francis had something on the hip that kind of dazed me for a wile, but afterwards I know we got a taxi and went to the theater. The tickets was there in my name and only cost me thirteen dollars and twenty cents.

Maybe you seen this show wile it was here. Some show! I didn't read the program to see who wrote it, but I guess the words was by Noah and the music took the highest awards at the St. Louis Fair. They had a good system on the gags. They didn't spring none but what you'd heard all your life and knew what was coming, so instead of just laughing at the point you laughed all the way through it.

I said to Ella, I said, "I bet the birds that run this don't want prohibition. If people paid $3.30 apiece and come in here sober they'd come back the next night with a machine gun."

"I think it's dandy," she says, "and you'll notice every seat is full. But listen! Will you do something for me? When this is over suggest that we go up to the Castle Roof for a wile."

"What for?" I said. "I'm sleepy."

"Just this once," she says. "You know what I told you about quick returns!"

Well, I give in and made the suggestion, and I never seen people so easy coaxed. I managed to get a ringside table for twenty-two bucks. Then I ast the boy how about getting a drink and he ast me if I knew any of the head waiters.

"I do," says Francis. "Tell Hector it's for Frank Griffin's party."

So we ordered four Scotch highballs and some chicken à la King, and then the dinge orchestra tore loose some jazz and I was expecting a dance with Ella, but before she could ask me Francis had ast her, and I had one with Kate.

"Your Wall Street friend's a fox," I says, "asking an old married lady to dance so's to stand in with the family."

"Old married lady!" said Kate. "Sis don't look a day over sixteen to-night."

"How are you and Francis coming?" I ast her.

"I don't know," she says. "He acts kind of shy. He hasn't hardly said a word to me all evening."

Well, they was another jazz and I danced it with Ella; then her and Francis had another one and I danced again with Kate. By this time our food and refreshments was served and the show was getting ready to start.

I could write a book on what I don't remember about that show. The first sip of their idear of a Scotch highball put me down for the count of eight and I was practic'lly unconscious till the waiter woke me up with a check for forty bucks.

Francis seen us home and said he would call up again soon, and when Ella and I was alone I made the remark that I didn't think he'd ever strain his larnix talking to Kate.

"He acts gun-shy when he's round her," I says. "You seem to be the one that draws him out."

"It's a good sign," she says. "A man's always embarrassed when he's with a girl he's stuck on. I'll bet you anything you want to bet that within a week something'll happen."

Well, she win. She'd of win if she'd of said three days instead of a week. It was a Wednesday night when we had that party, and on the Friday Francis called up and said he had tickets for the Palace. I'd been laid up mean wile with the Scotch influenza, so I told the gals to cut me out. I was still awake yet when Ella come in a little after midnight.

"Well," I said, "are we going to have a brother-in-law?"

"Mighty soon," she says.

So I ast her what had come off.

"Nothing—to-night," she says, "except this: He wrote me a note. He wants me to go with him to-morrow afternoon and look at a little furnished apartment. And he ast me if I could come without Sis, as he wants to pull a surprise on her. So I wondered if you couldn't think of some way to fix it so's I can sneak off for a couple of hours."

"Sure!" I said. "Just tell her you didn't sleep all night and you're wore out and you want to take a nap."

So she pulled this gag at lunch Saturday and Katie said she was tired too. She went up to her room and Ella snuck out to keep her date with Francis. In less than an hour she romped into our room again and throwed herself on the bed.

"Well," I says, "it must of been a little apartment if it didn't only take you this long to see it."

"Oh, shut up!" she said. "I didn't see no apartment. And don't say a word to me or I'll scream."

Well, I finally got her calmed down and she give me the details. It seems that she'd met Francis, and he'd got a taxi and they'd got in the taxi and they hadn't no sooner than got in the taxi when Francis give her a kiss.

"Quick returns," I says.

"I'll kill you if you say another word!" she says.

So I managed to keep still.

Well, I didn't know Francis' home address, and Wall Street don't run Sundays, so I spent the Sabbath training on a quart of rye that a bell hop picked up at a bargain sale somewheres for fifteen dollars. Mean wile Katie had been let in on the secret and staid in our room all day, moaning like a prune-fed calf.

"I'm afraid to leave her alone," says Ella. "I'm afraid she'll jump out the window."

"You're easily worried," I said. "What I'm afraid of is that she won't."

Monday morning finally come, as it generally always does, and I told the gals I was going to some first-class men's store and buy myself some ties and shirts that didn't look like a South Bend embalmer.

So the only store I knew about was H. L. Krause & Co. in Wall Street, but it turned out to be an office. I ast for Mr. Griffin and they ast me my name and I made one up, Sam Hall or something, and out he come.

If I told you the rest of it you'd think I was bragging. But I did bust a few records. Charley Brickley and Walter Eckersall both kicked five goals from field in one football game, and they was a bird named Robertson or something out at Purdue that kicked seven. Then they was one of the old-time ball players, Bobby Lowe or Ed Delehanty, that hit four or five home runs in one afternoon. And out to Toledo that time Dempsey made big Jess set down seven times in one round.

Well, listen! In a little less than three minutes I floored this bird nine times and I kicked him for eight goals from the field and I hit him over the fence for ten home runs. Don't talk records to me!

So that's what they meant in the clipping about a Hoosier cleaning up in Wall Street. But it's only a kid, see?

Lady Perkins

Along the first week in May they was a couple hot days, and Katie can't stand the heat. Or the cold, or the medium. Anyway, when it's hot she always says: "I'm simply stifling." And when it's cold: "I'm simply frozen." And when it ain't neither one: "I wished the weather would do one thing another." I don't s'pose she knows what she's saying when she says any one of them things, but she's one of these here gals that can't bear to see a conversation die out and thinks it's her place to come through with a wise crack whenever they's a vacuum.

So during this hot spell we was having dinner with a bird named Gene Buck that knowed New York like a book, only he hadn't never read a book, and Katie made the remark that she was simply stifling.

"If you think this is hot," says our friend, "just wait till the summer comes. The Old Town certainly steams up in the Old Summer Time."

So Kate asked him how people could stand it.

"They don't," he says. "All the ones that's got a piece of change ducks out somewheres where they can get the air."

"Where do they go?" Katie asked him.

"Well," he says, "the most of my pals goes to Newport or Maine or up in the Adirondacks. But of course them places is out of most people's reach. If I was you folks I'd go over on Long Island somewheres and either take a cottage or live in one of them good hotels."

"Where, for instance?" says my Mrs.

"Well," he said, "some people takes cottages, but the rents is something fierce, and besides, the desirable ones is probably all eat up by this time. But they's plenty good hotels where you get good service and swell meals and meet good people; they won't take in no riffraff. And they give you a pretty fair rate if they know you're going to make a stay."

So Ella asked him if they was any special one he could recommend.

"Let's think a minute," he says.

"Let's not strain ourself," I said.

"Don't get cute!" said the Mrs. "We want to get some real information and Mr. Buck can give it to us."

"How much would you be willing to pay?" said Buck.

It was Ella's turn to make a wise crack.

"Not no more than we have to," she says.

"I and my sister has got about eight thousand dollars per annum between us," said Katie, "though a thousand of it has got to go this year to a man that cheated us up on Riverside Drive.

"It was about a lease. But papa left us pretty well off; over a hundred and fifty thousand dollars."

"Don't be so secret with Mr. Buck," I says. "We've knew him pretty near a week now. Tell him about them four-dollar stockings you bought over on Fifth Avenue and the first time you put them on they got as many runs as George Sisler."

"Well," said Buck, "I don't think you'd have no trouble getting comfortable rooms in a good hotel on seven thousand dollars. If I was you I'd try the Hotel Decker. It's owned by a man named Decker."

"Why don't he call it the Griffith?" I says.

"It's located at Tracy Estates," says Buck. "That's one of the garden spots of Long Island. It's a great big place, right up to the minute, and they give you everything the best. And they's three good golf courses within a mile of the hotel."

The gals told him they didn't play no golf.

"You don't know what you've missed," he says.

"Well," I said, "I played a game once myself and missed a whole lot."

"Do they have dances?" asked Kate.

"Plenty of them," says Buck, "and the guests is the nicest people you'd want to meet. Besides all that, the meals is included in the rates, and they certainly set a nasty table."

"I think it sounds grand," said the Mrs. "How do you get there?"

"Go over to the Pennsylvania Station," says Buck, "and take the Long Island Railroad to Jamaica. Then you change to the Haverton branch. It don't only take a half hour altogether."

"Let's go over to-morrow morning and see can we get rooms," said Katie.

So Ella asked how that suited me.

"Go just as early as you want to," I says. "I got a date to run down to the Aquarium and see the rest of the fish."

"You won't make no mistake stopping at the Decker," says Buck.

So the gals thanked him and I paid the check so as he would have more to spend when he joined his pals up to Newport.

Well, when Ella and Kate come back the next afternoon, I could see without them telling me that it was all settled. They was both grinning like they always do when they've pulled something nutty.

"It's a good thing we met Mr. Buck," said the Mrs., "or we mightn't never of heard of this place. It's simply wonderful. A double room with a bath for you and I and a room with a bath for Katie. The meals is throwed in, and we can have it all summer."

"How much?" I asked her.

"Two hundred a week," she said. "But you must remember that's for all three of us and we get our meals free."

"And I s'pose they also furnish knobs for the bedroom doors," says I.

"We was awful lucky," said the wife. "These was the last two rooms they had, and they wouldn't of had those only the lady that had engaged them canceled her reservation."

"I wished I'd met her when I was single," I says.

"So do I," says Ella.

"But listen," I said. "Do you know what two hundred a week amounts to? It amounts to over ten thousand a year, and our income is seven thousand."

"Yes," says Katie, "but we aren't only going to be there twenty weeks, and that's only four thousand."

"Yes," I said, "and that leaves us three thousand for the other thirty-two weeks, to pay for board and room and clothes and show tickets and a permanent wave every other day."

"You forget," said Kate, "that we still got our principal, which we can spend some of it and not miss it."

"And you also forget," said the Mrs., "that the money belongs to Sis and I, not you."

"I've got a sweet chance of forgetting that," I said. "It's hammered into me three times a day. I hear about it pretty near as often as I hear that one of you's lost their new silk bag."

"Well, anyway," says Ella, "it's all fixed up and we move out there early to-morrow morning, so you'll have to do your packing to-night."

I'm not liable to celebrate the anniversary of the next day's trip. Besides the trunks, the gals had a suitcase and a grip apiece and I had a suitcase. So that give me five pieces of baggage to wrestle, because of course the gals had to carry their parasol in one hand and their wrist watch in the other. A redcap helped load us on over to the station, but oh you change at Jamaica! And when we got to Tracy Estates we seen that the hotel wasn't only a couple of blocks away, so the ladies said we might as well walk and save taxi fare.

I don't know how I covered them two blocks, but I do know that when I reeled into the Decker my hands and arms was paralyzed and Ella had to do the registering.

Was you ever out there? Well, I s'pose it's what you might call a family hotel, and a good many of the guests belongs to the cay-nine family. A few of the couples that can't afford dogs has got children, and you're always tripping over one or the other. They's a dining room for the grown-ups and another for the kids, wile the dogs and their nurses eats in the grillroom à la carte. One part of the joint is bachelor quarters. It's located right next to the dogs' dormitories, and they's a good deal of rivalry between the dogs and the souses to see who can make the most noise nights. They's also a ballroom and a couple card rooms and a kind of a summer parlor where the folks sets round in the evening and listen to a three-piece orchestra that don't know they's been any music wrote since Poets and Peasants. The men get up about eight o'clock and go down to New York to Business. They don't never go to work. About nine the women begins limping downstairs and either goes to call on their dogs or take them for a walk in the front yard. This is a great big yard with a whole lot of benches strewed round it, but you can't set on them in the daytime because the women or the nurses uses them for a place to read to the dogs or kids, and in the evenings you would have to share them with the waitresses, which you have already had enough of them during the day.

When the women has prepared themselves for the long day's grind with a four-course breakfast, they set round on the front porch and discuss the big questions of the hour, like for instance the last trunk murder or whether an Airedale is more loving than a Golden Bantam. Once in a wile one of them cracks that it looks like they was bound to be a panic pretty soon and a big drop in prices, and so forth. This shows they're broad-minded and are giving a good deal of thought to up-to-date topics. Every so often one of them'll say: "The present situation can't keep up." The hell it can't!

By one o'clock their appetites is whetted so keen from brain exercise that they make a bum out of a plate of soup and an order of Long Island duckling, which they figure is caught fresh every day, and they wind up with salad and apple pie à la mode and a stein of coffee. Then they totter up to their rooms to sleep it off before Dear gets home from Business.

Saturday nights everybody puts on their evening clothes like something was going to happen. But it don't. Sunday mornings the husbands and bachelors gets up earlier than usual to go to their real business, which is golf. The women-folks are in full possession of the hotel till Sunday night supper and wives and husbands don't see one another all day long, but it don't seem as long as if they did. Most of them's approaching their golden-wedding jubilee and haven't nothing more to say to each other that you could call a novelty. The husband may make the remark, Sunday night, that he would of broke one hundred and twenty in the afternoon round if the caddy hadn't of handed him a spoon when he asked for a nut pick, and the wife'll probably reply that she's got to go in Town some day soon and see a chiropodist. The rest of the Sabbath evening is spent in bridge or listening to the latest song hit from The Bohemian Girl.

The hotel's got all the modern conveniences like artificial light and a stopper in the bathtubs. They even got a barber and a valet, but you can't get a shave wile he's pressing your clothes, so it's pretty near impossible for a man to look their best at the same time.

Well, the second day we was there I bought me a deck of cards and got so good at solitary that pretty soon I could play fifty games between breakfast and lunch and a hundred from then till suppertime. During the first week Ella and Kate got on friendly terms with over a half dozen people—the head waiter, our waitress, some of the clerks and the manager and the two telephone gals. It wasn't from lack of trying that they didn't meet even more people. Every day one or the other of them would try and swap a little small talk with one of the other squatters, but it generally always wound up as a short monologue.

Ella said to me one day, she says: "I don't know if we can stick it out here or not. Every hotel I was ever at before, it was easy enough to make a lot of friends, but you could stick a bottle of cream alongside one of these people and it'd stay sweet a week. Unless they looked at it. I'm sick of talking to you and Sis and the hired help, and Kate's so lonesome that she cries herself to sleep nights."

Well, if I'd of only had sense enough to insist on staying we'd of probably packed up and took the next train to Town. But instead of that I said: "What's to prevent us from going back to New York?"

"Don't be silly!" says the Mrs. "We come out here to spend the summer and here is where we're going to spend the summer."

"All right," I says, "and by September I'll be all set to write a book on one-handed card games."

"You'd think," says Ella, "that some of these women was titled royalties the way they snap at you when you try and be friends with them. But they's only one in the bunch that's got any handle to her name; that's Lady Perkins."

I asked her which one was that.

"You know," says Ella. "I pointed her out to you in the dining room. She's a nice-looking woman, about thirty-five, that sets near our table and walks with a cane."

"If she eats like some of the rest of them," I says, "she's lucky they don't have to w'eel her."

"She's English," says Ella. "They just come over and her husband's in Texas on some business and left her here. She's the one that's got that dog."

"That dog!" I said. "You might just as well tell me she's the one that don't play the mouth organ. They've all got a dog."

"She's got two," said the wife. "But the one I meant is that big German police dog that I'm scared to death of him. Haven't you saw her out walking with him and the little chow?"

"Yes," I said, "if that's what it is. I always wondered what the boys in the Army was talking about when they said they eat chow."

"They probably meant chowchow," says the Mrs. "They wouldn't of had these kind of chows, because in the first place, who would eat a dog, and besides these kind costs too much."

"Well," I says, "I'm not interested in the price of chows, but if you want to get acquainted with Lady Perkins, why I can probably fix it for you."

"Yes, you'll fix it!" said Ella. "I'm beginning to think that if we'd of put you in storage for the summer the folks round here wouldn't shy away from us like we was leopards that had broke out of a pest-house. I wished you would try and dress up once in a wile and not always look like you was just going to do the chores. Then maybe I and Sis might get somewheres."

Well, of course when I told her I could probably fix it up with Lady Perkins, I didn't mean nothing. But it wasn't only the next morning when I started making good. I was up and dressed and downstairs about half past eight, and as the gals wasn't ready for their breakfast yet I went out on the porch and set down. They wasn't nobody else there, but pretty soon I seen Lady Perkins come up the path with her two whelps. When she got to the porch steps their nurse popped out of the servants' quarters and took them round to the grillroom for their breakfast. I s'pose the big one ordered sauerkraut and kalter Aufschnitt, wile the chow had tea and eggs fo yung. Anyway, the Perkins dame come up on the porch and flopped into the chair next to mine.

In a few minutes Ed Wurz, the manager of the hotel, showed, with a bag of golf instruments and a trick suit. He spotted me and asked me if I didn't want to go along with him and play.

"No," I said. "I only played once in my life."

"That don't make no difference," he says. "I'm a bum myself. I just play shinny, you might say."

"Well," I says, "I can't anyway, on account of my dogs. They been giving me a lot of trouble."

Of course I was referring to my feet, but he hadn't no sooner than went on his way when Lady Perkins swung round on me and says: "I didn't know you had dogs. Where do you keep them?"

At first I was going to tell her "In my shoes," but I thought I might as well enjoy myself, so I said: "They're in the dog hospital over to Haverton."

"What ails them?" she asked me.

Well, I didn't know nothing about cay-nine diseases outside of hydrophobia, which don't come till August, so I had to make one up.

"They got blanny," I told her.

"Blanny!" she says. "I never heard of it before."

"No," I said. "It hasn't only been discovered in this country just this year. It got carried up here from Peru some way another."

"Oh, it's contagious, then!" says Lady Perkins.

"Worse than measles or lockjaw," says I. "You take a dog that's been in the same house with a dog that's got blanny, and it's a miracle if they don't all get it."

She asked me if I'd had my dogs in the hotel.

"Only one day," I says, "the first day we come, about a week ago. As soon as I seen what was the matter with them, I took them over to Haverton in a sanitary truck."

"Was they mingling with the other dogs here?" she says.

"Just that one day," I said.

"Heavens!" said Lady Perkins. "And what's the symptoms?"

"Well," I said, "first you'll notice that they keep their tongue stuck out a lot and they're hungry a good deal of the time, and finally they show up with a rash."

"Then what happens?" she says.

"Well," said I, "unless they get the best of treatment, they kind of dismember."

Then she asked me how long it took for the symptoms to show after a dog had been exposed. I told her any time between a week and four months.

"My dogs has been awful hungry lately," she says, "and they most always keeps their tongue stuck out. But they haven't no rash."

"You're all right, then," I says. "If you give them treatments before the rash shows up, they's no danger."

"What's the treatment?" she asked me.

"You rub the back of their neck with some kind of dope," I told her. "I forget what it is, but if you say the word, I can get you a bottle of it when I go over to the hospital this afternoon."

"I'd be ever so much obliged," she says, "and I hope you'll find your dear ones a whole lot better."

"Dear ones is right," I said. "They cost a pile of jack, and the bird I bought them off of told me I should ought to get them insured, but I didn't. So if anything happens to them now, I'm just that much out."

Next she asked me what kind of dogs they was.

"Well," I said, "you might maybe never of heard of them, as they don't breed them nowheres only way down in Dakota. They call them yaphounds—I don't know why; maybe on account of the noise they make. But they're certainly a grand-looking dog and they bring a big price."

She set there a wile longer and then got up and went inside, probably to the nursery to look for signs of rash.

Of course I didn't tell the Mrs. and Kate nothing about this incidence. They wouldn't of believed it if I had of, and besides, it would be a knock-out if things broke right and Lady Perkins come up and spoke to me wile they was present, which is just what happened.

During the afternoon I strolled over to the drug store and got me an empty pint bottle. I took it up in the room and filled it with water and shaving soap. Then I laid low till evening, so as Perk would think I had went to Haverton.

I and Ella and Kate breezed in the dining room kind of late and we hadn't no more than ordered when I seen the Lady get up and start out. She had to pass right past us, and when I looked at her and smiled she stopped.

"Well," she said, "how's your dogs?"

I got up from the table.

"A whole lot better, thank you," says I, and then I done the honors. "Lady Perkins," I said, "meet the wife and sister-in-law."

The two gals staggered from their chairs, both pop-eyed. Lady Perkins bowed to them and told them to set down. If she hadn't the floor would of bounced up and hit them in the chin.

"I got a bottle for you," I said. "I left it upstairs and I'll fetch it down after supper."

"I'll be in the red card room," says Perk, and away she went.

I wished you could of see the two gals. They couldn't talk for a minute, for the first time in their life. They just set there with their mouth open like a baby blackbird. Then they both broke out with a rash of questions that come so fast I couldn't understand none of them, but the general idear was, What the hell!

"They's no mystery about it," I said. "Lady Perkins was setting out on the porch this morning and you two was late getting down to breakfast, so I took a walk, and when I come back she noticed that I kind of limped and asked me what ailed my feet. I told her they always swoll up in warm weather and she said she was troubled the same way and did I know any medicine that shrank them. So I told her I had a preparation and would bring her a bottle of it."

"But," says Kate, "I can't understand a woman like she speaking to a man she don't know."

"She's been eying me all week," I said. "I guess she didn't have the nerve to break the ice up to this morning; then she got desperate."

"She must of," said Ella.

"I wished," said Kate, "that when you introduce me to people you'd give them my name."

"I'm sorry," I said, "but I couldn't recall it for a minute, though your face is familiar."

"But listen," says the wife. "What ails your dogs is a corn. You haven't got no swelled feet and you haven't got no medicine for them."

"Well," I says, "what I give her won't hurt her. It's just a bottle of soap and water that I mixed up, and pretty near everybody uses that once in a wile without no bad after effects."

Now, the whole three of us had been eating pretty good ever since we'd came to the Decker. After living à la carte at Big Town prices for six months, the American plan was sweet patootie. But this night the gals not only skrimped themselves but they was in such a hurry for me to get through that my molars didn't hardly have time to identify what all was scampering past them. Ella finally got so nervous that I had to take off the feed bag without dipping my bill into the stewed rhubarb.

"Lady Perkins will get tired waiting for you," she says. "And besides, she won't want us horning in there and interrupting them after their game's started."

"Us!" said I. "How many do you think it's going to take to carry this bottle?"

"You don't mean to say we can't go with you!" said Kate.

"You certainly can't," I says. "I and the nobility won't have our little romance knocked for a gool by a couple of country gals that can't get on speaking terms with nobody but the chambermaid."

"But they'll be other people there," says Kate. "She can't play cards alone."

"Who told you she was going to play cards?" I says. "She picked the red card room because we ain't liable to be interrupted there. As for playing cards alone, what else have I done all week? But when I get there she won't have to play solitary. It'll be two-handed hearts; where if you was to crowd in, it couldn't be nothing but rummy."

Well, they finally dragged me from the table, and the gals took a seat in the lobby wile I went upstairs after the medicine. But I hadn't no sooner than got a hold of the bottle when Ella come in the room.

"Listen," she says. "They's a catch in this somewheres. You needn't to try and tell me that a woman like Lady Perkins is trying to start a flirtation with a yahoo. Let's hear what really come off."

"I already told you," I said. "The woman's nuts over me and you should ought to be the last one to find fault with her judgment."

Ella didn't speak for a wile. Then she says: "Well, if you're going to forget your marriage vows and flirt with an old hag like she, I guess two can play at that little game. They's several men round this hotel that I like their looks and all as they need is a little encouragement."

"More than a little, I guess," says I, "or else they'd of already been satisfied with what you and Kate has give them. They can't neither one of you pretend that you been fighting on the defense all week, and the reason you haven't copped nobody is because this place is a hotel, not a home for the blind."

I wrapped a piece of newspaper round the bottle and started for the door. But all of a sudden I heard snuffles and stopped.

"Look here," I said. "I been kidding you. They's no need for you to get sore and turn on the tear ducks. I'll tell you how this thing happened if you think you can see a joke."

So I give her the truth, and afterwards I says: "They'll be plenty of time for you and Kate to get acquainted with the dame, but I don't want you tagging in there with me to-night. She'd think we was too cordial. To-morrow morning, if you can manage to get up, we'll all three of us go out on the porch and lay for her when she brings the whelps back from their hike. She's sure to stop and inquire about my kennel. And don't forget, wile she's talking, that we got a couple of yaphounds that's suffering from blanny, and if she asks any questions let me do the answering, as I can think a lot quicker. You better tell Kate the secret, too, before she messes everything up, according to custom."

Then I and the Mrs. come downstairs and her and Katie went out to listen to the music while I beat it to the red card room. I give Perkie the bottle of rash poison and she thanked me and said she would have the dogs' governess slap some of it onto them in the morning. She was playing bridge w'ist with another gal and two dudes. To look at their faces they wasn't playing for just pins. I had sense enough to not talk, but I stood there watching them a few minutes. Between hands Perk introduced me to the rest of the party. She had to ask my name first. The other skirt at the table was a Mrs. Snell and one of the dudes was a Doctor Platt. I didn't get the name of Lady Perkins' partner.

"Mr. Finch," says Perk, "is also a dog fancier. But his dogs is sick with a disease called blanny and he's got them over to the dog hospital at Haverton."

"What kind of dogs?" asked Platt.

"I never heard of the breed before," says Perk. "They're yap-hounds."

"They raise them in South Dakota," I says.

Platt gives me a funny look and said: "I been in South Dakota several times and I never heard of a yaphound neither; or I never heard of a disease named blanny."

"I s'pose not," says I. "You ain't the only old-fashioned doctor that left themselves go to seed when they got out of school. I bet you won't admit they's such a thing as appendicitis.

Well, this got a laugh from Lady Perkins and the other dude, but it didn't go very big with Doc or Mrs. Snell. Wile Doc was trying to figure out a come-back I said I must go and look after my womenfolks. So I told the party I was glad to of met them and walked out.

I found Ella and Katie in the summer parlor, and they wasn't alone. A nice-looking young fella named Codd was setting alongside of them, and after we was introduced Ella leaned over and w'ispered to me that he was Bob Codd, the famous aviator. It come out that he had invented some new kind of an aeroplane and had come to demonstrate it to the Williams Company. The company—Palmer Williams and his brother, you know—they've got their flying field a couple miles from the hotel. Well, a guy with nerve enough to go up in one of them things certainly ain't going to hesitate about speaking to a strange gal when he likes their looks. So this Codd baby had give himself an introduction to my Mrs. and Kate, and I guess they hadn't sprained an ankle running away from him.

Of course Ella wanted to know how I'd came out with Lady Perkins. I told her that we hadn't had much chance to talk because she was in a bridge game with three other people, but I'd met them and they'd all seemed to fall for me strong. Ella wanted to know who they was and I told her their names, all but the one I didn't get. She squealed when I mentioned Mrs. Snell.

"Did you hear that, Sis?" she says to Kate. "Tom's met Mrs. Snell. That's the woman, you know, that wears them funny clothes and has the two dogs."

"You're describing every woman in the hotel," I said.

"But this is *the* Mrs. Snell," said the wife. "Her husband's the sugar man and she's the daughter of George Henkel, the banker. They say she's a wonderful bridge player and don't never play only for great big stakes. I'm wild to meet her."

"Yes," I said, "if they's one person you should ought to meet, it's a wonderful bridge player that plays for great big stakes, especially when our expenses is making a bum out of our income and you don't know a grand slam from no dice."

"I don't expect to gamble with her," says Ella. "But she's just the kind of people we want to know."

Well, the four of us set there and talked about this and that, and Codd said he hadn't had time to get his machine put together yet, but when he had her fixed and tested her a few times he would take me up for a ride.

"You got the wrong number," I says, "I don't feel flighty."

"Oh, I'd just love it!" said Kate.

"Well," says Codd, "you ain't barred. But I don't want to have no passengers along till I'm sure she's working O.K."

When I and Ella was upstairs she said that Codd had told them he expected to sell his invention to the Williamses for a cold million. And he had took a big fancy to Kate.

"Well," I said, "they say that the reckless aviators makes the best ones, so if him and Kate gets married he'll be better than ever. He won't give a damn after that."

"You're always saying something nasty about Sis," said the Mrs.; "but I know you just talk to hear yourself talk. If I thought you meant it I'd walk out on you."

"I'd hate to lose you," I says, "but if you took her along I wouldn't write it down as a total loss."

The following morning I and the two gals was down on the porch bright and early and in a few minutes, sure enough, along came Lady Perkins, bringing the menagerie back from the parade. She turned them over to the nurse and joined us. She said that Martha, the nurse, had used the rash poison and it had made a kind of lather on the dogs' necks and she didn't know whether to wash it off or not, but it had dried up in the sun. She asked me how many times a day the dope should ought to be put on, and I told her before every meal and at bedtime.

"But," I says, "it's best to not take the dogs right out in the sun where the lather'll dry. The blanny germ can't live in that kind of lather, so the longer it stays moist, why, so much the better."

Then she asked me was I going to Haverton to see my pets that day and I said yes, and she said she hoped I'd find them much improved. Then Ella cut in and said she understood that Lady Perkins was very fond of bridge.

"Yes, I am," says Perk. "Do you people play?"

"No, we don't," says Ella, "but we'd like to learn."

"It takes a long wile to learn to play good," said Perk. "But I do wished they was another real player in the hotel so as we wouldn't have to take Doctor Platt in. He knows the game, but he don't know enough to keep still. I don't mind people talking wile the cards is being dealt, but once the hands is picked up they ought to be absolute silence. Last night I lost about three hundred and seventy dollars just because he talked at the wrong time."

"Three hundred and seventy dollars!" said Kate. "My, you must play for big stakes!"

"Yes, we do," says Lady Perkins; "and when a person is playing for sums like that it ain't no time to trifle, especially when you're playing against an expert like Mrs. Snell."

"The game must be awfully exciting," said Ella. "I wished we could watch it sometime."

"I guess it wouldn't hurt nothing," says Perkie; "not if you kept still. Maybe you'd bring me luck."

"Was you going to play to-night?" asked Kate.

"No," says the Lady. "They's going to be a little dance here to-night and Mr. Snell's dance mad, so he insists on borrowing his wife for the occasion. Doctor Platt likes to dance too."

"We're all wild about it," says Kate. "Is this an invitation affair?"

"Oh, no," says Perk. "It's for the guests of the hotel."

Then she said good-by to us and went in the dining room. The rest of our conversation all day was about the dance and what should we wear, and how nice and democratic Lady Perkins was, and to hear her talk you wouldn't never know she had a title. I s'pose the gals thought she ought to stop every three or four steps and declare herself.

I made the announcement about noon that I wasn't going to partake in the grand ball. My corn was the alibi. But they wasn't no way to escape from dressing up and escorting the two gals into the grand ballroom and then setting there with them.

The dance was a knock-out. Outside of Ella and Kate and the aviator and myself, there was three couple. The Snells was there and so was Doctor Platt. He had a gal with him that looked like she might be his mother with his kid sister's clothes on. Then they was a pair of young shimmy shakers that ought to of been given their bottle and tucked in the hay at six P. M. A corn wouldn't of bothered them the way they danced; their feet wasn't involved in the transaction.

I and the Mrs. and Kate was the only ones there in evening clothes. The others had attended these functions before and knew that they wouldn't be enough suckers on hand to make any difference whether you wore a monkey suit or rompers. Besides, it wasn't Saturday night.

The music was furnished by the three-piece orchestra that usually done their murder in the summer parlor.

Ella was expecting me to introduce her and Kate to the Snell gal, but her and her husband was so keen for dancing that they called it off in the middle of the second innings and beat it upstairs. Then Ella said she wouldn't mind meeting Platt, but when he come past us and I spoke to him he give me a look like you would expect from a flounder that's been wronged.

So poor Codd danced one with Kate and one with Ella, and so on, and so on, till finally it got pretty late, a quarter to ten, and our party was the only merry-makers left in the joint. The orchestra looked over at us to see if we could stand some more punishment. The Mrs. told me to go and ask them to play a couple more dances before they quit. They done what I asked them, but maybe I got my orders mixed up.

The next morning I asked Wurz, the manager, how often the hotel give them dances.

"Oh," he says, "once or twice a month."

I told him I didn't see how they could afford it.

Kate went out after supper this next evening to take an automobile ride with Codd. So when I and Ella had set in the summer parlor a little wile, she proposed that we should go in and watch the bridge game. Well, I wasn't keen for it, but when you tell wife you don't want to do something she always says, "Why not?" and even if you've got a reason she'll make a monkey out of it. So we rapped at the door of the red card room and Lady Perkins said, "Come in," and in we went.

The two dudes and Mrs. Snell was playing with her again, but Perk was the only one that spoke.

"Set down," she said, "and let's see if you can bring me some luck."

So we drawed up a couple of chairs and set a little ways behind her. Her and the anonymous dude was partners against Doc and

Mrs. Snell, and they didn't change all evening. I haven't played only a few games of bridge, but I know a little about it, and I never see such hands as Perkie held. It was a misdeal when she didn't have the ace, king and four or five others of one suit and a few picture cards and aces on the side. When she couldn't get the bid herself she doubled the other pair and made a sucker out of them. I don't know what they was playing a point, but when they broke up Lady Perkins and her dude was something like seven hundred berries to the good.

I and Ella went to bed wile they was settling up, but we seen her on the porch in the morning. She smiled at us and says: "You two are certainly grand mascots! I hope you can come in and set behind me again to-night. I ain't even yet, but one more run of luck like last night's and I'll be a winner. Then," she says, "I s'pose I'll have to give my mascots some kind of a treat."

Ella was tickled to death and couldn't hardly wait to slip Sis the good news. Kate had been out late and overslept herself and we was half through breakfast when she showed up. The Mrs. told her about the big game and how it looked like we was in strong with the nobility, and Kate said she had some good news of her own; that Codd had as good as told her he was stuck on her.

"And he's going to sell his invention for a million," says Ella. "So I guess we wasn't as crazy coming out to this place as some people thought we was."

"Wait till the machine's made good," I said.

"It has already," says Kate. "He was up in it yesterday and everything worked perfect and he says the Williamses was wild over it. And what do you think's going to come off to-morrow morning? He's going to take me up with him."

"Oh, no, Sis!" said Ella. "S'pose something should happen!"

"No hope," says I.

"But even if something should happen," said Katie, "what would I care as long as it happened to Bob and I together!"

I told the waitress to bring me another order of fried mush.

"To-night," said Kate, "Bob's going in Town to a theater party with some boys he went to college with. So I can help you bring Lady Perkins good luck."

Something told me to crab this proposition and I tried, but it was passed over my veto. So the best I could do was to remind Sis, just before we went in the gambling den, to keep her mouth shut wile the play was going on.

Perk give us a smile of welcome and her partner smiled too.

For an hour the game went along about even. Kate acted like she was bored, and she didn't have nothing to say after she'd told them, wile somebody was dealing, that she was going to have an aeroplane ride in the morning. Finally our side begin to lose, and lose by big scores. They was one time when they was about sixteen hundred points to the bad. Lady Perkins didn't seem to be enjoying herself and when Ella addressed a couple of remarks to her the cat had her tongue.

But the luck switched round again and Lady Perk had all but caught up when the blow-off come.

It was the rubber game, with the score nothing and nothing. The Doc dealt the cards. I was setting where I could see his hand and Perk's both. Platt had the king, jack and ten and five other hearts. Lady Perkins held the ace and queen of hearts, the other three aces and everything else in the deck.

The Doc bid two hearts. The other dude and Mrs. Snell passed.

"Two without," says Lady Perkins.

"Three hearts," says Platt.

The other two passed again and Perk says: "Three without."

Katie had came strolling up and was pretty near behind Perk's chair.

"Well," says Platt, "it looks like——"

But we didn't find out what it looked like, as just then Katie says: "Heavens! Four aces! Don't you wished you was playing penny ante?"

It didn't take Lady Perkins no time at all to forget her title.

"You fool!" she screams, w'eeling round on Kate. "Get out of here, and get out of here quick, and don't never come near me again! I hope your aeroplane falls a million feet. You little fool!"

I don't know how the hand come out. We wasn't there to see it played.

Lady Perkins got part of her hope. The aeroplane fell all right, but only a couple of miles instead of a million feet. They say that they was a defect or something in poor Codd's engine. Anyway, he done an involuntary nose dive. Him and his invention was spilled all over Long Island. But Katie had been awake all night with the hysterics and Ella hadn't managed to get her to sleep till nine A.M. So when Codd had called for her Ella'd told him that Sis would go some other day. Can you beat it?

Wile I and Ella was getting ready for supper I made the remark that I s'posed we'd live in a vale of tears for the next few days.

"No," said Ella. "Sis is taking it pretty calm. She's sensible. She says if that could of happened, why the invention couldn't of been no good after all. And the Williamses probably wouldn't of give him a plugged dime for it."

Lady Perkins didn't only speak to me once afterwards. I seen her setting on the porch one day, reading a book. I went up to her and said: "Hello." They wasn't no answer, so I thought I'd appeal to her sympathies.

"Maybe you're still interested in my dogs," I said. "They was too far gone and the veter'nary had to order them shot."

"That's good," said Perk, and went on reading.

Three Without, Doubled

I

They ain't no immediate chance o' you gettin' ast out to our house to dinner—not w'ile round steak and General Motors is sellin' at the same price and common dog biscuit's ten cents a loaf. But you might have nothin' decent to do some evenin' and happen to drop in on the Missus and I for a call; so I feel like I ought to give you a little warnin' in case that comes off.

You know they's lots o' words that's called fightin' words. Some o' them starts a brawl, no matter who they're spoke to. You can't call nobody a liar without expectin' to lose a couple o' milk teeth—that is, if the party addressed has got somethin' besides lemon juice in his veins and ain't had the misfortune to fall asleep on the Panhandle tracks and be separated from his most prominent legs and arms. Then they's terms that don't hit you so much yourself, but reflects on your ancestors and prodigies, and you're supposed to resent 'em for the sake of honor and fix the speaker's map so as when he goes home his wife'll say: "Oh, kiddies! Come and look at the rainbow!"

Then they's other words and terms that you can call 'em to somebody and not get no rise; but call 'em to somebody else and the insurance companies could hold out on your widow by claimin' it was suicide. For instance, they's young Harold Greiner, one o' the bookkeepers down to the office. I could tell him he was an A. P. A., with a few adjectives, and he'd just smile and say: "Quit your flirtin'!" But I wouldn't never try that expression on Dan Cahill, the elevator starter, without bein' well out of his earshots. And I don't know what it means, at that.

Well, if you do come out to the house they's a term that you want to lay off of when the Missus is in the room. Don't say: "San Susie!"

It sounds harmless enough, don't it? They ain't nothin' to it even when it's transferred over from the Latin, "Without no cares." But just leave her hear it mentioned and watch her grab the two deadliest weapons that's within reach, one to use on you or whoever said it, and the other on me, on general principles.

You think I'm stringin' you, and I admit you got cause—that is, till you've heard the details of our latest plunge in the cesspools o' Society.

II

It was a Friday evenin' about three weeks ago when I come home and found the Wife quaverin' with excitement.

"Who do you think called up?" she ast me.

"I got no idear," I says.

"Guess!" says she.

So I had to guess.

"Josephus Daniels," I says. "Or Henry Ford. Or maybe it was that guy with the scar on his lip that you thought was smilin' at you the other day."

"You couldn't never guess," she says. "It was Mrs. Messenger."

"Which one?" I ast her. "You can't mean Mrs. A. D. T. Messenger."

"If you're so cute I won't tell you nothin' about it," says she.

"Don't make no rash threats," I says. "You're goin' to tell me some time and they's no use makin' yourself sick by tryin' to hold it in."

"You know very well what Mrs. Messenger I mean," she says. "It was Mrs. Robert Messenger that's husband owns this buildin' and the one at the corner, where they live at."

"Haven't you paid the rent?" I says.

"Do you think a woman like Mrs. Messenger would be buttin' into her husband's business?" says the Missus.

"I don't know what kind of a woman Mrs. Messenger is," I says. "But if I owned these here apartments and somebody fell behind in their rent, I wouldn't be surprised to see the owner's wife goin' right over to their flat and takin' it out o' their trousers pocket."

"Well," says the Wife, "we don't owe them no rent and that wasn't what she called up about. It wasn't no business call."

"Go ahead and spill it," I says. "My heart's weak."

"Well," she says, "I was just gettin' through with the lunch dishes and the phone rang."

"I bet you wondered who it was," says I.

"I thought it was Mrs. Hatch or somebody," says the Wife. "So I run to the phone and it was Mrs. Messenger. So the first thing she says was to explain who she was—just like I didn't know. And the next thing she ast was did I play bridge."

"And what did you tell her?" says I.

"What do you think I'd tell her?" says the Missus. "I told her yes."

"Wasn't you triflin' a little with the truth?" I ast her.

"Certainly not!" she says. "Haven't I played twice over to Hatches'? So then she ast me if my husband played bridge, too. And I told her yes, he did."

"What was the idear?" I says. "You know I didn't never play it in my life."

"I don't know no such a thing," she says. "For all as I know, you may play all day down to the office."

"No," I says; "we spend all our time down there playin' post-office with the scrubwomen."

"Well, anyway, I told her you did," says the Missus. "Don't you see they wasn't nothin' else I could tell her, because if I told her you didn't, that would of ended it."

"Ended what?" I says.

"We wouldn't of been ast to the party," says the Missus.

"Who told you they was goin' to be a party?" I says.

"I don't have to be told everything," says the Missus. "I got brains enough to know that Mrs. Messenger ain't callin' me up and astin' me do we play bridge just because she's got a headache or feels lonesome or somethin'. But it ain't only one party after all, and that's the best part of it. She ast us if we'd care to join the club."

"What club?" says I.

"Mrs. Messenger's club, the San Susie Club," says the Missus. "You've heard me speak about it a hundred times, and it's been mentioned in the papers once or twice, too—once, anyway, when the members give away them Christmas dinners last year."

"We can get into the papers," I says, "without givin' away no Christmas dinners."

"Who wants to get into the papers?" says the Wife. "I don't care nothin' about that."

"No," I says; "I suppose if a reporter come out here and ast for your pitcher to stick in the society columns, you'd pick up the carvin' knife and run him ragged."

"I'd be polite to him, at least," she says.

"Yes," says I; "it wouldn't pay to treat him rude; it'd even be justifiable to lock him in w'ile you was lookin' for the pitcher."

"If you'll kindly leave me talk you may find out what I got to say," she says. "I've told you about this club, but I don't suppose you ever paid any attention. It's a club that's made up from people that just lives in this block, twenty o' them altogether; and all but one couple either lives in this buildin' or in the buildin' the Messengers lives in. And they're all nice people, people with real class to them; not no tramps like most o' the ones we been runnin' round with. One o' them's Mr. and Mrs. Arthur Collins that used to live on Sheridan Road and still goes over to parties at some o' the most exclusive homes on the North Side. And they don't have nobody in the club that isn't congenial with each other, but all just a nice crowd o' real people that gets together once a week at one o' the members' houses and have a good time."

"How did these pillows o' Society happen to light on to us?" I ast her.

"Well," she says, "it seems like the Baileys, who belonged to the club, went to California last week to spend the winter. And they had to have a couple to take their place. And Mrs. Messenger says they wouldn't take nobody that didn't live in our block, and her and her husband looked over the list and we was the ones they picked out."

"Probably," I says, "that's because we was the only eligibles that can go out nights on account o' not havin' no children."

"The Pearsons ain't ast," she says, "and they ain't got no children."

"Well," I says, "what's the dues?"

"They ain't no dues," says the Missus. "But once in a w'ile, instead o' playin' bridge, everybody puts in two dollars apiece and have a theater party. But the regular program is for an evenin' o' bridge every Tuesday night, at different members' houses, somebody different actin' as hosts every week. And each couple puts up two dollars, makin' ten dollars for a gent's prize and ten dollars for a lady's. And the prizes is picked out by the lady that happens to be the hostess."

"That's a swell proposition for me," I says. "In the first place they wouldn't be a chance in the world for me to win a prize, because I don't know nothin' about the game. And, in the second place, suppose I had a whole lot o' luck and did win the prize, and come to find out it was a silver mustache cup that I wouldn't have no more use for than another Adam's apple! If they paid in cash they might be somethin' to it."

"If you win a prize you can sell it, can't you?" says the Missus. "Besides, the prizes don't count. It's gettin' in with the right kind o' people that makes the difference."

"Another thing," I says: "When it come our turn to have the party, where would we stick 'em all? We'd have to spread a sheet over the bathtub for one table, and have one couple set on the

edges and the other couple toss up for the washbasin and the
clothes-hamper. And another two couple'd have to kneel round
the bed, and another bunch could stand up round the bureau.
That'd leave the dinin'-room table for the fourth set; and for a
special treat the remainin' four could play in the parlor."

"We could hire chairs and tables," says the Missus. "We're goin'
to have to some time, anyway, when you or I die."

"You don't need to hire no tables for my funeral," I says. "If
the pallbearers or the quartet insists on shootin' craps they can
use the kitchen floor; or if they want beer and sandwiches you can
slip 'em the money to go down to the corner."

"They's no use worryin' about our end of it yet," says the Wife.
"We'll be new members and they won't expect us to give no party
till everybody else has had their turn."

"I only got one objection left," I says. "How am I goin' to get by
at a bridge party when I haven't no idear how many cards to deal?"

"I guess you can learn if I learnt," she says. "You're always talkin'
about what a swell card player you are. And besides, you've played
w'ist, and they ain't hardly any difference."

"And the next party is next Tuesday night?" I says.

"Yes," says the Missus, "at Mrs. Garrett's, the best player in the
club, and one o' the smartest women in Chicago, Mrs. Messenger
says. She lives in the same buildin' with the Messengers. And they's
dinner first and then we play bridge all evenin'."

"And maybe," I says, "before the evenin's over, I'll find out
what's trumps."

"You'll know all about the game before that," she says. "Right
after supper we'll get out the cards and I'll show you."

So right after supper she got out the cards and begun to show
me. But about all as I learnt was one thing, and that was that if
I died without no insurance, the Missus would stand a better show
o' supportin' herself by umpirin' baseball in the National League
than by teachin' in a bridge-w'ist university. She knew everything
except how much the different suits counted, and how many points
was in a game, and what honors meant, and who done the first
biddin', and how much to bid on what.

After about an hour of it I says:

"I can see you got this thing mastered, but you're like a whole lot of other people that knows somethin' perfect themselves but can't learn it to nobody else."

"No," she says; "I got to admit that I don't know as much as I thought I did. I didn't have no trouble when I was playin' with Mrs. Hatch and Mrs. Pearson and Mrs. Kramer; but it seems like I forgot all they learnt me."

"It's a crime," I says, "that we should have to pass up this chance to get in right just because we can't play a fool game o' cards. Why don't you call up Mrs. Messenger and suggest that the San Susies switches to pedro or five hundred or rummy, or somethin' that you don't need to take no college course in?"

"You're full o' brilliant idears," says the Missus. "They's only just the one game that Society plays, and that's bridge. Them other games is jokes."

"I've noticed you always treated 'em that way," I says. "But they wasn't so funny to me when it come time to settle."

"I'll tell you what we'll do," says the Missus: "We'll call up Mr. and Mrs. Hatch and tell 'em to come over here to-morrow night and give us a lesson."

"That'd be sweet," I says, "askin' them to learn us a game so as we could join a club that's right here in their neighborhood, but they ain't ever been ast to join it!"

"Why, you rummy!" she says. "We don't have to tell 'em why we want to learn. We'll just say that my two attempts over to their house has got me interested and I and you want to master the game so as we can spend many pleasant evenin's with them; because Mrs. Hatch has told me a hundred times that her and her husband would rather play bridge than eat."

So she called up Mrs. Hatch and sprung it on her; but it seemed like the Hatches had an engagement for Saturday night, but would be tickled to death to come over Monday evenin' and give us a work-out. After that was fixed we both felt kind of ashamed of ourselves, deceivin' people that was supposed to be our best friends.

"But, anyway," the Missus says, "the Hatches wouldn't never fit in with that crowd. Jim always looks like he'd dressed on the elevated and Mrs. Hatch can't talk about nothin' only shiropody."

On the Saturday I tried to slip one over by buyin' a book called *Auction Bridge*, and I read it all the way home from town and then left it on the car. It was a great book for a man that had learnt the rudderments and wanted to find out how to play the game right. But for me to try and get somethin' out of it was just like as though some kid'd learn the baseball guide by heart in kindeygarden and then ask Hugh Jennin's for the job in center-field. I did find out one thing from it though: it says that in every deal one o' the players was a dummy and just laid his cards down and left somebody else play 'em. So when I got home I says:

"We won't need no help from Jim Hatch and his wife. We can just be dummies all the evenin' and they won't nobody know if we're ignorant or not."

"That's impossible, to be dummy all the time," says the Missus.

"Not for me," I says. "I know it'll be tough for you, but you can chew a lot o' gum and you won't mind it so much."

"You don't understand," she says. "The dummy is the pardner o' the party that gets the bid. Suppose one o' the people that was playin' against you got the bid; then the other one'd be dummy and you'd have to play your hand."

"But I don't need to leave 'em have the bid," I says. "I can take it away from 'em."

"And if you take it away from 'em," she says, "then you got the bid yourself, and your pardner's dummy, not you."

Well, the Hatches breezed in Monday night and Mrs. Hatch remarked how tickled she was that we was goin' to learn, and what good times we four'd have playin' together. And the Missus and I pretended like we shared her raptures.

"Ain't you never played at all?" she ast me; and I told her no.

"The first thing," she says, "is how much the different suits count; and then they's the bids. And you got to pay attention to the conventions."

"I'm through with 'em forever," I says, "since they turned down Roosevelt."

Well, we started in and Hatch and the Missus played Mrs. Hatch and I. We kept at it till pretty near midnight, with three or four intermissions so as Hatch could relieve the strain on the ice-box. My w'ist education kept me from bein' much of a flivver when it come to playin' the cards; but, I don't care how bright a guy is, you can't learn everything about biddin' in one evenin', and you can't remember half what you learnt. I don't know what the score was when we got through, but the Hatches done most o' the execution and held most o' the cards, which is their regular habit.

"You'll get along all right," says Mrs. Hatch when they was ready to go. "But, o' course, you can't expect to master a game like bridge in a few hours. You want to keep at it."

"We're goin' to," says the Missus.

"Maybe it'd be a good idear," says Mrs. Hatch, "to play again soon before you forget what we learnt you. Why don't you come over to our house for another session to-morrow night?"

"Let's see; to-morrow night?" says the Missus, stallin'. "Why, no, we can't. We got an engagement."

So Mrs. Hatch stood there like she was expectin' to hear what it was.

"We're goin' to a party," says the Wife.

"Oh, tell me about it!" says Mrs. Hatch.

"Well," says the Missus, "it ain't really a party; it's just a kind of a party; some old friends that's visitin' in town."

"Maybe they'll play bridge with you," says Mrs. Hatch.

"Oh, no," says the Missus, blushin'. "It'll probably be rummy or pedro; or maybe we'll just go to the pitchers."

"Why don't you go over to the Acme?" says Mrs. Hatch. "They got Chaplin in *The Street Sweeper*. We're goin', and we could meet you and all go together."

"N-no," says the Wife. "You see, one of our friends has just lost his wife and I know he wouldn't feel like goin' to see somethin' funny."

"He's already laughed himself sick," I says.

Well, we wouldn't make no date with 'em and they finally blew with the understandin' that we was to go to their house and play some night soon. When they'd went the Missus says:

"I feel like a criminal, deceivin' 'em like that. But I just couldn't tell 'em the truth. Bertha Hatch is the most jealous thing in the world and it would just about kill her to know that we was in on somethin' good without she and Jim."

"If you hadn't ast 'em over," I says, "we'd of been just as well off and you wouldn't of had to make a perjure out o' yourself."

"What do you mean, we'd of been just as well off?" she says. "They done what we expected of 'em, learnt us the game."

"Yes," I says; "and you could take all I remember o' the lesson and feed it to a gnat and he'd say: 'Hurry up with the soup course!' "

III

Well, Mrs. Garrett had called up to say that the feed before the game would begin at seven bells; so I and the Missus figured on bein' on hand at half past six, so as to get acquainted with some of our fellow club members and know what to call 'em when we wanted the gravy passed or somethin'. But I had trouble with my studs and it wasn't till pretty near twenty minutes to seven that we rung the Garretts' bell. The hired girl let us in and left us standin' in the hall w'ile she went to tell Mrs. Garrett we was there. Pretty soon the girl come back and says she would take our wraps and that Mrs. Garrett would be with us in a few minutes. So we was showed into the livin'-room.

The apartment was on the second floor and looked about twice as big as our'n.

"What do you suppose this costs 'em?" ast the Missus.

"About fifty-five a month," I says.

"You're crazy!" says she. "They got this big livin'-room and two big bedrooms, and a maid's room and a sun parlor, besides their dinin'-room and kitchen and bath. They're lucky if they ain't stuck for seventy."

"I'll bet you!" I says. "I'll bet you it's nearer fifty-five than seventy."

"How much'll you bet?" she says.

"Anything you say," says I.

"Well," she says, "I've got a cinch, and I need a pair o' black silk stockin's. My others has begun to run."

"All right," I says, "A pair o' black silk stockin's to fifty cents cash."

"You're on," she says. "And I'll call up the agent to-morrow and find out."

Well, it must of been pretty near seven o'clock when Mrs. Garrett finally showed up.

"Good evenin'," she says. "I suppose this must be our new members. I'm awfully glad you could come and I'm sorry I wasn't quite ready."

"That's all right," I says. "I'm glad to know they's others has trouble gettin' into their evenin' clo'es. I suppose people that does it often enough finally get to be experts."

"I didn't have no trouble," says Mrs. Garrett; "only I didn't expect nobody till seven o'clock. You must of misunderstood me and thought I said half past six."

Then Mr. Garrett come in and shook hands with us, and then the rest o' the folks begun to arrive and we was introduced to them all. I didn't catch all their names, only Mr. and Mrs. Messenger and Mr. and Mrs. Collins and a Mr. and Mrs. Sparks. Mrs. Garrett says dinner was ready and I was glad to hear it.

They set me down between Mrs. Messenger and a lady that I didn't get her name.

"Well," I says to Mrs. Messenger, "now we know you personally, we can pay the rent direct without botherin' to go to the real-estate office."

"I'm afraid that wouldn't do," she says. "Our agent's entitled to his commissions. And besides, I wouldn't know how much to take or nothin' about it."

"We pay thirty-five," I says, "and that's all as you could ast for, seein' we only got the four rooms and no sun parlor. Thirty-two and a half would be about the right price."

"You'll have to argue that out with the agent," she says.

I was kind of expectin' a cocktail; but nothin' doin'. The hired girl brought in some half sandwiches, made o' toast, with some-thin' on 'em that looked like BB shot and tasted like New Year's mornin'.

"Don't we get no liquid refreshments?" I ast Mrs. Messenger.

"No, indeed," she says. "The San Susie's a dry club."

"You should ought to call it the San Sousy, then," says I.

The Missus was settin' next to Mr. Garrett and I could hear 'em talkin' about what a nice neighborhood it was and how they liked their flats. I thought I and the Missus might as well settle our bet then and there, so I spoke to Mr. Garrett acrost the table.

"Mr. Garrett," I says, "w'ile we was waitin' for you and your wife to get dressed, I and the Missus made a little bet, a pair o' silk stockin' against half a buck. I got to pay out two dollars here for the prize and the Missus claims her other stockin's has begun to run; so you might say we're both a little anxious."

"Is it somethin' I can settle?" he ast.

"Yes, sir," I says, "because we was bettin' on the rent you paid for this apartment. The Missus says seventy a month and I says fifty-five."

"I never decide against a lady," he says. "You better buy the stockin's before the others run so far that they can't find their way home."

"If I lose, I lose," says I. "But if you're stuck sixty-five or better, the Missus must of steered me wrong about the number o' rooms you got. I'll pay, though, because I don't never welsh on a bet. So this party's really costin' me two and a half instead o' two."

"Maybe you'll win the prize," says Mr. Garrett.

"They ain't much chance," I says. "I ain't played this game for a long w'ile."

"Why, your wife was just tellin' me you played last night," he says.

"I mean," says I, "that I didn't play for a long w'ile before last night; not for thirty-six years," I says.

Well, when everybody'd got through chokin' down the shot, they brought in some drowned toadstools, and then some little slices o' beef about the size of a checker, and seven Saratoga chips apiece, and half a dozen string beans. Those that was still able to set up under this load finished up on sliced tomatoes that was caught too young and a nickel's worth of ice-cream and an eye-dropper full o' coffee.

"Before I forget it," says Mrs. Collins, w'ile we was staggerin' out o' the dinin'-room, "you're all comin' to my house next Tuesday night."

I was walkin' right behind her.

"And I got a suggestion for you," I says, low enough so as they couldn't nobody else hear: "Throw some o' the prize money into the dinner; and if they's any skimpin' to be done, do it on the prizes."

She didn't say nothin' back, because Mrs. Garrett had started to hand us the little cards that showed where we was to play.

"I suppose I better tell you our rules," she says to me. "Each table plays four deals. Then the winners moves w'ile the losers sets still, except at the first table, where the winners sets still and the losers moves. You change pardners after every four deals. You count fifty for a game and a hundred and fifty for a rubber."

"The way I been playin'," I says, "it was thirty for a game."

"I never heard o' that," she says; but I noticed when we got to playin' that everybody that made thirty points called it a game.

"Don't we see the prizes before we start?" I ast her. "I want to know whether to play my best or not."

"If you win the prize and don't like it," she says, "I guess you can get it exchanged."

"They tell me you're the shark amongst the womenfolks," says I; "so it's a safe bet that you didn't pick out no lady's prize that isn't O.K."

I noticed some o' the other men was slippin' her their ante; so I parted with a two-spot. Then I found where I was to set at. It was Table Number Three, Couple Number One. My pardner was a strappin' big woman with a name somethin' like Rowley or Phillips. Our opponents was Mrs. Garrett and Mr. Messenger. Mrs. Garrett looked like she'd been livin' on the kind of a meal she'd gave us, and Mr. Messenger could of set in the back seat of a flivver with two regular people without crowdin' nobody. So I says to my pardner:

"Well, pardner, we got 'em outweighed, anyway."

They was two decks o' cards on the table. I grabbed one o' them and begun to deal 'em face up.

"First jack," I says.

"If you don't mind, we'll cut for deal," says Mrs. Garrett.

So we cut the cards and it seemed like the low cut got the deal and that was Mrs. Garrett herself.

"Which deck'll we play with?" I ast.

"Both o' them," says Mrs. Garrett. "Mr. Messenger'll make them red ones for you."

"Make 'em!" I says. "Well, Messenger, I didn't know you was a card factory."

Messenger laughed; but the two ladies didn't get it. Mrs. Garrett dealt and it was her turn to bid.

"One without," she says.

"I'd feel better if I had one within," says I.

"Are you goin' to bid or not?" she ast me.

"I thought it was the dealer's turn first," I says.

"I've made my bid," she says. "I bid one without."

"One without lookin', or what?" I says.

"One no trump, if I got to explain it," she says.

"Oh, that's different," I says; but I found out that most all o' them said "One without" when they meant one no trump.

I looked at my hand; but about all as I had was four hearts, with the king and jack high.

"Pardner," I says, "I don't see nothin' I can bid, unless it'd be one heart. Does that hit you?"

"No talkin' acrost the boards," says Mrs. Garrett. "And besides, one heart ain't over my bid."

So I passed and Mr. Messenger bid two spades. Then my pardner passed and Mrs. Garrett thought it over a w'ile and then bid two without. So I passed again and the rest o' them passed, and it was my first lead.

Well, I didn't have only one spade—the eight-spot—and I knew it wouldn't do my hand no good as long as I couldn't trump in with it; so I led it out. Messenger was dummy, and he laid his hand down. He had about eight spades, with the ace and queen high.

"I might as well take a chance," says Mrs. Garrett, and she throwed on Messenger's ten-spot.

Out come my pardner with the king, and it was our trick.

"What kind of a lead was that?" says Mrs. Garrett to me.

"Pretty good one, I guess," says I. "It fooled you, anyway."

And she acted like she was sore as a boil. Come to find out, she'd thought I was leadin' from the king and was goin' to catch it later on.

Well, her and Messenger took all the rest o' the tricks except my king o' hearts, and they had a game on us, besides forty for their four aces.

"I could of made a little slam as well as not," she says when it was over. "But I misunderstood our friend's lead. It's the first time I ever seen a man lead from a sneak in no trump."

"I'll do a whole lot o' things you never seen before," I says.

"I don't doubt it," says she, still actin' like I'd spilled salad dressin' on her skirt.

It was my first bid next time and hearts was my only suit again. I had the ace, queen and three others.

"Pardner," I says, "I'm goin' to bid one heart and if you got somethin' to help me out with, don't let 'em take it away from me."

"I'll double a heart," says Messenger.

"Oh, somebody else is gettin' cute!" says I. "Well, I'll double right back at you."

"Will you just wait till it comes your turn?" says Mrs. Garrett. "And besides, you can't redouble."

"I guess I can," says I. "I've got five o' them."

"It's against our rules," she says.

So my partner done nothin', as usual, and Mrs. Garrett bid one without again.

"I guess you want to play 'em all," I says; "but you'll have to come higher'n that. I'm goin' to bid two hearts."

"Two no trump," says Messenger, and my pardner says "Pass" once more.

"You'll get a sore throat sayin' that," I told her. "Don't you never hold nothin'?"

"It don't look like it," she says.

"Maybe you don't know what's worth biddin' on," I says.

"Maybe she'd better take a few lessons from you," says Mrs. Garrett.

"No," I says, kiddin' her. "You don't want no more female experts in the club or you might have to buy some cut glass once in a w'ile instead o' winnin' it."

Well, I bid three hearts; but Mrs. Garrett come up to three no trump and I couldn't go no higher. This time I led out my ace o' hearts, hopin' maybe to catch their king; but I didn't get it. And Mrs. Garrett copped all the rest of 'em for a little slam.

"If your husband ever starts drinkin' hard," I says, "you can support yourself by sellin' some o' your horseshoes to the Russian government."

It wasn't no lie, neither. I never seen such hands as that woman held, and Messenger's was pretty near as good. In the four deals they grabbed two rubbers and a couple o' little slams, and when they left our table they had over nine hundred to our nothin'.

Mr. Collins and another woman was the next ones to set down with us. The rules was to change pardners and Collins took the one I'd been playin' with. And what does she do but get lucky and they give us another trimmin', though nothin' near as bad as the first one. My pardner, this time, was a woman about forty-eight, and she acted like it was way past her bedtime. When it was her turn to say somethin' we always had to wait about five minutes, and all the other tables was through a long w'ile before us. Once she says:

"You'll have to excuse me to-night. I don't somehow seem to be able to keep my mind on the game."

"No," I says; "but I bet you'd perk up if the lady's prize was a mattress. When you're goin' to be up late you should ought to take a nap in the afternoon."

Well, sir, my next pardner wasn't nobody else but the Missus. She'd started at the fourth table and lost the first time, but win the second. She come along with the husband o' the pardner I'd just had; so here we was family against family, you might say.

"What kind o' luck you been havin'?" the fella ast me.

"No luck at all," I says. "But if you're anywheres near as sleepy as your Missus, I and my wife should ought to clean up this time."

We didn't. They held all the cards except in one hand, and that was one my Missus tried to play. I bid first and made it a no trump, as they was three aces in my hand. Old Slumber began to talk in her sleep and says: "Two diamonds." The Missus bid two hearts. Mr. Sleeper passed, and so did I, as I didn't have a single heart in my hand and figured the Missus probably had 'em all. She had six, with the king high and then the nine-spot. Our female opponent had only two, and that left five for her husband, includin' the ace, queen and jack. We was set three.

"Nice work!" I says to the Missus. "You're the Philadelphia Athletics of auction bridge."

"What was you biddin' no trump on?" she says. "I thought, o' course, you'd have one high heart and some suit."

"You don't want to start thinkin' at your age," I says. "You can't learn an old dog new tricks."

Mrs. Nap's husband cut in.

"O' course," he says, "it's a man's privilege to call your wife anything you feel like callin' her. But your Missus don't hardly look old to me."

"No, not comparatively speakin'," I says, and he shut up.

They moved on and along come Garrett and Mrs. Messenger. I and Mrs. Messenger was pardners and I thought for a w'ile we was goin' to win. But Garrett and the Missus had a bouquet o' four-leaf clovers in the last two deals and licked us. Garrett wasn't supposed to be as smart as his wife, but he was fox enough to keep biddin' over my Missus, so as he'd do the playin' instead o' she.

It wasn't till pretty near the close o' the evenin's entertainment that I got away from that table and moved to Number Two. When I set down there it was I and Mrs. Collins against her husband and Mrs. Sleeper.

"Well, Mrs. Collins," I says, "I'll try and hold some good hands for you and maybe I can have two helpin's o' the meat when we come to your house."

The other lady opened her eyes long enough to ask who was winnin'.

"Oh, Mrs. Garrett's way ahead," says Mrs. Collins. "She's got a score o' somethin' like three thousand. And Mr. Messenger is high amongst the men."

"Who's next to the leadin' lady?" I ast her.

"I guess I am," she says. "But I'm three hundred behind Mrs. Garrett."

Well, the luck I'd just bumped into stayed with me and I and Mrs. Collins won and moved to the head table. Waitin' there for us was our darlin' hostess and Messenger, the two leaders in the pennant race. It was give out that this was to be the last game.

When Mrs. Garrett realized who was goin' to be her pardner I wisht you could of seen her face!

"This is an unexpected pleasure," she says to me. "I thought you liked the third table so well you was goin' to stay there all evenin'."

"I did intend to," I says; "but I seen you up here and I heard you was leadin' the league, so I thought I'd like to help you finish in front."

"I don't need no help," she says. "All I ast is for you to not overbid your hands, and I'll do the rest."

"How many are you, Mrs. Garrett?" ast Mrs. Collins.

"Thirty-two hundred and sixty," she says.

"Oh, my!" says Mrs. Collins, "I'm hopeless. I'm only twenty-nine hundred and forty-eight. And how about you, Mr. Messenger?"

"Round thirty-one hundred," he says.

"Yes," says Mrs. Garrett, "and I don't believe any o' the rest o' the men is within five hundred o' that."

"Well, Messenger," I says, "if the men's prize happens to be a case o' beer or a steak smothered in onions, don't forget that I'm payin' you thirty-five a month for a thirty-dollar flat."

Now, I'd of gave my right eye to see Mrs. Collins beat Mrs. Garrett out. But I was goin' to do my best for Mrs. Garrett just the same, because I don't think it's square for a man to not try and play your hardest all the time in any kind of a game, no matter where your sympathies lays. So when it come my turn to bid on the first hand, and I seen the ace and king and four other hearts in my hand, I raised Mrs. Collins' bid o' two diamonds, and Mrs. Garrett made it two no trump and got away with it. On the next two deals Messenger and Mrs. Collins made a game, and Mrs. Garrett got set a trick once on a bid o' five clubs. The way the score was when it come to the last deal, I figured that if Mrs. Collins and Messenger made another game and rubber, the two wom-en'd be mighty close to even.

Mrs. Garrett dealt 'em, and says:

"One without."

"Two spades," says Mrs. Collins.

Well, sir, they wasn't a spade in my hand, and I seen that if Mrs. Collins got it we was ruined on account o' me not havin' a trump. And w'ile I wanted Mrs. Collins to win I was goin' to do my best to not let her. So I says:

"Two without."

"You know what you're doin', do you?" says Mrs. Garrett.

"What do you mean, know what I'm doin'?" I says.

"No talkin' acrost the boards," says Messenger.

"All right," I says; "but you can depend on me, pardner, not to throw you down."

Well, Messenger passed and so did Mrs. Garrett; but Mrs. Collins wasn't through.

"Three spades," she says.

"Three without," says I.

"I hope it's all right," says Mrs. Garrett.

"I'll tell you one thing," I says; "it's a whole lot all-righter than if she played it in spades."

Messenger passed again and ditto for my pardner.

"I'll double," says Mrs. Collins, and we let it go at that.

Man, oh, man! You ought to seen our genial hostess when I laid down my cards! And heard her, too! Her face turned all three colors o' Old Glory. She slammed her hand down on the table, face up.

"I won't play it!" she hollers. "I won't be made a fool of! This poor idiot deliberately told me he had spades stopped, and look at his hand!"

"You're mistaken, Mrs. Garrett," I says. "I didn't say nothin' about spades."

"Shut your mouth!" she says. "That's what you ought to done all evenin'."

"I might as well of," I says, "for all the good it done me to keep it open at dinner."

Everybody in the room quit playin' and rubbered. Finally Garrett got up from where he was settin' and come over.

"What seems to be the trouble?" he says. "This ain't no barroom."

"Nobody'd ever suspect it o' bein'," I says.

"Look what he done!" says Mrs. Garrett. "He raised my no-trump bid over three spades without a spade in his hand."

"Well," says Mr. Garrett, "they's no use gettin' all fussed up over a game o' cards. The thing to do is pick up your hand and play it out and take your medicine."

"I can set her three," said Mrs. Collins. "I got seven spades, with the ace, king and queen, and I'll catch her jack on the third lead."

"And I got the ace o' hearts," says Messenger. "Even if it didn't take a trick it'd make aces easy; so our three hundred above the line gives Mrs. Collins a score of about ten more'n Mrs. Garrett."

"All right, then," says Garrett. "Mrs. Collins is entitled to the lady's prize."

"I don't want to take it," says Mrs. Collins.

"You got to take it," says Garrett.

And he give his wife a look that meant business. Anyway, she got up and went out o' the room, and when she come back she was smilin'. She had two packages in her hand, and she give one to Messenger and one to Mrs. Collins.

"There's the prizes," she says; "and I hope you'll like 'em."

Messenger unwrapped his'n and it was one o' them round leather cases that you use to carry extra collars in when you're travelin'. Messenger had told me earlier in the evenin' that he hadn't been outside o' Chicago in six years.

Mrs. Collins' prize was a chafin'-dish.

"I don't blame Mrs. Garrett for bein' so crazy to win it," I says to her when they couldn't nobody hear. "Her and Garrett both must get hungry along about nine or ten P. M."

"I hate to take it," says Mrs. Collins.

"I wouldn't feel that way," I says. "I guess Mrs. Garrett will chafe enough without it."

When we was ready to go I shook hands with the host and hostess and says I was sorry if I'd pulled a boner.

"It was to be expected," says Mrs. Garrett.

"Yes," I says; "a man's liable to do most anything when he's starvin' to death."

The Messengers and Collinses was a little ways ahead of us on the stairs and I wanted we should hurry and catch up with 'em.

"You let 'em go!" says the Missus. "You've spoiled everything now without doin' nothin' more. Every time you talk you insult some-body."

"I ain't goin' to insult them," I says. "I'm just goin' to ask 'em to go down to the corner and have a drink."

"You are not!" she says.

But she's just as good a prophet as she is a bridge player. They wouldn't go along, though, sayin' it was late and they wanted to get to bed.

"Well, if you won't, you won't," says I. "We'll see you all a week from to-night. And don't forget, Mrs. Collins, that I'm responsible for you winnin' that chafin'-dish, and I'm fond o' welsh rabbits."

I was glad that we didn't have to go far to our buildin'. The

Missus was pleasant company, just like a bloodhound with the rabies. I left her in the vestibule and went down to help Mike close up. He likes to be amongst friends at a sad hour like that.

At breakfast the next mornin' the Wife was more calm.

"Dearie," she says, "they don't neither one of us class as bridge experts. I'll admit I got a lot to learn about the game. What we want to do is play with the Hatches every evenin' this week, and maybe by next Tuesday night we'll know somethin'."

"I'm willin'," I says.

"I'll call Mrs. Hatch up this forenoon," she says, "and see if they want us to come over there this evenin'. But if we do go remember not to mention our club or tell 'em anything about the party."

Well, she had news for me when I got home.

"The San Susies is busted up," she says. "Not forever, but for a few months anyway. Mrs. Messenger called up to tell me."

"What's the idear?" I says.

"I don't know exactly," says the Missus. "Mrs. Messenger says that the Collinses had boxes for the opera every Tuesday night and the rest didn't feel like goin' on without the Collinses, and they couldn't all o' them agree on another night."

"I don't see why they should bust it up on account o' one couple," I says. "Why didn't you tell 'em about the Hatches? They're right here in the neighborhood and can play bridge as good as anybody."

"I wouldn't think o' doin' it," says she. "They may play all right, but think o' how they talk and how they dress!"

"Well," I says, "between you and I, I ain't goin' to take cyanide over a piece o' news like this. Somehow it don't appeal to me to vote myself dry every Tuesday night all winter—to say nothin' o' two dollars a week annual dues to help buy a prize that I got no chance o' winnin' and wouldn't know what to do with it if I had it."

"It'd of been nice, though," she says, "to make friends with them people."

"Well," I says, "I'll feel a little more confident o' doin' that if I see 'em once a year—or not at all."

IV

I can tell you the rest of it in about a minute. The Missus had became resigned and everything was goin' along smooth till last

Tuesday evenin'. They was a new Chaplin show over to the Acme and we was on our way to see it. At the entrance to the buildin' where the Messengers lives we seen Mr. and Mrs. Hatch.

"Hello, there!" says the Wife. "Better come along with us to the Acme."

"Not to-night," says Mrs. Hatch. "We're tied up every Tuesday evenin'."

"Some club?" ast the Missus.

"Yes," says Mrs. Hatch. "It's a bridge club—the San Susie. The Messengers and Collinses and Garretts and us and some other people's in it. Two weeks ago we was to Collinses', and last week to Beardsleys'; and to-night the Messengers is the hosts."

The Missus tried to say somethin', and couldn't.

"I been awful lucky," says Mrs. Hatch. "I win the prize at Collinses'. It was a silver pitcher—the prettiest you ever seen!"

The Missus found her voice.

"Do you have dinner, too?" she ast.

"I should say we do!" says Mrs. Hatch. "And simply grand stuff to eat! It was nice last week at Beardsleys'; but you ought to been at Collinses'! First, they was an old-fashioned beefsteak supper; and then, when we was through playin', Mrs. Collins made us welsh rabbits in her chafin'-dish."

"That don't tempt me," I says. "I'd just as soon try and eat a raw mushrat as a welsh rabbit."

"Well, we got to be goin' in," says Hatch.

"Good night," says Mrs. Hatch; "and I wisht you was comin' with us."

The pitcher we seen was called *The Fly Cop*. Don't never waste a dime on it. They ain't a laugh in the whole show!

A Visit to the Garrisons

For the benefit of folks that is planning or building new homes, or nests as I call them, or have moved into homes all ready built and don't know what to do with all their space, I will try and describe something I seen the other night which it strikes me like it will solve a problem for a big majority of families besides adding to the gen. appearance and comfort of the home (nest).

A couple named Garrison who we met them a couple times at different parties asked us to come over and play mah jongg some evening so we went over to their house which they had just finished building it and Mrs. Garrison says did we want to see the house so of course we says yes and they showed us over it and the most of it was a good deal like other houses but they was one room which was in the way of a novelty and that is what I am going to try and describe.

This room was a kind of a small room next to the living room.

"I don't dast come in here unless I am invited," said Mrs. Garrison. "It is Mr. Garrison's den."

"His what?" I asked her.

"His den," says Mrs. Garrison.

The Mrs. and I was both obliged to laugh at the quaint idear of calling a room a den.

"Mr. Garrison comes in here when he doesn't want to be disturbed," says Mrs. Garrison. "Not even I or Junior dast disturb him."

"Junior!" I says. "Who is Junior?"

"Junior is our son," says Mrs. Garrison. "His real name is Ralph, after his daddy, but we thought if they was two Ralphs in the house, we would get all mixed up. So we call little Ralph Junior."

"A good idear," I could not help from saying.

Well, the den, as they call it, was furnished with one easy chair, a couch, a straight chair and a desk. They was two pillows on the couch and one of them red and blue and had the word Pennsylvania worked on it.

"Oh, is your husband a railroad man?" asked my Mrs. who is kind of ignorant.

"You mean the pillow?" says Mrs. Garrison. "No, that's for the University of Pennsylvania, where he attended."

Everybody laughed at my wife's mistake.

The other pillow was maroon and gold and had a big M in the middle of it. Mrs. Garrison exclaimed that this was for Minnesota where her brother attended the university.

"What did he study?" I asked her.

"Pharmacy," said Mrs. Garrison with a smile.

But what I want to describe mostly is the ornaments with which the den, as they call it, was decorated. On one side of the door as you went in was a giant pine cone.

"My goodness, is that a real pine cone?" asked my wife.

"Yes," said Mr. Garrison, speaking for the first time in several moments.

On the walls on either side of the window was a pair of antlers.

"What pretty antlers," says my wife.

"Ralph shot them himself," said Mrs. Garrison. "I mean he shot the deer they belonged to."

"That was up in Wisconsin, in 1903," says Mr. Garrison. "No, it was 1904."

Another wall was adorned with a mounted tarpon and a sail-fish.

"Ralph caught those himself," said Mrs. Garrison. "He caught them a little way out from Palm Beach."

"What year?" asked my Mrs.

"1919," said Mr. Garrison.

Leaning up against one corner of the den was a mandolin in a case. Mr. Garrison exclaimed laughingly that he had not played it for several years. Other decorations in the room was two shot guns, several pieces of fishing tackle, kodak pictures of the time the Garrisons drove from Chicago to the Coast, a pair of foils, pennants of all the big colleges and last but not least a rather risky picture called September Morn.

"I am always threatening to tear that down and throw it away," says Mrs. Garrison.

"You better not!" says her husband.

"Aren't you terrible!" says Mrs. Garrison.

The laughter was general.

That is about all I remember in regards to the den, but it seems to me like it strikes a new cord in the matter of hominess.

After we was through admiring the den we went in the living room and Mrs. Garrison got out the mah jongg set and we played till after ten o'clock. During the evening Mr. Garrison served us a couple drinks of gin and ginger ale.

"I call it a squirrel rickey," said Mr. Garrison and the laughter was general.

"I bet you would never know that Ralph made this gin himself," says Mrs. Garrison.

The Mrs. and I nudged each other.

Some Like Them Cold

N. Y., Aug. 3.

DEAR MISS GILLESPIE: How about our bet now as you bet me I would forget all about you the minute I hit the big town and would never write you a letter. Well girlie it looks like you lose so pay me. Seriously we will call all bets off as I am not the kind that bet on a sure thing and it sure was a sure thing that I would not forget a girlie like you and all that is worrying me is whether it may not be the other way round and you are wondering who this fresh guy is that is writeing you this letter. I bet you are so will try and refreshen your memory.

Well girlie I am the handsome young man that was wondering round the Lasalle st. station Monday and "happened" to sit down beside of a mighty pretty girlie who was waiting to meet her sister from Toledo and the train was late and I am glad of it because if it had not of been that little girlie and I would never of met. So for once I was a lucky guy but still I guess it was time I had some luck as it was certainly tough luck for you and I to both be liveing in Chi all that time and never get together till a half hour before I was leaveing town for good.

Still "better late than never" you know and maybe we can make up for lost time though it looks like we would have to do our make-ing up at long distants unless you make good on your threat and come to N. Y. I wish you would do that little thing girlie as it looks like that was the only way we would get a chance to play round together as it looks like they was little or no chance of me comeing back to Chi as my whole future is in the big town. N. Y. is the only spot and specially for a man that expects to make my liveing in the song writeing game as here is the Mecca for that line of work and no matter how good a man may be they don't get no recognition unless they live in N. Y.

Well girlie you asked me to tell you all about my trip. Well I remember you saying that you would give anything to be makeing it yourself but as far as the trip itself was conserned you ought to be thankfull you did not have to make it as you would of sweat your head off. I know I did specially wile going through Ind. Monday p. m. but Monday night was the worst of all trying to sleep and finely I give it up and just layed there with the prespiration rolling off of me though I was laying on top of the covers and nothing on but my underwear.

Yesterday was not so bad as it rained most of the a. m. comeing through N. Y. state and in the p. m. we road along side of the Hudson all p. m. Some river girlie and just looking at it makes a man forget all about the heat and everything else except a certain girlie who I seen for the first time Monday and then only for a half hour but she is the kind of a girlie that a man don't need to see her only once and they would be no danger of forgetting her. There I guess I better lay off that subject or you will think I am a "fresh guy."

Well that is about all to tell you about the trip only they was one amuseing incidence that come off yesterday which I will tell you. Well they was a dame got on the train at Toledo Monday and had the birth opp. mine but I did not see nothing of her that night as I was out smokeing till late and she hit the hay early but yesterday a. m. she come in the dinner and sit at the same table with me and tried to make me and it was so raw that the dinge waiter seen it and give me the wink and of course I paid no tension and I waited till she got through so as they would be no danger of her folling me out but she stopped on the way out to get a tooth pick and when I come out she was out on the platform with it so I tried to brush right by but she spoke up and asked me what time it was and I told her and she said she geussed her watch was slow so I said maybe it just seemed slow on acct. of the company it was in.

I don't know if she got what I was driveing at or not but any way she give up trying to make me and got off at Albany. She was a good looker but I have no time for gals that tries to make strangers on a train.

Well if I don't quit you will think I am writeing a book but will expect a long letter in answer to this letter and we will see if you can keep your promise like I have kept mine. Don't dissapoint me girlie as I am all alone in a large city and hearing from you will keep me from getting home sick for old Chi though I never thought so much of the old town till I found out you lived there. Don't think that is kidding girlie as I mean it.

You can address me at this hotel as it looks like I will be here right along as it is on 47th st. right off of old Broadway and handy to everything and am only paying $21 per wk. for my rm. and could of got one for $16 but without bath but am glad to pay the differents as am lost without my bath in the A. M. and sometimes at night too.

Tomorrow I expect to commence fighting the "battle of Broadway" and will let you know how I come out that is if you answer this letter. In the mean wile girlie au reservoir and don't do nothing I would not do.

Your new friend (?)

CHAS. F. LEWIS.

Chicago, Ill., Aug. 6.

MY DEAR MR. LEWIS: Well, that certainly was a "surprise party" getting your letter and you are certainly a "wonder man" to keep your word as I am afraid most men of your sex are gay deceivers but maybe you are "different." Any way it sure was a surprise and will gladly pay the bet if you will just tell me what it was we bet. Hope it was not money as I am a "working girl" but if it was not more than a dollar or two will try to dig it up even if I have to "beg, borrow or steal."

Suppose you will think me a "case" to make a bet and then forget what it was, but you must remember, Mr. Man, that I had just met you and was "dazzled." Joking aside I was rather "fussed" and will tell you why. Well, Mr. Lewis, I suppose you see lots of girls like the one you told me about that you saw on the train who tried to "get acquainted" but I want to assure you that I am not one of those kind and sincerely hope you will believe me when I tell you that you was the first man I ever spoke to meeting them like that and my friends and the people who know me would simply faint if they knew I ever spoke to a man without a "proper introduction."

Believe me, Mr. Lewis, I am not that kind and I don't know now why I did it only that you was so "different" looking if you know what I mean and not at all like the kind of men that usually try to force their attentions on every pretty girl they see. Lots of times I act on impulse and let my feelings run away from me and sometimes I do things on the impulse of the moment which I regret them later on, and that is what I did this time, but hope you won't give me cause to regret it and I know you won't as I know you are not that kind of a man a specially after what you told me about the girl on the train. But any way as I say, I was in a "daze" so can't remember what it was we bet, but will try and pay it if it does not "break" me.

Sis's train got in about ten minutes after yours had gone and when she saw me what do you think was the first thing she said? Well, Mr. Lewis, she said: "Why Mibs (That is a pet name some of my friends have given me) what has happened to you? I never seen you have as much color." So I passed it off with some remark about the heat and changed the subject as I certainly was not going to tell her that I had just been talking to a man who I had never met or she would of dropped dead from the shock. Either that or she would not of believed me as it would be hard for a person who knows me well to imagine me doing a thing like that as I have quite a reputation for "squelching" men who try to act fresh. I don't mean anything personal by that, Mr. Lewis, as am a good judge of character and could tell without you telling me that you are not that kind.

Well, Sis and I have been on the "go" ever since she arrived as I took yesterday and today off so I could show her the "sights" though she says she would be perfectly satisfied to just sit in the apartment and listen to me "rattle on." Am afraid I am a great talker, Mr. Lewis, but Sis says it is as good as a show to hear me talk as I tell things in such a different way as I cannot help from seeing the humorous side of everything and she says she never gets tired of listening to me, but of course she is my sister and thinks the world of me, but she really does laugh like she enjoyed my craziness.

Maybe I told you that I have a tiny little apartment which a girl friend of mine and I have together and it is hardly big enough to turn round in, but still it is "home" and I am a great home girl and hardly ever care to go out evenings except occasionally to the theatre or dance. But even if our "nest" is small we are proud of it and Sis complimented us on how cozy it is and how "homey" it looks and she said she did not see how we could afford to have everything so nice and Edith (my girl friend) said: "Mibs deserves all the credit for that. I never knew a girl who could make a little money go a long ways like she can." Well, of course she is my best friend and always saying nice things about me, but I do try and I hope I get results. Have always said that good taste and being careful is a whole lot more important than lots of money though it is nice to have it.

You must write and tell me how you are getting along in the "battle of Broadway" (I laughed when I read that) and whether the publishers like your songs though I know they will. Am crazy to hear them and hear you play the piano as I love good jazz music even better than classical, though I suppose it is terrible to say such a thing. But I usually say just what I think though sometimes I wish afterwards I had not of. But still I believe it is better for a girl to be her own self and natural instead of always acting. But am afraid I will never have a chance to hear you play unless you come back to Chi and pay us a visit as my "threat" to come to New York was just a "threat" and I don't see any hope of ever getting there unless some rich New Yorker should fall in love with me and take me there to live. Fine chance for poor little me, eh Mr. Lewis?

Well, I guess I have "rattled on" long enough and you will think I am writing a book unless I quit and besides, Sis has asked me as a special favor to make her a pie for dinner. Maybe you don't know it, Mr. Man, but I am quite famous for my pie and pastry, but I don't suppose a "genius" is interested in common things like that.

Well, be sure and write soon and tell me what N.Y. is like and all about it and don't forget the little girlie who was "bad" and spoke to a strange man in the station and have been blushing over it ever since.

Your friend (?)

MABELLE GILLESPIE.

N. Y., Aug. 10.

DEAR GIRLIE: I bet you will think I am a fresh guy commenceing that way but Miss Gillespie is too cold and a man can not do nothing cold in this kind of weather specially in this man's town which is the hottest place I ever been in and I guess maybe the reason why

New Yorkers is so bad is because they think they are all ready in
H—— and can not go no worse place no matter how they behave
themselves. Honest girlie I certainly envy you being where there is
a breeze off the old Lake and Chi may be dirty but I never heard
of nobody dying because they was dirty but four people died here
yesterday on acct. of the heat and I seen two different women flop
right on Broadway and had to be taken away in the ambulance and
it could not of been because they was dressed too warm because it
would be impossible for the women here to leave off any more
cloths.

Well have not had much luck yet in the battle of Broadway as all
the heads of the big music publishers is out of town on their vacation and the big boys is the only ones I will do business with as it
would be silly for a man with the stuff I have got to waste my time
on somebody that is just on the staff and have not got the final say.
But I did play a couple of my numbers for the people up to Levy's
and Goebel's and they went crazy over them in both places. So it
looks like all I have to do is wait for the big boys to get back and
then play my numbers for them and I will be all set. What I want
is to get taken on the staff of one of the big firms as that gives a man
the inside and they will plug your numbers more if you are on the
staff. In the mean wile have not got nothing to worry me but am
just seeing the sights of the big town as have saved up enough
money to play round for a wile and any way a man that can play
piano like I can don't never have to worry about starveing. Can
certainly make the old music box talk girlie and am always good
for a $75 or $100 job.

Well have been here a week now and on the go every minute and
I thought I would be lonesome down here but no chance of that as
I have been treated fine by the people I have met and have sure
met a bunch of them. One of the boys liveing in the hotel is a vaudeville actor and he is a member of the Friars club and took me
over there to dinner the other night and some way another the
bunch got wise that I could play piano so of course I had to sit
down and give them some of my numbers and everybody went crazy
over them. One of the boys I met there was Paul Sears the song
writer but he just writes the lyrics and has wrote a bunch of hits
and when he heard some of my melodies he called me over to one

side and said he would like to work with me on some numbers. How is that girlie as he is one of the biggest hit writers in N. Y.

N. Y. has got some mighty pretty girlies and I guess it would not be hard to get acquainted with them and in fact several of them has tried to make me since I been here but I always figure that a girl must be something wrong with her if she tries to make a man that she don't know nothing about so I pass them all up. But I did meet a couple of pips that a man here in the hotel went up on Riverside Drive to see them and insisted on me going along and they got on some way that I could make a piano talk so they was nothing but I must play for them so I sit down and played some of my own stuff and they went crazy over it.

One of the girls wanted I should come up and see her again, and I said I might but I think I better keep away as she acted like she wanted to vamp me and I am not the kind that likes to play round with a gal just for their company and dance with them etc. but when I see the right gal that will be a different thing and she won't have to beg me to come and see her as I will camp right on her trail till she says yes. And it won't be none of these N. Y. fly by nights neither. They are all right to look at but a man would be a sucker to get serious with them as they might take you up and next thing you know you would have a wife on your hands that don't know a dish rag from a waffle iron.

Well girlie will quit and call it a day as it is too hot to write any more and I guess I will turn on the cold water and lay in the tub a wile and then turn in. Don't forget to write to

Your friend,

CHAS. F. LEWIS.

DEAR MR. MAN: Hope you won't think me a "silly Billy" for starting my letter that way but "Mr. Lewis" is so formal and "Charles" is too much the other way and any way I would not dare call a man by their first name after only knowing them only two weeks. Though I may as well confess that Charles is my favorite name for a man and have always been crazy about it as it was my father's name. Poor old dad, he died of cancer three years ago, but left enough insurance so that mother and we girls were well provided for and do not have to do anything to support ourselves though I have been earning my own living for two years to make things easier for mother and also because I simply can't bear to be doing nothing as I feel like a "drone." So I flew away from the "home nest" though mother felt bad about it as I was her favorite and she always said I was such a comfort to her as when I was in the house she never had to worry about how things would go.

But there I go gossiping about my domestic affairs just like you would be interested in them though I don't see how you could be though personaly I always like to know all about my friends, but I know men are different so will try and not bore you any longer. Poor Man, I certainly feel sorry for you if New York is as hot as all that. I guess it has been very hot in Chi, too, at least everybody has been complaining about how terrible it is. Suppose you will wonder why I say "I guess" and you will think I ought to know if it is hot. Well, sir, the reason I say "I guess" is because I don't feel the heat like others do or at least I don't let myself feel it. That sounds crazy I know, but don't you think there is a good deal in mental suggestion and not letting yourself feel things? I believe that if a person simply won't allow themselves to be affected by disagreeable things, why such things won't bother them near as much. I know it works with me and that is the reason why I am never cross when things go wrong and "keep smiling" no matter what happens and as far as the heat is concerned, why I just don't let myself feel it and my friends say I don't even look hot no matter if the weather is boiling and Edith, my girl friend, often says that I am like a breeze and it cools her off just to have me come in the room. Poor Edie suffers terribly during the hot weather and says it almost makes her mad at me to see how cool and unruffled I look when everybody else is perspiring and have red faces etc.

I laughed when I read what you said about New York being so hot that people thought it was the "other place." I can appreciate a joke, Mr. Man, and that one did not go "over my head." Am still laughing at some of the things you said in the station though they probably struck me funnier than they would most girls as I always see the funny side and sometimes something is said and I laugh and the others wonder what I am laughing at as they cannot see anything in it themselves, but it is just the way I look at things so of course I cannot explain to them why I laughed and they think I am crazy.

But I had rather part with almost anything rather than my sense of humour as it helps me over a great many rough spots.

Sis has gone back home though I would of liked to of kept her here much longer, but she had to go though she said she would of liked nothing better than to stay with me and just listen to me "rattle on." She always says it is just like a show to hear me talk as I always put things in such a funny way and for weeks after she has been visiting me she thinks of some of the things I said and laughs over them. Since she left Edith and I have been pretty quiet though poor Edie wants to be on the "go" all the time and tries to make me go out with her every evening to the pictures and scolds me when I say I had rather stay home and read and calls me a "book worm." Well, it is true that I had rather stay home with a good book than go to some crazy old picture and the last two nights I have been reading myself to sleep with Robert W. Service's poems. Don't you love Service or don't you care for "highbrow" writings?

Personly there is nothing I love more than to just sit and read a good book or sit and listen to somebody play the piano, I mean if they can really play and I really believe I like popular music better than the classical though I suppose that is a terrible thing to confess, but I love all kinds of music but a specially the piano when it is played by somebody who can really play.

Am glad you have not "fallen" for the "ladies" who have tried to make your acquaintance in New York. You are right in thinking there must be something wrong with girls who try to "pick up" strange men as no girl with self respect would do such a thing and when I say that, Mr. Man, I know you will think it is a funny thing for me to say on account of the way our friendship started, but I mean it and I assure you that was the first time I ever done such a thing in my life and would never of thought of doing it had I not known you were the right kind of a man as I flatter myself that I am a good judge of character and can tell pretty well what a person is like by just looking at them and I assure you I had made up my mind what kind of a man you were before I allowed myself to answer your opening remark. Otherwise I am the last girl in the world that would allow myself to speak to a person without being introduced to them.

When you write again you must tell me all about the girl on Riverside Drive and what she looks like and if you went to see her again and all about her. Suppose you will think I am a little old "curiosity shop" for asking all those questions and will wonder why I want to know. Well, sir, I won't tell you why, so there, but I insist on you answering all questions and will scold you if you don't. Maybe you will think that the reason why I am so curious is because I am "jealous" of the lady in question. Well, sir, I won't tell you whether I am or not, but will keep you "guessing." Now, don't you wish you knew?

Must close or you will think I am going to "rattle on" forever or maybe you have all ready become disgusted and torn my letter up. If so all I can say is poor little me—she was a nice little girl and meant well, but the man did not appreciate her.

There! Will stop or you will think I am crazy if you do not all ready.

Yours (?)

MABELLE.

N. Y., Aug. 20.

DEAR GIRLIE: Well girlie I suppose you thought I was never going to answer your letter but have been busier than a one armed paper hanger the last week as have been working on a number with Paul Sears who is one of the best lyric writers in N. Y. and has turned out as many hits as Berlin or Davis or any of them. And believe me girlie he has turned out another hit this time that is he and I have done it together. It is all done now and we are just waiting for the best chance to place it but will not place it nowheres unless we get the right kind of a deal but maybe will publish it ourselves.

The song is bound to go over big as Sears has wrote a great lyric and I have give it a great tune or at least every body that has heard it goes crazy over it and it looks like it would go over bigger than any song since Mammy and would not be surprised to see it come out the hit of the year. If it is handled right we will make a bbl. of money and Sears says it is a cinch we will clean up as much as $25000 apiece which is pretty fair for one song but this one is not like the most of them but has got a great lyric and I have wrote a melody that will knock them out of their seats. I only wish you could hear it girlie and hear it the way I play it. I had to play it over and over about 50 times at the Friars last night.

I will copy down the lyric of the chorus so you can see what it is

like and get the idea of the song though of course you can't tell
much about it unless you hear it played and sang. The title of the
song is When They're Like You and here is the chorus:

> "Some like them hot, some like them cold.
> Some like them when they're not too darn old.
> Some like them fat, some like them lean.
> Some like them only at sweet sixteen.
> Some like them dark, some like them light.
> Some like them in the park, late at night.
> Some like them fickle, some like them true,
> But the time I like them is when they're like you."

How is that for a lyric and I only wish I could play my melody
for you as you would go nuts over it but will send you a copy as
soon as the song is published and you can get some of your friends
to play it over for you and I know you will like it though it is a
different melody when I play it or when somebody else plays it.

Well girlie you will see how busy I have been and am libel to
keep right on being busy as we are not going to let the grass grow
under our feet but as soon as we have got this number placed we
will get busy on another one as a couple like that will put me on
Easy st. even if they don't go as big as we expect but even 25 grand
is a big bunch of money and if a man could only turn out one hit
a year and make that much out of it I would be on Easy st. and no
more hammering on the old music box in some cabaret.

Who ever we take the song to we will make them come across
with one grand for advance royaltys and that will keep me going till
I can turn out another one. So the future looks bright and rosey to
yours truly and I am certainly glad I come to the big town though
sorry I did not do it a whole lot quicker.

This is a great old town girlie and when you have lived here a wile
you wonder how you ever stood for a burg like Chi which is just a
hick town along side of this besides being dirty etc. and a man is a
sucker to stay there all their life specially a man in my line of work
as N. Y. is the Mecca for man that has got the musical gift. I figure
that all the time I spent in Chi I was just wasteing my time and
never really started to live till I come down here and I have to laugh
when I think of the boys out there that is trying to make a liveing
in the song writeing game and most of them starve to death all their

life and the first week I am down here I meet a man like Sears and the next thing you know we have turned out a song that will make us a fortune.

Well girlie you asked me to tell you about the girlie up on the Drive that tried to make me and asked me to come and see her again. Well I can assure you you have no reasons to be jealous in that quarter as I have not been back to see her as I figure it is wasteing my time to play round with a dame like she that wants to go out somewheres every night and if you married her she would want a house on 5th ave. with a dozen servants so I have passed her up as that is not my idea of home.

What I want when I get married is a real home where a man can stay home and work and maybe have a few of his friends in once in a wile and entertain them or go to a good musical show once in a wile and have a wife that is in sympathy with you and not nag at you all the wile but be a real help mate. The girlie up on the Drive would run me ragged and have me in the poor house inside of a year even if I was makeing 25 grand out of one song. Besides she wears a make up that you would have to blast to find out what her face looks like. So I have not been back there and don't intend to see her again so what is the use of me telling you about her. And the only other girlie I have met is a sister of Paul Sears who I met up to his house wile we was working on the song but she don't hardly count as she has not got no use for the boys but treats them like dirt and Paul says she is the coldest proposition he ever seen.

Well I don't know no more to write and besides have got a date to go out to Paul's place for dinner and play some of my stuff for him so as he can see if he wants to set words to some more of my melodies. Well don't do nothing I would not do and have as good a time as you can in old Chi and will let you know how we come along with the song.

CHAS. F. LEWIS.

Chicago, Ill., Aug. 23.

DEAR MR. MAN: I am thrilled to death over the song and think the words awfully pretty and am crazy to hear the music which I know must be great. It must be wonderful to have the gift of writing songs and then hear people play and sing them and just think of making $25,000 in such a short time. My, how rich you will be and I certainly congratulate you though am afraid when you are rich and famous you will have no time for insignificant little me or will you be an exception and remember your "old" friends even when you are up in the world? I sincerely hope so.

Will look forward to receiving a copy of the song and will you be sure and put your name on it? I am all ready very conceited just to think that I know a man that writes songs and makes all that money.

Seriously I wish you success with your next song and I laughed when I read your remark about being busier than a one armed paper hanger. I don't see how you think up all those comparisons and crazy things to say. The next time one of the girls asks me to go out with them I am going to tell them I can't go because I am busier than a one armed paper hanger and then they will think I made it up and say: "The girl is clever."

Seriously I am glad you did not go back to see the girl on the Drive and am also glad you don't like girls who makes themselves up so much as I think it is disgusting and would rather go round looking like a ghost than put artificial color on my face. Fortunately I have a complexion that does not need "fixing" but even if my coloring was not what it is I would never think of lowering myself to "fix" it. But I must tell you a joke that happened just the other day when Edith and I were out at lunch and there was another girl in the restaurant whom Edie knew and she introduced her to me and I noticed how this girl kept staring at me and finally she begged my pardon and asked if she could ask me a personal question and I said yes and she asked me if my complexion was really "mine." I assured her it was and she said: "Well, I thought so because I did not think anybody could put it on so artistically. I certainly envy you." Edie and I both laughed.

Well, if that girl envies me my complexion, why I envy you living in New York. Chicago is rather dirty though I don't let that part of it bother me as I bathe and change my clothing so often that the dirt does not have time to "settle." Edie often says she cannot see how I always keep so clean looking and says I always look like I had just stepped out of a band box. She also calls me a fish (jokingly) because I spend so much time in the water. But seriously I do love to bathe and never feel so happy as when I have just "cleaned up" and put on fresh clothing.

Edie has just gone out to see a picture and was cross at me because I would not go with her. I told her I was going to write a letter and she wanted to know to whom and I told her and she said: "You write to him so often that a person would almost think you was in love with him." I just laughed and turned it off, but she does say the most embarrassing things and I would be angry if it was anybody but she that said them.

Seriously I had much rather sit here and write letters or read or just sit and dream than go out to some crazy old picture show except once in awhile I do like to go to the theater and see a good play and a specially a musical play if the music is catchy. But as a rule I am contented to just stay home and feel cozy and lots of evenings Edie and I sit here without saying hardly a word to each other though she would love to talk but she knows I had rather be quiet and she often says it is just like living with a deaf and dumb mute to live with me because I make so little noise round the apartment. I guess I was born to be a home body as I so seldom care to go "gadding."

Though I do love to have company once in awhile, just a few congenial friends whom I can talk to and feel at home with and play cards or have some music. My friends love to drop in here, too, as they say Edie and I always give them such nice things to eat. Though poor Edie has not much to do with it, I am afraid, as she hates anything connected with cooking which is one of the things I love best of anything and I often say that when I begin keeping house in my own home I will insist on doing most of my own work as I would take so much more interest in it than a servant, though I would want somebody to help me a little if I could afford it as I often think a woman that does all her own work is liable to get so tired that she loses interest in the bigger things of life like books and music. Though after all what bigger thing is there than home making a specially for a woman?

I am sitting in the dearest old chair that I bought yesterday at a little store on the North Side. That is my one extravagance, buying furniture and things for the house, but I always say it is economy in the long run as I will always have them and have use for them and when I can pick them up at a bargain I would be silly not to. Though heaven knows I will never be "poor" in regards to furniture and rugs and things like that as mother's house in Toledo is full of lovely things which she says she is going to give to Sis and myself as soon as we have real homes of our own. She is going to give me the first choice as I am her favorite. She has the loveliest old things that you could not buy now for love or money including lovely old rugs and a piano which Sis wanted to have a player attachment put on it but I said it would be an insult to the piano so we did not get one. I am funny about things like that, a specially old furniture and feel towards them like people whom I love.

Poor mother, I am afraid she won't live much longer to enjoy her lovely old things as she has been suffering for years from stomach trouble and the doctor says it has been worse lately instead of better and her heart is weak besides. I am going home to see her a few days this fall as it may be the last time. She is very cheerful and always says she is ready to go now as she has had enough joy out of life and all she would like would be to see her girls settled down in their own homes before she goes.

There I go, talking about my domestic affairs again and I will bet you are bored to death though personly I am never bored when my friends tell me about themselves. But I won't "rattle on" any longer, but will say good night and don't forget to write and tell me how you come out with the song and thanks for sending me the words to it. Will you write a song about me some time? I would be thrilled to death! But I am afraid I am not the kind of girl that inspires men to write songs about them, but am just a quiet "mouse" that loves home and am not giddy enough to be the heroine of a song.

Well, Mr. Man, good night and don't wait so long before writing again to

Yours (?)

MABELLE.

N. Y., Sept. 8.

DEAR GIRLIE: Well girlie have not got your last letter with me so cannot answer what was in it as I have forgotten if there was anything I was supposed to answer and besides have only a little time to write as I have a date to go out on a party with the Sears. We are going to the Georgie White show and afterwards somewheres for supper. Sears is the boy who wrote the lyric to my song and it is him and his sister I am going on the party with. The sister is a cold fish that has no use for men but she is show crazy and insists on Paul taking her to 3 or 4 of them a week.

Paul wants me to give up my room here and come and live with them as they have plenty of room and I am running a little low on money but don't know if I will do it or not as am afraid I would freeze to death in the same house with a girl like the sister as she is ice cold but she don't hang round the house much as she is always takeing trips or going to shows or somewheres.

So far we have not had no luck with the song. All the publishers we have showed it to has went crazy over it but they won't make the right kind of a deal with us and if they don't loosen up and give us a decent royalty rate we are libel to put the song out ourselves and show them up. The man up to Goebel's told us the song was O. K. and he liked it but it was more of a production number than anything else and ought to go in a show like the Follies but they won't be in N. Y. much longer and what we ought to do is hold it till next spring.

Mean wile I am working on some new numbers and also have taken a position with the orchestra at the Wilton and am going to work there starting next week. They pay good money $60 and it will keep me going.

Well girlie that is about all the news. I believe you said your father was sick and hope he is better and also hope you are getting along O. K. and take care of yourself. When you have nothing else to do write to your friend,

Chas. F. Lewis.

Chicago, Ill., Sept. 11.

Dear Mr. Lewis: Your short note reached me yesterday and must say I was puzzled when I read it. It sounded like you was mad at me though I cannot think of any reason why you should be. If there was something I said in my last letter that offended you I wish you would tell me what it was and I will ask your pardon though I cannot remember anything I could of said that you could take offense at. But if there was something, why I assure you, Mr. Lewis, that I did not mean anything by it. I certainly did not intend to offend you in any way.

Perhaps it is nothing I wrote you, but you are worried on account of the publishers not treating you fair in regards to your song and that is why your letter sounded so distant. If that is the case I hope that by this time matters have rectified themselves and the future looks brighter. But any way, Mr. Lewis, don't allow yourself to worry over business cares as they will all come right in the end and I always think it is silly for people to worry themselves sick over temporary troubles, but the best way is to "keep smiling" and look for the "silver lining" in the cloud. That is the way I always do and no matter what happens, I manage to smile and my girl friend, Edie, calls me Sunny because I always look on the bright side.

Remember also, Mr. Lewis, that $60 is a salary that a great many men would like to be getting and are living on less than that and supporting a wife and family on it. I always say that a person can get along on whatever amount they make if they manage things in the right way.

So if it is business troubles, Mr. Lewis, I say don't worry, but look on the bright side. But if it is something I wrote in my last letter that offended you I wish you would tell me what it was so I can apologize as I assure you I meant nothing and would not say anything to hurt you for the world.

Please let me hear from you soon as I will not feel comfortable until I know I am not to blame for the sudden change.

Sincerely,
Mabelle Gillespie.

N. Y., Sept. 24.

Dear Miss Gillespie: Just a few lines to tell you the big news or at least it is big news to me. I am engaged to be married to Paul Sears' sister and we are going to be married early next month and live in Atlantic City where the orchestra I have been playing with has got an engagement in one of the big cabarets.

I know this will be a surprise to you as it was even a surprise to me as I did not think I would ever have the nerve to ask the girlie the big question as she was always so cold and acted like I was just in the way. But she said she supposed she would have to marry somebody some time and she did not dislike me as much as most of the other men her brother brought round and she would marry me with the understanding that she would not have to be a slave and work round the house and also I would have to take her to a show or somewheres every night and if I could not take her myself she would "run wild" alone. Atlantic City will be O. K. for that as a lot of new shows opens down there and she will be able to see them before they get to the big town. As for her being a slave, I would hate to think of marrying a girl and then have them spend their lives in druggery round the house. We are going to live in a hotel till we find something better but will be in no hurry to start house keeping as we will have to buy all new furniture.

Betsy is some doll when she is all fixed up and believe me she knows how to fix herself up. I don't know what she uses but it is weather proof as I have been out in a rain storm with her and we both got drowned but her face stayed on. I would almost think it was real only she tells me different.

Well girlie I may write to you again once in a wile as Betsy says she don't give a dam if I write to all the girls in the world just so I don't make her read the answers but that is all I can think of to say now except good bye and good luck and may the right man come along soon and he will be a lucky man getting a girl that is such a good cook and got all that furniture etc.

But just let me give you a word of advice before I close and that is don't never speak to strange men who you don't know nothing about as they may get you wrong and think you are trying to make them. It just happened that I knew better so you was lucky in my case but the luck might not last.

Your friend,

CHAS. F. LEWIS.

Chicago, Ill., Sept. 27.

MY DEAR MR. LEWIS: Thanks for your advice and also thank your fiance for her generosity in allowing you to continue your correspondence with her "rivals," but personly I have no desire to take advantage of that generosity as I have something better to do than read letters from a man like you, a specially as I have a man friend who is not so generous as Miss Sears and would strongly object to my continuing a correspondence with another man. It is at his request that I am writing this note to tell you not to expect to hear from me again.

Allow me to congratulate you on your engagement to Miss Sears and I am sure she is to be congratulated too, though if I met the lady I would be tempted to ask her to tell me her secret, namely how she is going to "run wild" on $60.

Sincerely,

MABELLE GILLESPIE.

I Can't Breathe

July 12.

I am staying here at the Inn for two weeks with my Uncle Nat and Aunt Jule and I think I will keep a kind of a diary while I am here to help pass the time and so I can have a record of things that happen though goodness knows there isn't lightly to anything happen, that is anything exciting with Uncle Nat and Aunt Jule making the plans as they are both at least 35 years old and maybe older.

Dad and mother are abroad to be gone a month and me coming here is supposed to be a recompence for them not taking me with them. A fine recompence to be left with old people that come to a place like this to rest. Still it would be a heavenly place under different conditions, for instance if Walter were here, too. It would be heavenly if he were here, the very thought of it makes my heart stop.

I can't stand it. I won't think about it.

This is our first seperation since we have been engaged, nearly 17 days. It will 17 days tomorrow. And the hotel orchestra at dinner this evening played that old thing "Oh how I miss you tonight" and it seemed as if they must be playing it for my benefit though of course the person in that song is talking about how they miss their mother though of course I miss mother too, but a person gets used to missing their mother and it isn't like Walter or the person you are engaged to.

But there won't be any more seperations much longer, we are

going to be married in December even if mother does laugh when I talk to her about it because she says I am crazy to even think of getting married at 18.

She got married herself when she was 18, but of course that was "different," she wasn't crazy like I am, she knew whom she was marrying. As if Walter were a policeman or a foreigner or something. And she says she was only engaged once while I have been engaged at least five times a year since I was 14, of course it really isn't as bad as that and I have really only been really what I call engaged six times altogether, but is getting engaged my fault when they keep insisting and hammering at you and if you didn't say yes they would never go home.

But it is different with Walter. I honestly believe if he had not asked me I would have asked him. Of course I wouldn't have, but I would have died. And this is the first time I have ever been engaged to be really married. The other times when they talked about when should we get married I just laughed at them, but I hadn't been engaged to Walter ten minutes when he brought up the subject of marriage and I didn't laugh. I wouldn't be engaged to him unless it was to be married. I couldn't stand it.

Anyway mother may as well get used to the idea because it is "No Foolin'" this time and we have got our plans all made and I am going to be married at home and go out to California and Hollywood on our honeymoon. December, five months away. I can't stand it. I can't wait.

There were a couple of awfully nice looking boys sitting together alone in the dining-room tonight. One of them wasn't so much, but the other was cute. And he——

There's the dance orchestra playing "Always," what they played at the Biltmore the day I met Walter. "Not for just an hour not for just a day." I can't live. I can't breathe.

July 13

This has been a much more exciting day than I expected under the circumstances. In the first place I got two long night letters, one from Walter and one from Gordon Flint. I don't see how Walter ever had the nerve to send his, there was everything in it and it must have been horribly embarrassing for him while the telegraph

operator was reading it over and counting the words to say nothing
of embarrassing for the operator.

But the one from Gordon was a kind of a shock. He just got back
from a trip around the world, left last December to go on it and got
back yesterday and called up our house and Helga gave him my
address, and his telegram, well it was nearly as bad as Walter's. The
trouble is that Gordon and I were engaged when he went away, or
at least he thought so and he wrote to me right along all the time
he was away and sent cables and things and for a while I answered
his letters, but then I lost track of his itinery and couldn't write to
him any more and when I got really engaged to Walter I couldn't let
Gordon know because I had no idea where he was besides not
wanting to spoil his trip.

And now he still thinks we are engaged and he is going to call
me up tomorrow from Chicago and how in the world can I explain
things and get him to understand because he is really serious and
I like him ever and ever so much and in lots of ways he is nicer than
Walter, not really nicer but better looking and there is no comparison between their dancing. Walter simply can't learn to dance, that
is really dance. He says it is because he is flat footed, he says that as
a joke, but it is true and I wish to heavens it wasn't.

All forenoon I thought and thought and thought about what to
say to Gordon when he calls up and finally I couldn't stand thinking
about it any more and just made up my mind I wouldn't think
about it any more. But I will tell the truth though it will kill me to
hurt him.

I went down to lunch with Uncle Nat and Aunt Jule and they
were going out to play golf this afternoon and were insisting that
I go with them, but I told them I had a headache and then I had
a terrible time getting them to go without me. I didn't have a headache at all and just wanted to be alone to think about Walter and
besides when you play with Uncle Nat he is always correcting your
stance or your swing or something and always puts his hands on my
arms or shoulders to show me the right way and I can't stand it to
have old men touch me, even if they are your uncle.

I finally got rid of them and I was sitting watching the tennis
when that boy that I saw last night, the cute one, came and sat right
next to me and of course I didn't look at him and I was going to

smoke a cigarette and found I had left my lighter upstairs and I started to get up and go after it when all of a sudden he was offering me his lighter and I couldn't very well refuse it without being rude. So we got to talking and he is even cuter than he looks, the most original and wittiest person I believe I ever met and I haven't laughed so much in I don't know how long.

For one thing he asked me if I had heard Rockefeller's song and I said no and he began singing "Oil alone." Then he asked me if I knew the orange juice song and I told him no again and he said it was "Orange juice sorry you made me cry." I was in hysterics before we had been together ten minutes.

His name is Frank Caswell and he has been out of Dartmouth a year and is 24 years old. That isn't so terribly old, only two years older than Walter and three years older than Gordon. I hate the name Frank, but Caswell is all right and he is so cute.

He was out in California last winter and visited Hollywood and met everybody in the world and it is fascinating to listen to him. He met Norma Shearer and he said he thought she was the prettiest thing he had ever seen. What he said was "I did think she was the prettiest girl in the world, till today." I was going to pretend I didn't get it, but I finally told him to be sensible or I would never be able to believe anything he said.

Well, he wanted me to dance with him tonight after dinner and the next question was how to explain how we had met each other to Uncle Nat and Aunt Jule. Frank said he would fix that all right and sure enough he got himself introduced to Uncle Nat when Uncle Nat came in from golf and after dinner Uncle Nat introduced him to me and Aunt Jule too and we danced together all evening, that is not Aunt Jule. They went to bed, thank heavens.

He is a heavenly dancer, as good as Gordon. One dance we were dancing and for one of the encores the orchestra played "In a cottage small by a waterfall" and I simply couldn't dance to it. I just stopped still and said "Listen, I can't bear it, I can't breathe" and poor Frank thought I was sick or something and I had to explain that that was the tune the orchestra played the night I sat at the next table to Jack Barrymore at Barney Gallant's.

I made him sit out that encore and wouldn't let him talk till they got through playing it. Then they played something else and I was all right again and Frank told me about meeting Jack Barrymore. Imagine meeting him. I couldn't live.

I promised Aunt Jule I would go to bed at eleven and it is way past that now, but I am all ready for bed and have just been writing this. Tomorrow Gordon is going to call up and what will I say to him? I just won't think about it.

July 14

Gordon called up this morning from Chicago and it was wonderful to hear his voice again though the connection was terrible. He asked me if I still loved him and I tried to tell him no, but I knew that would mean an explanation and the connection was so bad that I never could make him understand so I said yes, but I almost whispered it purposely, thinking he wouldn't hear me, but he heard me all right and he said that made everything all right with the world. He said he thought I had stopped loving him because I had stopped writing.

I wish the connection had been decent and I could have told him how things were, but now it is terrible because he is planning to get to New York the day I get there and heaven knows what I will do because Walter will be there, too. I just won't think about it.

Aunt Jule came in my room just after I was through talking to Gordon, thank heavens. The room was full of flowers. Walter had sent me some and so had Frank. I got another long night letter from Walter, just as silly as the first one. I wish he would say those things in letters instead of night letters so everybody in the world wouldn't see them. Aunt Jule wanted me to read it aloud to her. I would have died.

While she was still in the room, Frank called up and asked me to play golf with him and I said all right and Aunt Jule said she was glad my headache was gone. She was trying to be funny.

I played golf with Frank this afternoon. He is a beautiful golfer and it is thrilling to watch him drive, his swing is so much more graceful than Walter's. I asked him to watch me swing and tell me what was the matter with me, but he said he couldn't look at anything but my face and there wasn't anything the matter with that.

He told me the boy who was here with him had been called home and he was glad of it because I might have liked him, the other boy, better than himself. I told him that couldn't be possible and he

asked me if I really meant that and I said of course, but I smiled
when I said it so he wouldn't take it too seriously.

We danced again tonight and Uncle Nat and Aunt Jule sat with
us a while and danced a couple of dances themselves, but they were
really there to get better acquainted with Frank and see if he was
all right for me to be with. I know they certainly couldn't have enjoyed their own dancing, no old people really can enjoy it because
they can't really *do* anything.

They were favorably impressed with Frank I think, at least Aunt
Jule didn't say I must be in bed at eleven, but just not to stay up
too late. I guess it is a big surprise to a girl's parents and aunts and
uncles to find out that the boys you go around with are all right,
they always seem to think that if I seem to like somebody and the
person pays a little attention to me, why he must be a convict or a
policeman or a drunkard or something queer.

Frank had some more songs for me tonight. He asked me if I
knew the asthma song and I said I didn't and he said "Oh, you
must know that. It goes yes, sir, asthma baby." Then he told me
about the underwear song, "I underwear my baby is tonight." He
keeps you in hysterics and yet he has his serious side, in fact he was
awfully serious when he said good night to me and his eyes simply
shown. I wish Walter were more like him in some ways, but I
mustn't think about that.

July 15

I simply can't live and I know I'll never sleep tonight. I am in a
terrible predicament or rather I won't know whether I really am or
not till tomorrow and that is what makes it so terrible.

After we had danced two or three dances, Frank asked me to go
for a ride with him and we went for a ride in his car and he had had
some cocktails and during the ride he had some drinks out of a flask
and finally he told me he loved me and I said not to be silly, but he
said he was perfectly serious and he certainly acted that way. He
asked me if I loved anybody else and I said yes and he asked if I
didn't love him more than anybody else and I said yes, but only
because I thought he had probably had too much to drink and
wouldn't remember it anyway and the best thing to do was humor
him under the circumstances.

Then all of a sudden he asked me when I could marry him and

I said, just as a joke, that I couldn't possibly marry him before December. He said that was a long time to wait, but I was certainly worth waiting for and he said a lot of other things and maybe I humored him a little too much, but that is just the trouble, I don't know.

I was absolutely sure he was tight and would forget the whole thing, but that was early in the evening, and when we said good night he was a whole lot more sober than he had been and now I am not sure how it stands. If he doesn't remember anything about it, of course I am all right. But if he does remember and if he took me seriously, I will simply have to tell him about Walter and maybe about Gordon, too. And it isn't going to be easy. The suspense is what is maddening and I know I'll never live through this night.

July 16

I can't stand it, I can't breathe, life is impossible. Frank remembered everything about last night and firmly believes we are engaged and going to be married in December. His people live in New York and he says he is going back when I do and have them meet me.

Of course it can't go on and tomorrow I will tell him about Walter or Gordon or both of them. I know it is going to hurt him terribly, perhaps spoil his life and I would give anything in the world not to have had it happen. I hate so to hurt him because he is so nice besides being so cute and attractive.

He sent me the loveliest flowers this morning and called up at ten and wanted to know how soon he could see me and I hope the girl wasn't listening in because the things he said were, well like Walter's night letters.

And that is another terrible thing, today I didn't get a night letter from Walter, but there was a regular letter instead and I carried it around in my purse all this afternoon and evening and never remembered to read it till ten minutes ago when I came up in the room. Walter is worried because I have only sent him two telegrams and written him one letter since I have been here, he would be a lot more worried if he knew what has happened now, though of course it can't make any difference because he is the one I am really engaged to be married to and the one I told mother I was going to marry in December and I wouldn't dare tell her it was somebody else.

I met Frank for lunch and we went for a ride this afternoon and he was so much in love and so lovely to me that I simply did not have the heart to tell him the truth, I am surely going to tell him tomorrow and telling him today would have just meant one more day of unhappiness for both of us.

He said his people had plenty of money and his father had offered to take him into partnership and he might accept, but he thinks his true vocation is journalism with a view to eventually writing novels and if I was willing to undergo a few hardships just at first we would probably both be happier later on if he was doing something he really liked. I didn't know what to say, but finally I said I wanted him to suit himself and money wasn't everything.

He asked me where I would like to go on my honeymoon and I suppose I ought to have told him my honeymoon was all planned, that I was going to California, with Walter, but all I said was that I had always wanted to go to California and he was enthusiastic and said that is where we would surely go and he would take me to Hollywood and introduce me to all those wonderful people he met there last winter. It nearly takes my breath away to think of it, going there with someone who really knows people and has the entrée.

We danced again tonight, just two or three dances, and then went out and sat in the tennis-court, but I came upstairs early because Aunt Jule had acted kind of funny at dinner. And I wanted to be alone, too, and think, but the more I think the worse it gets.

Sometimes I wish I were dead, maybe that is the only solution and it would be best for everyone concerned. I *will* die if things keep on the way they have been. But of course tomorrow it will be all over, with Frank I mean, for I must tell him the truth no matter how much it hurts us both. Though I don't care how much it hurts me. The thought of hurting him is what is driving me mad. I can't bear it.

July 18

I have skipped a day. I was busy every minute of yesterday and so exhausted when I came upstairs that I was tempted to fall into bed with all my clothes on. First Gordon called me up from Chicago to remind me that he would be in New York the day I got there and that when he comes he wants me all to himself all the time and we can make plans for our wedding. The connection was bad again and I just couldn't explain to him about Walter.

I had an engagement with Frank for lunch and just as we were going in another long distance call came, from Walter this time. He wanted to know why I haven't written more letters and sent him more telegrams and asked me if I still loved him and of course I told him yes because I really do. Then he asked if I had met any men here and I told him I had met one, a friend of Uncle Nat's. After all it was Uncle Nat who introduced me to Frank. He reminded me that he would be in New York on the 25th which is the day I expect to get home, and said he would have theater tickets for that night and we would go somewhere afterwards and dance.

Frank insisted on knowing who had kept me talking so long and I told him it was a boy I had known a long while, a very dear friend of mine and a friend of my family's. Frank was jealous and kept asking questions till I thought I would go mad. He was so serious and kind of cross and gruff that I gave up the plan of telling him the truth till some time when he is in better spirits.

I played golf with Frank in the afternoon and we took a ride last night and I wanted to get in early because I had promised both Walter and Gordon that I would write them long letters, but Frank wouldn't bring me back to the Inn till I had named a definite date in December. I finally told him the 10th and he said all right if I was sure that wasn't a Sunday. I said I would have to look it up, but as a matter of fact I know the 10th falls on a Friday because the date Walter and I have agreed on for our wedding is Saturday the 11th.

Today has just been the same thing over again, two more night letters, a long distance call from Chicago, golf and a ride with Frank, and the room full of flowers. But tomorrow I am going to tell Frank and I am going to write Gordon a long letter and tell him, too, because this simply can't go on any longer. I can't breathe. I can't live.

July 21

I wrote to Gordon yesterday, but I didn't say anything about Walter because I don't think it is a thing a person ought to do by letter. I can tell him when he gets to New York and then I will be sure that he doesn't take it too hard and I can promise him that I will be friends with him always and make him promise not to do anything silly, while if I told it to him in a letter there is no telling what he would do, there all alone.

And I haven't told Frank because he hasn't been feeling well, he is terribly sunburned and it hurts him terribly so he can hardly play golf or dance, and I want him to be feeling his best when I do tell him, but whether he is all right or not I simply must tell him to-morrow because he is actually planning to leave here on the same train with us Saturday night and I can't let him do that.

Life is so hopeless and it could be so wonderful. For instance how heavenly it would be if I could marry Frank first and stay married to him five years and he would be the one who would take me to Hollywood and maybe we could go on parties with Norman Kerry and Jack Barrymore and Buster Collier and Marion Davies and Lois Moran.

And at the end of five years Frank could go into journalism and write novels and I would only be 23 and I could marry Gordon and he would be ready for another trip around the world and he could show me things better than someone who had never seem them before.

Gordon and I would separate at the end of five years and I would be 28 and I know of lots of women that never even got married the first time till they were 28 though I don't suppose that was their fault, but I would marry Walter then, for after all he is the one I really love and want to spend most of my life with and I wouldn't care whether he could dance or not when I was that old. Before long we would be as old as Uncle Nat and Aunt Jule and I certainly wouldn't want to dance at their age when all you can do is just hobble around the floor. But Walter is so wonderful as a companion and we would enjoy the same things and be pals and maybe we would begin to have children.

But that is all impossible though it wouldn't be if older people just had sense and would look at things the right way.

It is only half past ten, the earliest I have gone to bed in weeks, but I am worn out and Frank went to bed early so he could put cold cream on his sunburn.

Listen, diary, the orchestra is playing "Limehouse Blues." The first tune I danced to with Merle Oliver, two years ago. I can't stand it. And how funny that they should play that old tune tonight of all nights, when I have been thinking of Merle off and on all day, and I hadn't thought of him before in weeks and weeks. I wonder where he is, I wonder if it is just an accident or if it means I am going to see him again. I simply mustn't think about it or I'll die.

July 22

I knew it wasn't an accident. I knew it must mean something, and it did.

Merle is coming here today, here to this Inn, and just to see me. And there can only be one reason. And only one answer. I knew that when I heard his voice calling from Boston. How could I ever had thought I loved anyone else? How could he ever have thought I meant it when I told him I was engaged to George Morse?

A whole year and he still cares and I still care. That shows we were always intended for each other and for no one else. I won't make *him* wait till December. I doubt if we even wait till dad and mother get home. And as for a honeymoon I will go with him to Long Beach or the Bronx Zoo, wherever he wants to take me.

After all this is the best way out of it, the only way. I won't have to say anything to Frank, he will guess when he sees me with Merle. And when I get home Sunday and Walter and Gordon call me up, I will invite them both to dinner and Merle can tell them himself, with two of them there it will only hurt each one half as much as if they were alone.

The train is due at 2:40, almost three hours from now. I can't wait. And what if it should be late? I can't stand it.

Zone of Quiet

"Well," said the Doctor briskly, "how do you feel?"

"Oh, I guess I'm all right," replied the man in bed. "I'm still kind of drowsy, that's all."

"You were under the anesthetic an hour and a half. It's no wonder you aren't wide awake yet. But you'll be better after a good night's rest, and I've left something with Miss Lyons that'll make you sleep. I'm going along now. Miss Lyons will take good care of you."

"I'm off at seven o'clock," said Miss Lyons. "I'm going to a show with my G. F. But Miss Halsey's all right. She's the night floor nurse. Anything you want, she'll get it for you. What can I give him to eat, Doctor?"

"Nothing at all; not till after I've been here tomorrow. He'll be better off without anything. Just see that he's kept quiet. Don't let him talk, and don't talk to him; that is, if you can help it."

"Help it!" said Miss Lyons. "Say, I can be old lady Sphinx herself when I want to! Sometimes I sit for hours—not alone, neither—and never say a word. Just think and think. And dream.

"I had a G. F. in Baltimore, where I took my training; she used to call me Dummy. Not because I'm dumb like some people—you know—but because I'd sit there and not say nothing. She'd say, 'A penny for your thoughts, Eleanor.' That's my first name—Eleanor."

"Well, I must run along. I'll see you in the morning."

"Good-by, Doctor," said the man in bed, as he went out.

"Good-by, Doctor Cox," said Miss Lyons as the door closed.

"He seems like an awful nice fella," said Miss Lyons. "And a good doctor, too. This is the first time I've been on a case with him. He gives a girl credit for having some sense. Most of these doctors treat us like they thought we were Mormons or something. Like Doctor Holland. I was on a case with him last week. He treated me like I was a Mormon or something. Finally, I told him, I said, 'I'm not as dumb as I look.' She died Friday night."

"Who?" asked the man in bed.

"The woman; the case I was on," said Miss Lyons.

"And what did the doctor say when you told him you weren't as dumb as you look?"

"I don't remember," said Miss Lyons. "He said, 'I hope not,' or something. What *could* he say? Gee! It's quarter to seven. I hadn't no idear it was so late. I must get busy and fix you up for the night. And I'll tell Miss Halsey to take good care of you. We're going to see 'What Price Glory?' I'm going with my G. F. Her B. F. gave her the tickets and he's going to meet us after the show and take us to supper.

"Marian—that's my G. F.—she's crazy wild about him. And he's crazy about her, to hear her tell it. But I said to her this noon—she called me up on the phone—I said to her, 'If he's so crazy about you, why don't he propose? He's got plenty of money and no strings tied to him, and as far as I can see there's no reason why he shouldn't marry you if he wants you as bad as you say he does.' So she said maybe he was going to ask her tonight. I told her, 'Don't be silly! Would he drag me along if he was going to ask you?'

"That about him having plenty of money, though, that's a joke. He told her he had and she believes him. I haven't met him yet, but he looks in his picture like he's lucky if he's getting twenty-five dollars a week. She thinks he must be rich because he's in Wall Street. I told her, I said, 'That being in Wall Street don't mean nothing. What does he do there? is the question. You know they have to have janitors in those buildings just the same like anywhere else.' But she thinks he's God or somebody.

"She keeps asking me if I don't think he's the best looking thing I ever saw. I tell her yes, sure, but between you and I, I don't believe anybody'd ever mistake him for Richard Barthelmess.

"Oh, say! I saw him the other day, coming out of the Algonquin! He's the best looking thing! Even better looking than on the screen. Roy Stewart."

"What about Roy Stewart?" asked the man in bed.

"Oh, he's the fella I was telling you about," said Miss Lyons. "He's my G. F.'s B. F."

"Maybe I'm a D. F. not to know, but would you tell me what a B. F. and G. F. are?"

"Well, you *are* dumb, aren't you!" said Miss Lyons. "A G. F., that's a girl friend, and a B. F. is a boy friend. I thought everybody knew that.

"I'm going out now and find Miss Halsey and tell her to be nice to you. But maybe I better not."

"Why not?" asked the man in bed.

"Oh, nothing. I was just thinking of something funny that happened last time I was on a case in this hospital. It was the day the man had been operated on and he was the best looking somebody you ever saw. So when I went off duty I told Miss Halsey to be nice to him, like I was going to tell her about you. And when I came back in the morning he was dead. Isn't that funny?"

"Very!"

"Well," said Miss Lyons, "did you have a good night? You look a lot better, anyway. How'd you like Miss Halsey? Did you notice her ankles? She's got pretty near the smallest ankles I ever saw. Cute. I remember one day Tyler—that's one of the internes—he said if he could just see our ankles, mine and Miss Halsey's, he wouldn't know which was which. Of course we don't look anything alike other ways. She's pretty close to thirty and—well, nobody'd ever take her for Julia Hoyt. Helen."

"Who's Helen?" asked the man in bed.

"Helen Halsey. Helen; that's her first name. She was engaged to a man in Boston. He was going to Tufts College. He was going to be a doctor. But he died. She still carries his picture with her. I tell her she's silly to mope about a man that's been dead four years. And besides a girl's a fool to marry a doctor. They've got too many alibis.

"When I marry somebody, he's got to be a somebody that has regular office hours like he's in Wall Street or somewhere. Then when he don't come home, he'll have to think up something better than being 'on a case.' I used to use that on my sister when we were living together. When I happened to be out late, I'd tell her I was on a case. She never knew the difference. Poor sis! She married a terrible oil can! But she didn't have the looks to get a real somebody. I'm making this for her. It's a bridge table cover for her birthday. She'll be twenty-nine. Don't that seem old?"

"Maybe to you; not to me," said the man in bed.

"You're about forty, aren't you?" said Miss Lyons.

"Just about."

"And how old would you say I am?"

"Twenty-three."

"I'm twenty-five," said Miss Lyons. "Twenty-five and forty. That's fifteen years' difference. But I know a married couple that the husband is forty-five and she's only twenty-four, and they get along fine."

"I'm married myself," said the man in bed.

"You would be!" said Miss Lyons. "The last four cases I've been on was all married men. But at that, I'd rather have any kind of a man than a woman. I hate women! I mean sick ones. They treat a nurse like a dog, especially a pretty nurse. What's that you're reading?"

" 'Vanity Fair,' " replied the man in bed.

" 'Vanity Fair.' I thought that was a magazine."

"Well, there's a magazine *and* a book. This is the book."

"Is it about a girl?"

"Yes."

"I haven't read it yet. I've been busy making this thing for my sister's birthday. She'll be twenty-nine. It's a bridge table cover. When you get that old, about all there is left is bridge or cross-word puzzles. Are you a puzzle fan? I did them religiously for a while, but I got sick of them. They put in such crazy words. Like one day they had a word with only three letters and it said 'A e-longated fish' and the first letter had to be an *e*. And only three letters. That *couldn't* be right! So I said if they put things wrong like that, what's the use? Life's too short. And we only live once. When you're dead, you stay a long time dead.

"That's what a B. F. of mine used to say. He was a caution! But he was crazy about me. I might of married him only for a G. F. telling him lies about me. And called herself my friend! Charley Pierce."

"Who's Charley Pierce?"

"That was my B. F. that the other girl lied to him about me. I told him, I said, 'Well, if you believe all them stories about me, maybe we better part once and for all. I don't want to be tied up to a somebody that believes all the dirt they hear about me.' So he said he didn't really believe it and if I would take him back he wouldn't quarrel with me no more. But I said I thought it was best for us to part. I got their announcement two years ago, while I was still in training in Baltimore."

"Did he marry the girl that lied to him about you?"

"Yes, the poor fish! And I bet he's satisfied! They're a match for each other! He was all right, though, at that, till he fell for her. He used to be so thoughtful of me, like I was his sister or something.

"I like a man to *respect* me. Most fellas wants to kiss you before they know your name.

"Golly! I'm sleepy this morning! And got a right to be, too. Do you know what time I got home last night, or this morning, rather? Well, it was half past three. What would mama say if she could see her little girl now! But we did have a good time. First we went to the show—'What Price Glory?'—I and my G. F.—and afterwards her B. F. met us and took us in a taxi down to Barney Gallant's. Peewee Byers has got the orchestra there now. Used to be with Whiteman's. Gee! How he can dance! I mean Roy."

"Your G. F.'s B. F.?"

"Yes, but I don't believe he's as crazy about her as she thinks he is. Anyway—but this is a secret—he took down the phone number of the hospital while Marian was out powdering her nose, and he said he'd give me a ring about noon. Gee! I'm sleepy! Roy Stewart!"

"Well," said Miss Lyons, "how's my patient? I'm twenty minutes late, but honest, it's a wonder I got up at all! Two nights in succession is too much for this child!"

"Barney Gallant's again?" asked the man in bed.

"No, but it was dancing, and pretty near as late. It'll be different tonight. I'm going to bed just the minute I get home. But I did have a dandy time. And I'm just crazy about a certain somebody."

"Roy Stewart?"

"How'd you guess it? But honest, he's wonderful! And so different than most of the fellas I've met. He says the craziest things, just keeps you in hysterics. We were talking about books and reading, and he asked me if I liked poetry—only he called it 'poultry'—and I said I was wild about it and Edgar M. Guest was just about my favorite, and then I asked him if he liked Kipling and what do you think he said? He said he didn't know; he'd never kipled.

"He's a scream! We just sat there in the house till half past eleven and didn't do nothing but just talk and the time went like we was at a show. He's better than a show. But finally I noticed how late it was and I asked him didn't he think he better be going and he said he'd go if I'd go with him, so I asked him where could we go at that hour of night, and he said he knew a road-house just a little ways away, and I didn't want to go, but he said we wouldn't stay for only just one dance, so I went with him. To the Jericho Inn.

"I don't know what the woman thought of me where I stay, going out that time of night. But he *is* such a wonderful dancer and such a perfect gentleman! Of course we had more than one dance and it was after two o'clock before I knew it. We had some gin, too, but he just kissed me once and that was when we said good night."

"What about your G. F., Marian? Does she know?"

"About Roy and I? No. I always say that what a person don't know don't hurt them. Besides, there's nothing *for* her to know—yet. But listen: If there was a chance in the world for her, if I thought he cared anything about her, I'd be the last one in the world to accept his intentions. I hope I'm not that kind! But as far as anything serious between them is concerned, well, it's cold. I happen to *know* that! She's not the girl for him.

"In the first place, while she's pretty in a way, her complexion's bad and her hair's scraggy and her figure, well, it's like some woman in the funny pictures. And she's not peppy enough for Roy. She'd rather stay home than do anything. Stay home! It'll be time enough for that when you can't get anybody to take you out.

"She'd never make a wife for him. He'll be a rich man in another year; that is, if things go right for him in Wall Street like he expects. And a man's as rich as he'll be wants a wife that can live up to it and entertain and step out once in a while. He don't want a wife that's a drag on him. And he's too good-looking for Marian. A fella as good-looking as him needs a pretty wife or the first thing you know some girl that is pretty will steal him off of you. But it's silly to talk about them marrying each other. He'd have to ask her first, and he's not going to. I know! So I don't feel at all like I'm trespassing.

"Anyway, you know the old saying, everything goes in love. And I—— But I'm keeping you from reading your book. Oh, yes; I almost forgot a T. L. that Miss Halsey said about you. Do you know what a T. L. is?"

"Yes."

"Well, then, you give me one and I'll give you this one."

"But I haven't talked to anybody but the Doctor. I can give you one from myself. He asked me how I liked you and I said all right."

"Well, that's better than nothing. Here's what Miss Halsey said: She said if you were shaved and fixed up, you wouldn't be bad. And now I'm going out and see if there's any mail for me. Most of my mail goes to where I live, but some of it comes here sometimes. What I'm looking for is a letter from the state board telling me if I passed my state examination. They ask you the craziest questions. Like 'Is ice a disinfectant?' Who cares! Nobody's going to waste ice to kill germs when there's so much of it needed in high-balls. Do you like high-balls? Roy says it spoils whisky to mix it with water. He takes it straight. He's a terror! But maybe you want to read."

"Good morning," said Miss Lyons. "Did you sleep good?"

"Not so good," said the man in bed. "I——"

"I bet you got more sleep than I did," said Miss Lyons. "He's the most persistent somebody I ever knew! I asked him last night, I said, 'Don't you never get tired of dancing?' So he said, well, he did get tired of dancing with some people, but there was others who he never got tired of dancing with them. So I said, 'Yes, Mr. Jollier, but I wasn't born yesterday and I know apple sauce when I hear it and I bet you've told that to fifty girls.' I guess he really did mean it, though.

"Of course most anybody'd rather dance with slender girls than stout girls. I remember a B. F. I had one time in Washington. He said dancing with me was just like dancing with nothing. That sounds like he was insulting me, but it was really a compliment. He meant it wasn't any effort to dance with me like with some girls. You take Marian, for instance, and while I'm crazy about her, still that don't make her a good dancer and dancing with her must be a good deal like moving the piano or something.

"I'd die if I was fat! People are always making jokes about fat people. And there's the old saying, 'Nobody loves a fat man.' And it's even worse with a girl. Besides people making jokes about them and don't want to dance with them and so forth, besides that they're always trying to reduce and can't eat what they want to. I bet, though, if I was fat, I'd eat everything in sight. Though I guess not, either. Because I hardly eat anything as it is. But they do make jokes about them.

"I'll never forget one day last winter, I was on a case in Great Neck and the man's wife was the fattest thing! So they had a radio in the house and one day she saw in the paper where Bugs Baer was going to talk on the radio and it would probably be awfully funny because he writes so crazy. Do you ever read his articles? But this woman, she was awfully sensitive about being fat and I nearly died sitting there with her listening to Bugs Baer, because his whole talk was all about some fat woman and he said the craziest things, but I couldn't laugh on account of she being there in the room with me. One thing he said was that the woman, this woman he was talking about, he said she was so fat that she wore a wrist watch on her thumb. Henry J. Belden."

"Who is Henry J. Belden? Is that the name of Bugs Baer's fat lady?"

"No, you crazy!" said Miss Lyons. "Mr. Belden was the case I was on in Great Neck. He died."

"It seems to me a good many of your cases die."

"Isn't it a scream!" said Miss Lyons. "But it's true; that is, it's been true lately. The last five cases I've been on has all died. Of course it's just luck, but the girls have been kidding me about it and calling me a jinx, and when Miss Halsey saw me here the evening of the day you was operated, she said, 'God help him!' That's the night floor nurse's name. But you're going to be mean and live through it and spoil my record, aren't you? I'm just kidding. Of course I want you to get all right.

"But it *is* queer, the way things have happened, and it's made me feel kind of creepy. And besides, I'm not like some of the girls and don't care. I get awfully fond of some of my cases and I hate to see them die, especially if they're men and not very sick and treat you half-way decent and don't yell for you the minute you go out of the room. There's only one case I was ever on where I didn't mind her dying and that was a woman. She had nephritis. Mrs. Judson.

"Do you want some gum? I chew it just when I'm nervous. And I always get nervous when I don't have enough sleep. You can bet I'll stay home tonight, B. F. or no B. F. But anyway he's got an engagement tonight, some directors' meeting or something. He's the busiest somebody in the world. And I told him last night, I said, 'I should think you'd need sleep, too, even more than I do because you have to have all your wits about you in your business or those big bankers would take advantage and rob you. You can't afford to be sleepy,' I told him.

"So he said, 'No, but of course it's all right for you, because if you go to sleep on your job, there's no danger of you doing any damage except maybe give one of your patients a bichloride of mercury tablet instead of an alcohol rub.' He's terrible! But you can't help from laughing.

"There was four of us in the party last night. He brought along his B. F. and another girl. She was just blah, but the B. F. wasn't so bad, only he insisted on me helping him drink a half a bottle of Scotch, and on top of gin, too. I guess I was the life of the party; that is, at first. Afterwards I got sick and it wasn't so good.

"But at first I was certainly going strong. And I guess I made quite a hit with Roy's B. F. He knows Marian, too, but he won't say anything, and if he does, I don't care. If she don't want to lose her beaus, she ought to know better than to introduce them to all the pretty girls in the world. I don't mean that I'm any Norma Talmadge, but at least—well—but I sure was sick when I *was* sick!

"I must give Marian a ring this noon. I haven't talked to her since the night she introduced me to him. I've been kind of scared. But I've got to find out what she knows. Or if she's sore at me. Though I don't see how she can be, do you? But maybe you want to read."

"I called Marian up, but I didn't get her. She's out of town but she'll be back tonight. She's been out on a case. Hudson, New York, That's where she went. The message was waiting for her when she got home the other night, the night she introduced me to Roy."

"Good morning," said Miss Lyons.
"Good morning," said the man in bed. "Did you sleep enough?"
"Yes," said Miss Lyons. "I mean no, not enough."
"Your eyes look bad. They almost look as if you'd been crying."
"Who? Me? It'd take more than—I mean, I'm not a baby! But go on and read your book."

"Well, good morning," said Miss Lyons. "And how's my patient? And this is the last morning I can call you that, isn't it? I think you're mean to get well so quick and leave me out of a job. I'm just kidding. I'm glad you're all right again, and I can use a little rest myself."

"Another big night?" asked the man in bed.

"Pretty big," said Miss Lyons. "And another one coming. But tomorrow I won't ever get up. Honest, I danced so much last night that I thought my feet would drop off. But he certainly is a dancing fool! And the nicest somebody to talk to that I've met since I came to this town. Not a smart Alex and not always trying to be funny like some people, but just nice. He understands. He seems to know just what you're thinking. George Morse."

"George Morse!" exclaimed the man in bed.

"Why yes," said Miss Lyons. "Do you know him?"

"No. But I thought you were talking about this Stewart, this Roy."

"Oh, him!" said Miss Lyons. "I should say not! He's private property; other people's property, not mine. He's engaged to my G. F. Marian. It happened day before yesterday, after she got home from Hudson. She was on a case up there. She told me about it night before last. I told her congratulations. Because I wouldn't hurt her feelings for the world! But heavens! what a mess she's going to be in, married to that dumb-bell. But of course some people can't be choosey. And I doubt if they ever get married unless some friend loans him the price of a license.

"He's got her believing he's in Wall Street, but I bet if he ever goes there at all, it's to sweep it. He's one of these kind of fellas that's got a great line for a little while, but you don't want to live with a clown. And I'd hate to marry a man that all he thinks about is to step out every night and dance and drink.

"I had a notion to tell her what I really thought. But that'd only of made her sore, or she'd of thought I was jealous or something. As if I couldn't of had him myself! Though even if he wasn't so awful, if I'd liked him instead of loathed him, I wouldn't of taken him from her on account of she being my G. F. And especially while she was out of town.

"He's the kind of a fella that'd marry a nurse in the hopes that some day he'd be an invalid. You know, that kind.

"But say—did you ever hear of J. P. Morgan and Company? That's where my B. F. works, and he don't claim to own it neither. George Morse.

"Haven't you finished that book yet?"

PART THREE

Success Story, U.S.A.

Champion

Midge Kelly scored his first knockout when he was seventeen. The knockee was his brother Connie, three years his junior and a cripple. The purse was a half dollar given to the younger Kelly by a lady whose electric had just missed bumping his soul from his frail little body.

Connie did not know Midge was in the house, else he never would have risked laying the prize on the arm of the least comfortable chair in the room, the better to observe its shining beauty. As Midge entered from the kitchen, the crippled boy covered the coin with his hand, but the movement lacked the speed requisite to escape his brother's quick eye.

"Watcha got there?" demanded Midge.

"Nothin'," said Connie.

"You're a one legged liar!" said Midge.

He strode over to his brother's chair and grasped the hand that concealed the coin.

"Let loose!" he ordered.

Connie began to cry.

"Let loose and shut up your noise," said the elder, and jerked his brother's hand from the chair arm.

The coin fell onto the bare floor. Midge pounced on it. His weak mouth widened in a triumphant smile.

"Nothin', huh?" he said. "All right, if it's nothin' you don't want it."

"Give that back," sobbed the younger.

"I'll give you a red nose, you little sneak! Where'd you steal it?"

"I didn't steal it. It's mine. A lady give it to me after she pretty near hit me with a car."

"It's a crime she missed you," said Midge.

Midge started for the front door. The cripple picked up his

crutch, rose from his chair with difficulty, and, still sobbing, came toward Midge. The latter heard him and stopped.

"You better stay where you're at," he said.

"I want my money," cried the boy.

"I know what you want," said Midge.

Doubling up the fist that held the half dollar, he landed with all his strength on his brother's mouth. Connie fell to the floor with a thud, the crutch tumbling on top of him. Midge stood beside the prostrate form.

"Is that enough?" he said. "Or do you want this, too?"

And he kicked him in the crippled leg.

"I guess that'll hold you," he said.

There was no response from the boy on the floor. Midge looked at him a moment, then at the coin in his hand, and then went out into the street, whistling.

An hour later, when Mrs. Kelly came home from her day's work at Faulkner's Steam Laundry, she found Connie on the floor, moaning. Dropping on her knees beside him, she called him by name a score of times. Then she got up and, pale as a ghost, dashed from the house. Dr. Ryan left the Kelly abode about dusk and walked toward Halsted Street. Mrs. Dorgan spied him as he passed her gate.

"Who's sick, Doctor?" she called.

"Poor little Connie," he replied. "He had a bad fall."

"How did it happen?"

"I can't say for sure, Margaret, but I'd almost bet he was knocked down."

"Knocked down!" exclaimed Mrs. Dorgan.

"Why, who—?"

"Have you seen the other one lately?"

"Michael? No, not since mornin'. You can't be thinkin'——"

"I wouldn't put it past him, Margaret," said the doctor gravely. "The lad's mouth is swollen and cut, and his poor, skinny little leg is bruised. He surely didn't do it to himself and I think Helen suspects the other one."

"Lord save us!" said Mrs. Dorgan. "I'll run over and see if I can help."

"That's a good woman," said Doctor Ryan, and went on down the street.

Near midnight, when Midge came home, his mother was sitting at Connie's bedside. She did not look up.

"Well," said Midge, "what's the matter?"

She remained silent. Midge repeated his question.

"Michael, you know what's the matter," she said at length.

"I don't know nothin," said Midge.

"Don't lie to me, Michael. What did you do to your brother?"

"Nothin'."

"You hit him."

"Well, then, I hit him. What of it? It ain't the first time."

Her lips pressed tightly together, her face like chalk, Ellen Kelly rose from her chair and made straight for him. Midge backed against the door.

"Lay off'n me, Ma. I don't want to fight no woman."

Still she came on breathing heavily.

"Stop where you're at, Ma," he warned.

There was a brief struggle and Midge's mother lay on the floor before him.

"You ain't hurt, Ma. You're lucky I didn't land good. And I told you to lay off'n me."

"God forgive you, Michael!"

Midge found Hap Collins in the showdown game at the Royal.

"Come on out a minute," he said.

Hap followed him out on the walk.

"I'm leavin' town for a w'ile," said Midge.

"What for?"

"Well, we had a little run-in up to the house. The kid stole a half buck off'n me, and when I went after it he cracked me with his crutch. So I nailed him. And the old lady came at me with a chair and I took it off'n her and she fell down."

"How is Connie hurt?"

"Not bad."

"What are you runnin' away for?"

"Who the hell said I was runnin' away? I'm sick and tired o' gettin' picked on; that's all. So I'm leavin' for a w'ile and I want a piece o' money."

"I ain't only got six bits," said Happy.

"You're in bad shape, ain't you? Well, come through with it."

Happy came through.

"You oughtn't to hit the kid," he said.

"I ain't astin' you who can I hit," snarled Midge. "You try to put somethin' over on me and you'll get the same dose. I'm goin' now."

"Go as far as you like," said Happy, but not until he was sure that Kelly was out of hearing.

Early the following morning, Midge boarded a train for Milwaukee. He had no ticket, but no one knew the difference. The conductor remained in the caboose.

On a night six months later, Midge hurried out of the "stage door" of the Star Boxing Club and made for Duane's saloon, two blocks away. In his pocket were twelve dollars, his reward for having battered up one Demon Dempsey through the six rounds of the first preliminary.

It was Midge's first professional engagement in the manly art. Also it was the first time in weeks that he had earned twelve dollars.

On the way to Duane's he had to pass Niemann's. He pulled his cap over his eyes and increased his pace until he had gone by. Inside Niemann's stood a trusting bartender, who for ten days had staked Midge to drinks and allowed him to ravage the lunch on a promise to come in and settle the moment he was paid for the "prelim."

Midge strode into Duane's and aroused the napping bartender by slapping a silver dollar on the festive board.

"Gimme a shot," said Midge.

The shooting continued until the wind-up at the Star was over and part of the fight crowd joined Midge in front of Duane's bar. A youth in the early twenties, standing next to young Kelly, finally summoned sufficient courage to address him.

"Wasn't you in the first bout?" he ventured.

"Yeh," Midge replied.

"My name's Hersch," said the other.

Midge received the startling information in silence.

"I don't want to butt in," continued Mr. Hersch, "but I'd like to buy you a drink."

"All right," said Midge, "but don't overstrain yourself."

Mr. Hersch laughed uproariously and beckoned to the bartender.

"You certainly gave that wop a trimmin' to-night," said the buyer of the drink, when they had been served. "I thought you'd kill him."

"I would if I hadn't let up," Midge replied. "I'll kill 'em all."

"You got the wallop all right," the other said admiringly.

"Have I got the wallop?" said Midge. "Say, I can kick like a mule. Did you notice them muscles in my shoulders?"

"Notice 'em? I couldn't help from noticin' 'em," said Hersch. "I says to the fella settin' alongside o' me, I says: 'Look at them shoulders! No wonder he can hit,' I says to him."

"Just let me land and it's good-by, baby," said Midge. "I'll kill 'em all."

The oral manslaughter continued until Duane's closed for the night. At parting, Midge and his new friend shook hands and arranged for a meeting the following evening.

For nearly a week the two were together almost constantly. It was Hersch's pleasant rôle to listen to Midge's modest revelations concerning himself, and to buy every time Midge's glass was empty. But there came an evening when Hersch regretfully announced that he must go home to supper.

"I got a date for eight bells," he confided. "I could stick till then, only I must clean up and put on the Sunday clo'es, 'cause she's the prettiest little thing in Milwaukee."

"Can't you fix it for two?" asked Midge.

"I don't know who to get," Hersch replied. "Wait, though. I got a sister and if she ain't busy, it'll be O.K. She's no bum for looks herself."

So it came about that Midge and Emma Hersch and Emma's brother and the prettiest little thing in Milwaukee foregathered at Wall's and danced half the night away. And Midge and Emma danced every dance together, for though every little onestep seemed to induce a new thirst of its own, Lou Hersch stayed too sober to dance with his own sister.

The next day, penniless at last in spite of his phenomenal ability to make someone else settle, Midge Kelly sought out Doc Hammond, matchmaker for the Star, and asked to be booked for the next show.

"I could put you on with Tracy for the next bout," said Doc.

"What's they in it?" asked Midge.

"Twenty if you cop," Doc told him.

"Have a heart," protested Midge. "Didn't I look good the other night?"

"You looked all right. But you aren't Freddie Welsh yet by a consid'able margin."

"I ain't scared of Freddie Welsh or none of 'em," said Midge.

"Well, we don't pay our boxers by the size of their chests," Doc said. "I'm offerin' you this Tracy bout. Take it or leave it."

"All right; I'm on," said Midge, and he passed a pleasant afternoon at Duane's on the strength of his booking.

Young Tracy's manager came to Midge the night before the show. "How do you feel about this go?" he asked.

"Me?" said Midge. "I feel all right. What do you mean, how do I feel?"

"I mean," said Tracy's manager, "that we're mighty anxious to win, 'cause the boy's got a chanct in Philly if he cops this one."

"What's your proposition?" asked Midge.

"Fifty bucks," said Tracy's manager.

"What do you think I am, a crook? Me lay down for fifty bucks. Not me!"

"Seventy-five, then," said Tracy's manager.

The market closed on eighty and the details were agreed on in short order. And the next night Midge was stopped in the second round by a terrific slap on the forearm.

This time Midge passed up both Niemann's and Duane's, having a sizable account at each place, and sought his refreshment at Stein's farther down the street.

When the profits of his deal with Tracy were gone, he learned, by first-hand information from Doc Hammond and the match-makers at the other "clubs," that he was no longer desired for even the cheapest of preliminaries. There was no danger of his starving or dying of thirst while Emma and Lou Hersch lived. But he made up his mind, four months after his defeat by Young Tracy, that Milwaukee was not the ideal place for him to live.

"I can lick the best of 'em," he reasoned, "but there ain't no more chanct for me here. I can maybe go east and get on some-wheres. And besides——"

But just after Midge had purchased a ticket to Chicago with

the money he had "borrowed" from Emma Hersch "to buy shoes," a heavy hand was laid on his shoulders and he turned to face two strangers.

"Where are you goin', Kelly?" inquired the owner of the heavy hand.

"Nowheres," said Midge. "What the hell do you care?"

The other stranger spoke:

"Kelly, I'm employed by Emma Hersch's mother to see that you do right by her. And we want you to stay here till you've done it."

"You won't get nothin' but the worst of it, monkeying with me," said Midge.

Nevertheless, he did not depart for Chicago that night. Two days later, Emma Hersch became Mrs. Kelly, and the gift of the groom, when once they were alone, was a crushing blow on the bride's pale cheek.

Next morning, Midge left Milwaukee as he had entered it— by fast freight.

"They's no use kiddin' ourself any more," said Tommy Haley. "He might get down to thirty-seven in a pinch, but if he done below that a mouse could stop him. He's a welter; that's what he is and he knows it as well as I do. He's growed like a weed in the last six mont's. I told him, I says, 'If you don't quit growin' they won't be nobody for you to box, only Willard and them.' He says, 'Well, I wouldn't run away from Willard if I weighed twenty pounds more.''

"He must hate himself," said Tommy's brother.

"I never seen a good one that didn't," said Tommy. "And Midge is a good one; don't make no mistake about that. I wisht we could of got Welsh before the kid growed so big. But it's too late now. I won't make no holler, though, if we can match him up with the Dutchman."

"Who do you mean?"

"Young Goetz, the welter champ. We mightn't not get so much dough for the bout itself, but it'd roll in afterward. What a drawin' card we'd be, 'cause the people pays their money to see the fella with the wallop, and that's Midge. And we'd keep the title just as long as Midge could make the weight."

"Can't you land no match with Goetz?"

"Sure, 'cause he needs the money. But I've went careful with the kid so far and look at the results I got! So what's the use of takin' a chanct? The kid's comin' every minute and Goetz is goin' back faster'n big Johnson did. I think we could lick him now; I'd bet my life on it. But six mont's from now they won't be no risk. He'll of licked hisself before that time. Then all as we'll have to do is sign up with him and wait for the referee to stop it. But Midge is so crazy to get at him now that I can't hardly hold him back."

The brothers Haley were lunching in a Boston hotel. Dan had come down from Holyoke to visit with Tommy and to watch the latter's protégé go twelve rounds, or less, with Bud Cross. The bout promised little in the way of a contest, for Midge had twice stopped the Baltimore youth and Bud's reputation for gameness was all that had earned him the date. The fans were willing to pay the price to see Midge's hay-making left, but they wanted to see it used on an opponent who would not jump out of the ring the first time he felt its crushing force. But Cross was such an opponent, and his willingness to stop boxing-gloves with his eyes, ears, nose and throat had long enabled him to escape the horrors of honest labor. A game boy was Bud, and he showed it in his battered, swollen, dis-colored face.

"I should think," said Dan Haley, "that the kid'd do whatever you tell him after all you done for him."

"Well," said Tommy, "he's took my dope pretty straight so far, but he's so sure of hisself that he can't see no reason for waitin'. He'll do what I say, though; he'd be a sucker not to."

"You got a contrac' with him?"

"No, I don't need no contrac'. He knows it was me that drug him out o' the gutter and he ain't goin' to turn me down now, when he's got the dough and bound to get more. Where'd he of been at if I hadn't listened to him when he first come to me? That's pretty near two years ago now, but it seems like last week. I was settin' in the s'loon acrost from the Pleasant Club in Philly, waitin' for McCann to count the dough and come over, when this little bum blowed in and tried to stand the house off for a drink. They told him nothin' doin' and to beat it out o' there, and then he seen me and come over to where I was settin' and ast me wasn't I a boxin' man and I told him who I was. Then he ast me for money to buy a shot and I told him to set down and I'd buy it for him.

"Then we got talkin' things over and he told me his name and told me about fightin' a couple o' prelims out to Milwaukee. So I says, 'Well, boy, I don't know how good or how rotten you are, but you won't never get nowheres trainin' on that stuff.' So he says he'd cut it out if he could get on in a bout and I says I would give him a chanct if he played square with me and didn't touch no more to drink. So we shook hands and I took him up to the hotel with me and give him a bath and the next day I bought him some clo'es. And I staked him to eats and sleeps for over six weeks. He had a hard time breakin' away from the polish, but finally I thought he was fit and I give him his chanct. He went on with Smiley Sayer and stopped him so quick that Smiley thought sure he was poisoned.

"Well, you know what he's did since. The only beatin' in his record was by Tracy in Milwaukee before I got hold of him, and he's licked Tracy three times in the last year.

"I've gave him all the best of it in a money way and he's got seven thousand bucks in cold storage. How's that for a kid that was in the gutter two years ago? And he'd have still more yet if he wasn't so nuts over clo'es and got to stop at the good hotels and so forth."

"Where's his home at?"

"Well, he ain't really got no home. He came from Chicago and his mother canned him out o' the house for bein' no good. She give him a raw deal, I guess, and he says he won't have nothin' to do with her unlest she comes to him first. She's got a pile o' money, he says, so he ain't worryin' about her."

The gentleman under discussion entered the café and swaggered to Tommy's table, while the whole room turned to look.

Midge was the picture of health despite a slightly colored eye and an ear that seemed to have no opening. But perhaps it was not his healthiness that drew all eyes. His diamond horse-shoe tie pin, his purple cross-striped shirt, his orange shoes and his light blue suit fairly screamed for attention.

"Where you been?" he asked Tommy. "I been lookin' all over for you."

"Set down," said his manager.

"No time," said Midge. "I'm goin' down to the w'arf and see 'em unload the fish."

"Shake hands with my brother Dan," said Tommy.

Midge shook with the Holyoke Haley.

"If you're Tommy's brother, you're O. K. with me," said Midge, and the brothers beamed with pleasure.

Dan moistened his lips and murmured an embarrassed reply, but it was lost on the young gladiator.

"Leave me take twenty," Midge was saying. "I prob'ly won't need it, but I don't like to be caught short."

Tommy parted with a twenty dollar bill and recorded the transaction in a small black book the insurance company had given him for Christmas.

"But," he said, "it won't cost you no twenty to look at them fish. Want me to go along?"

"No," said Midge hastily. "You and your brother here prob'ly got a lot to say to each other."

"Well," said Tommy, "don't take no bad money and don't get lost. And you better be back at four o'clock and lay down a w'ile."

"I don't need no rest to beat this guy," said Midge. "He'll do enough layin' down for the both of us."

And laughing even more than the jest called for, he strode out through the fire of admiring and startled glances.

The corner of Boylston and Tremont was the nearest Midge got to the wharf, but the lady awaiting him was doubtless a more dazzling sight than the catch of the luckiest Massachusetts fisherman. She could talk, too—probably better than the fish.

"O you Kid!" she said, flashing a few silver teeth among the gold. "O you fighting man!"

Midge smiled up at her.

"We'll go somewheres and get a drink," he said. "One won't hurt."

In New Orleans, five months after he had rearranged the map of Bud Cross for the third time, Midge finished training for his championship bout with the Dutchman.

Back in his hotel after the final workout, Midge stopped to chat with some of the boys from up north, who had made the long trip to see a champion dethroned, for the result of this bout was so nearly a foregone conclusion that even the experts had guessed it.

Tommy Haley secured the key and the mail and ascended to the Kelly suite. He was bathing when Midge came in, half hour later.

"Any mail?" asked Midge.

"There on the bed," replied Tommy from the tub.

Midge picked up the stack of letters and post-cards and glanced them over. From the pile he sorted out three letters and laid them on the table. The rest he tossed into the waste-basket. Then he picked up the three and sat for a few moments holding them, while his eyes gazed off into space. At length he looked again at the three unopened letters in his hand; then he put one in his pocket and tossed the other two at the basket. They missed their target and fell on the floor.

"Hell!" said Midge, and stooping over picked them up.

He opened one postmarked Milwaukee and read:

DEAR HUSBAND:

I have wrote to you so manny times and got no anser and I dont know if you ever got them, so I am writeing again in the hopes you will get this letter and anser. I dont like to bother you with my trubles and I would not only for the baby and I am not asking you should write to me but only send a little money and I am not asking for myself but the baby has not been well a day sence last Aug. and the dr. told me she cant live much longer unless I give her better food and thats impossible the way things are. Lou has not been working for a year and what I make dont hardley pay for the rent. I am not asking for you to give me any money, but only you should send what I loaned when convenient and I think it amts. to about $36.00. Please try and send that amt. and it will help me, but if you cant send the whole amt. try and send me something.

Your wife,

EMMA.

Midge tore the letter into a hundred pieces and scattered them over the floor.

"Money, money, money!" he said. "They must think I'm made o' money. I s'pose the old woman's after it too."

He opened his mother's letter:

dear Michael Connie wonted me to rite and say you must beet the dutch-man and he is sur you will and wonted me to say we wont you to rite and tell us about it, but I gess you havent no time to rite or we herd from you long beffore this but I wish you would rite jest a line or 2 boy becaus it wuld be better for Connie than a barl of medisin. It wuld help me to keep things going if you send me money now and then when you can spair it but if you cant send no money try and fine time to rite a letter onley a few lines and it will please Connie. jest think boy he hasent got out of bed in over 3 yrs. Connie says good luck.

Your Mother,
Ellen F. Kelly.

"I thought so," said Midge. "They're all alike."
The third letter was from New York. It read:

Hon:—This is the last letter you will get from me before your champ, but I will send you a telegram Saturday, but I can't say as much in a telegram as in a letter and I am writeing this to let you know I am thinking of you and praying for good luck.

Lick him good hon and don't wait no longer than you have to and don't forget to wire me as soon as its over. Give him that little old left of yours on the nose hon and don't be afraid of spoiling his good looks because he couldn't be no homlier than he is. But don't let him spoil my baby's pretty face. You won't will you hon.

Well hon I would give anything to be there and see it, but I guess you love Haley better than me or you wouldn't let him keep me away. But when your champ hon we can do as we please and tell Haley to go to the devil.

Well hon I will send you a telegram Saturday and I almost forgot to tell you I will need some more money, a couple hundred say and you will have to wire it to me as soon as you get this. You will won't you hon.

I will send you a telegram Saturday and remember hon I am pulling for you.

Well good-by sweetheart and good luck.

Grace.

"They're all alike," said Midge. "Money, money, money."

Tommy Haley, shining from his ablutions, came in from the adjoining room.

"Thought you'd be layin' down," he said.

"I'm goin' to," said Midge, unbuttoning his orange shoes.

"I'll call you at six and you can eat up here without no bugs to pester you. I got to go down and give them birds their tickets."

"Did you hear from Goldberg?" asked Midge.

"Didn't I tell you? Sure; fifteen weeks at five hundred, if we win. And we can get a guarantee o' twelve thousand, with privileges either in New York or Milwaukee."

"Who with?"

"Anybody that'll stand up in front of you. You don't care who it is, do you?"

"Not me. I'll make 'em all look like a monkey."

"Well you better lay down a w'ile."

"Oh, say, wire two hundred to Grace for me, will you? Right away; the New York address."

"Two hundred! You just sent her three hundred last Sunday."

"Well, what the hell do you care?"

"All right, all right. Don't get sore about it. Anything else?"

"That's all," said Midge, and dropped onto the bed.

"And I want the deed done before I come back," said Grace as she rose from the table. "You won't fall down on me, will you, hon?"

"Leave it to me," said Midge. "And don't spend no more than you have to."

Grace smiled a farewell and left the café. Midge continued to sip his coffee and read his paper.

They were in Chicago and they were in the middle of Midge's first week in vaudeville. He had come straight north to reap the rewards of his glorious victory over the broken down Dutchman. A fortnight had been spent in learning his act, which consisted of a gymnastic exhibition and a ten minutes' monologue on the various excellences of Midge Kelly. And now he was twice daily turning 'em away from the Madison Theater.

His breakfast over and his paper read, Midge sauntered into the lobby and asked for his key. He then beckoned to a bell-boy, who had been hoping for that very honor.

"Find Haley, Tommy Haley," said Midge. "Tell him to come up to my room."

"Yes, sir, Mr. Kelly," said the boy, and proceeded to break all his former records for diligence.

Midge was looking out of his seventh-story window when Tommy answered the summons.

"What'll it be?" inquired his manager.

There was a pause before Midge replied.

"Haley," he said, "twenty-five per cent's a whole lot o' money."

"I guess I got it comin', ain't I?" said Tommy.

"I don't see how you figger it. I don't see where you're worth it to me."

"Well," said Tommy, "I didn't expect nothin' like this. I thought you was satisfied with the bargain. I don't want to beat nobody out o' nothin', but I don't see where you could have got anybody else that would of did all I done for you."

"Sure, that's all right," said the champion. "You done a lot for me in Philly. And you got good money for it, didn't you?"

"I ain't makin' no holler. Still and all, the big money's still ahead of us yet. And if it hadn't of been for me, you wouldn't of never got within grabbin' distance."

"Oh, I guess I could of went along all right," said Midge. "Who was it that hung that left on the Dutchman's jaw, me or you?"

"Yes, but you wouldn't been in the ring with the Dutchman if it wasn't for how I handled you."

"Well, this won't get us nowheres. The idear is that you ain't worth no twenty-five per cent now and it don't make no diff'rence what come off a year or two ago."

"Don't it?" said Tommy. "I'd say it made a whole lot of difference."

"Well, I say it don't and I guess that settles it."

"Look here, Midge," Tommy said, "I thought I was fair with you, but if you don't think so, I'm willin' to hear what you think is fair. I don't want nobody callin' me a Sherlock. Let's go down to business and sign up a contrac'. What's your figger?"

"I ain't namin' no figger," Midge replied. "I'm sayin' that twenty-five's too much. Now what are you willin' to take?"

"How about twenty?"

"Twenty's too much," said Kelly.

"What ain't too much?" asked Tommy.

"Well, Haley, I might as well give it to you straight. They ain't nothin' that ain't too much."

"You mean you don't want me at no figger?"

"That's the idear."

There was a minute's silence. Then Tommy Haley walked toward the door.

"Midge," he said, in a choking voice, "you're makin' a big mistake, boy. You can't throw down your best friends and get away with it. That damn woman will ruin you."

Midge sprang from his seat.

"You shut your mouth!" he stormed. "Get out o' here before they have to carry you out. You been spongin' off o' me long enough. Say one more word about the girl or about anything else and you'll get what the Dutchman got. Now get out!"

And Tommy Haley, having a very vivid memory of the Dutchman's face as he fell, got out.

Grace came in later, dropped her numerous bundles on the lounge and perched herself on the arm of Midge's chair.

"Well?" she said.

"Well," said Midge, "I got rid of him."

"Good boy!" said Grace. "And now I think you might give me that twenty-five per cent."

"Besides the seventy-five you're already gettin'?" said Midge.

"Don't be no grouch, hon. You don't look pretty when you're grouchy."

"It ain't my business to look pretty," Midge replied.

"Wait till you see how I look with the stuff I bought this mornin'!"

Midge glanced at the bundles on the lounge.

"There's Haley's twenty-five per cent," he said, "and then some."

The champion did not remain long without a manager. Haley's successor was none other than Jerome Harris, who saw in Midge a better meal ticket than his popular-priced musical show had been.

The contract, giving Mr. Harris twenty-five per cent of Midge's earnings, was signed in Detroit the week after Tommy Haley had heard his dismissal read. It had taken Midge just six days to learn that a popular actor cannot get on without the ministrations of a man who thinks, talks and means business. At first Grace objected to the new member of the firm, but when Mr. Harris had demanded and secured from the vaudeville people a one-hundred dollar increase in Midge's weekly stipend, she was convinced that the champion had acted for the best.

"You and my missus will have some great old times," Harris told Grace. "I'd of wired her to join us here, only I seen the Kid's bookin' takes us to Milwaukee next week, and that's where she is."

But when they were introduced in the Milwaukee hotel, Grace admitted to herself that her feeling for Mrs. Harris could hardly be called love at first sight. Midge, on the contrary, gave his new manager's wife the many times over and seemed loath to end the feast of his eyes.

"Some doll," he said to Grace when they were alone.

"Doll is right," the lady replied, "and sawdust where her brains ought to be."

"I'm li'ble to steal that baby," said Midge, and he smiled as he noted the effect of his words on his audience's face.

On Tuesday of the Milwaukee week the champion successfully defended his title in a bout that the newspapers never reported. Midge was alone in his room that morning when a visitor entered without knocking. The visitor was Lou Hersch.

Midge turned white at sight of him.

"What do you want?" he demanded.

"I guess you know," said Lou Hersch. "Your wife's starvin' to death and your baby's starvin' to death and I'm starvin' to death. And you're dirty with money."

"Listen," said Midge, "if it wasn't for you, I wouldn't never saw your sister. And, if you ain't man enough to hold a job, what's that to me? The best thing you can do is keep away from me."

"You give me a piece o' money and I'll go."

Midge's reply to the ultimatum was a straight right to his brother-in-law's narrow chest.

"Take that home to your sister."

And after Lou Hersch had picked himself up and slunk away, Midge thought: "It's lucky I didn't give him my left or I'd of croaked him. And if I'd hit him in the stomach, I'd of broke his spine."

There was a party after each evening performance during the Milwaukee engagement. The wine flowed freely and Midge had more of it than Tommy Haley ever would have permitted him. Mr. Harris offered no objection, which was possibly just as well for his own physical comfort.

In the dancing between drinks, Midge had his new manager's wife for a partner as often as Grace. The latter's face as she floundered round in the arms of the portly Harris, belied her frequent protestations that she was having the time of her life.

Several times that week, Midge thought Grace was on the point of starting the quarrel he hoped to have. But it was not until Friday night that she accommodated. He and Mrs. Harris had disappeared after the matinee and when Grace saw him again at the close of the night show, she came to the point at once.

"What are you tryin' to pull off?" she demanded.

"It's none o' your business, is it?" said Midge.

"You bet it's my business; mine and Harris's. You cut it short or you'll find out."

"Listen," said Midge, "have you got a mortgage on me or somethin'? You talk like we was married."

"We're goin' to be, too. And to-morrow's as good a time as any."

"Just about," Midge said. "You got as much chanct o' marryin' me to-morrow as the next day or next year and that ain't no chanct at all."

"We'll find out," said Grace.

"You're the one that's got somethin' to find out."

"What do you mean?"

"I mean I'm married already."

"You lie!"

"You think so, do you? Well, s'pose you go to this here address and get acquainted with my missus."

Midge scrawled a number on a piece of paper and handed it to her. She stared at it unseeingly.

"Well," said Midge. "I ain't kiddin' you. You go there and ask for Mrs. Michael Kelly, and if you don't find her, I'll marry you to-morrow before breakfast."

Still Grace stared at the scrap of paper. To Midge it seemed an age before she spoke again.

"You lied to me all this w'ile."

"You never ast me was I married. What's more, what the hell

diff'rence did it make to you? You got a split, didn't you? Better'n fifty-fifty."

He started away.

"Where you goin'?"

"I'm goin' to meet Harris and his wife."

"I'm goin' with you. You're not goin' to shake me now."

"Yes, I am, too," said Midge quietly. "When I leave town to-morrow night, you're going to stay here. And if I see where you're goin' to make a fuss, I'll put you in a hospital where they'll keep you quiet. You can get your stuff to-morrow mornin' and I'll slip you a hundred bucks. And then I don't want to see no more o' you. And don't try and tag along now or I'll have to add another K. O. to the old record."

When Grace returned to the hotel that night, she discovered that Midge and the Harrises had moved to another. And when Midge left town the following night, he was again without a manager, and Mr. Harris was without a wife.

Three days prior to Midge Kelly's ten-round bout with Young Milton in New York City, the sporting editor of *The News* assigned Joe Morgan to write two or three thousand words about the champion to run with a picture lay-out for Sunday.

Joe Morgan dropped in at Midge's training quarters Friday afternoon. Midge, he learned, was doing road work, but Midge's manager, Wallie Adams, stood ready and willing to supply reams of dope about the greatest fighter of the age.

"Let's hear what you've got," said Joe, "and then I'll try to fix up something."

So Wallie stepped on the accelerator of his imagination and shot away.

"Just a kid; that's all he is; a regular boy. Get what I mean? Don't know the meanin' o' bad habits. Never tasted liquor in his life and would prob'bly get sick if he smelled it. Clean livin' put him up where he's at. Get what I mean? And modest and unassumin' as a school girl. He's so quiet you wouldn't never know he was round. And he'd go to jail before he'd talk about himself.

"No job at all to get him in shape, 'cause he's always that way. The only trouble we have with him is gettin' him to light into

these poor bums they match him up with. He's scared he'll hurt
somebody. Get what I mean? He's tickled to death over this match
with Milton, 'cause everybody says Milton can stand the gaff.
Midge'll maybe be able to cut loose a little this time. But the last
two bouts he had, the guys hadn't no business in the ring with
him, and he was holdin' back all the w'ile for the fear he'd kill
somebody. Get what I mean?"

"Is he married?" inquired Joe.

"Say, you'd think he was married to hear him rave about them
kiddies he's got. His fam'ly's up in Canada to their summer home
and Midge is wild to get up there with 'em. He thinks more o'
that wife and them kiddies than all the money in the world. Get
what I mean?"

"How many children has he?"

"I don't know, four or five, I guess. All boys and every one of
'em a dead ringer for their dad."

"Is his father living?"

"No, the old man died when he was a kid. But he's got a grand
old mother and a kid brother out in Chi. They're the first ones
he thinks about after a match, them and his wife and kiddies.
And he don't forget to send the old woman a thousand bucks
after every bout. He's goin to buy her a new home as soon as they
pay him off for this match."

"How about his brother? Is he going to tackle the game?"

"Sure, and Midge says he'll be a champion before he's twenty
years old. They're a fightin' fam'ly and all of 'em honest and
straight as a die. Get what I mean? A fella that I can't tell you
his name come to Midge in Milwaukee onct and wanted him to
throw a fight and Midge give him such a trimmin' in the street
that he couldn't go on that night. That's the kind he is. Get what
I mean?"

Joe Morgan hung around the camp until Midge and his trainers
returned.

"One o' the boys from *The News*," said Wallie by way of introduction. "I been givin' him your fam'ly hist'ry."

"Did he give you good dope?" he inquired.

"He's some historian," said Joe.

"Don't call me no names," said Wallie smiling. "Call us up if they's anything more you want. And keep your eyes on us Monday night. Get what I mean?"

The story in Sunday's *News* was read by thousands of lovers of the manly art. It was well written and full of human interest. Its slight inaccuracies went unchallenged, though three readers, besides Wallie Adams and Midge Kelly, saw and recognized them. The three were Grace, Tommy Haley and Jerome Harris and the comments they made were not for publication.

Neither the Mrs. Kelly in Chicago nor the Mrs. Kelly in Milwaukee knew that there was such a paper as the New York *News*. And even if they had known of it and that it contained two columns of reading matter about Midge, neither mother nor wife could have bought it. For *The News* on Sunday is a nickel a copy.

Joe Morgan could have written more accurately, no doubt, if instead of Wallie Adams, he had interviewed Ellen Kelly and Connie Kelly and Emma Kelly and Lou Hersch and Grace and Jerome Harris and Tommy Haley and Hap Collins and two or three Milwaukee bartenders.

But a story built on their evidence would never have passed the sporting editor.

"Suppose you can prove it," that gentleman would have said, "It wouldn't get us anything but abuse to print it. The people don't want to see him knocked. He's champion."

A Caddy's Diary

Wed. Apr. 12.

I am 16 of age and am a caddy at the Pleasant View Golf Club but only temporary as I expect to soon land a job some wheres as asst pro as my game is good enough now to be a pro but to young looking. My pal Joe Bean also says I have not got enough swell head to make a good pro but suppose that will come in time, Joe is a wise cracker.

But first will put down how I come to be writeing this diary, we have got a member name Mr Colby who writes articles in the news-papers and I hope for his sakes that he is a better writer then he plays golf but any way I cadded for him a good many times last yr and today he was out for the first time this yr and I cadded for him and we got talking about this in that and something was mentioned in regards to the golf articles by Alex Laird that comes out every Sun in the paper Mr Colby writes his articles for so I asked Mr Colby did he know how much Laird got paid for the articles and he said he did not know but supposed that Laird had to split 50-50 with who ever wrote the articles for him. So I said don't he write the articles himself and Mr Colby said why no he guessed not. Laird may be a master mind in regards to golf he said, but that is no sign he can write about it as very few men can write decent let alone a pro. Writeing is a nag.

How do you learn it I asked him.

Well he said read what other people writes and study them and write things yourself, and maybe you will get on to the nag and maybe you wont.

Well Mr Colby I said do you think I could get on to it?

Why he said smileing I did not know that was your ambition to be a writer.

Not exactly was my reply, but I am going to be a golf pro myself and maybe some day I will get good enough so as the papers will want I should write them articles and if I can learn to write them myself why I will not have to hire another writer and split with them.

Well said Mr Colby smileing you have certainly got the right temperament for a pro, they are all big hearted fellows.

But listen Mr Colby I said if I want to learn it would not do me no good to copy down what other writers have wrote, what I would have to do would be write things out of my own head.

That is true said Mr Colby.

Well I said what could I write about?

Well said Mr Colby why don't you keep a diary and every night after your supper set down and write what happened that day and write who you cadded for and what they done only leave me out of it. And you can write down what people say and what you think and etc., it will be the best kind of practice for you, and once in a wile you can bring me your writeings and I will tell you the truth if they are good or rotten.

So that is how I come to be writeing this diary is so as I can get some practice writeing and maybe if I keep at it long enough I can get on to the nag.

Friday, Apr. 14.

We been haveing Apr. showers for a couple days and nobody out on the course so they has been nothing happen that I could write down in my diary but dont want to leave it go to long or will never learn the trick so will try and write a few lines about a caddys life and some of our members and etc.

Well I and Joe Bean is the 2 oldest caddys in the club and I been cadding now for 5 yrs and quit school 3 yrs ago tho my mother did not like it for me to quit but my father said he can read and write and figure so what is the use in keeping him there any longer as greek and latin dont get you no credit at the grocer, so they lied about my age to the trunce officer and I been cadding every yr from March till Nov and the rest of the winter I work around Heismans store in the village.

Dureing the time I am cadding I genally always manage to play at lease 9 holes a day myself on wk days and some times 18 and am never more then 2 or 3 over par figures on our course but it is a cinch.

I played the engineers course 1 day last summer in 75 which is some golf and some of our members who has been playing 20 yrs would give their right eye to play as good as myself.

I use to play around with our pro Jack Andrews till I got so as I could beat him pretty near every time we played and now he wont play with me no more, he is not a very good player for a pro but they claim he is a good teacher. Personly I think golf teachers is a joke tho I am glad people is suckers enough to fall for it as I expect to make my liveing that way. We have got a member Mr Dunham who must of took 500 lessons in the past 3 yrs and when he starts to shoot he trys to remember all the junk Andrews has learned him and he gets dizzy and they is no telling where the ball will go and about the safest place to stand when he is shooting is between he and the hole.

I dont beleive the club pays Andrews much salery but of course he makes pretty fair money giveing lessons but his best graft is a 3 some which he plays 2 and 3 times a wk with Mr Perdue and Mr Lewis and he gives Mr Lewis a stroke a hole and they genally break some wheres near even but Mr Perdue made a 83 one time so he thinks that is his game so he insists on playing Jack even, well they always play for $5.00 a hole and Andrews makes $20.00 to $30.0 per round and if he wanted to cut loose and play his best he could make $50.00 to $60.00 per round but a couple of wallops like that and Mr Perdue might get cured so Jack figures a small stedy income is safer.

I have got a pal name Joe Bean and we pal around together as he is about my age and he says some comical things and some times will wisper some thing comical to me wile we are cadding and it is all I can do to help from laughing out loud, that is one of the first things a caddy has got to learn is never laugh out loud only when a member makes a joke. How ever on the days when theys ladies on the course I dont get a chance to caddy with Joe because for some reason another the woman folks dont like Joe to caddy for them wile on the other hand they are always after me tho I am no Othello for looks or do I seek their flavors, in fact it is just the opp and I try to keep in the back ground when the fair sex appears on the seen as cadding for ladies means you will get just so much money and no more as theys no chance of them loosning up. As Joe says the rule against tipping is the only rule the woman folks keeps.

Theys one lady how ever who I like to caddy for as she looks like Lillian Gish and it is a pleasure to just look at her and I would caddy for her for nothing tho it is hard to keep your eye on the ball when you are cadding for this lady, her name is Mrs Doane.

Sat. Apr. 15.

This was a long day and am pretty well wore out but must not get behind in my writing practice. I and Joe carried all day for Mr Thomas and Mr Blake. Mr Thomas is the vice president of one of the big banks down town and he always slips you a $1.00 extra per round but beleive me you earn it cadding for Mr Thomas,

there is just 16 clubs in his bag includeing 5 wood clubs tho he
has not used the wood in 3 yrs but says he has got to have them
along in case his irons goes wrong on him. I dont know how bad
his irons will have to get before he will think they have went
wrong on him but personly if I made some of the tee shots he
made today I would certainly considder some kind of a change
of weppons.

Mr Thomas is one of the kind of players that when it has took
him more than 6 shots to get on the green he will turn to you and
say how many have I had caddy and then you are suppose to pretend like you was thinking a minute and then say 4, then he will
say to the man he is playing with well I did not know if I had shot
4 or 5 but the caddy says it is 4. You see in this way it is not him
that is cheating but the caddy but he makes it up to the caddy afterwards with a $1.00 tip.

Mr Blake gives Mr Thomas a stroke a hole and they play a
$10.00 nassua and niether one of them wins much money from the
other one but even if they did why $10.00 is chickens food to men
like they. But the way they crab and squak about different things
you would think their last $1.00 was at stake. Mr Thomas started
out this A. M. with a 8 and a 7 and of course that spoilt the day
for him and me to. Theys lots of men that if they dont make a
good score on the first 2 holes they will founder all the rest of the
way around and raze H with their caddy and if I was laying out
a golf course I would make the first 2 holes so darn easy that you
could not help from getting a 4 or better on them and in that
way everybody would start off good natured and it would be a
few holes at lease before they begun to turn sour.

Mr Thomas was beat both in the A. M. and P. M. in spite of
my help as Mr Blake is a pretty fair counter himself and I heard
him say he got a 88 in the P. M. which is about a 94 but any way
it was good enough to win. Mr Blakes regular game is about a 90
takeing his own figures and he is one of these cocky guys that takes
his own game serious and snears at men that cant break 100 and
if you was to ask him if he had ever been over 100 himself he
would say not since the first yr he begun to play. Well I have
watched a lot of those guys like he and I will tell you how they
keep from going over 100 namely by doing just what he done this

A. M. when he come to the 13th hole. Well he missed his tee shot and dubbed along and finely he got in a trap on his 4th shot and I seen him take 6 wallops in the trap and when he had took the 6th one his ball was worse off then when he started so he picked it up and marked a X down on his score card. Well if he had of played out the hole why the best he could of got was a 11 by hole-ing his next niblick shot but he would of probly got about a 20 which would of made him around 108 as he admitted takeing a 88 for the other 17 holes. But I bet if you was to ask him what score he had made he would say O I was terrible and I picked up on one hole but if I had of played them all out I guess I would of had about a 92.

These is the kind of men that laughs themselfs horse when they hear of some dub takeing 10 strokes for a hole but if they was made to play out every hole and mark down their real score their card would be decorated with many a big casino.

Well as I say I had a hard day and was pretty sore along towards the finish but still I had to laugh at Joe Bean on the 15th hole which is a par 3 and you can get there with a fair drive and personly I am genally hole high with a midiron, but Mr Thomas topped his tee shot and dubbed a couple with his mashie and was still quiet a ways off the green and he stood studing the situation a minute and said to Mr Blake well I wonder what I better take here. So Joe Bean was standing by me and he said under his breath take my advice and quit you old rascal.

Mon. Apr. 17.

Yesterday was Sun and I was to wore out last night to write as I cadded 45 holes. I cadded for Mr Colby in the A. M. and Mr Langley in the P. M. Mr Thomas thinks golf is wrong on the sabath tho as Joe Bean says it is wrong any day the way he plays it.

This A. M. they was nobody on the course and I played 18 holes by myself and had a 5 for a 76 on the 18th hole but the wind got a hold of my drive and it went out of bounds. This P. M. they was 3 of us had a game of rummy started but Miss Rennie and Mrs Thomas come out to play and asked for me to caddy for them, they are both terrible.

Mrs Thomas is Mr Thomas wife and she is big and fat and

shakes like jell and she always says she plays golf just to make her skinny and she dont care how rotten she plays as long as she is getting the exercise, well maybe so but when we find her ball in a bad lie she aint never sure it is hers till she picks it up and smells it and when she puts it back beleive me she don't cram it down no gopher hole.

Miss Rennie is a good looker and young and they say she is engaged to Chas Crane, he is one of our members and is the best player in the club and dont cheat hardly at all and he has got a job in the bank where Mr Thomas is the vice president. Well I have cadded for Miss Rennie when she was playing with Mr Crane and I have cadded for her when she was playing alone or with another lady and I often think if Mr Crane could hear her talk when he was not around he would not be so stuck on her. You would be surprised at some of the words that falls from those fare lips.

Well the 2 ladies played for 2 bits a hole and Miss Rennie was haveing a terrible time wile Mrs Thomas was shot with luck on the greens and sunk 3 or 4 putts that was murder. Well Miss Rennie used some expressions which was best not repeated but towards the last the luck changed around and it was Miss Rennie that was sinking the long ones and when they got to the 18th tee Mrs Thomas was only 1 up.

Well we had started pretty late and when we left the 17th green Miss Rennie made the remark that we would have to hurry to get the last hole played, well it was her honor and she got the best drive she made all day about 120 yds down the fair way. Well Mrs Thomas got nervous and looked up and missed her ball a ft and then done the same thing right over and when she finely hit it she only knocked it about 20 yds and this made her lay 3. Well her 4th went wild and lit over in the rough in the apple trees. It was a cinch Miss Rennie would win the hole unless she dropped dead.

Well we all went over to hunt for Mrs Thomas ball but we would of been lucky to find it even in day light but now you could not hardly see under the trees, so Miss Rennie said drop another ball and we will not count no penalty. Well it is some job any time to make a woman give up hunting for a lost ball and all the more so when it is going to cost her 2 bits to play the hole out so there we stayed for at lease 10 minutes till it was so dark we could not see each other let alone a lost ball and finely Mrs Thomas said well it looks like we could not finish, how do we stand? Just like she did not know how they stood.

You had me one down up to this hole said Miss Rennie.

Well that is finishing pretty close said Mrs Thomas.

I will have to give Miss Rennie credit that what ever word she thought of for this occasion she did not say it out loud but when she was paying me she said I might of give you a quarter tip only I have to give Mrs Thomas a quarter she dont deserve so you dont get it.

Fat chance I would of had any way.

Thurs. Apr. 20.

Well we been haveing some more bad weather but today the weather was all right but that was the only thing that was all right. This P. M. I cadded double for Mr Thomas and Chas Crane the club champion who is stuck on Miss Rennie. It was a 4 some with he and Mr Thomas against Mr Blake and Jack Andrews the pro, they was only playing best ball so it was really just a match between Mr Crane and Jack Andrews and Mr Crane win by 1 up. Joe Bean cadded for Jack and Mr Blake. Mr Thomas was terrible and I put in a swell P. M. lugging that heavy bag of his besides Mr Cranes bag.

Mr Thomas did not go off of the course as much as usual but he kept hitting behind the ball and he run me ragged replacing his divots but still I had to laugh when he was playing the 4th hole which you have to drive over a ravine and every time Mr Thomas misses his tee shot on this hole why he makes a squak about the ravine and says it ought not to be there and etc.

Today he had a terrible time getting over it and afterwards he said to Jack Andrews this is a joke hole and ought to be changed. So Joe Bean wispered to me that if Mr Thomas kept on playing like he was the whole course would be changed.

Then a little wile later when we come to the long 9th hole Mr Thomas got a fair tee shot but then he whiffed twice missing the ball by a ft and the 3d time he hit it but it only went a little ways and Joe Bean said that is 3 trys and no gain, he will have to punt.

But I must write down about my tough luck, well we finely

got through the 18 holes and Mr Thomas reached down in his pocket for the money to pay me and he genally pays for Mr Crane to when they play together as Mr Crane is just a employ in the bank and dont have much money but this time all Mr Thomas had was a $20.00 bill so he said to Mr Crane I guess you will have to pay the boy Charley so Charley dug down and got the money to pay me and he paid just what it was and not a dime over, where if Mr Thomas had of had the change I would of got a $1.00 extra at lease and maybe I was not sore and Joe Bean to because of course Andrews never gives you nothing and Mr Blake dont tip his caddy unless he wins.

They are a fine bunch of tight wads said Joe and I said well Crane is all right only he just has not got no money.

He aint all right no more than the rest of them said Joe.

Well at lease he dont cheat on his score I said.

And you know why that is said Joe, neither does Jack Andrews cheat on his score but that is because they play to good. Players like Crane and Andrews that goes around in 80 or better cant cheat on their score because they make the most of the holes in around 4 strokes and the 4 strokes includes their tee shot and a couple of putts which everybody is right there to watch them when they make them and count them right along with them. So if they make a 4 and claim a 3 why people would just laugh in their face and say how did the ball get from the fair way on to the green, did it fly? But the boys that takes 7 and 8 strokes to a hole can shave their score and you know they are shaveing it but you have to let them get away with it because you cant prove nothing. But that is one of the penaltys for being a good player, you cant cheat.

To hear Joe tell it pretty near everybody are born crooks, well maybe he is right.

Wed. Apr. 26.

Today Mrs Doane was out for the first time this yr and asked for me to caddy for her and you bet I was on the job. Well how are you Dick she said, she always calls me by name. She asked me what had I been doing all winter and was I glad to see her and etc.

She said she had been down south all winter and played golf

pretty near every day and would I watch her and notice how much she had improved.

Well to tell the truth she was no better then last yr and wont never be no better and I guess she is just to pretty to be a golf player but of course when she asked me did I think her game was improved I had to reply yes indeed as I would not hurt her feelings and she laughed like my reply pleased her. She played with Mr and Mrs Carter and I carried the 2 ladies bags wile Joe Bean cadded for Mr Carter. Mrs Carter is a ugly dame with things on her face and it must make Mr Carter feel sore when he looks at Mrs Doane to think he married Mrs Carter but I suppose they could not all marry the same one and besides Mrs Doane would not be a sucker enough to marry a man like he who drinks all the time and is pretty near always stood, tho Mr Doane who she did marry aint such a H of a man himself tho dirty with money.

They all gave me the laugh on the 3d hole when Mrs Doane was makeing her 2d shot and the ball was in the fair way but laid kind of bad and she just ticked it and then she asked me if winter rules was in force and I said yes so we teed her ball up so as she could get a good shot at it and they gave me the laugh for saying winter rules was in force.

You have got the caddys bribed Mr Carter said to her.

But she just smiled and put her hand on my sholder and said Dick is my pal. That is enough of a bribe to just have her touch you and I would caddy all day for her and never ask for a cent only to have her smile at me and call me her pal.

Sat. Apr. 29.

Today they had the first club tournament of the yr and they have a monthly tournament every month and today was the first one, it is a handicap tournament and everybody plays in it and they have prizes for low net score and low gross score and etc. I cadded for Mr Thomas today and will tell what happened.

They played a 4 some and besides Mr Thomas we had Mr Blake and Mr Carter and Mr Dunham. Mr Dunham is the worst man player in the club and the other men would not play with him a specialy on a Saturday only him and Mr Blake is partners together in business. Mr Dunham has got the highest handicap in the club which is 50 but it would have to be 150 for him to win a prize. Mr Blake and Mr Carter has got a handicap of about 15 a piece I think and Mr Thomas is 30, the first prize for the low net score for the day was a dozen golf balls and the second low score a ½ dozen golf balls and etc.

Well we had a great battle and Mr Colby ought to been along to write it up or some good writer. Mr Carter and Mr Dunham played partners against Mr Thomas and Mr Blake which ment that Mr Carter was playing Thomas and Blakes best ball, well Mr Dunham took the honor and the first ball he hit went strate off to the right and over the fence outside of the grounds, well he done the same thing 3 times. Well when he finely did hit one in the course why Mr Carter said why not let us not count them 3 first shots of Mr Dunham as they was just practice. Like H we wont count them said Mr Thomas we must count every shot and keep our scores correct for the tournament.

All right said Mr Carter.

Well we got down to the green and Mr Dunham had about 11 and Mr Carter sunk a long putt for a par 5, Mr Blake all ready had 5 strokes and so did Mr Thomas and when Mr Carter sunk his putt why Mr Thomas picked his ball up and said Carter wins the hole and I and Blake will take 6s. Like H you will said Mr Carter, this is a tournament and we must play every hole out and keep our scores correct. So Mr Dunham putted and went down in 13 and Mr Blake got a 6 and Mr Thomas missed 2 easy putts and took a 8 and maybe he was not boiling.

Well it was still their honor and Mr Dunham had one of his dizzy spells on the 2d tee and he missed the ball twice before he hit it and then Mr Carter drove the green which is only a midiron shot and then Mr Thomas stepped up and missed the ball just like Mr Dunham. He was wild and yelled at Mr Dunham no man could play golf playing with a man like you, you would spoil anybodys game.

Your game was all ready spoiled said Mr Dunham, it turned sour on the 1st green.

You would turn anybody sour said Mr Thomas.

Well Mr Thomas finely took a 8 for the hole which is a par 3 and it certainly looked bad for him winning a prize when he started out with 2 8s, and he and Mr Dunham had another terrible time on No 3 and wile they was messing things up a 2 some come up behind us and hollered fore and we left them go through tho it was Mr Clayton and Mr Joyce and as Joe Bean said they was probly dissapointed when we left them go through as they are the kind that feels like the day is lost if they cant write to some committee and preffer charges.

Well Mr Thomas got a 7 on the 3d and he said well it is no wonder I am off of my game today as I was up ½ the night with my teeth.

Well said Mr Carter if I had your money why on the night before a big tournament like this I would hire somebody else to set up with my teeth.

Well I wished I could remember all that was said and done but any way Mr Thomas kept getting sore and sore and we got to the 7th tee and he had not made a decent tee shot all day so Mr Blake said to him why dont you try the wood as you cant do no worse?

By Geo I beleive I will said Mr Thomas and took his driver out of the bag which he had not used it for 3 yrs.

Well he swang and zowie away went the ball pretty near 8 inchs distants wile the head of the club broke off clean and saled 50 yds down the course. Well I have got a hold on myself so as I dont never laugh out loud and I beleive the other men was scarred to laugh or he would of killed them so we all stood there in silents waiting for what would happen.

Well without saying a word he come to where I was standing and took his other 4 wood clubs out of the bag and took them to a tree which stands a little ways from the tee box and one by one he swang them with all his strength against the trunk of the tree and smashed them to H and gone, all right gentlemen that is over he said.

Well to cut it short Mr Thomas score for the first 9 was a even 60 and then we started out on the 2d 9 and you would not think it was the same man playing, on the first 3 holes he made 2 4s and a 5 and beat Mr Carter even and followed up with a 6 and a 5 and that is how he kept going up to the 17th hole.

What has got in to you Thomas said Mr Carter.

Nothing said Mr Thomas only I broke my hoodoo when I broke them 5 wood clubs.

Yes I said to myself and if you had broke them 5 wood clubs 3 yrs ago I would not of broke my back lugging them around.

Well we come to the 18th tee and Mr Thomas had a 39 which give him a 99 for 17 holes, well everybody drove off and as we was following along why Mr Klabor come walking down the course from the club house on his way to the 17th green to join some friends and Mr Thomas asked him what had he made and he said he had turned in a 93 but his handicap is only 12 so that give him a 81.

That wont get me no wheres he said as Charley Crane made a 75.

Well said Mr Thomas I can tie Crane for low net if I get a 6 on this hole.

Well it come his turn to make his 2d and zowie he hit the ball pretty good but they was a hook on it and away she went in to the woods on the left, the ball laid in behind a tree so as they was only one thing to do and that was waste a shot getting it back on the fair so that is what Mr Thomas done and it took him 2 more to reach the green.

How many have you had Thomas said Mr Carter when we was all on the green.

Let me see said Mr Thomas and then turned to me, how many have I had caddy?

I dont know I said.

Well it is either 4 or 5 said Mr Thomas.

I think it is 5 said Mr Carter.

I think it is 4 said Mr Thomas and turned to me again and said how many have I had caddy?

So I said 4.

Well said Mr Thomas personly I was not sure myself but my caddy says 4 and I guess he is right.

Well the other men looked at each other and I and Joe Bean looked at each other but Mr Thomas went ahead and putted and was down in 2 putts.

Well he said I certainly come to life on them last 9 holes.

So he turned in his score as 105 and with his handicap of 30 why that give him a net of 75 which was the same as Mr Crane so instead of Mr Crane getting 1 dozen golf balls and Mr Thomas getting ½ a dozen golf balls why they will split the 1st and 2d prize makeing 9 golf balls a piece.

Tues. May 2.

This was the first ladies day of the season and even Joe Bean had to carry for the fair sex. We cadded for a 4 some which was Miss Rennie and Mrs Thomas against Mrs Doane and Mrs Carter. I guess if they had of kept their score right the total for the 4 of them would of ran well over a 1000.

Our course has a great many trees and they seemed to have a traction for our 4 ladies today and we was in amongst the trees more then we was on the fair way.

Well said Joe Bean theys one thing about cadding for these dames, it keeps you out of the hot sun.

And another time he said he felt like a boy scout studing wood craft.

These dames is always up against a stump he said.

And another time he said that it was not fair to charge these dames regular ladies dues in the club as they hardly ever used the course.

Well it seems like they was a party in the village last night and of course the ladies was talking about it and Mrs Doane said what a lovely dress Miss Rennie wore to the party and Miss Rennie said she did not care for the dress herself.

Well said Mrs Doane if you want to get rid of it just hand it over to me.

I wont give it to you said Miss Rennie but I will sell it to you at ½ what it cost me and it was a bargain at that as it only cost me a $100.00 and I will sell it to you for $50.00.

I have not got $50.00 just now to spend said Mrs Doane and besides I dont know would it fit me.

Sure it would fit you said Miss Rennie, you and I are exactly the same size and figure, I tell you what I will do with you I will play you golf for it and if you beat me you can have the gown for nothing and if I beat you why you will give me $50.00 for it.

All right but if I loose you may have to wait for your money said Mrs Doane.

So this was on the 4th hole and they started from there to play for the dress and they was both terrible and worse then usual on acct of being nervous as this was the biggest stakes they had either of them ever played for tho the Doanes has got a bbl of money and $50.00 is chickens food.

Well we was on the 16th hole and Mrs Doane was 1 up and Miss Rennie sliced her tee shot off in the rough and Mrs Doane landed in some rough over on the left so they was clear across the course from each other. Well I and Mrs Doane went over to her ball and as luck would have it it had come to rest in a kind of a groove where a good player could not hardly make a good shot of it let alone Mrs Doane. Well Mrs Thomas was out in the middle of the course for once in her life and the other 2 ladies was over on the right side and Joe Bean with them so they was nobody near Mrs Doane and I.

Do I have to play it from there she said. I guess you do was my reply.

Why Dick have you went back on me she said and give me one of her looks.

Well I looked to see if the others was looking and then I kind of give the ball a shove with my toe and it come out of the groove and laid where she could get a swipe at it.

This was the 16th hole and Mrs Doane win it by 11 strokes to 10 and that made her 2 up and 2 to go. Miss Rennie win the 17th but they both took a 10 for the 18th and that give Mrs Doane the match.

Well I wont never have a chance to see her in Miss Rennies dress but if I did I aint sure that I would like it on her.

Fri. May 5.

Well I never thought we would have so much excitement in the club and so much to write down in my diary but I guess I better get busy writeing it down as here it is Friday and it was Wed. A. M. when the excitement broke loose and I was getting ready to play around when Harry Lear the caddy master come running out with the paper in his hand and showed it to me on the first page.

It told how Chas Crane our club champion had went south with $8000 which he had stole out of Mr Thomas bank and a swell looking dame that was a stenographer in the bank had elloped with him and they had her picture in the paper and I will say she is a pip but who would of thought a nice quiet young man like Mr Crane was going to prove himself a gay Romeo and a specialy as he was engaged to Miss Rennie tho she now says she broke their engagement a month ago but any way the whole affair has certainly give everybody something to talk about and one of the caddys Lou Crowell busted Fat Brunner in the nose because Fat claimed to of been the last one that cadded for Crane. Lou was really the last one and cadded for him last Sunday which was the last time Crane was at the club.

Well everybody was thinking how sore Mr Thomas would be and they would better not mention the affair around him and etc. but who should show up to play yesterday but Mr Thomas himself and he played with Mr Blake and all they talked about the whole P. M. was Crane and what he had pulled.

Well Thomas said Mr Blake I am curious to know if the thing come as a surprise to you or if you ever had a hunch that he was libel to do a thing like this.

Well Blake said Mr Thomas I will admit that the whole thing come as a complete suprise to me as Crane was all most like my son you might say and I was going to see that he got along all right and that is what makes me sore is not only that he has proved himself dishonest but that he could be such a sucker as to give up a bright future for a sum of money like $8000 and a doll face girl that cant be no good or she would not of let him do it. When you think how young he was and the carreer he might of had why it certainly seems like he sold his soul pretty cheap.

That is what Mr Thomas had to say or at lease part of it as I cant remember a ½ of all he said but any way this P. M. I cadded for Mrs Thomas and Mrs Doane and that is all they talked about to, and Mrs Thomas talked along the same lines like her husband and said she had always thought Crane was to smart a young man to pull a thing like that and ruin his whole future.

He was getting $4000 a yr said Mrs Thomas and everybody liked him and said he was bound to get ahead so that is what makes it such a silly thing for him to of done, sell his soul for $8000 and a pretty face.

Yes indeed said Mrs Doane.

Well all the time I was listening to Mr Thomas and Mr Blake and Mrs Thomas and Mrs Doane why I was thinking about something which I wanted to say to them but it would of ment me looseing my job so I kept it to myself but I sprung it on my pal Joe Bean on the way home tonight.

Joe I said what do these people mean when they talk about Crane selling his soul?

Why you know what they mean said Joe, they mean that a person that does something dishonest for a bunch of money or a gal or any kind of a reward why the person that does it is selling his soul.

All right I said and it dont make no differents does it if the reward is big or little?

Why no said Joe only the bigger it is the less of a sucker the person is that goes after it.

Well I said here is Mr Thomas who is vice president of a big bank and worth a bbl of money and it is just a few days ago when he lied about his golf score in order so as he would win 9 golf balls instead of a ½ a dozen.

Sure said Joe.

And how about his wife Mrs Thomas I said, who plays for 2 bits a hole and when her ball dont lie good why she picks it up and pretends to look at it to see if it is hers and then puts it back in a good lie where she can sock it.

And how about my friend Mrs Doane that made me move her ball out of a rut to help her beat Miss Rennie out of a party dress.

Well said Joe what of it?

Well I said it seems to me like these people have got a lot of nerve to pan Mr Crane and call him a sucker for doing what he done, it seems to me like $8000 and a swell dame is a pretty fair reward compared with what some of these other people sells their soul for, and I would like to tell them about it.

Well said Joe go ahead and tell them but maybe they will tell you something right back.

What will they tell me?

Well said Joe they might tell you this, that when Mr Thomas asks you how many shots he has had and you say 4 when you know he has had 5, why you are selling your soul for a $1.00 tip. And when you move Mrs Doanes ball out of a rut and give it a good lie, what are you selling your soul for? Just a smile.

O keep your mouth shut I said to him.

I am going to said Joe and would advice you to do the same.

"In Conference"

Harvey Hester entered the outer office of Kramer & Company, Efficiency Engineers. He approached the girl at the desk.

"I want to see Mr. Lansing," he said.

"A. M. or A. T.?" inquired the girl.

"Mr. A. T. Lansing," Hester replied.

"What is your name?"

"Harvey Hester."

The girl pressed a button and wrote something on a slip of paper. A boy appeared. She gave him the paper.

"For Mr. A. T. Lansing," she said.

The boy went away. Presently a young lady in mannish attire came out.

"I am Mr. Lansing's secretary," she said. "Did you want to see him personally?"

"I did and do," said Hester.

"Well, just now he's in conference," said the secretary. "Perhaps you would like to wait."

"Listen. This is pretty important——"

"I'm sorry, but it's against the rules to disturb any of the officers in conference."

"How long will the conference last?"

"It's hard to say," replied the secretary. "They just got through one conference and they're beginning another. It may be ten minutes and it may be an hour."

"But listen——"

"I'm sorry, but there's nothing for you to do but call again, or else wait."

"I'll wait," snapped Hester, "but I won't wait long!"

The conferees were sitting around the big table in the conference room. At the head of the table was J. H. Carlisle, president of the firm.

"Where is L. M.?" he inquired crossly. "This is the fifth conference he's been late to this morning. And we've had only six."

"Well, J. H. C.," said R. L. Jamieson, a vice-president, "I don't think we ought to wait for him. If we drag along this way we won't be able to get in a dozen conferences all day. And a dozen was the absolute minimum agreed on."

"That's all right, R. L.," said K. M. Dewey, another vice-president, "but it happens that L. M. is the one that asked for this conference, and he's the only one that knows what it's about. So we'd——"

At this moment the door opened and the tardy one entered. He was L. M. Croft, one of the vice-presidents.

"I'm sorry to be late," he apologized, addressing J. H. C.

"I was talking over the phone to J. P. The reason I asked for this conference," he continued, "was to get your thought on a proposition that came up about twenty minutes ago. There was a post-card in the mail addressed to the firm. It was from the main post-office. It says they are holding a letter for us which reached them unstamped. If we sign the card and send it to them, together with a two-cent stamp, they will forward us the letter. Otherwise they will send it to the Dead Letter Office. The question is, is the letter worth the time and expense of sending for it?"

"Who is the letter from, L. M.?" The inquirer was S. P. Daniels, one of the vice-presidents.

"The card didn't say, S. P.," replied Croft.

"My suggestion, J. H. C. and gentlemen," said A. M. Lansing, a vice-president, "is to write to whoever is in charge of that office, authorize him to open the letter, see who it's from and what it's about, and if he thinks it important, to let us know, and then we can mail the required stamp."

"It's a mighty ticklish business, gentlemen," ventured Vice-President T. W. Havers. "I have a brother, G. K. Havers. He's a pharmaceutical dispenser at a drug store on upper Broadway. He received a card like this from a branch post-office. He signed the card and sent the stamp, and the letter turned out to be nothing but advertising matter from a realtor."

"Why, T. W.," said A. T. Lansing, "you never told any one of us you had a brother."

"Oh, yes, A. T.," replied Havers. "I've got two other brothers besides G. K. One of them, N. D., is a mortuary artisan and the other, V. F., is a garbage practitioner in Harrisburg."

"I'm one of a family of seven boys," put in Vice-President B. B. Nordyke.

"I was born in Michigan," said H. J. Milton, the firm's secretary, "in a little bit of town called Watervliet."

"I'm a Yankee myself," said S. P. Daniels, "born and raised in Hingham, Massachusetts."

"How far is that from North Attleboro?" asked K. M. Dewey.

"It's right near Boston, K. M.," answered S. P. "It's a suburb of Boston."

"Philadelphia has some mighty pretty suburbs," said A. M. Lansing. "Don't you think so, R. L.?"

"I haven't been there for fifteen years, A. M.," replied R. L. Jamieson. "Last time I was there was in 1909."

"That was fifteen years ago, R. L.," remarked T. W. Havers.

"That's what I say, T. W., fifteen years," said Jamieson.

"I thought you said fourteen years," rejoined Havers.

"Let's see," put in C. T. Miller, treasurer of the firm. "Where was I fifteen years ago? Oh, yes, I was a bibliopolistic actuary in southern Ohio. I was selling Balzac complete for twenty-six dollars."

"Did you read Jimmie Montague's poem in the Record this morning, Z. H.?" inquired F. X. Murphy of Z. H. Holt.

"No, F. X.," replied Holt. "I don't go in for that highbrow stuff and anyways, when I get through my day's work here, I'm too tired to read."

"What do you do with yourself evenings, Z. H.?" asked A. T., the younger of the Lansings.

"Oh, maybe play the player piano or go to a movie or go to bed," said Holt.

"I bet there's none of you spends your evenings like I do," said young Lansing. "Right after dinner, the wife and I sit down in the living room and I tell her everything that I've done down here during the day."

"Don't she get bored?" asked S. P. Daniels.

"I should say not, S. P.!" replied young Lansing. "She loves it!"

"My sister Minnie—she married L. F. Wilcox, the tire people— she was over to the house last night," announced L. M. Croft. "She was reading us a poem by this Amy Leslie, the woman that got up this free verse. I couldn't make much out of it."

"Gentlemen," said J. H. C. at this juncture, "have you any more suggestions in regards to this unstamped letter? How about you, Z. H.?" he added, turning to Holt.

"Well, I'll tell you, J. H. C.," replied Holt, "a thing like this has got to be handled mighty careful. It may be all right, and it may be a hoax, and it may be out and out blackmail. I remember a some- what similar case that occurred in my home town, Marengo, Illinois."

"Did you know the Lundgrens there?" asked L. M. Croft.

"Yes, indeed, L. M.," answered Holt. "I used to go into Chicago to see Carl pitch. He was quite a card player, too. But this case I speak of, why, it seems that S. W. Kline—he was a grass truncater around town—why, he received an anonymous post-card with no name signed to it. It didn't even say who it was from. All it said was that if he would be at a certain corner at a certain hour on a certain day, he would find out something that he'd like to know."

"What?" interrupted the elder Lansing.

"I was saying," said Holt, "that in my home town, Marengo, Illi- nois, there was a man named S. W. Kline who got an anonymous post-card with no name signed to it, and it said that if he would be at a certain corner at a certain hour on a certain day, he would find out something that he'd like to know."

"What?" repeated the elder Lansing.

"Never mind, Z. H.," said J. H. C. "Tell us what happened."

"Nothing," said Holt. "Kline never went near the place."

"That reminds me," put in K. M. Dewey, "of a funny thing that came off in St. Louis. That's when I was with the P. D. advertising department. One afternoon the postman brought the mail to our house and my wife looked it over and found a letter addressed to some name like Jennings or Galt or something like that. It wasn't for us at all. So she laid for the postman next day and gave him back the letter. She said, 'Look here, here's a letter that don't belong to us at all. It's for somebody else.' I forget now just what the name was. Anyway, he took the letter and I guess he delivered it to the right people."

"I got some pretty good Scotch myself for fifty-six dollars a case," said S. P. Daniels. "It's old James Buchanan."

"Where did you get it, S. P.?" inquired Paul Sickles.

"I've got the phone number home," replied Daniels. "I'll bring it to you to-morrow, Paul."

Sickles was the only man in the outfit who was not an officer, so they called him Paul instead of by his initials.

"Prohibition's a joke!" said T. W. Havers.

"People drink now'days that never drank before," said S. P. Daniels.

"Even nice women are drinking," said L. M. Croft.

"I think you'll see light wines and beer before it's over," said K. M. Dewey.

J. H. C. spoke again.

"But what about this letter?"

"It seems funny to me," said A. T. Lansing, "that the people in the post-office don't open it and find out what it's all about. Why, my wife opens my personal mail, and when I'm home I open hers."

"Don't she care?" asked S. P. Daniels.

"No, S. P.," said the younger Lansing. "She thinks everything I do is all right."

"My wife got a letter last week with no stamp on it at all," said Sickles. "The stamp must have dropped off. All it was anyways was a circular about mah jongg sets."

"Do you play with flowers, Paul?" asked K. M. Dewey.

"Why——"

Harvey Hester, in the outer office, looked at his watch for the twentieth time; then got up and went to the girl at the desk.

"Please have Mr. Lansing's secretary come out here again," he said.

"A. M. or A. T.?" asked the girl.

"A. T.," said Hester.

The secretary came out.

"Listen," said Hester. "If I can't see Mr. Lansing right this minute it'll be too late."

"I'm sorry, but I can't interrupt him when he's in conference."

"All right," said Hester. "Will you please give him this message? You've got my name. Mr. Lansing and I were in school together and were more or less friendly. Well, I was tipped off this morning —I don't need to tell you how—I was tipped off that Mrs. Lansing is leaving for Chicago on the 12:05 train. And she isn't leaving alone. She's eloping. I thought Mr. Lansing might want to try to stop her."

"What time is it now?"

"Seven minutes of twelve," said Hester. "He can just make it."

"But he's still in conference," said the secretary.

The Love Nest

"I'll tell you what I'm going to do with you, Mr. Bartlett," said the great man. "I'm going to take you right out to my home and have you meet the wife and family; stay to dinner and all night. We've got plenty of room and extra pajamas, if you don't mind them silk. I mean that'll give you a chance to see us just as we are. I mean you can get more that way than if you sat here a whole week, asking me questions."

"But I don't want to put you to a lot of trouble," said Bartlett.

"Trouble!" The great man laughed. "There's no trouble about it. I've got a house that's like a hotel. I mean a big house with lots of servants. But anyway I'm always glad to do anything I can for a writing man, especially a man that works for Ralph Doane. I'm very fond of Ralph. I mean I like him personally besides being a great editor. I mean I've known him for years and when there's anything I can do for him, I'm glad to do it. I mean it'll be a pleasure to have you. So if you want to notify your family——"

"I haven't any family," said Bartlett.

"Well, I'm sorry for you! And I bet when you see mine, you'll wish you had one of your own. But I'm glad you can come and we'll start now so as to get there before the kiddies are put away for the night. I mean I want you to be sure and see the kiddies. I've got three."

"I've seen their pictures," said Bartlett. "You must be very proud of them. They're all girls, aren't they?"

"Yes, sir; three girls. I wouldn't have a boy. I mean I always wanted girls. I mean girls have got a lot more zip to them. I mean they're a lot zippier. But let's go! The Rolls is down-stairs and if we start now we'll get there before dark. I mean I want you to see the place while it's still daylight."

The great man—Lou Gregg, president of Modern Pictures, Inc. —escorted his visitor from the magnificent office by a private door and down a private stairway to the avenue, where the glittering car with its glittering chauffeur waited.

"My wife was in town today," said Gregg as they glided northward, "and I hoped we could ride out together, but she called up about two and asked would I mind if she went on home in the Pierce. She was through with her shopping and she hates to be away from the house and the kiddies any longer than she can help. Celia's a great home girl. You'd never know she was the same girl now as the girl I married seven years ago. I mean she's different. I mean she's not the same. I mean her marriage and being a mother has developed her. Did you ever see her? I mean in pictures?"

"I think I did once," replied Bartlett. "Didn't she play the young sister in 'The Cad'?"

"Yes, with Harold Hodgson and Marie Blythe."

"I thought I'd seen her. I remember her as very pretty and vivacious."

"She certainly was! And she is yet! I mean she's even prettier, but of course she ain't a kid, though she looks it. I mean she was only seventeen in that picture and that was ten years ago. I mean she's twenty-seven years old now. But I never met a girl with as much zip as she had in those days. It's remarkable how marriage changes them. I mean nobody would ever thought Celia Sayles would turn out to be a sit-by-the-fire. I mean she still likes a good time, but her home and kiddies come first. I mean her home and kiddies come first."

"I see what you mean," said Bartlett.

An hour's drive brought them to Ardsley-on-Hudson and the great man's home.

"A wonderful place!" Bartlett exclaimed with a heroic semblance of enthusiasm as the car turned in at an *arc de triomphe* of a gateway and approached a white house that might have been mistaken for the Yale Bowl.

"It ought to be!" said Gregg. "I mean I've spent enough on it. I mean these things cost money."

He indicated with a gesture the huge house and Urbanesque landscaping.

"But no amount of money is too much to spend on home. I mean it's a good investment if it tends to make your family proud and satisfied with their home. I mean every nickel I've spent here is like so much insurance; It insures me of a happy wife and family. And what more can a man ask!"

Bartlett didn't know, but the topic was forgotten in the business of leaving the resplendent Rolls and entering the even more resplendent reception hall.

"Forbes will take your things," said Gregg. "And, Forbes, you may tell Dennis that Mr. Bartlett will spend the night." He faced the wide stairway and raised his voice. "Sweetheart!" he called.

From above came the reply in contralto: "Hello, sweetheart!"

"Come down, sweetheart. I've brought you a visitor."

"All right, sweetheart, in just a minute."

Gregg led Bartlett into a living-room that was five laps to the mile and suggestive of an Atlantic City auction sale.

"Sit there," said the host, pointing to a balloon-stuffed easy chair, "and I'll see if we can get a drink. I've got some real old Bourbon that I'd like you to try. You know I come from Chicago and I always liked Bourbon better than Scotch. I mean I always preferred it to Scotch. Forbes," he addressed the servant, "we want a drink. You'll find a full bottle of that Bourbon in the cupboard."

"It's only half full, sir," said Forbes.

"Half full! That's funny! I mean I opened it last night and just took one drink. I mean it ought to be full."

"It's only half full," repeated Forbes, and went to fetch it.

"I'll have to investigate," Gregg told his guest. "I mean this ain't the first time lately that some of my good stuff has disappeared. When you keep so many servants, it's hard to get all honest ones. But here's Celia!"

Bartlett rose to greet the striking brunette who at this moment made an entrance so Delsarte as to be almost painful. With never a glance at him, she minced across the room to her husband and took a half interest in a convincing kiss.

"Well, sweetheart," she said when it was at last over.

"This is Mr. Bartlett, sweetheart," said her husband. "Mr. Bartlett, meet Mrs. Gregg."

Bartlett shook his hostess's proffered two fingers.

"I'm so pleased!" said Celia in a voice reminiscent of Miss Claire's imitation of Miss Barrymore.

"Mr. Bartlett," Gregg went on, "is with Mankind, Ralph Doane's magazine. He is going to write me up; I mean us."

"No, you mean you," said Celia. "I'm sure the public is not interested in great men's wives."

"I am sure you are mistaken, Mrs. Gregg," said Bartlett politely. "In this case at least. You are worth writing up aside from being a great man's wife."

"I'm afraid you're a flatterer, Mr. Bartlett," she returned. "I have been out of the limelight so long that I doubt if anybody remembers me. I'm no longer an artist; merely a happy wife and mother."

"And I claim, sweetheart," said Gregg, "that it takes an artist to be that."

"Oh, no, sweetheart!" said Celia. "Not when they have you for a husband!"

The exchange of hosannahs was interrupted by the arrival of Forbes with the tray.

"Will you take yours straight or in a highball?" Gregg inquired of his guest. "Personally I like good whiskey straight. I mean mixing it with water spoils the flavor. I mean whisky like this, it seems like a crime to mix it with water."

"I'll have mine straight." said Bartlett, who would have preferred a high-ball.

While the drinks were being prepared, he observed his hostess more closely and thought how much more charming she would be if she had used finesse in improving on nature. Her cheeks, her mouth, her eyes, and lashes had been, he guessed, far above the average in beauty before she had begun experimenting with them. And her experiments had been clumsy. She was handsome in spite of her efforts to be handsomer.

"Listen, sweetheart," said her husband. "One of the servants has been helping himself to this Bourbon. I mean it was a full bottle last night and I only had one little drink out of it. And now it's less than half full. Who do you suppose has been at it?"

"How do I know, sweetheart? Maybe the groceryman or the iceman or somebody."

"But you and I and Forbes are the only ones that have a key. I mean it was locked up."

"Maybe you forgot to lock it."

"I never do. Well, anyway, Bartlett, here's a go!"

"Doesn't Mrs. Gregg indulge?" asked Bartlett.

"Only a cocktail before dinner," said Celia. "Lou objects to me drinking whisky, and I don't like it much anyway."

"I don't object to you drinking whisky, sweetheart. I just object to you drinking to excess. I mean I think it coarsens a woman to drink. I mean it makes them coarse."

"Well, there's no argument, sweetheart. As I say, I don't care whether I have it or not."

"It certainly is great Bourbon!" said Bartlett, smacking his lips and putting his glass back on the tray.

"You bet it is!" Gregg agreed. "I mean you can't buy that kind of stuff any more. I mean it's real stuff. You help yourself when you want another. Mr. Bartlett is going to stay all night, sweetheart. I told him he could get a whole lot more of a line on us that way than just interviewing me in the office. I mean I'm tongue-tied when it comes to talking about my work and my success. I mean it's better to see me out here as I am, in my home, with my family. I mean my home life speaks for itself without me saying a word."

"But, sweetheart," said his wife, "what about Mr. Latham?"

"Gosh! I forgot all about him! I must phone and see if I can call it off. That's terrible! You see," he explained to Bartlett, "I made a date to go up to Tarrytown tonight, to K. L. Latham's, the sugar people. We're going to talk over the new club. We're going to have a golf club that will make the rest of them look like a toy. I mean a real golf club! They want me to kind of run it. And I was to go up there tonight and talk it over. I'll phone and see if I can postpone it."

"Oh, don't postpone it on my account!" urged Bartlett. "I can come out again some other time, or I can see you in town."

"I don't see how you *can* postpone it, sweetheart," said Celia. "Didn't he say old Mr. King was coming over from White Plains? They'll be mad at you if you don't go."

"I'm afraid they would resent it, sweetheart. Well, I'll tell you. You can entertain Mr. Bartlett and I'll go up there right after dinner and come back as soon as I can. And Bartlett and I can talk when I get back. I mean we can talk when I get back. How is that?"

"That suits me," said Bartlett.

"I'll be as entertaining as I can," said Celia, "but I'm afraid that isn't very entertaining. However, if I'm too much of a bore, there's plenty to read."

"No danger of my being bored," said Bartlett.

"Well, that's all fixed then," said the relieved host. "I hope you'll excuse me running away. But I don't see how I can get out of it. I mean with old King coming over from White Plains. I mean he's an old man. But listen, sweetheart—where are the kiddies? Mr. Bartlett wants to see them."

"Yes, indeed!" agreed the visitor.

"Of course you'd say so!" Celia said. "But we *are* proud of them! I suppose all parents are the same. They all think their own children are the only children in the world. Isn't that so, Mr. Bartlett? Or haven't you any children?"

"I'm sorry to say I'm not married."

"Oh, you poor thing! We pity him, don't we, sweetheart? But why aren't you, Mr. Bartlett? Don't tell me you're a woman hater!"

"Not now, anyway," said the gallant Bartlett.

"Do you get that, sweetheart? He's paying you a pretty compliment."

"I heard it, sweetheart. And now I'm sure he's a flatterer. But I must hurry and get the children before Hortense puts them to bed."

"Well," said Gregg when his wife had left the room, "would you say she's changed?"

"A little, and for the better. She's more than fulfilled her early promise."

"I think so," said Gregg. "I mean I think she was a beautiful girl and now she's an even more beautiful woman. I mean wifehood and maternity have given her a kind of a—well, you know

—I mean a kind of a pose. I mean a pose. How about another drink?"

They were emptying their glasses when Celia returned with two of her little girls.

"The baby's in bed and I was afraid to ask Hortense to get her up again. But you'll see her in the morning. This is Norma and this is Grace. Girls, this is Mr. Bartlett."

The girls received this news calmly.

"Well, girls," said Bartlett.

"What do you think of them, Bartlett?" demanded their father. "I mean what do you think of them?"

"They're great!" replied the guest with creditable warmth.

"I mean aren't they pretty?"

"I should say they are!"

"There, girls! Why don't you thank Mr. Bartlett?"

"Thanks," murmured Norma.

"How old are you, Norma?" asked Bartlett.

"Six," said Norma.

"Well," said Bartlett. "And how old is Grace?"

"Four," replied Norma.

"Well," said Bartlett. "And how old is baby sister?"

"One and a half," answered Norma.

"Well," said Bartlett.

As this seemed to be final, "Come, girls," said their mother. "Kiss daddy good night and I'll take you back to Hortense."

"I'll take them," said Gregg. "I'm going up-stairs anyway. And you can show Bartlett around. I mean before it gets any darker."

"Good night, girls," said Bartlett, and the children murmured a good night.

"I'll come and see you before you're asleep," Celia told them. And after Gregg had led them out, "Do you really think they're pretty?" she asked Bartlett.

"I certainly do. Especially Norma. She's the image of you," said Bartlett.

"She looks a little like I used to," Celia admitted. "But I hope she doesn't look like me now. I'm too old looking."

"You look remarkably young!" said Bartlett. "No one would believe you were the mother of three children."

"Oh, Mr. Bartlett! But I mustn't forget I'm to 'show you around.' Lou is so proud of our home!"

"And with reason," said Bartlett.

"It *is* wonderful! I call it our love nest. Quite a big nest, don't you think? Mother says it's too big to be cosy; she says she can't think of it as a home. But I always say a place is whatever one makes of it. A woman can be happy in a tent if they love each other. And miserable in a royal palace without love. Don't you think so, Mr. Bartlett?"

"Yes, indeed."

"Is this really such wonderful Bourbon? I think I'll just take a sip of it and see what it's like. It can't hurt me if it's so good. Do you think so, Mr. Bartlett?"

"I don't believe so."

"Well then, I'm going to taste it and if it hurts me it's your fault."

Celia poured a whisky glass two-thirds full and drained it at a gulp.

"It *is* good, isn't it?" she said. "Of course I'm not much of a judge as I don't care for whisky and Lou won't let me drink it. But he's raved so about this Bourbon that I did want to see what it was like. You won't tell on me, will you, Mr. Bartlett?"

"Not I!"

"I wonder how it would be in a high-ball. Let's you and I have just one. But I'm forgetting I'm supposed to show you the place. We won't have time to drink a high-ball and see the place too before Lou comes down. Are you so crazy to see the place?"

"Not very."

"Well, then, what do you say if we have a high-ball? And it'll be a secret between you and I."

They drank in silence and Celia pressed a button by the door.

"You may take the bottle and tray," she told Forbes. "And now," she said to Bartlett, "we'll go out on the porch and see as much as we can see. You'll have to guess the rest."

Gregg, having changed his shirt and collar, joined them.

"Well," he said to Bartlett, "have you seen everything?"

"I guess I have, Mr. Gregg," lied the guest readily. "It's a wonderful place!"

"We like it. I mean it suits us. I mean it's my idear of a real home. And Celia calls it her love nest."

"So she told me," said Bartlett.

"She'll always be sentimental," said her husband.

He put his hand on her shoulder, but she drew away.

"I must run up and dress," she said.

"Dress!" exclaimed Bartlett, who had been dazzled by her flowered green chiffon.

"Oh, I'm not going to really dress," she said. "But I couldn't wear this thing for dinner!"

"Perhaps you'd like to clean up a little, Bartlett," said Gregg. "I mean Forbes will show you your room if you want to go up."

"It might be best," said Bartlett.

Celia, in a black lace dinner gown, was rather quiet during the elaborate meal. Three or four times when Gregg addressed her, she seemed to be thinking of something else and had to ask, "What did you say, sweetheart?" Her face was red and Bartlett imagined that she had "sneaked" a drink or two besides the two helpings of Bourbon and the cocktail that had preceded dinner.

"Well, I'll leave you," said Gregg when they were in the living-room once more. "I mean the sooner I get started, the sooner I'll be back. Sweetheart, try and keep your guest awake and don't let him die of thirst. *Au revoir,* Bartlett. I'm sorry, but it can't be helped. There's a fresh bottle of the Bourbon, so go to it. I mean help yourself. It's too bad you have to drink alone."

"It *is* too bad, Mr. Bartlett," said Celia when Gregg had gone.

"What's too bad?" asked Bartlett.

"That you have to drink alone. I feel like I wasn't being a good hostess to let you do it. In fact, I refuse to let you do it. I'll join you in just a little wee sip."

"But it's so soon after dinner!"

"It's never too soon! I'm going to have a drink myself and if you don't join me, you're a quitter."

She mixed two life-sized high-balls and handed one to her guest.

"Now we'll turn on the radio and see if we can't stir things up. There! No, no! Who cares about the old baseball! Now! This is better! Let's dance."

"I'm sorry, Mrs. Gregg, but I don't dance."

"Well, you're an old cheese! To make me dance alone! 'All alone, yes, I'm all alone.' "

There was no affectation in her voice now and Bartlett was amazed at her unlabored grace as she glided around the big room.

"But it's no fun alone," she complained. "Let's shut the damn thing off and talk."

"I love to watch you dance," said Bartlett.

"Yes, but I'm no Pavlowa," said Celia as she silenced the radio. "And besides, it's time for a drink."

"I've still got more than half of mine."

"Well, you had that wine at dinner, so I'll have to catch up with you."

She poured herself another high-ball and went at the task of "catching up."

"The trouble with you, Mr.—now isn't that a scream! I can't think of your name."

"Bartlett."

"The trouble with you, Barker—do you know what's the trouble with you? You're too sober. See? You're too damn sober! That's the whole trouble, see? If you weren't so sober, we'd be better off. See? What I can't understand is how you can be so sober and me so high."

"You're not used to it."

"Not used to it! That's the cat's pajamas! Say, I'm like this half the time, see? If I wasn't, I'd die!"

"What does your husband say?"

"He don't say because he don't know. See, Barker? There's nights when he's out and there's a few nights when I'm out myself. And there's other nights when we're both in and I pretend I'm sleepy and I go up-stairs. See? But I don't go to bed. See? I have a little party all by myself. See? If I didn't, I'd die!"

"What do you mean, you'd die?"

"You're dumb, Barker! You may be sober, but you're dumb! Did you fall for all that apple sauce about the happy home and the contented wife? Listen, Barker—I'd give anything in the world to be out of this mess. I'd give anything to never see him again."

"Don't you love him any more? Doesn't he love you? Or what?"

"Love! I never did love him! I didn't know what love was! And all his love is for himself!"

"How did you happen to get married?"

"I was a kid; that's the answer. A kid and ambitious. See? He was a director then and he got stuck on me and I thought he'd make me a star. See, Barker? I married him to get myself a chance. And now look at me!"

"I'd say you were fairly well off."

"Well off, am I? I'd change places with the scum of the earth just to be free! See, Barker? And I could have been a star without any help if I'd only realized it. I had the looks and I had the talent. I've got it yet. I could be a Swanson and get myself a marquis; maybe a prince! And look what I did get! A self-satisfied, self-centered——! I thought he'd *make* me! See, Barker? Well, he's made me all right; he's made me a chronic mother and it's a wonder I've got any looks left.

"I fought at first. I told him marriage didn't mean giving up my art, my life work. But it was no use. He wanted a beautiful wife and beautiful children for his beautiful home. Just to show us off. See? I'm part of his chattels. See, Barker? I'm just like his big diamond or his cars or his horses. And he wouldn't stand for his wife 'lowering' herself to act in pictures. Just as if pictures hadn't made him!

"You go back to your magazine tomorrow and write about our love nest. See, Barker? And be sure and don't get mixed and call it a baby ranch. Babies! You thought little Norma was pretty. Well, she is. And what is it going to get her? A rich ——— of a husband that treats her like a ———! That's what it'll get her if I don't interfere. I hope I don't last long enough to see her grow up, but if I do, I'm going to advise her to run away from home and live her own life. And *be* somebody! Not a *thing* like I am! See, Barker?"

"Did you ever think of a divorce?"

"Did I ever think of one! Listen—but there's no chance. I've got nothing on him, and no matter what he had on me, he'd never let the world know it. He'd keep me here and torture me like he does now, only worse. But I haven't done anything wrong, see? The men I might care for, they're all scared of him and his money

and power. See, Barker? And the others are just as bad as him.
Like fat old Morris, the hotel man, that everybody thinks he's a
model husband. The reason he don't step out more is because he's
too stingy. But I could have him if I wanted him. Every time he
gets near enough to me, he squeezes my hand. I guess he thinks
it's a nickel, the tight old ———! But come on, Barker. Let's
have a drink. I'm running down."

"I think it's about time you were running up—up-stairs," said
Bartlett. "If I were you, I'd try to be in bed and asleep when Gregg
gets home."

"You're all right, Barker. And after this drink I'm going to do
just as you say. Only I thought of it before you did, see? I think
of it lots of nights. And tonight you can help me out by telling
him I had a bad headache."

Left alone, Bartlett thought a while, then read, and finally dozed
off. He was dozing when Gregg returned.

"Well, well, Bartlett," said the great man, "did Celia desert you?"

"It was perfectly all right, Mr. Gregg. She had a headache and
I told her to go to bed."

"She's had a lot of headaches lately; reads too much, I guess.
Well, I'm sorry I had this date. It was about a new golf club and
I had to be there. I mean I'm going to be president of it. I see
you consoled yourself with some of the Bourbon. I mean the bottle
doesn't look as full as it did."

"I hope you'll forgive me for helping myself so generously," said
Bartlett. "I don't get stuff like that every day!"

"Well, what do you say if we turn in? We can talk on the way
to town tomorrow. Though I guess you won't have much to ask
me. I guess you know all about us. I mean you know all about
us now."

"Yes, indeed, Mr. Gregg. I've got plenty of material if I can
just handle it."

Celia had not put in an appearance when Gregg and his guest
were ready to leave the house next day.

"She always sleeps late," said Gregg. "I mean she never wakes
up very early. But she's later than usual this morning. Sweetheart!"
he called up the stairs.

"Yes, sweetheart," came the reply.

"Mr. Bartlett's leaving now. I mean he's going."

"Oh, good-by, Mr. Bartlett. Please forgive me for not being down to see you off."

"You're forgiven, Mrs. Gregg. And thanks for your hospitality."

"Good-by, sweetheart!"

"Good-by, sweetheart!"

A Day with Conrad Green

Conrad Green woke up depressed and, for a moment, could not think why. Then he remembered. Herman Plant was dead; Herman Plant, who had been his confidential secretary ever since he had begun producing; who had been much more than a secretary —his champion, votary, shield, bodyguard, tool, occasional lackey, and the butt of his heavy jokes and nasty temper. For forty-five dollars a week.

Herman Plant was dead, and this Lewis, recommended by Ezra Peebles, a fellow entrepreneur, had not, yesterday, made a good first impression. Lewis was apparently impervious to hints. You had to tell him things right out, and when he did understand he looked at you as if you were a boob. And insisted on a salary of sixty dollars right at the start. Perhaps Peebles, who, Green knew, hated him almost enough to make it fifty-fifty, was doing him another dirty trick dressed up as a favor.

After ten o'clock, and still Green had not had enough sleep. It had been nearly three when his young wife and he had left the Bryant-Walkers'. Mrs. Green, the former Marjorie Manning of the Vanities chorus, had driven home to Long Island, while he had stayed in the rooms he always kept at the Ambassador.

Marjorie had wanted to leave a good deal earlier; through no lack of effort on her part she had been almost entirely ignored by her aristocratic host and hostess and most of the guests. She had confided to her husband more than once that she was sick of the whole such-and-such bunch of so-and-so's. As far as she was concerned, they could all go to hell and stay there! But Green had been rushed by the pretty and stage-struck Joyce Brainard, wife of the international polo star, and had successfully combated his own wife's importunities till the Brainards themselves had gone.

Yes, he could have used a little more sleep, but the memory of the party cheered him. Mrs. Brainard, excited by his theatrical aura and several highballs, had been almost affectionate. She had promised to come to his office some time and talk over a stage career which both knew was impossible so long as Brainard lived. But, best of all, Mr. and Mrs. Green would be listed in the papers as among those present at the Bryant-Walkers', along with the Vanderbecks, the Suttons, and the Schuylers, and that would just about be the death of Peebles and other social sycophants of "show business." He would order all the papers now and look for his name. No; he was late and must get to his office. No telling what a mess things were in without Herman Plant. And, by the way, he mustn't forget Plant's funeral this afternoon.

He bathed, telephoned for his breakfast, and his favorite barber, dressed in a symphony of purple and gray, and set out for Broadway, pretending not to hear the "There's Conrad Green!" spoken in awed tones by two flappers and a Westchester realtor whom he passed en route.

Green let himself into his private office, an office of luxurious, exotic furnishings, its walls adorned with expensive landscapes and a Zuloaga portrait of his wife. He took off his twenty-five dollar velour hat, approved of himself in the large mirror, sat down at his desk, and rang for Miss Jackson.

"All the morning papers," he ordered, "and tell Lewis to come in."

"I'll have to send out for the papers," said Miss Jackson, a tired-looking woman of forty-five or fifty.

"What do you mean, send out? I thought we had an arrangement with that boy to leave them every morning."

"We did. But the boy says he can't leave them any more till we've paid up to date."

"What do we owe?"

"Sixty-five dollars."

"Sixty-five dollars! He's crazy! Haven't you been paying him by the week?"

"No. You told me not to."

"I told you nothing of the kind! Sixty-five dollars! He's trying to rob us!"

"I don't believe so, Mr. Green," said Miss Jackson. "He showed me his book. It's more than thirty weeks since he began, and you know we've never paid him."

"But hell! There isn't sixty-five dollars' worth of newspapers ever been printed! Tell him to sue us! And now send out for the papers and do it quick! After this we'll get them down at the corner every morning and pay for them. Tell Lewis to bring me the mail."

Miss Jackson left him, and presently the new secretary came in. He was a man under thirty, whom one would have taken for a high school teacher rather than a theatrical general's aide-de-camp.

"Good morning, Mr. Green," he said.

His employer disregarded the greeting.

"Anything in the mail?" he asked.

"Not much of importance. I've already answered most of it. Here are a few things from your clipping bureau and a sort of dunning letter from some jeweler in Philadelphia."

"What did you open that for?" demanded Green, crossly. "Wasn't it marked personal?"

"Look here, Mr. Green," said Lewis quietly: "I was told you had a habit of being rough with your employees. I want to warn you that I am not used to that sort of treatment and don't intend to get used to it. If you are decent with me, I'll work for you. Otherwise I'll resign."

"I don't know what you're talking about, Lewis. I didn't mean to be rough. It's just my way of speaking. Let's forget it and I'll try not to give you any more cause to complain."

"All right, Mr. Green. You told me to open all your mail except the letters with that one little mark on them——"

"Yes, I know. Now let's have the clippings."

Lewis laid them on the desk.

"I threw away about ten of them that were all the same—the announcement that you had signed Bonnie Blue for next season. There's one there that speaks of a possible partnership between you and Sam Stein——"

"What a nerve he's got, giving out a statement like that. Fine chance of me mixing myself up with a crook like Stein! Peebles says he's a full stepbrother to the James boys. So is Peebles himself, for that matter. What's this long one about?"

"It's about that young composer, Casper Ettelson. It's by Deems Taylor of the *World*. There's just a mention of you down at the bottom."

"Read it to me, will you? I've overstrained my eyes lately."

The dead Herman Plant had first heard of that recent eye strain twenty years ago. It amounted to almost total blindness where words of over two syllables were concerned.

"So far," Lewis read, "Ettelson has not had a book worthy of his imaginative, whimsical music. How we would revel in an Ettelson score with a Barrie libretto and a Conrad Green production."

"Who is this Barrie?" asked Green.

"I suppose it's James M. Barrie," replied Lewis, "the man who wrote Peter Pan."

"I thought that was written by a fella over in England," said Green.

"I guess he does live in England. He was born in Scotland. I don't know where he is now."

"Well, find out if he's in New York, and, if he is, get a hold of him. Maybe he'll do a couple of scenes for our next show. Come in, Miss Jackson. Oh, the papers!"

Miss Jackson handed them to him and went out. Green turned first to the society page of the *Herald Tribune*. His eye trouble was not so severe as to prevent his finding that page. And he could read his name when it was there to be read.

Three paragraphs were devoted to the Bryant-Walker affair, two of them being lists of names. And Mr. and Mrs. Conrad Green were left out.

"—— !" commented Green, and grabbed the other papers. The *World* and *Times* were searched with the same hideous result. And the others did not mention the party at all.

"—— !" repeated Green. "I'll get somebody for this!" Then, to Lewis: "Here! Take this telegram. Send it to the managing editors of all the morning papers; you'll find their names pasted on Plant's desk. Now: 'Ask your society editor why my name was not on list of guests at Bryant-Walker dinner Wednesday night. Makes no difference to me, as am not seeking and do not need publicity, but it looks like conspiracy, and thought you ought to be informed, as have always been good friend of your paper, as well as steady advertiser.' I guess that's enough."

"If you'll pardon a suggestion," said Lewis, "I'm afraid a telegram like this would just be laughed at."

"You send the telegram; I'm not going to have a bunch of cheap reporters make a fool of me!"

"I don't believe you can blame the reporters. There probably weren't reporters there. The list of guests is generally given out by the people who give the party."

"But listen——" Green paused and thought. "All right. Don't send the telegram. But if the Bryant-Walkers are ashamed of me, why the hell did they invite me? I certainly didn't want to go and they weren't under obligations to me. I never——"

As if it had been waiting for its cue, the telephone rang at this instant, and Kate, the switchboard girl, announced that the Bryant-Walkers' secretary was on the wire.

"I am speaking for Mrs. Bryant-Walker," said a female voice. "She is chairman of the committee on entertainment for the Women's Progress Bazaar. The bazaar is to open on the third of next month and wind up on the evening of the fifth with a sort of vaudeville entertainment. She wanted me to ask you——"

Green hung up with an oath.

"That's the answer!" he said. "The damn grafters!"

Miss Jackson came in again.

"Mr. Robert Blair is waiting to see you."

"Who is he?"

"You know. He tried to write some things for one of the shows last year."

"Oh, yes. Say, did you send flowers to Plant's house?"

"I did," replied Miss Jackson. "I sent some beautiful roses."

"How much?"

"Forty-five dollars," said Miss Jackson.

"Forty-five dollars for roses! And the man hated flowers even when he was alive! Well, send in this Blair."

Robert Blair was an ambitious young free lance who had long been trying to write for the stage, but with little success.

"Sit down, Blair," said Green. "What's on your mind?"

"Well, Mr. Green, my stuff didn't seem to suit you last year, but this time I think I've got a scene that can't miss."

"All right. If you want to leave it here, I'll read it over."

"I haven't written it out. I thought I'd tell you the idea first."

"Well, go ahead, but cut it short; I've got a lot of things to do today. Got to go to old Plant's funeral for one thing."

"I bet you miss him, don't you?" said Blair sympathetically.

"Miss him! I should say I do! A lovable character and"—with a glance at Lewis—"the best secretary I'll ever have. But let's hear your scene."

"Well," said Blair, "it may not sound like much the way I tell it, but I think it'll work out great. Well, the police get a report that a woman has been murdered in her home, and they go there and find her husband, who is acting very nervous. They give him the third degree, and he finally breaks down and admits he killed her. They ask him why, and he tells them he is very fond of beans, and on the preceding evening he came home to dinner and asked her what there was to eat, and she told him she had lamb chops, mashed potatoes, spinach, and apple pie. So he says, 'No beans?' and she says, 'No beans.' So he shoots her dead. Of course, the scene between the husband and wife is acted out on the stage. Then——"

"It's no good!" said Conrad Green. "In the first place, it takes too many people, all those policemen and everybody."

"Why, all you need is two policemen and the man and his wife. And wait till I tell you the rest of it."

"I don't like it; it's no good. Come back again when you've got something."

When Blair had gone Green turned to Lewis.

"That's all for just now," he said, "but on your way out tell Miss Jackson to get a hold of Martin and say I want him to drop in here as soon as he can."

"What Martin?" asked Lewis.

"She'll know—Joe Martin, the man that writes most of our librettos."

Alone, Conrad Green crossed the room to his safe, opened it, and took out a box on which was inscribed the name of a Philadelphia jeweler. From the box he removed a beautiful rope of matched pearls and was gazing at them in admiration when Miss Jackson came in; whereupon he hastily replaced them in their case and closed the safe.

"That man is here again," said Miss Jackson, "That man Hawley from *Gay New York.*"

"Tell him I'm not in."

"I did, but he says he saw you come in and he's going to wait till you'll talk to him. Really, Mr. Green, I think it would be best in the long run to see him. He's awfully persistent."

"All right; send him in," said Green, impatiently, "though I have no idea what he can possibly want of me."

Mr. Hawley, dapper and eternally smiling, insisted on shaking hands with his unwilling host, who had again sat down at his desk.

"I think," he said, "we've met before."

"Not that I know of," Green replied shortly.

"Well, it makes no difference, but I'm sure you've read our little paper, *Gay New York.*"

"No," said Green. "All I have time to read is manuscripts."

"You don't know what you're missing," said Hawley. "It's really a growing paper, with a big New York circulation, and a circulation that is important from your standpoint."

"Are you soliciting subscriptions?" asked Green.

"No. Advertising."

"Well, frankly, Mr. Hawley, I don't believe I need any advertising. I believe that even the advertising I put in the regular daily papers is a waste of money."

"Just the same," said Hawley, "I think you'd be making a mistake not to take a page in *Gay New York.* It's only a matter of fifteen hundred dollars."

"Fifteen hundred dollars! That's a joke! Nobody's going to hold *me* up!"

"Nobody's trying to, Mr. Green. But I might as well tell you that one of our reporters came in with a story the other day—well, it was about a little gambling affair in which some of the losers sort of forgot to settle, and—well, my partner was all for printing it, but I said I had always felt friendly toward you and why not give you a chance to state your side of it?"

"I don't know what you're talking about. If your reporter has got my name mixed up in a gambling story he's crazy."

"No. He's perfectly sane and very, very careful. We make a specialty of careful reporters and we're always sure of our facts."

Conrad Green was silent for a long, long time. Then he said:

"I tell you, I don't know what gambling business you refer to, and furthermore, fifteen hundred dollars is a hell of a price for a page in a paper like yours. But still, as you say, you've got the kind of circulation that might do me good. So if you'll cut down the price——"

"I'm sorry, Mr. Green, but we never do that."

"Well, then, of course you'll have to give me a few days to get my ad fixed up. Say you come back here next Monday afternoon."

"That's perfectly satisfactory, Mr. Green," said Hawley, "and I assure you that you're not making a mistake. And now I won't keep you any longer from your work."

He extended his hand, but it was ignored, and he went out, his smile a little broader than when he had come in. Green remained at his desk, staring straight ahead of him and making semi-audible references to certain kinds of dogs as well as personages referred to in the Old and New Testaments. He was interrupted by the entrance of Lewis.

"Mr. Green," said the new secretary, "I have found a check for forty-five dollars, made out to Herman Plant. I imagine it is for his final week's pay. Would you like to have me change it and make it out to his widow?"

"Yes," said Green. "But no; wait a minute. Tear it up and I'll make out my personal check to her and add something to it."

"All right," said Lewis, and left.

"Forty-five dollars' worth of flowers," said Green to himself, and smiled for the first time that morning.

He looked at his watch and got up and put on his beautiful hat.

"I'm going to lunch," he told Miss Jackson on his way through the outer office. "If Peebles or anybody important calls up, tell them I'll be here all afternoon."

"You're not forgetting Mr. Plant's funeral?"

"Oh, that's right. Well, I'll be here from one-thirty to about three."

A head waiter at the Astor bowed to him obsequiously and escorted him to a table near a window, while the occupants of several other tables gazed at him spellbound and whispered, "Conrad Green."

A luncheon of clams, sweetbreads, spinach, strawberry ice cream, and small coffee seemed to satisfy him. He signed his check and then tipped his own waiter and the head waiter a dollar apiece, the two tips falling just short of the cost of the meal.

Joe Martin, his chief librettist, was waiting when he got back to his office.

"Oh, hello, Joe!" he said, cordially. "Come right inside. I think I've got something for you."

Martin followed him in and sat down without waiting for an invitation. Green seated himself at his desk and drew out his cigarette case.

"Have one, Joe?"

"Not that kind!" said Martin, lighting one of his own. "You've got rotten taste in everything but gals."

"And librettists," replied Green, smiling.

"But here's what I wanted to talk about. I couldn't sleep last night, and I just laid there and an idea came to me for a comedy scene. I'll give you the bare idea and you can work it out. It'll take a girl and one of the comics, maybe Fraser, and a couple of other men that can play.

"Well, the idea is that the comic is married to the girl. In the first place, I'd better mention that the comic is crazy about beans. Well, one night the comic—no, wait a minute. The police get word that the comic's wife has been murdered and two policemen come to the comic's apartment to investigate. They examine the corpse and find out she's been shot through the head. They ask the comic if he knows who did it and he says no, but they keep after him, and finally he breaks down and admits that he did it himself.

"But he says, 'Gentlemen, if you'll let me explain the circumstances, I don't believe you'll arrest me.' So they tell him to explain, and he says that he came home from work and he was very hungry and he asked his wife what they were going to have for dinner. So she tells him—clams and sweetbreads and spinach and strawberry ice cream and coffee. So he asks her if she isn't going to have any beans and she says no, and he shoots her. What do you think you could do with that idea?"

"Listen, Connie," said Martin: "You've only got half the scene, and you've got that half wrong. In the second place, it was played a whole season in the Music Box and it was written by Bert Kalmar and Harry Ruby. Otherwise I can do a whole lot with it."

"Are you sure you're right?"

"I certainly am!"

"Why, that damn little thief? He told me it was his!"

"Who?" asked Martin.

"Why, that Blair, that tried to butt in here last year. I'll fix him!"

"I thought you said it was your own idea."

"Hell, no! Do you think I'd be stealing stuff, especially if it was a year old?"

"Well," said Martin, "when you get another inspiration like this, give me a ring and I'll come around. Now I've got to hurry up to the old Stadium and see what the old Babe does in the first inning."

"I'm sorry, Joe. I thought it was perfectly all right."

"Never mind! You didn't waste much of my time. But after this you'd better leave the ideas to me. So long!"

"Good-by, Joe; and thanks for coming in."

Martin went and Green pressed the button for Miss Jackson.

"Miss Jackson, don't ever let that young Blair in here again. He's a faker!"

"All right, Mr. Green. But don't you think it's about time you were starting for the funeral? It's twenty minutes of three."

"Yes. But let's see: where is Plant's house?"

"It's up on One Hundred and Sixtieth street, just off Broadway."

"My God! Imagine living there! Wait a minute, Miss Jackson. Send Lewis here."

"Lewis," he said, when the new secretary appeared, "I ate something this noon that disagreed with me. I wanted to go up to Plant's funeral, but I really think it would be dangerous to try it. Will you go up there, let them know who you are, and kind of represent me? Miss Jackson will give you the address."

"Yes, sir," said Lewis, and went out.

Almost immediately the sanctum door opened again and the

beautiful Marjorie Green, née Manning, entered unannounced. Green's face registered not altogether pleasant surprise.

"Why, hello, dear!" he said. "I didn't know you were coming to town today.

"I never told you I wasn't," his wife replied.

They exchanged the usual connubial salutations.

"I supposed you noticed," said Mrs. Green, "that our names were not on the list of guests at the party."

"No; I haven't had time to look at the papers. But what's the difference?"

"No difference at all, of course. But do you know what I think? I think we were invited just because those people want to get something out of you, for some benefit or something."

"A fine chance! I hope they try it!"

"However, that's not what I came to talk about."

"Well, dear, what is it?"

"I thought maybe you'd remember something."

"What, honey?"

"Why—oh, well, there's no use talking about it if you've forgotten."

Green's forehead wrinkled in deep thought; then suddenly his face brightened.

"Of course I haven't forgotten! It's your birthday!"

"You just thought of it now!"

"No such a thing! I've been thinking of it for weeks!"

"I don't believe you! If you had been, you'd have said something, and"—his wife was on the verge of tears—"you'd have given me some little thing, just any little thing."

Once more Green frowned, and once more brightened up.

"I'll prove it to you," he said, and walked rapidly to the safe.

In a moment he had placed in her hands the jewel box from Philadelphia. In another moment she had opened it, gasped at the beauty of its contents, and thrown her arms around his neck.

"Oh, dearest!" she cried. "Can you ever forgive me for doubting you?"

She put the pearls to her mouth as if she would eat them.

"But haven't you been terribly extravagant?"

"I don't consider anything too extravagant for you."

"You're the best husband a girl ever had!"

"I'm glad you're pleased," said Green.

"Pleased! I'm overwhelmed. And to think I imagined you'd forgotten! But I'm not going to break up your whole day. I know you want to get out to poor old Plant's funeral. So I'll run along. And maybe you'll take me to dinner somewhere tonight."

"I certainly will! You be at the Ambassador about six-thirty and we'll have a little birthday party. But don't you want to leave the pearls here now?"

"I should say not! They're going to stay with me forever! Anyone that tries to take them will do it over my dead body!"

"Well, good-by, then, dear."

"Till half past six."

Green, alone again, kicked shut the door of his safe and returned to his desk, saying in loud tones things which are not ordinarily considered appropriate to the birthday of a loved one. The hubbub must have been audible to Miss Jackson outside, but perhaps she was accustomed to it. It ceased at another unannounced entrance, that of a girl even more beautiful than the one who had just gone out. She looked at Green and laughed.

"My God! You look happy!" she said.

"Rose!"

"Yes, it's Rose. But what's the matter with you?"

"I've had a bad day."

"But isn't it better now?"

"I didn't think you were coming till tomorrow."

"But aren't you glad I came today?"

"You bet I am!" said Green. "And if you'll come here and kiss me I'll be all the gladder."

"No. Let's get our business transacted first."

"What business?"

"You know perfectly well! Last time I saw you you insisted that I must give up everybody else but you. And I promised you it would be all off between Harry and I if—— Well, you know. There was a little matter of some pearls."

"I meant everything I said."

"Well, where are they?"

"They're all bought and all ready for you. But I bought them in Philadelphia and for some damn reason they haven't got here yet."

"Got here yet! Were they so heavy you couldn't bring them with you?"

"Honest, dear, they'll be here day after tomorrow at the latest."

" 'Honest' is a good word for you to use! Do you think I'm dumb? Or is it that you're so used to lying that you can't help it?"

"If you'll let me explain——"

"Explain hell! We made a bargain and you haven't kept your end of it. And now——"

"But listen——"

"I'll listen to nothing! You know where to reach me and when you've kept your promise you can call me up. Till then—Well, Harry isn't such bad company."

"Wait a minute, Rose!"

"You've heard all I've got to say. Good-by!"

And she was gone before he could intercept her.

Conrad Green sat as if stunned. For fifteen minutes he was so silent and motionless that one might have thought him dead. Then he shivered as if with cold and said aloud:

"I'm not going to worry about them any more. To hell with all of them!"

He drew the telephone to him and took off the receiver.

"Get me Mrs. Bryant-Walker."

And after a pause:

"Is this Mrs. Bryant-Walker. No, I want to speak to her personally. This is Conrad Green. Oh, hello, Mrs. Walker. Your secretary called me up this morning, but we were cut off. She was saying something about a benefit. Why, yes, certainly, I'll be glad to. As many of them as you want. If you'll just leave it all in my hands I'll guarantee you a pretty good entertainment. It's no bother at all. It's a pleasure. Thank you. Good-by."

Lewis came in.

"Well, Lewis, did you get to the funeral?"

"Yes, Mr. Green, and I saw Mrs. Plant and explained the circumstances to her. She said you had always been very kind to her husband. She said that during the week of his illness he talked of you nearly all the time and expressed confidence that if he died you would attend his funeral. So she wished you had been there."

"Good God! So do I!" said Conrad Green.

Mr. Frisbie

I am Mr. Allen Frisbie's chauffeur. Allen Frisbie is a name I made up because they tell me that if I used the real name of the man I am employed by that he might take offense and start trouble though I am sure he will never see what I am writing as he does not read anything except the American Golfer but of course some of his friends might call his attention to it. If you knew who the real name of the man is it would make more interesting reading as he is one of the 10 most wealthiest men in the United States and a man who everybody is interested in because he is so famous and the newspapers are always writing articles about him and sending high salary reporters to interview him but he is a very hard man to reproach or get an interview with and when they do he never tells them anything.

That is how I come to be writing this article because about two weeks ago a Mr. Kirk had an appointment to interview Mr. Frisbie for one of the newspapers and I drove him to the station after the interview was over and he said to me your boss is certainly a tough egg to interview and getting a word out of him is like pulling turnips.

"The public do not know anything about the man," said Mr. Kirk. "They know he is very rich and has got a wife and a son and a daughter and what their names are but as to his private life and his likes and dislikes he might just as well be a monk in a convent."

"The public knows he likes golf," I said.

"They do not know what kind of a game he plays."

"He plays pretty good," I said.

"How good?" said Mr. Kirk.

"About 88 or 90," I said.

"So is your grandmother," said Mr. Kirk.

He only meant the remark as a comparison but had either of my grandmothers lived they would both have been over 90. Mr. Kirk did not believe I was telling the truth about Mr. Frisbie's game and he was right though was I using real names I would not admit it as Mr. Frisbie is very sensitive in regards to his golf.

Mr. Kirk kept pumping at me but I am used to being pumped at and Mr. Kirk finally gave up pumping at me as he found me as closed mouth as Mr. Frisbie himself but he made the remark that he wished he was in my place for a few days and as close to the old man as I am and he would then be able to write the first real article which had ever been written about the old man. He called Mr. Frisbie the old man.

He said it was too bad I am not a writer so I could write up a few instance about Mr. Frisbie from the human side on account of being his caddy at golf and some paper or magazine would pay me big. He said if you would tell me a few instance I would write them up and split with you but I said no I could not think of anything which would make an article but after Mr. Kirk had gone I got to thinking it over and thought to myself maybe I could be a writer if I tried and at least there is no harm in trying so for the week after Mr. Kirk's visit I spent all my spare time writing down about Mr. Frisbie only at first I used his real name but when I showed the article they said for me not to use real names but the public would guess who it was anyway and that was just as good as using real names.

So I have gone over the writing again and changed the name to Allen Frisbie and other changes and here is the article using Allen Frisbie.

When I say I am Mr. Frisbie's chauffeur I mean I am his personal chauffeur. There are two other chauffeurs who drive for the rest of the family and run errands. Had I nothing else to do only drive I might well be turned a man of leisure as Mr. Frisbie seldom never goes in to the city more than twice a week and even less oftener than that does he pay social visits.

His golf links is right on the place an easy walk from the house to the first tee and here is where he spends a good part of each and every day playing alone with myself in the roll of caddy. So one would not be far from amiss to refer to me as Mr. Frisbie's caddy rather than his chauffeur but it was as a chauffeur that I was engaged and can flatter myself that there are very few men of my calling who would not gladly exchange their salary and position for mine.

Mr. Frisbie is a man just this side of 60 years of age. Almost 10 years ago he retired from active business with money enough to put him in a class with the richest men in the United States and since then his investments have increased their value to such an extent so that now he is in a class with the richest men in the United States.

It was soon after his retirement that he bought the Peter Vischer estate near Westbury, Long Island. On this estate there was a 9 hole golf course in good condition and considered one of the best private 9 hole golf courses in the United States but Mr. Frisbie would have had it plowed up and the land used for some other usage only for a stroke of chance which was when Mrs. Frisbie's brother came over from England for a visit.

It was during while this brother-in-law was visiting Mr. Frisbie that I entered the last named employee and was an onlooker when Mr. Frisbie's brother-in-law persuaded his brother-in-law to try the game of golf. As luck would have it Mr. Frisbie's first drive was so good that his brother-in-law would not believe he was a new beginner till he had seen Mr. Frisbie shoot again but that first perfect drive made Mr. Frisbie a slave of the game and without which there would be no such instance as I am about to relate.

I would better explain at this junction that I am not a golfer but I have learned quite a lot of knowledge about the game by cadding for Mr. Frisbie and also once or twice in company with my employer have picked up some knowledge of the game by witnessing players like Bobby Jones and Hagen and Sarazen and Smith in some of their matches. I have only tried it myself on a very few occasions when I was sure Mr. Frisbie could not observe me and will confide that in my own mind I am convinced that with a little practise that I would have little trouble defeating Mr. Frisbie but will never seek to prove same for reasons which I will leave it to the reader to guess the reasons.

One day shortly after Mr. Frisbie's brother-in-law had ended his visit I was cadding for Mr. Frisbie and as had become my custom keeping the score for him when a question arose as to whether he had taken 7 or 8 strokes on the last hole. A 7 would have given him a total of 63 for the 9 holes while a 8 would have made it 64. Mr. Frisbie tried to recall the different strokes but was not certain and asked me to help him.

As I remembered it he had sliced his 4th. wooden shot in to a trap but had recovered well and got on to the green and then had taken 3 putts which would make him a 8 but by some slip of the tongue when I started to say 8 I said 7 and before I could correct myself Mr. Frisbie said yes you are right it was a 7.

"That is even 7s," said Mr. Frisbie.

"Yes," I said.

On the way back to the house he asked me what was my salary which I told him and he said well I think you are worth more than that and from now on you will get $25.00 more per week.

On another occasion when 9 more holes had been added to the course and Mr. Frisbie was playing 18 holes regular every day he came to the last hole needing a 5 to break 112 which was his best score.

The 18th. hole is only 120 yards with a big green but a brook in front and traps in back of it. Mr. Frisbie got across the brook with his second but the ball went over in to the trap and it looked like bad business because Mr. Frisbie is even worse with a niblick than almost any other club except maybe the No. 3 and 4 irons and the wood.

Well I happened to get to the ball ahead of him and it laid there burred in the deep sand about a foot from a straight up and down bank 8 foot high where it would have been impossible for any man alive to oust it in one stroke but as luck would have it I stumbled and gave the ball a little kick and by chance it struck the side of the bank and stuck in the grass and Mr. Frisbie got it up on the green in one stroke and was down in 2 putts for his 5.

"Well that is my record 111 or 3 over 6s," he said.

Now my brother had a couple of tickets for the polo at Meadowbrook the next afternoon and I am a great lover of horses flesh so I said to Mr. Frisbie can I go to the polo tomorrow afternoon and

he said certainly any time you want a afternoon off do not hesitate
to ask me but a little while later there was a friend of mine going
to get married at Atlantic City and Mr. Frisbie had just shot a
128 and broke his spoon besides and when I mentioned about going
to Atlantic City for my friend's wedding he snapped at me like a
wolf and said what did I think it was the xmas holidays.

Personally I am a man of simple tastes and few wants and it is
very seldom when I am not satisfied to take my life and work as
they come and not seek fear or favor but of course there are times
in every man's life when they desire something a little out of the
ordinary in the way of a little vacation or perhaps a financial ac-
commodation of some kind and in such cases I have found Mr.
Frisbie a king amongst men provide it one uses discretion in choosing the moment of their reproach but a variable tyrant if one uses
bad judgment in choosing the moment of their reproach.

You can count on him granting any reasonable request just after
he has made a good score or even a good shot where as a person
seeking a favor when he is off his game might just swell ask President Coolidge to do the split.

I wish to state that having learned my lesson along these lines I
did not use my knowledge to benefit myself alone but have on the
other hand utilized same mostly to the advantage of others especially the members of Mr. Frisbie's own family. Mr. Frisbie's wife
and son and daughter all realized early in my employment that I
could handle Mr. Frisbie better than anyone else and without me
ever exactly divulging the secret of my methods they just naturally
began to take it for granted that I could succeed with him where
they failed and it became their habit when they sought something
from their respective spouse and father to summons me as their
adviser and advocate.

As an example of the above I will first sight an example in
connection with Mrs. Frisbie. This occurred many years ago and
was the instance which convinced her beyond all doubt that I was
a expert on the subject of managing her husband.

Mrs. Frisbie is a great lover of music but unable to perform on
any instrument herself. It was her hope that one of the children
would be a pianiste and a great deal of money was spent on piano
lessons for both Robert the son and Florence the daughter but all

in vain as neither of the two showed any talent and their teachers one after another gave them up in despair.

Mrs. Frisbie at last became desirous of purchasing a player piano and of course would consider none but the best but when she brooched the subject to Mr. Frisbie he turned a deaf ear as he said pianos were made to be played by hand and people who could not learn same did not deserve music in the home.

I do not know how often Mr. and Mrs. Frisbie disgust the matter pro and con.

Personally they disgust it in my presence any number of times and finally being a great admirer of music myself and seeing no reason why a man of Mr. Frisbie's great wealth should deny his wife a harmless pleasure such as a player piano I suggested to the madam that possibly if she would leave matters to me the entire proposition might be put over. I can no more than fail I told her and I do not think I will fail so she instructed me to go ahead as I could not do worse than fail which she had already done herself.

I will relate the success of my plan as briefly as possible. Between the house and the golf course there was a summer house in which Mrs. Frisbie sat reading while Mr. Frisbie played golf. In this summer house she could sit so as to not be visible from the golf course. She was to sit there till she heard me whistle the strains of "Over There" where at she was to appear on the scene like she had come direct from the house and the fruits of our scheme would then be known.

For two days Mrs. Frisbie had to console herself with her book as Mr. Frisbie's golf was terrible and there was no moment when I felt like it would not be courting disaster to summons her on the scene but during the 3rd. afternoon his game suddenly improved and he had shot the 1st. 9 holes in 53 and started out on the 10th. with a pretty drive when I realized the time had come.

Mrs. Frisbie appeared promptly in answer to my whistling and walked rapidly up to Mr. Frisbie like she had hurried from the house and said there is a man at the house from that player piano company and he says he will take $50.00 off the regular price if I order today and please let me order one as I want one so much.

"Why certainly dear go ahead and get it dear," said Mr. Frisbie and that is the way Mrs. Frisbie got her way in regards to a player

piano. Had I not whistled when I did but waited a little longer
it would have spelt ruination to our schemes as Mr. Frisbie took a
12 on the 11th. hole and would have bashed his wife over the head
with a No. 1 iron had she even asked him for a toy drum.

I have been of assistance to young Mr. Robert Frisbie the son
with reference to several items of which I will only take time to
touch on one item with reference to Mr. Robert wanting to drive a
car. Before Mr. Robert was 16 years of age he was always after Mr.
Frisbie to allow him to drive one of the cars and Mr. Frisbie always
said him nay on the grounds that it is against the law for a person
under 16 years of age to drive a car.

When Mr. Robert reached the age of 16 years old however this
excuse no longer held good and yet Mr. Frisbie continued to say
Mr. Robert nay in regards to driving a car. There is plenty of
chauffeurs at your beckon call said Mr. Frisbie to drive you where
ever and when ever you wish to go but of course Mr. Robert like
all youngsters wanted to drive himself and personally I could see
no harm in it as I personally could not drive for him and the other
2 chauffeurs in Mr. Frisbie's employee at the time were just as
lightly to wreck a car as Mr. Robert so I promised Mr. Robert that
I would do my best towards helping him towards obtaining permission to drive one of the cars.

"Leave it to me" was my bequest to Mr. Robert and sure enough
my little strategy turned the trick though Mr. Robert did not have
the patience like his mother to wait in the summer house till a fa-
vorable moment arrived so it was necessary for me to carry through
the entire proposition by myself.

The 16th. hole on our course is perhaps the most difficult hole
on our course at least it has always been a variable tartar for Mr.
Frisbie.

It is about 350 yards long in lenth and it is what is called a
blind hole as you can not see the green from the tee as you drive
from the tee up over a hill with a direction flag as the only guide
and down at the bottom of the hill there is a brook a little over
225 yards from the tee which is the same brook which you come to
again on the last hole and in all the times Mr. Frisbie has played
around the course he has seldom never made this 16th. hole in less

than 7 strokes or more as his tee shot just barely skins the top of the hill giving him a down hill lie which upsets him so that he will miss the 2d. shot entirely or top it and go in to the brook.

Well I generally always stand up on top of the hill to watch where his tee shot goes and on the occasion referred to he got a pretty good tee shot which struck on top of the hill and rolled half way down and I hurried to the ball before he could see me and I picked it up and threw it across the brook and when he climbed to the top of the hill I pointed to where the ball laid the other side of the brook and shouted good shot Mr. Frisbie. He was overjoyed and beamed with joy and did not suspect anything out of the way though in realty he could not hit a ball more than 160 yards if it was teed on the summit of Pike's Peak.

Fate was on my side at this junction and Mr. Frisbie hit a perfect mashie shot on to the green and sunk his 2d. put for the only 4 of his career on this hole. He was almost delirious with joy and you may be sure I took advantage of the situation and before we were fairly off the green I said to him Mr. Frisbie if you do not need me tomorrow morning do you not think it would be a good time for me to learn Mr. Robert to drive a car.

"Why certainly he is old enough now to drive a car and it is time he learned."

I now come to the main instance of my article which is in regards to Miss Florence Frisbie who is now Mrs. Henry Craig and of course Craig is not the real name but you will soon see that what I was able to do for her was no such childs play like gaining consent for Mr. Robert to run a automobile or Mrs. Frisbie to purchase a player piano but this was a matter of the up most importance and I am sure the reader will not consider me a vain bragger when I claim that I handled it with some skill.

Miss Florence is a very pretty and handsome girl who has always had a host of suiters who paid court to her on account of being pretty as much as her great wealth and I believe there has been times when no less than half a dozen or more young men were paying court to her at one time. Well about 2 years ago she lost her heart to young Henry Craig and at the same time Mr. Frisbie told her in no uncertain turns that she must throw young Craig over board and marry his own choice young Junior Holt or he would cut her off without a dime.

Holt and Craig are not the real names of the two young men referred to though I am using their real first names namely Junior and Henry. Young Holt is a son of Mr. Frisbie's former partner in business and a young man who does not drink or smoke and has got plenty of money in his own rights and a young man who any father would feel safe in trusting their daughter in the bands of matrimony. Young Craig at that time had no money and no position and his parents had both died leaving nothing but debts.

"Craig is just a tramp and will never amount to anything," said Mr. Frisbie. "I have had inquirys made and I understand he drinks when anyone will furnish him the drinks. He has never worked and never will. Junior Holt is a model young man from all accounts and comes of good stock and is the only young man I know whose conduct and habits are such that I would consider him fit to marry my daughter."

Miss Florence said that Craig was not a tramp and she loved him and would not marry anyone else and as for Holt he was terrible but even if he was not terrible she would never consider undergoing the bands of matrimony with a man named Junior.

"I will elope with Henry if you do not give in," she said.

Mr. Frisbie was not alarmed by this threat as Miss Florence has a little common sense and would not be lightly to elope with a young man who could hardly finance a honeymoon trip on the subway. But neither was she showing any signs of yielding in regards to his wishes in regards to young Holt and things began to take on the appearance of a dead lock between father and daughter with neither side showing any signs of yielding.

Miss Florence grew pale and thin and spent most of her time in her room instead of seeking enjoyment amongst her friends as was her custom. As for Mr. Frisbie he was always a man of iron will and things began to take on the appearance of a dead lock with neither side showing any signs of yielding.

It was when it looked like Miss Florence was on the verge of a serious illness when Mrs. Frisbie came to me and said we all realize that you have more influence with Mr. Frisbie than anyone else and is there any way you can think of to get him to change his status towards Florence and these 2 young men because if something is not done right away I am afraid of what will happen. Miss Florence likes you and has a great deal of confidence in you said Mrs. Frisbie so will you see her and talk matters over with her and see if you can not think up some plan between you which will put a end to this situation before my poor little girl dies.

So I went to see Miss Florence in her bedroom and she was a sad sight with her eyes red from weeping and so pale and thin and yet her face lit up with a smile when I entered the room and she shook hands with me like I was a long lost friend.

"I asked my mother to send you," said Miss Florence. "This case looks hopeless but I know you are a great fixer as far as Father is concerned and you can fix it if anyone can. Now I have got a idea which I will tell you and if you like it it will be up to you to carry it out."

"What is your idea?"

"Well," said Miss Florence, "I think that if Mr. Craig the man I love could do Father a favor why Father would not be so set against him."

"What kind of a favor?"

"Well Mr. Craig plays a very good game of golf and he might give Father some pointers which would improve Father's game."

"Your father will not play golf with anyone and certainly not with a good player and besides that your father is not the kind of a man that wants anyone giving him pointers. Personally I would just as leaf go up and tickle him as tell him that his stance is wrong."

"Then I guess my idea is not so good."

"No," I said and then all of a sudden I had a idea of my own. "Listen Miss Florence does the other one play golf?"

"Who?"

"Young Junior Holt."

"Even better than Mr. Craig."

"Does your father know that?"

"Father does not know anything about him or he would not like him so well."

Well I said I have got a scheme which may work or may not work but no harm to try and the first thing to be done is for you to spruce up and pretend like you do not feel so unkindly towards young Holt after all. The next thing is to tell your father that Mr. Holt never played golf and never even saw it played but would like to watch your father play so he can get the hang of the game.

And then after that you must get Mr. Holt to ask your father to let him follow him around the course and very secretly you must tip Mr. Holt off that your father wants his advice. When ever your father does anything wrong Mr. Holt is to correct him. Tell him your father is crazy to improve his golf but is shy in regards to asking for help.

There is a lot of things that may happen to this scheme but if it should go through why I will guarantee that at least half your troubles will be over.

Well as I said there was a lot of things that might have happened to spoil my scheme but nothing did happen and the very next afternoon Mr. Frisbie confided in me that Miss Florence seemed to feel much better and seemed to have changed her mind in regards to Mr. Holt and also said that the last named had expressed a desire to follow Mr. Frisbie around the golf course and learn something about the game.

Mr. Holt was a kind of a fat pudgy young man with a kind of a sneering smile and the first minute I saw him I wished him the worst.

For a second before Mr. Frisbie started to play I was certain we were lost as Mr. Frisbie remarked where have you been keeping yourself Junior that you never watched golf before. But luckily young Holt took the remark as a joke and made no reply. Right afterwards the storm clouds began to gather in the sky. Mr. Frisbie sliced his tee shot.

"Mr. Frisbie," said young Holt, "there was several things the matter with you then but the main trouble was that you stood too close to the ball and cut across it with your club head and besides that you swang back faster than Alex Smith and you were off your balance and you gripped too hard and you jerked instead of hitting with a smooth follow through."

Well, Mr. Frisbie gave him a queer look and then made up his mind that Junior was trying to be humorous and he frowned at him so as he would not try it again but when we located the ball in the rough and Mr. Frisbie asked me for his spoon young Holt said Oh take your mashie Mr. Frisbie never use a wooden club in a place like that and Mr. Frisbie scowled and mumbled under his breath and missed the ball with his spoon and missed it again and then took a midiron and just dribbled it on to the fairway and finally got on the green in 7 and took 3 putts.

I suppose you might say that this was one of the quickest golf matches on record as it ended on the 2d. tee. Mr. Frisbie tried to drive and sliced again. Then young Holt took a ball from my pocket and a club from the bag and said here let me show you the swing and drove the ball 250 yards straight down the middle of the course.

I looked at Mr. Frisbie's face and it was puffed out and a kind of a purple black color. Then he burst and I will only repeat a few of the more friendlier of his remarks.

"Get to hell and gone of my place. Do not never darken my doors again. Just show up around here one more time and I will blow out what you have got instead of brains. You lied to my girl and you tried to make a fool out of me. Get out before I sick my dogs on you and tear you to pieces."

Junior most lightly wanted to offer some word of explanation or to demand one on his own account but saw at a glance how useless same would be. I heard later that he saw Miss Florence and that she just laughed at him.

"I made a mistake about Junior Holt," said Mr. Frisbie that evening. "He is no good and must never come to this house again."

"Oh Father and just when I was beginning to like him," said Miss Florence.

Well like him or not like him she and the other young man Henry Craig were married soon afterwards which I suppose Mr. Frisbie permitted the bands in the hopes that same would rile Junior Holt.

Mr. Frisbie admitted he had made a mistake in regards to the last named but he certainly was not mistaken when he said that young Craig was a tramp and would never amount to anything.

Well I guess I have rambled on long enough about Mr. Frisbie.

Sun Cured

It seems there were two New Yorkers, C. L. Walters and Ernie Fretts. They met on a train Florida bound. Fretts was in the insurance business, over in Brooklyn.

"I'm in the insurance business, over in Brooklyn," said Fretts. "Handle all kinds of insurance. I started when I was just a kid, twenty years ago, and now I've got it built up so's I don't need to worry. It runs itself. I guess that's the trouble. I mean I got too much time on my hands, and I play around too much. Why, say, it's a wonder I ain't dead, the way I been going. I bet I ain't been to bed before two, three o'clock the last six months. You can't go that pace and not feel it."

"It's bound to tell on a man after a w'ile," said Walters. "Now you take me——"

"So I'm about all in," said Fretts. "And the funny part of it is I didn't realize it. I wouldn't of thought nothing about it only for the girl I got in my office. You couldn't hardly call her a girl, either; she's a woman about fifty-three and looks like a Channel swimmer. That's the kind to have in your office. I had a regular Miss America once, the first year I was in business for myself, and we were so busy petting each other that we couldn't even answer the phone. I didn't sell enough insurance that year to keep her in typewriter erl. The smartest play I ever made in my life was getting rid of her.

"This woman I got now—well, you'd about as soon think of making love to a horse. And she's as smart as a man; you don't have to tell her nothing. And where do you think I got her? In an emplerment agency."

"Now you take me——" said Walters.

"So as I was telling you, I come in the office one day last week, along about noon, and hadn't been to bed in thirty-six hours, and

Miss Clancy—that's the woman I got in the office—she give me one look and said, 'Mr. Fretts,' she said, 'don't think I am butting in on your private affairs, but you better be careful or you will kill yourself. If you will take my advice,' she said, 'lay off for a month or two and go to Florida or somewheres and rest up. Get away from these friends of yours for a w'ile.'

"She said, 'You know you can trust me to handle the business,' she said, 'and if you will take a vacation for a month or two, you will feel like a new man. You use' to play golf and tennis and enjer yourself in things that was good for you,' she said, 'and now look at you! I bet you ain't taken no real exercise in four years. And you don't sleep and you don't eat. Just pack up and go down to Palm Beach or Miami or some place and take a little exercise and lay around in the sun and read, or just lay there and relax yourself. You got nothing in the world to worry about and if something does come up that needs your personal attention, I will let you know. But I won't anner you,' she said, 'unless it's absolutely necessary and I don't think it will be.'

"She knows me so well that she could see what kind of shape I was in. I tell you I was a wreck, but wouldn't of thought nothing of it only for her calling my attention. I tell you I was a wreck."

"You and me both," said Walters. "Now in my case——"

"So I promised her I'd think it over and that night I went on another party—without a wink of sleep, mind you—and I told a pal of mine, Ben Drew—he's in the furniture business in Brooklyn, in partners with his brother, and a great pal of mine—I told him what Miss Clancy had said, and they was a couple of girls with us. Bonnie Werner, the girl I been going around with, she was with us, and a girl named Stevens that Ben had picked up somewheres; they were both along on the party.

"The Werner girl thinks I'm going to marry her. Fine chance!

"Anyway, she overheard me telling Ben about this Florida idear and she was all ears. She made some crack about Palm Beach being a grand place for a honeymoon. I guess she thought I was steweder than I really was. I kept right on talking to Ben and he was cockeyed and got all steamed up over the idear and said he would go along with me. He would of been right on this train, too, only for his brother getting sick. But he's going to jern me next week."

"I tried to persuade a friend of mine——"

"We got rid of the girls and sat up all that night in a poker game and I was half asleep, and at that I win over seven hundred dollars. We was playing deuces wild and they was one hand where I had three deuces and drew to them and caught a five and nine of clubs. Well, I and a fella named Garvey bet back and forth and he finally called me and laid down a deuce and three tens. I was so gone by this time that I couldn't talk, so I just throwed down my hand face up and somebody said, 'My Lord! A straight flush!' So they give me the pot and I thought all the w'ile that what I had was four nines. That shows——"

"I don't like deuces wild," said Walters. "What's the——"

"I finally got home about noon and called up the office and then slept five or six hours and by that time I was ready for another party. But when I showed up at the office on Wednesday, Miss Clancy bawled me out again and I promised I'd take her advice. Well, I hadn't played golf or tennis for years and meanw'ile I'd moved three or four times and when I come to look for my golf-clubs and tennis racket, well, they'd disappeared. And I couldn't find a bathing-suit either, or my fishing-tackle. So all this stuff I'm taking along, it's all new; I had to buy an entire new outfit—seventy-some dollars for a set of golf-clubs and a bag, fourteen dollars for a tennis racket, and thirty-odd dollars for fishing-tackle. And besides that, a bathing-suit that I paid thirty-two dollars for it, but it'll knock 'em dead.

"I don't know how my golf game will be after laying off so long; I expect it'll come back to me after the first couple of days. The last time I played was out on Long Island, at the Engineers'; must of been four, five years ago. I remember I shot an eighty-seven and win over a hundred dollars. Tennis is my game, though, and I can't hardly wait to get at it again. What I'm planning to do is get up early in the morning, have breakfast, play two or three sets of tennis, then go swimming and maybe lay around on the beach for an hour; have lunch and then get in eighteen holes of golf and another little swim; then have my dinner, probably up in my room, and go to bed around nine, ten o'clock. Three weeks and I'll be in the pink!"

"Now you take me," said Walters, "and——"

"Yes," said Fretts, "but you probably use some judgment, or maybe you're married and don't——"

"No, I'm——"

"I don't believe they's a man living could of went the pace I been going and stood up under it. Ben Drew—he's a pal of mine—he says I'm a marvel. He said, 'Ernie, you're a marvel!' Why listen: Here's what I did three weeks ago, just for an example. That was right after New Year's eve. Of course I was on parties morning, night and noon all through the holidays and wound up with a bat that started New Year's eve and lasted till Monday morning, the third. I slept a w'ile Monday forenoon and showed up at the office about three o'clock. Miss Clancy—the girl I got in the office—she give me a message to call up a pal of mine, Ben Drew.

"I called him up and he had a date with a girl he had picked up somewhere named Stevens, and would I and my girl come along. That's a girl named Bonnie Werner that I been going with. She thinks I'm going to marry her, and I suppose everybody's entitled to their opinion. Anyway, I couldn't leave Ben in a hole so I said all right and he and I got together around five o'clock and loaded up on cocktails and later we jerned the girls and made the rounds and wound up at a Black and Tan, and I and Ben both got pie-eyed and finally sent the girls home mad and we stayed and got in a crap game and I win two three hundred dollars. The game broke up at noon.

"I went straight to the office and Miss Clancy give me a message to call up Miss Werner; that's the girl I was with the night before, Monday. She was sore on account of me not seeing her home and said if I didn't take her out this night—Tuesday—why, it was all off between her and I. Well, Tuesday nights we always have a big poker game and I told her I couldn't get out of the game, but I would see her Wednesday night. I was praying she'd stay sore and carry out her threat and I wouldn't have to bother with her no more. But no; she backed down and said Wednesday would be k. o.

"So I got in the poker game and it not only lasted all Tuesday night and all day Wednesday, but all night Wednesday night. I got outside of five, six bottles of Ben Drew's Scotch and win a hundred and seventy dollars. I snatched three, four hours sleep Thursday forenoon and when I showed up at the office, the girl, the Werner girl, was waiting for me.

"To keep her from making a scene I had to promise to devote the rest of the week to her, and the next three nights, we made the rounds of all the different jernts, dancing and drinking rat-poison. Now that's just one week, but it's like all the other weeks. No wonder Miss Clancy said I looked terrible!"

"A man can't go that pace and not feel it. I know in my case——"

"So I need just this kind of a trip—go down there where I don't know nobody and no girls pestering me all the w'ile, and be outdoors all day and exercise and breathe God's fresh air. Three, four weeks of that life and the boys in Brooklyn and New York won't recognize me. And besides that, I never been to Florida and I'm anxious to look it over and see if it's all they claim. They tell me a man can pick up some great bargains there now and if I find something I like, I'm liable to grab off a piece of it, not for speculation, but maybe build myself a little place to spend the winter months. I hate cold weather and snow and they's no sense in a man in my position hanging around New York and freezing to death when I could just as well be enjering myself in a clean, wholesome way, in the sunshine."

"You take me, now——"

"You're probably a fella that uses some judgment and eat regular, or maybe you got a wife and family to make you behave. But I got nobody only my friends, though I guess I got more of them than any man in Brooklyn. That's one of my troubles, having too many friends, but only for them, I wouldn't be where I am, I mean in business. A man in my business has got to have friends, or they wouldn't have no business."

"In my business, too. I'm——"

"This must be Fayetteville we're coming to," said Fretts. "I've got to send a wire to a pal of mine, Ben Drew. He's in Brooklyn now, but he's going to jern me next week down in Miami."

It seems that the two New Yorkers happened to be on the same train a month later, northward bound from Jacksonville.

"Hello, there," said Walters.

"Fine," replied Fretts, regarding the other somewhat vaguely.

"I come down on the same train with you a month ago," said Walters.

"That's right," said Fretts. "We come down on the same train together."

"Well, what do you think of Florida?"

"No place like it in the world!" said Fretts, warming up. "Say, I could write a book! I wished I'd kept a diary of the month I been there. Only nobody would believe it."

"Where was you? Palm Beach?"

"No, Miami. That is, I guess we drove up to Palm Beach one night. I don't know."

"Where did you stop in Miami?"

"Over at the Beach, at the Flamingo."

"What did they charge you there?"

"I've got no idear. I paid them with a check," said Fretts.

"It's American plan, ain't it?"

"No. Yes, yes, it's American plan."

"And how was the meals?"

"Meals! I don't know. I didn't hear anybody say anything about them."

"I thought——"

"After this, I'm going to take all my vacations in the winter and spend them right there. That's the Garden Spot of God's Green Footstool!"

"So you bought yourself a place?"

"No, I didn't buy nothing; that is, no real estate. I met some guy the second day that was talking about a big bargain in some development he was interested in, and I promised I'd go out and look at it. He called up a couple of times to remind me of my promise, so to keep him from pestering me, I finally did go out there, but they was no moon, so I couldn't tell much about it."

"I thought——"

"Listen till you hear something funny. When I got to the hotel, they told me my room was still occupied, but the guy was just moving out and I could move in inside of an hour. Well, they made the fella pack up in a hurry and he overlooked two bottles of Plymouth gin. So there was the two bottles staring me in the eye and I was afraid he'd come back after them, so I phoned up to another fella's room that had rode over with me in the taxi from the station and he come down and we had ten, eleven Tom Collinses just as fast as we could drink them.

"Then we filled up the both bottles with water and fixed them like they hadn't been opened, and sure enough, the bird come back for his treasure. He said he was on his way to Key West and had got clear over near to Miami station when he recalled leaving the gin and he had enough time to come back for it and still catch his train yet. That's one thing about Florida trains—you can't miss them no matter what time you get there. He said it was a good thing for him that his room had been inherited by an honest man. I'd like to heard what he said when he took his first swig out of those bottles.

"Well, I and the other fella, the fella that split the gin with me— he's a fella named Leo Hargrave, from Cleveland; got a foundry there or something—the two of us went up in his room and polished off a bottle of Scotch and then it was time to dress for dinner. That's all I done about dinner the whole month I was in Miami—I dressed for it, but I never got it. Hargrave said he knew a swell jernt out near Hialeah and we hired a car and drove out there and it was a place where you dined and danced, but we wasn't hungry and we didn't have nobody to dance with. So we just ordered some drinks——"

"Did you have any trouble getting drinks?"

"Yes. You had to call a waiter. Well, we stayed there till pretty close to midnight and then drove back towards the beach and stopped at another jernt where you play roulette. There's a game I always been wild about and I'd of been satisfied to send for my baggage and settle right down for the month. But Hargrave was dance mad and he said we would have to find some girls to travel around with. He said he knew one girl; he would call her up in the morning, and maybe she had a friend.

"I told him to never mind about a friend, because it's been my experience that when you ask a girl to bring along a girl friend, the girl friend generally always looks like she had charge of the linen room at a two dollar hotel. So we stayed up till the telegraph office was open and then I sent a letter to New York, to a girl I been going around with, a girl named Bonnie Werner, and told her to jump in an upper and jern me."

"Did she come?"

"Sure, she come. She thinks I'm going to marry her. But she couldn't get there till two, three days later and in the meanwhile,

I run around with Hargrave and his dame. I wasn't lonesome, though; not as long as they was plenty of Scotch and a roulette w'eel, and besides that, I found a poker game, to say nothing about a couple dandy fellas lives there at the Beach and love to just sit around and hit up the old barber shop harmony—Jim Allison and Jess Andrew.

"But I didn't really strike my stride till Miss Werner got in. From that time on, I went some pace! And of course it was even worse when Ben Drew showed up. He's a pal of mine, in partners with his brother in the furniture business in Brooklyn. He was going to come down with me, but his brother got sick and held him up a week. He brought a girl named Stevens that he picked up somewheres, and with Miss Werner and I, and Ben Drew and the Stevens dame, and Hargrave and his girl, that made six of us that stuck together all the w'ile; that is, for the first few nights. After that, we'd get the girls all wore out by one, two o'clock and chase them home and then I and Ben and Hargrave, we'd play the w'eel or sit in a game of stud.

"It was the same schedule, day after day, the whole time I was there. The party would start out along about seven, eight o'clock in the evening and go to whatever place we hadn't been to the night before. We'd dance till, say, one o'clock and then chase the women home and do a little serious gambling. The poker game generally broke up a little before noon. That would give us fellas the afternoon to sleep, w'ile the girls would do their shopping or go to the polo or waste their time some way another. About six o'clock, I'd get up and have the barber come in and shave me and then I'd dress and be all set for the roll-call."

"But I thought——"

"From the first day, I didn't wear nothing but dinner clothes. And I brought along a trunk full of white pants and knickers that I never even unpacked.

"You'd have to get Miss Werner or one of the other girls to tell you the different places we went. They all looked alike to me—just jernts, with tables and waiters and an orchestra."

"But the weather was beautiful——"

"So I heard somebody say. I guess it's a great climate, if that's what a man is looking for. They say California's another garden spot and that's another place I've always intended to go. But of course it takes longer."

"The California climate," said Walters, "is probably just as good——"

"I've always intended to go out there. But of course it takes longer. Four, five days on a train is too much. A fella don't get no sun or air. I always feel cooped up on a train."

"How was the golf?"

"I didn't get to play golf; never had my clubs out of the bag. But I heard somebody telling Ben Drew that they had four, five fine courses around Miami."

"Play any tennis?"

"No, I didn't have time for tennis. They got some swell courts right by the hotel, but even at that, when you change into your tennis clothes and play four, five sets and then take a bath and dress again, why, it means a waste of two hours."

"Go fishing?"

"Fishing! That's a whole day! And as far as bathing is concerned, why, it looks like they was a law that you couldn't swim only at noon time, just when a man's ready for the hay."

"How far is the ocean from the hotel where you stopped?"

"I don't know. I didn't get over there. You see you can't do everything at a place like that. It would wear you out. I'm thirty-eight years old and when a man gets that age, you've got to watch your-step. You can't go in for athaletics like you was a kid.

"I'm in the insurance business in Brooklyn, and one of the things we learn in our business is that a man is taking chances if he goes in too strong for sports after a certain age. You can't be a youngster all your life."

"Did your friends go home ahead of you?"

"Do you mean Ben Drew and Miss Werner and the Stevens girl? No, Ben, he's back there in a compartment dead to the world and he said he'd shoot anybody that woke him up this side of Manhattan Transfer.

"And the girls—they look like they'd just stepped out of a waste-pipe."

"You look pretty good yourself, better than last time I seen you."

"I should! A trip like this was just what I needed—away from the office a whole month and longer and ain't even given business a thought.

"That's where so many men make mistakes—not taking a vacation; or if they do take one, they keep in touch with their office all the time and sperl the whole trip, worrying. I got a girl that can run my business pretty near as good as I can myself—not a girl, either; a woman about fifty-three years old; a Miss Clancy.

"She's the one that realized the shape I was in and insisted on me taking this trip. And how her face will light up when I walk in that office Monday morning—or maybe Monday afternoon—and she sees what this has done for me!"

Now and Then

Nassau, Bahamas, Feb. 3.

DEAREST ESTHER:

Bob is asleep and I will snatch these few minutes to write you a letter, but it may not be very long because he is liable to wake up any moment and insist that I stop writing and "pay some attention" to him. He is honestly jealous of you and I being friends or of me caring for anybody besides him enough to write to them. Isn't that too silly for words and yet it thrills me to have him be that way and shows that I am really everything in his life. He is a regular child where I am concerned and can't bear to have me even mention my old friends or things that happened before I met him.

Esther, I am tickled to death now that we didn't go on our honeymoon right after we were married, but waited these seven months when Bob can have a real vacation and don't have to be worrying about business all of the time. Just think we might never have seen this place if we hadn't made up our minds to wait and Esther it is just heaven, so beautiful and quaint that it is like a place in some other world.

Well I will begin at the beginning and tell you everything about our trip like I promised though I am afraid it won't be very interesting as in the first place I was deathly seasick all the way down on the boat, but it may sound funny but I am honestly glad I was because Bob was so perfectly dear and would not leave me for a minute though he is a wonderful sailor himself and I being sick must have simply ruined the trip for him. Well I was just in misery for three nights and two days, but as soon as the boat stopped Monday morning I was all right again and able to take in all the sights.

The boat has to anchor out in the harbor on account of the water being too shallow near land so we were all loaded on to a tender and brought to the dock here and then we had to wait around while they inspected our baggage because this is a British port though they didn't open anything at all but just put chalk marks on it and Bob says about the only thing the customs inspectors look for these days is liquor and they realize nobody would try and smuggle liquor to this place as it would be like bringing coal to New Castle, Pa.

Next we got into a two seated carriage and drove to the hotel and Bob talked to the Negro driver and of course all the drivers and people like that here are Negroes but not like our Negroes at home, they talk with a kind of English accent and you can't hardly understand them half the time. Our room is wonderful and faces on the water which is wonderful, all different shades of green and blue and purple, it makes a person wish they were a painter it is so wonderful in coloring.

At lunch time Bob told the head waiter to put us as far as he could from other people. Bob says he used to be one of the most sociable men in the world but since he married me he don't want anything to do with other people and the more we can keep to ourselves just we two the better he likes it. The head waiter give us a table in a corner near a window and when another couple came in and sat at the next table Bob actually got mad at them like nobody had a right to be in the same dining room with us almost.

After lunch I unpacked or rather I directed the unpacking and Bob did the real work as he won't let me lift my hand to really do anything as he says he would never forgive himself if I overdid. At five o'clock the hotel orchestra began playing out on the lawn where they have a dance floor and serve tea and drinks and Bob and I had some tea and cakes and danced four dances.

Most of the other people around us were drinking highballs and things and Bob said he didn't blame them, if he had to dance with some of the women here he would want to drink enough first to blind him. But he said he wanted his eyes clear when he looked at me and as for drinking anything why just being with me and touching me made him intoxicated. He does say the nicest things and puts them so differently.

He is beginning to wake up so this will have to be "continued in our next."

With love,
IRMA.

Nassau, Bahamas, Feb. 6.

DEAREST ESTHER:

We are having such a heavenly time that it seems criminal to not share it with somebody but of course it is just us being here together alone that makes it so heavenly. It is simply heavenly here and I don't see why people go other places when they can come here and I guess maybe they don't know about this place or perhaps it seems more wonderful to me than it really is on account of being here with Bob and that is what makes it so wonderful. Anyway I was never so happy in my life and am already dreading the time when it will be time to start home.

The first day we got here there was a young couple introduced themselves to Bob after dinner that evening and wanted to know did we want to play bridge with them. As you know I don't play bridge and Bob says he can't take any interest in games unless I am in them so he told these people we were going out for a sail and after we were alone he said he hated to tell a lie so we would have to go out for a sail so he would not have told those people a lie, so he hired a sail boat and it was simply heavenly sailing in the moonlight just Bob and I and the man sailing the boat who never looked at us.

The moonlight here is heavenly and I don't believe there is any other place where it is so wonderful and it was so wonderful that Bob and I had to laugh at the idea of staying in a stuffy hotel and playing cards when you could be out sailing in the moonlight though I suppose it would bore some people.

The next morning we got on the hotel boat and went over to the bathing beach and went in swimming and the water was wonderful but Bob didn't like it at first as he said there was too many people around and he hated to have other men see me in my bathing suit so he and I walked away along the beach where there was nobody else and we went in the water there. It was kind of weedy and not as nice as the regular beach as there was also some rocks in the place we went in and I stubbed my toe on one of them, but Bob said he would rather I stubbed my toe than have a lot of men staring at me, but he was awfully nice about my toe and kept asking me how it felt.

Bob is a wonderful swimmer and I tried to make him go out and enjoy himself in the deep water, but he wouldn't leave me for a second and he said he would never forgive himself if he left me and something happened to me. I told him I would stay in shallow water and there would be no danger, but he said he had heard that sharks and baracudas sometimes came right up to the beach and bit women if they were alone.

We came back to the hotel for lunch and in the afternoon we took a ride on the glass bottom boat to the sea garden. It is a boat with a glass bottom and you can see right through it and they took us to a place where the bottom of the sea is just like a garden with things growing in it and fish. It was simply heavenly, but Bob got kind of mad because there was a man that spoke to me, the man didn't mean anything, but Bob gave him a terrible look and the incident kind of spoiled the trip.

We had dinner in our room as Bob said there was too many people in the dining room. We went to bed early and the orchestra was playing out on the lawn and it was heavenly just lying there listening and finally they sang some native Bahamian songs and Bob just loved them and is going to try and get them to take home with us.

He is through shaving and all dressed and this will have to be "continued in our next" as he gets impatient if I am not ready to do things with him when he is ready to do them.

Yours,
IRMA.

Nassau, Bahamas, Feb. 10.

DEAREST ESTHER:

What do you think I did today? Well you will never guess so I may as well tell you. I played golf. I suppose I ought not to say I really played it but I played at it though Bob said I had a beautiful swing and he was amazed at how quickly I picked it up.

Bob of course is a splendid golf player and brought his clubs along, but up to today I couldn't make him play as he said it was no fun for him to do anything if I was not doing it with him, but yesterday we took a carriage ride and went past the golf course and Bob said he would like to try it and I said why didn't he and then he said he would if I would go along and play with him. Well at first I thought he was joking, but he was in dead earnest and he said he did not see any reason why I did not learn the game and then in the summer time we could play together and he would not have to play around with a lot of stupid men who always wanted to bet and then get sore when he beats them.

Well I finally agreed to try it and he borrowed some clubs from Jock Hutchinson who is the teacher down here and we went out on the linx and the first time I swang at the ball I missed it entirely, but I hit it the next time and did better after that and we played nine holes and Bob said my score was 92 which was good for a beginner. We are going to play again tomorrow and every day we are down here. It is really wonderful exercise and as long as Bob won't play without me I feel like I really ought to play with him because he really enjoys the game so much.

It took us an hour to get out there and an hour to get back, but we could have made it in ten minutes each way if we had gone in an automobile, but Bob won't use the automobiles here as he says the carriages look more in keeping with the place they are so quaint and it would be sacrilegious to use the automobiles. Well Esther won't you be proud of me when I am a real golfer and maybe I will have a chance to teach you the game some time when Bob is away on business.

We had a narrow escape when we got back to the hotel. Just as we were coming in the door a man got out of a car right behind us that Bob knows and it was just luck that he didn't see Bob. He is from Chicago and Bob says he is an awfully nice man and he does business with him sometimes, but he says our whole trip would be ruined if we couldn't be alone just by ourselves all the time we are here and not see anybody else, that is to talk to them. So we are having dinner in our room again so as not to take any chance of seeing this man and maybe his wife is here with him and we would have to spend an evening with them or something. I hope they will go away soon and not bother us.

I had some pictures taken the second day we were here by a man who takes pictures of all the hotel guests and then if you like them you can buy some of them. They were finished today and the man showed them to us and I wanted to buy two or three of each as they were awfully good, but Bob said I could only buy one of each and that would be for him and he didn't want me sending my pictures around to other people, so I guess you will just have to remember what I look like and get along without my picture.

Last night the orchestra played out on the lawn and Bob and I danced a couple of dances and were sitting there watching the others and the assistant manager of the hotel was there and he came to our table and asked me to dance and I almost started to get up when Bob answered for me and said he was sorry but I had turned my ankle in swimming.

I know the man had seen me dancing just a few minutes before and I don't know what he thought, but he was awfully nice about it and said maybe we could have a dance some other time.

After he had gone away Bob said I wasn't to speak to him next time I saw him or he would take it as an encouragement and ask me to dance with him again.

Must close now as Bob has finished the letters he was writing and wants to be read aloud to. I don't read aloud very well, but he says he loves to have me as he can sit and look at me while I read and it don't make any difference if I read well or not because he is too busy looking at me to pay any attention to what I am reading.

Love,

IRMA.

Nassau, Bahamas, Feb. 13.

DEAREST ESTHER:

I know I promised to write you every other day while we were down here, but I am afraid I will have to ask you to release me from my promise. I suppose I could tell you a fib and say I don't have time to write, but that would be a fib and the real reason I can't write to you any more is because it makes Bob mad and I won't do anything behind his back so I know you will understand if you don't hear from me again and as soon as I get home and Bob's vacation is over, I will come and see you and tell you about the rest of our trip, that is anything that might be interesting.

Bob don't like to have me write for two reasons, in the first place he is jealous of all my old friends and he says I am his wife now and all my time belongs to him and he don't want me wasting it writing to other people even if they are old friends and secondly he don't like the idea of me telling anybody the things we do down here as he says this belated honeymoon as he calls it is sacred between him and me and it is nobody's else business what we do down here.

Please try and understand Esther and forgive me and you know I love you and wouldn't do anything in the world to hurt your feelings, but I am married to Bob now and his feelings are to be considered above everything else. We are having such a heavenly time that I simply can't do anything that would spoil it in any way.

Your friend,
IRMA.

Nassau, Bahamas, Feb. 5.

DEAREST ESTHER:

Well Esther here we are Bob and I "honeymooning" again and it hardly seems possible that three years have gone by since we were in Nassau before, but don't you think it was a wonderful idea coming back to the place where we had such a heavenly time the winter after we were married and this is the first time Bob has had a real vacation since then and he has certainly earned it and I know he will enjoy every minute down here even if we keep to ourselves and just rest and "loaf."

I am feeling all right again after being terribly seasick all the way down from New York. I though it was quite rough, but Bob said it was just like a billiard table and he was quite provoked at me being sick and threatened to leave me home the next time he was going anywhere on a boat. He said he did not see how I ever sat through a dinner party as he would think the waves in the finger bowl would upset me. Bob just loves to tease me.

When we went in the dining room for lunch today the same head

waiter was there as the last time and he remembered us after three
years and gave us the same corner table we had the last time.
Imagine him remembering us after three years, but after lunch Bob
stopped and talked to him about giving us another table in the
middle of the room and not so far off from everybody as he said it
would not seem like we were in a big hotel way off from everybody
like that. So tonight he is going to change us.

I have had quite a busy afternoon unpacking and getting settled.
Bob went out with some men he met on the boat to play golf as
he said he couldn't very well get out of it and he thought I would
be too worn out to play with him after my seasickness. I am afraid
he will be bothered to death by all the different people he met on
the boat which he couldn't help because of course I was unable to
leave my stateroom for meals and they put him at a big table with a
lot of other people but he can always manage to discourage new
acquaintances if they begin to make a nuisance of themselves.

Will have to close as Bob promised he would be back in time for
a few dances before it is time to dress for dinner, but it is after six
now and the orchestra will soon stop playing, but I suppose they
were slow getting their golf game started the first day or maybe he
has had trouble getting away from those other men.

With love,

IRMA.

Nassau, Bahamas, Feb. 7.

DEAREST ESTHER:

Well it is nearly bed time but I don't feel like going to bed till
Bob comes in and he is downstairs playing bridge with a woman
and her husband and the woman's sister that he met on the boat.
I have hardly seen him at all today as he was not feeling well this
morning and would not go to the beach swimming as he said he
thought it had upset his stomach swallowing the salt water, but he
insisted on me going without him and he introduced me to a friend
of his from Chicago a Mr. Granville who was here three years ago
with his wife but his wife has since died. Bob said Mr. Granville
was a great swimmer and would see that I did not drown and
would teach me to swim.

Well I wouldn't let him teach me to swim because I hate to have a strange man come near me in swimming, but he was awfully nice to me, but I didn't stay in long as I hate to enjoy myself when Bob is not feeling well.

Bob and I had lunch together and he felt better and arranged a golf game with some people he met on the boat. I asked him if he was sure he ought to play when he didn't feel well, but he said it was swimming that upset him and not golf. I asked him if he wasn't ever going to play golf again with me and he said yes some time, but he said it wasn't much fun playing with me as I am so terrible that we can't play any kind of a match and he likes to play with people he can bet with and he also said I look so awkward when I try to play that he is afraid people will laugh at me.

Yesterday I asked him if he didn't want to go out in the glass bottom boat and look at the sea garden as we did when we were here before and he said yes we would go tomorrow, meaning today, but when I reminded him of it he told me to go alone or find somebody else to go with as he couldn't get any thrill out of looking at a bunch of dirty sea weed. He did keep his promise to take me to tea out on the lawn where they dance.

The golf match had tired him out though and he wouldn't dance but he would not admit he was tired but said he didn't like the music and wished the orchestra would get up to date and play something besides old native tunes that the Negroes down here made up. They really only played the native songs for one dance, but Bob has no ear and don't know one tune from another. He insisted on me dancing with Mr. Granville whom he invited to our table.

We had tea and Bob said he felt like he needed something stronger than tea and he drank four highballs so I knew he wasn't telling the truth when he said the golf hadn't made him tired.

I was really very tired myself and I suggested that it would be a good thing for both of us if we had dinner in our room and we would go to bed right after and I would read to him. He said he wouldn't like anything better though he could hardly understand me when I read because I mumble my words so, but he had asked some people he met on the boat to have a cocktail with him and they were people who might help him in a business way so he couldn't get out of it, but if I met them too why it would mean we would probably have them on our hands the rest of the time we are here so he thought it would be a good idea for me to have dinner by myself and go to bed when I felt like it.

After dinner he phoned up to say that he got tangled up in a bridge game with these people and I had better go to bed and not wait for him. But I know he will have some things to tell me about these people when he comes in and he tells things in such an amusing way that I hate to miss it and maybe by tomorrow morning he won't remember half the things that happened.

The weather has been heavenly and we are having a simply wonderful time and I wish some time you could come down here and spend a week or two as it is simply heavenly and I don't believe there is another place like it in the world.

Am out of stationery so this will have to be "continued in our next."

Love,
IRMA.

Nassau, Bahamas, Feb. 8.

DEAREST ESTHER:

I have been having dinner in the room again as I did not feel like dressing up and going downstairs. Bob was tired out too and wanted to stay here with me, but those people he met on the boat insisted on him having a cocktail with them and as long as he had to get dressed for that he thought he might as well eat in the dining room and now he is playing bridge with them again as they couldn't find a fourth without him. They are a Mr. and Mrs. Griffin and Mrs. Griffin's sister, Miss Cutts, and he met them on the boat coming down. Mr. Griffin is in a position to do Bob some good in a business way and that is why Bob don't like to refuse their invitations.

This morning I went over to the beach with Mr. Granville and Bob played golf with some people he met on the boat. As we were coming back from the beach a man stopped us who takes pictures and he wanted to take a picture of Mr. Granville and me together but I thought that wouldn't look right so I let him take my picture alone and while he was taking it Bob came along and he had just come back from his golf game and when he saw me getting my picture taken he teased me about it and said I must think I was a movie star, or somebody, getting my picture taken all the time.

I said I was just having it taken for him and he said I needn't waste money on pictures of myself for him as he already had enough of them and I better send these to my friends who were always asking me for my picture. So if they are good I will send you one and send some to the other girls too.

This afternoon Bob went out to play golf and I was sitting on the porch reading and Mr. Granville came along and invited me to take a drive with him and I was tired reading so I accepted and we took a carriage though Bob says it is silly to ride in the old broken down carriages they have got here when you can get a car and get to places ten times as fast but we were in no hurry so we took a carriage and drove past the golf club and they have got a bathing beach out there too and we stopped for a minute to watch the people in swimming and there was Bob swimming with Miss Cutts whom he met on the boat coming down.

Well he didn't see us and I didn't say anything to him about it when he came home but he is just a child Esther and he knew I would think it was bad for him to go in swimming when the salt water affects him so and that is why he went in swimming where he thought I wouldn't see him and I only hope he don't get sick again.

He had promised to take me for a moonlight sail tonight, but I could see that his golf and his swim had worn him out and besides that the Griffins made him stay down on the lawn when they got back from the golf club and he didn't want to offend them but felt so tired that he had to take some highballs and then Miss Cutts practically made him dance with her twice and he was tired enough without that, but he never would have told me all the things he had had to do and probably would have gone sailing with me if I had reminded him of it, but I had watched him dancing from my window which fronts on the lawn and I knew how he must feel so I pretended I had forgotten all about our sail.

Poor Bob he wasn't a bit like his usual cheerful self when he got up in the room and he would have given anything to get out of his engagement tonight and he was so cross that when I tried to persuade him to stay here by hinting that I was getting lonesome staying all by myself with nothing to do, he said, "What would you do if I was here? All you ever do is read or write letters. Why don't you write to your friend Esther and tell her your troubles?"

So I just laughed it off but I do get a little lonesome sometimes and wish he could get rid of these people he met on the boat. It is so heavenly here and such a wonderful place and we could be having such a heavenly time if it wasn't for the Griffins. Isn't it a darn shame that a man can't get away from business even on his vacation when he hasn't had one in three years?

With love,

IRMA.

Miami, Fla., Feb. 11.

DEAREST ESTHER:

You will probably be surprised at me writing to you from this place. I arrived here by boat from Nassau this morning and was sick all the way and now I am waiting for train time. I leave here tonight for home and will arrive there Thursday forenoon. I am crazy to see you Esther and I am writing to know if you can't come and visit me for a few days next week. We will go to a show every night or do anything you want to do. I just want to see you and have a nice visit.

Bob is staying on at Nassau for two more weeks as he loves it there and it agrees with him so well. I love it too and think it is the most heavenly place I ever went to, but there is so much to do there that a person simply gets worn out and both Bob and I agreed that I wasn't strong enough to stand the pace and would be better off at home.

I will be expecting a wire from you as soon as you get this. Wire me at home and I will try and get tickets for things I know you will want to see. Please come Esther. Any day will do and the sooner the better, but don't disappoint me.

Your friend,

IRMA.

My Own Beauty Secrets

In a recent issue of a weekly a lady star in a English revue, namely Miss Renslaw, who is undoubtedly one of the prettiest ladies that ever just happened, give a interview to a gal which the title of it was a woman's duty to be beautiful plus.

What Miss Renslaw seems to of meant by plus was that you should ought to be smart as well as beautiful. In other words if a gal is just beautiful without no brains why after a wile you get tired of setting around and just looking at her because you think to yourself I could get a copy of the Madonna and set there and look at that and between looks I could read the paper and find out where Sharkey was going to train. But if it is a live gal setting there why it seems kind of rude to read the papers and the gal should ought to be able to say something besides I, yes or no when you talk to her.

Well Miss Renslaw in this article tells not only how she keeps beautiful but also how she also keeps snappy and I will quote her following words:

"A woman should give over a few minutes every day to reading something good. Memorize two lines of poetry a day, a paragraph or two of good prose. Add a few words daily to your vocabulary. Do this for no other reason than to keep mentally active, enthusiastic and consequently young."

So much for keeping the brains alert. Now in regards to how to keep beautiful. Miss Renslaw says:

"Take a warm bath then lie flat on your back, draw the knees up so that the base of the spine may feel the soothing caress of the mattress. Lie thus for fifteen minutes with every fibre and nerve relaxed."

Now then, gals, Miss Renslaw has certainly showed you how to be

338

beautiful and bright and also she adds a little hint in regards to how to keep the pores of the skin closed—"first you cleanse the face thoroughly, then with a tiny brush or a piece of clean cloth, apply the unbeaten white of a egg to the skin. Let the albumen dry on the skin etc."

But that don't tell the male sex how to be pretty and clever at one and the same time but at least one person has wrote in and requested me to tell them how I do it.

Well, gents, when I go to bed nights, if ever, I always do one knee up in a plaster cast to be sure it won't go nowheres. Then I always lay down on my left side and memorize a couple of paragraphs of the official football guide. Like for inst.:

"The service is a fault as provided for by Rule 9, or if the ball served touches the server's partner or anything which he wears or carries."

"In case a player is hindered in makeing a stroke by anything not within his control, except a permanent fixture of the court, the point shall be replayed."

By this time I am generally always so exhausted that I have to call in a chiropracter, but only for a few hours. After that I uncast my knee and set up in bed and read the first few pages of the Syracuse telephone directory. Then I lay back again and scream a few moments to keep my throat clear. The next step is to call up a general practitioner and try and find out what is the matter. His name is usually Dr. Patterson but you can't depend on that. Before finely retireing for the night I see that all the pores is closed and all the doors is locked. Then I dust my face off with a whisk broom.

When dawn comes I always get up and like Miss Renslaw try and add a few words to my vocabulary. Like for inst., yesterday morning I put on the following nouns:

Wham

Kurtell

Grafe.

The first two mean that a caravan is just starting out and the noun grafe means that you ain't paid your insurance.

That is about all of my system, gents, and as for comparisons why look at my picture and then look at Miss Renslaw and judge for yourself.

The Golden Honeymoon

Mother says that when I start talking I never know when to stop.
But I tell her the only time I get a chance is when she ain't around,
so I have to make the most of it. I guess the fact is neither one of us
would be welcome in a Quaker meeting, but as I tell Mother, what
did God give us tongues for if He didn't want we should use them?
Only she says He didn't give them to us to say the same thing over
and over again, like I do, and repeat myself. But I say:

"Well, Mother," I say, "when people is like you and I and been
married fifty years, do you expect everything I say will be something
you ain't heard me say before? But it may be new to others, as they
ain't nobody else lived with me as long as you have."

So she says:

"You can bet they ain't, as they couldn't nobody else stand you
that long."

"Well," I tell her, "you look pretty healthy."

"Maybe I do," she will say, "but I looked even healthier before
I married you."

You can't get ahead of Mother.

Yes, sir, we was married just fifty years ago the seventeenth day of
last December and my daughter and son-in-law was over from Trenton to help us celebrate the Golden Wedding. My son-in-law is John
H. Kramer, the real estate man. He made $12,000 one year and is
pretty well thought of around Trenton; a good, steady, hard
worker. The Rotarians was after him a long time to join, but he
kept telling them his home was his club. But Edie finally made him
join. That's my daughter.

Well, anyway, they come over to help us celebrate the Golden
Wedding and it was pretty crimpy weather and the furnace don't
seem to heat up no more like it used to and Mother made the
remark that she hoped this winter wouldn't be as cold as the last,

referring to the winter previous. So Edie said if she was us, and nothing to keep us home, she certainly wouldn't spend no more winters up here and why didn't we just shut off the water and close up the house and go down to Tampa, Florida? You know we was there four winters ago and staid five weeks, but it cost us over three hundred and fifty dollars for hotel bill alone. So Mother said we wasn't going no place to be robbed. So my son-in-law spoke up and said that Tampa wasn't the only place in the South, and besides we didn't have to stop at no high price hotel but could rent us a couple rooms and board out somewheres, and he had heard that St. Petersburg, Florida, was *the* spot and if we said the word he would write down there and make inquiries.

Well, to make a long story short, we decided to do it and Edie said it would be our Golden Honeymoon and for a present my son-in-law paid the difference between a section and a compartment so as we could have a compartment and have more privatecy. In a compartment you have an upper and lower berth just like the regular sleeper, but it is a shut in room by itself and got a wash bowl. The car we went in was all compartments and no regular berths at all. It was all compartments.

We went to Trenton the night before and staid at my daughter and son-in-law and we left Trenton the next afternoon at 3.23 P.M.

This was the twelfth day of January. Mother set facing the front of the train, as it makes her giddy to ride backwards. I set facing her, which does not affect me. We reached North Philadelphia at 4.03 P.M. and we reached West Philadelphia at 4.14, but did not go into Broad Street. We reached Baltimore at 6.30 and Washington, D.C., at 7.25. Our train laid over in Washington two hours till another train come along to pick us up and I got out and strolled up the platform and into the Union Station. When I come back, our car had been switched on to another track, but I remembered the name of it, the La Belle, as I had once visited my aunt out in Oconomowoc, Wisconsin, where there was a lake of that name, so I had no difficulty in getting located. But Mother had nearly fretted herself sick for fear I would be left.

"Well," I said, "I would of followed you on the next train."

"You could of," said Mother, and she pointed out that she had the money.

"Well," I said, "we are in Washington and I could of borrowed from the United States Treasury. I would of pretended I was an Englishman."

Mother caught the point and laughed heartily.

Our train pulled out of Washington at 9.40 P.M. and Mother and I turned in early, I taking the upper. During the night we passed through the green fields of old Virginia, though it was too dark to tell if they was green or what color. When we got up in the morning, we was at Fayetteville, North Carolina. We had breakfast in the dining car and after breakfast I got in conversation with the man in the next compartment to ours. He was from Lebanon, New Hampshire, and a man about eighty years of age. His wife was with him, and two unmarried daughters and I made the remark that I should think the four of them would be crowded in one compartment, but he said they had made the trip every winter for fifteen years and knowed how to keep out of each other's way. He said they was bound for Tarpon Springs.

We reached Charleston, South Carolina, at 12.50 P.M. and arrived at Savannah, Georgia, at 4.20. We reached Jacksonville, Florida, at 8.45 P.M. and had an hour and a quarter to lay over there, but Mother made a fuss about me getting off the train, so we had the darky make up our berths and retired before we left Jacksonville. I didn't sleep good as the train done a lot of hemming and hawing, and Mother never sleeps good on a train as she says she is always worrying that I will fall out. She says she would rather have the upper herself, as then she would not have to worry about me, but I tell her I can't take the risk of having it get out that I allowed my wife to sleep in an upper berth. It would make talk.

We was up in the morning in time to see our friends from New Hampshire get off at Tarpon Springs, which we reached at 6.53 A.M.

Several of our fellow passengers got off at Clearwater and some at Belleair, where the train backs right up to the door of the mammoth hotel. Belleair is the winter headquarters for the golf dudes and everybody that got off there had their bag of sticks, as many as ten and twelve in a bag. Women and all. When I was a young man we called it shinny and only needed one club to play with and about one game of it would of been a-plenty for some of these dudes, the way we played it.

The train pulled into St. Petersburg at 8.20 and when we got off the train you would think they was a riot, what with all the darkies barking for the different hotels.

I said to Mother, I said:

"It is a good thing we have got a place picked out to go to and don't have to choose a hotel, as it would be hard to choose amongst them if every one of them is the best."

She laughed.

We found a jitney and I give him the address of the room my son-in-law had got for us and soon we was there and introduced ourselves to the lady that owns the house, a young widow about forty-eight years of age. She showed us our room, which was light and airy with a comfortable bed and bureau and washstand. It was twelve dollars a week, but the location was good, only three blocks from Williams Park.

St. Pete is what folks calls the town, though they also call it the Sunshine City, as they claim they's no other place in the country where they's fewer days when Old Sol don't smile down on Mother Earth, and one of the newspapers gives away all their copies free every day when the sun don't shine. They claim to of only give them away some sixty-odd times in the last eleven years. An other nickname they have got for the town is "the Poor Man's Palm Beach," but I guess they's men that comes there that could borrow as much from the bank as some of the Willie boys over to the other Palm Beach.

During our stay we paid a visit to the Lewis Tent City, which is the headquarters for the Tin Can Tourists. But maybe you ain't heard about them. Well, they are an organization that takes their vacation trips by auto and carries everything with them. That is, they bring along their tents to sleep in and cook in and they don't patronize no hotels or cafeterias, but they have got to be bona fide auto campers or they can't belong to the organization.

They tell me they's over 200,000 members to it and they call themselves the Tin Canners on account of most of their food being put up in tin cans. One couple we seen in the Tent City was a couple from Brady, Texas, named Mr. and Mrs. Pence, which the old man is over eighty years of age and they had came in their auto all the way from home, a distance of 1,641 miles. They took five weeks for the trip, Mr. Pence driving the entire distance.

The Tin Canners hails from every State in the Union and in the summer time they visit places like New England and the Great Lakes region, but in the winter the most of them comes to Florida and scatters all over the State. While we was down there, they was a national convention of them at Gainesville, Florida, and they elected a Fredonia, New York, man as their president. His title is Royal Tin Can Opener of the World. They have got a song wrote up which everybody has got to learn it before they are a member:

> "The tin can forever! Hurrah, boys! Hurrah!
>   Up with the tin can! Down with the foe!
> We will rally round the campfire, we'll rally once again,
>   Shouting, 'We auto camp forever!' "

That is something like it. And the members has also got to have a tin can fastened on to the front of their machine.

I asked Mother how she would like to travel around that way and she said:

"Fine, but not with an old rattle brain like you driving."

"Well," I said, "I am eight years younger than this Mr. Pence who drove here from Texas."

"Yes," she said, "but he is old enough to not be skittish."

You can't get ahead of Mother.

Well, one of the first things we done in St. Petersburg was to go to the Chamber of Commerce and register our names and where we was from as they's great rivalry amongst the different States in regards to the number of their citizens visiting in town and of course our little State don't stand much of a show, but still every little bit helps, as the fella says. All and all, the man told us, they was eleven thousand names registered, Ohio leading with some fifteen hundred-odd and New York State next with twelve hundred. Then come Michigan, Pennsylvania and so on down, with one man each from Cuba and Nevada.

The first night we was there, they was a meeting of the New York-New Jersey Society at the Congregational Church and a man from Ogdensburg, New York State, made the talk. His subject was Rainbow Chasing. He is a Rotarian and a very convicting speaker, though I forget his name.

Our first business, of course, was to find a place to eat and after trying several places we run on to a cafeteria on Central Avenue that suited us up and down. We eat pretty near all our meals there and it averaged about two dollars per day for the two of us, but the food was well cooked and everything nice and clean. A man don't mind paying the price if things is clean and well cooked.

On the third day of February, which is Mother's birthday, we spread ourselves and eat supper at the Poinsettia Hotel and they charged us seventy-five cents for a sirloin steak that wasn't hardly big enough for one.

I said to Mother: "Well," I said, "I guess it's a good thing every day ain't your birthday or we would be in the poorhouse."

"No," says Mother, "because if every day was my birthday, I would be old enough by this time to of been in my grave long ago."

You can't get ahead of Mother.

In the hotel they had a card-room where they was several men and ladies playing five hundred and this new fangled whist bridge. We also seen a place where they was dancing, so I asked Mother would she like to trip the light fantastic toe and she said no, she was too old to squirm like you have got to do now days. We watched some of the young folks at it awhile till Mother got disgusted and said we would have to see a good movie to take the taste out of our mouth. Mother is a great movie heroyne and we go twice a week here at home.

But I want to tell you about the Park. The second day we was there we visited the Park, which is a good deal like the one in Tampa, only bigger, and they's more fun goes on here every day than you could shake a stick at. In the middle they's a big bandstand and chairs for the folks to set and listen to the concerts, which they give you music for all tastes, from Dixie up to classical pieces like Hearts and Flowers.

Then all around they's places marked off for different sports and games—chess and checkers and dominoes for folks that enjoys those kind of games, and roque and horse-shoes for the nimbler ones. I used to pitch a pretty fair shoe myself, but ain't done much of it in the last twenty years.

Well, anyway, we bought a membership ticket in the club which costs one dollar for the season, and they tell me that up to a couple years ago it was fifty cents, but they had to raise it to keep out the riffraff.

Well, Mother and I put in a great day watching the pitchers and she wanted I should get in the game, but I told her I was all out of practice and would make a fool of myself, though I seen several men pitching who I guess I could take their measure without no practice. However, they was some good pitchers, too, and one boy from Akron, Ohio, who could certainly throw a pretty shoe. They told me it looked like he would win the championship of the United States in the February tournament. We come away a few days before they held that and I never did hear if he win. I forget his name, but he was a clean cut young fella and he has got a brother in Cleveland that's a Rotarian.

Well, we just stood around and watched the different games for two or three days and finally I set down in a checker game with a man named Weaver from Danville, Illinois. He was a pretty fair checker player, but he wasn't no match for me, and I hope that don't sound like bragging. But I always could hold my own on a checker-board and the folks around here will tell you the same thing. I played with this Weaver pretty near all morning for two or three mornings and he beat me one game and the only other time it looked like he had a chance, the noon whistle blowed and we had to quit and go to dinner.

While I was playing checkers, Mother would set and listen to the band, as she loves music, classical or no matter what kind, but any-way she was setting there one day and between selections the woman next to her opened up a conversation. She was a woman about Mother's own age, seventy or seventy-one, and finally she asked Mother's name and Mother told her her name and where she was from and Mother asked her the same question, and who do you think the woman was?

Well, sir, it was the wife of Frank M. Hartsell, the man who was engaged to Mother till I stepped in and cut him out, fifty-two years ago!

Yes, sir!

You can imagine Mother's surprise! And Mrs. Hartsell was sur-prised, too, when Mother told her she had once been friends with her husband, though Mother didn't say how close friends they had been, or that Mother and I was the cause of Hartsell going out West. But that's what we was. Hartsell left his town a month after the engagement was broke off and ain't never been back since. He had went out to Michigan and became a veterinary, and that is where he had settled down, in Hillsdale, Michigan, and finally married his wife.

Well, Mother screwed up her courage to ask if Frank was still living and Mrs. Hartsell took her over to where they was pitching horse-shoes and there was old Frank, waiting his turn. And he knowed Mother as soon as he seen her, though it was over fifty years. He said he knowed her by her eyes.

"Why, it's Lucy Frost!" he says, and he throwed down his shoes and quit the game.

Then they come over and hunted me up and I will confess I wouldn't of knowed him. Him and I is the same age to the month, but he seems to show it more, some way. He is balder for one thing. And his beard is all white, where mine has still got a streak of brown in it. The very first thing I said to him, I said:

"Well, Frank, that beard of yours makes me feel like I was back north. It looks like a regular blizzard."

"Well," he said, "I guess yourn would be just as white if you had it dry cleaned."

But Mother wouldn't stand that.

"Is that so!" she said to Frank. "Well, Charley ain't had no tobacco in his mouth for over ten years!"

And I ain't!

Well, I excused myself from the checker game and it was pretty close to noon, so we decided to all have dinner together and they was nothing for it only we must try their cafeteria on Third Avenue. It was a little more expensive than ours and not near as good, I thought. I and Mother had about the same dinner we had been having every day and our bill was $1.10. Frank's check was $1.20 for he and his wife. The same meal wouldn't of cost them more than a dollar at our place.

After dinner we made them come up to our house and we all set in the parlor, which the young woman had give us the use of to entertain company. We begun talking over old times and Mother said she was a-scared Mrs. Hartsell would find it tiresome listening to we three talk over old times, but as it turned out they wasn't much chance for nobody else to talk with Mrs. Hartsell in the company. I have heard lots of women that could go it, but Hartsell's wife takes the cake of all the women I ever seen. She told us the family history of everybody in the State of Michigan and bragged for a half hour about her son, who she said is in the drug business in Grand Rapids, and a Rotarian.

When I and Hartsell could get a word in edgeways we joked one another back and forth and I chafed him about being a horse doctor.

"Well, Frank," I said, "you look pretty prosperous, so I suppose they's been plenty of glanders around Hillsdale."

"Well," he said, "I've managed to make more than a fair living. But I've worked pretty hard."

"Yes," I said, "and I suppose you get called out all hours of the night to attend births and so on."

Mother made me shut up.

Well, I thought they wouldn't never go home and I and Mother was in misery trying to keep awake, as the both of us generally always takes a nap after dinner. Finally they went, after we had made an engagement to meet them in the Park the next morning, and Mrs. Hartsell also invited us to come to their place the next night and play five hundred. But she had forgot that they was a meeting of the Michigan Society that evening, so it was not till two evenings later that we had our first card game.

Hartsell and his wife lived in a house on Third Avenue North and had a private setting room besides their bedroom. Mrs. Hartsell couldn't quit talking about their private setting room like it was something wonderful. We played cards with them, with Mother and Hartsell partners against his wife and I. Mrs. Hartsell is a miserable card player and we certainly got the worst of it.

After the game she brought out a dish of oranges and we had to pretend it was just what we wanted, though oranges down there is like a young man's whiskers; you enjoy them at first, but they get to be a pesky nuisance.

We played cards again the next night at our place with the same partners and I and Mrs. Hartsell was beat again. Mother and Hartsell was full of compliments for each other on what a good team they made, but the both of them knowed well enough where the secret of their success laid. I guess all and all we must of played ten different evenings and they was only one night when Mrs. Hartsell and I come out ahead. And that one night wasn't no fault of hern.

When we had been down there about two weeks, we spent one evening as their guest in the Congregational Church, at a social give by the Michigan Society. A talk was made by a man named Bitting of Detroit, Michigan, on How I was Cured of Story Telling. He is a big man in the Rotarians and give a witty talk.

A woman named Mrs. Oxford rendered some selections which Mrs. Hartsell said was grand opera music, but whatever they was my daughter Edie could of give her cards and spades and not made such a hullaballoo about it neither.

Then they was a ventriloquist from Grand Rapids and a young woman about forty-five years of age that mimicked different kinds of birds. I whispered to Mother that they all sounded like a chicken, but she nudged me to shut up.

After the show we stopped in a drug store and I set up the refreshments and it was pretty close to ten o'clock before we finally turned in. Mother and I would of preferred tending the movies, but Mother said we mustn't offend Mrs. Hartsell, though I asked her had we came to Florida to enjoy ourselves or to just not offend an old chatterbox from Michigan.

I felt sorry for Hartsell one morning. The women folks both had an engagement down to the chiropodist's and I run across Hartsell in the Park and he foolishly offered to play me checkers.

It was him that suggested it, not me, and I guess he repented himself before we had played one game. But he was too stubborn to give up and set there while I beat him game after game and the worst part of it was that a crowd of folks had got in the habit of watching me play and there they all was, looking on, and finally they seen what a fool Frank was making of himself, and they began to chafe him and pass remarks. Like one of them said:

"Who ever told you you was a checker player!"

And:

"You might maybe be good for tiddle-de-winks, but not checkers!"

I almost felt like letting him beat me a couple games. But the crowd would of knowed it was a put up job.

Well, the women folks joined us in the Park and I wasn't going to mention our little game, but Hartsell told about it himself and admitted he wasn't no match for me.

"Well," said Mrs. Hartsell, "checkers ain't much of a game anyway, is it?" She said: "It's more of a children's game, ain't it? At least, I know my boy's children used to play it a good deal."

"Yes, ma'am," I said. "It's a children's game the way your husband plays it, too."

Mother wanted to smooth things over, so she said:

"Maybe they's other games where Frank can beat you."

"Yes," said Mrs. Hartsell, "and I bet he could beat you pitching horse-shoes."

"Well," I said, "I would give him a chance to try, only I ain't pitched a shoe in over sixteen years."

"Well," said Hartsell, "I ain't played checkers in twenty years."

"You ain't never played it," I said.

"Anyway," says Frank, "Lucy and I is your master at five hundred."

Well, I could of told him why that was, but had decency enough to hold my tongue.

It had got so now that he wanted to play cards every night and when I or Mother wanted to go to a movie, any one of us would have to pretend we had a headache and then trust to goodness that they wouldn't see us sneak into the theater. I don't mind playing cards when my partner keeps their mind on the game, but you take a woman like Hartsell's wife and how can they play cards when they have got to stop every couple seconds and brag about their son in Grand Rapids?

Well, the New York-New Jersey Society announced that they was goin to give a social evening too and I said to Mother, I said:

"Well, that is one evening when we will have an excuse not to play five hundred."

"Yes," she said, "but we will have to ask Frank and his wife to go to the social with us as they asked us to go to the Michigan social."

"Well," I said, "I had rather stay home than drag that chatterbox everywheres we go."

So Mother said:

"You are getting too cranky. Maybe she does talk a little too much but she is good hearted. And Frank is always good company."

So I said:

"I suppose if he is such good company you wished you had of married him."

Mother laughed and said I sounded like I was jealous. Jealous of a cow doctor!

Anyway we had to drag them along to the social and I will say that we give them a much better entertainment than they had given us.

Judge Lane of Paterson made a fine talk on business conditions and a Mrs. Newell of Westfield imitated birds, only you could really tell what they was the way she done it. Two young women from Red Bank sung a choral selection and we clapped them back and they gave us Home to Our Mountains and Mother and Mrs. Hartsell both had tears in their eyes. And Hartsell, too.

Well, some way or another the chairman got wind that I was there and asked me to make a talk and I wasn't even going to get up, but Mother made me, so I got up and said:

"Ladies and gentlemen," I said. "I didn't expect to be called on for a speech on an occasion like this or no other occasion as I do not set myself up as a speech maker, so will have to do the best I can, which I often say is the best anybody can do."

Then I told them the story about Pat and the motorcycle, using the brogue, and it seemed to tickle them and I told them one or two other stories, but altogether I wasn't on my feet more than twenty or twenty-five minutes and you ought to of heard the clapping and hollering when I set down. Even Mrs. Hartsell admitted that I am quite a speechifier and said if I ever went to Grand Rapids, Michigan, her son would make me talk to the Rotarians.

When it was over, Hartsell wanted we should go to their house and play cards, but his wife reminded him that it was after 9.30 P.M., rather a late hour to start a card game, but he had went crazy on the subject of cards, probably because he didn't have to play partners with his wife. Anyway, we got rid of them and went home to bed.

It was the next morning, when we met over to the Park, that Mrs. Hartsell made the remark that she wasn't getting no exercise so I suggested that why didn't she take part in the roque game.

She said she had not played a game of roque in twenty years, but if Mother would play she would play. Well, at first Mother wouldn't hear of it, but finally consented, more to please Mrs. Hartsell than anything else.

Well, they had a game with a Mrs. Ryan from Eagle, Nebraska, and a young Mrs. Morse from Rutland, Vermont, who Mother had met down to the chiropodist's. Well, Mother couldn't hit a flea and they all laughed at her and I couldn't help from laughing at her myself and finally she quit and said her back was too lame to stoop over. So they got another lady and kept on playing and soon Mrs. Hartsell was the one everybody was laughing at, as she had a long shot to hit the black ball, and as she made the effort her teeth fell out on to the court. I never seen a woman so flustered in my life. And I never heard so much laughing, only Mrs. Hartsell didn't join in and she was madder than a hornet and wouldn't play no more, so the game broke up.

Mrs. Hartsell went home without speaking to nobody, but Hartsell stayed around and finally he said to me, he said:

"Well, I played you checkers the other day and you beat me bad and now what do you say if you and me play a game of horse-shoes?"

I told him I hadn't pitched a shoe in sixteen years, but Mother said:

"Go ahead and play. You used to be good at it and maybe it will come back to you."

Well, to make a long story short, I give in. I oughtn't to of never tried it, as I hadn't pitched a shoe in sixteen years, and I only done it to humor Hartsell.

Before we started, Mother patted me on the back and told me to do my best, so we started in and I seen right off that I was in for it, as I hadn't pitched a shoe in sixteen years and didn't have my distance. And besides, the plating had wore off the shoes so that they was points right where they stuck into my thumb and I hadn't throwed more than two or three times when my thumb was raw and it pretty near killed me to hang on to the shoe, let alone pitch it.

Well, Hartsell throws the awkwardest shoe I ever seen pitched and to see him pitch you wouldn't think he would ever come nowheres near, but he is also the luckiest pitcher I ever seen and he made some pitches where the shoe lit five and six feet short and then schoonered up and was a ringer. They's no use trying to beat that kind of luck.

They was a pretty fair size crowd watching us and four or five other ladies besides Mother, and it seems like, when Hartsell pitches, he has got to chew and it kept the ladies on the anxious seat as he don't seem to care which way he is facing when he leaves go.

You would think a man as old as him would of learnt more manners.

Well, to make a long story short, I was just beginning to get my distance when I had to give up on account of my thumb, which I showed it to Hartsell and he seen I couldn't go on, as it was raw and bleeding. Even if I could of stood it to go on myself, Mother wouldn't of allowed it after she seen my thumb. So anyway I quit and Hartsell said the score was nineteen to six, but I don't know what it was. Or don't care, neither.

Well, Mother and I went home and I said I hoped we was through with the Hartsells as I was sick and tired of them, but it seemed like she had promised we would go over to their house that evening for another game of their everlasting cards.

Well, my thumb was giving me considerable pain and I felt kind of out of sorts and I guess maybe I forgot myself, but anyway, when we was about through playing Hartsell made the remark that he wouldn't never lose a game of cards if he could always have Mother for a partner.

So I said:

"Well, you had a chance fifty years ago to always have her for a partner, but you wasn't man enough to keep her."

I was sorry the minute I had said it and Hartsell didn't know what to say and for once his wife couldn't say nothing. Mother tried to smooth things over by making the remark that I must of had something stronger than tea or I wouldn't talk so silly. But Mrs. Hartsell had froze up like an iceberg and hardly said good night to us and I bet her and Frank put in a pleasant hour after we was gone.

As we was leaving, Mother said to him: "Never mind Charley's nonsense, Frank. He is just mad because you beat him all hollow pitching horseshoes and playing cards."

She said that to make up for my slip, but at the same time she certainly riled me. I tried to keep ahold of myself, but as soon as we was out of the house she had to open up the subject and begun to scold me for the break I had made.

Well, I wasn't in no mood to be scolded. So I said:

"I guess he is such a wonderful pitcher and card player that you wished you had married him."

"Well," she said, "at least he ain't a baby to give up pitching because his thumb has got a few scratches."

"And how about you," I said, "making a fool of yourself on the roque court and then pretending your back is lame and you can't play no more!"

"Yes," she said, "but when you hurt your thumb I didn't laugh at you, and why did you laugh at me when I sprained my back?"

"Who could help from laughing!" I said.

"Well," she said, "Frank Hartsell didn't laugh."

"Well," I said, "why didn't you marry him?"

"Well," said Mother, "I almost wished I had!"

"And I wished so, too!" I said.

"I'll remember that!" said Mother, and that's the last word she said to me for two days.

We seen the Hartsells the next day in the Park and I was willing to apologize, but they just nodded to us. And a couple days later we heard they had left for Orlando, where they have got relatives.

I wished they had went there in the first place.

Mother and I made it up setting on a bench.

"Listen, Charley," she said. "This is our Golden Honeymoon and we don't want the whole thing spoilt with a silly old quarrel."

"Well," I said, "did you mean that about wishing you had married Hartsell?"

"Of course not," she said, "that is, if you didn't mean that you wished I had, too."

So I said:

"I was just tired and all wrought up. I thank God you chose me instead of him as they's no other woman in the world who I could of lived with all these years."

"How about Mrs. Hartsell?" says Mother.

"Good gracious!" I said. "Imagine being married to a woman that plays five hundred like she does and drops her teeth on the roque court!"

"Well," said Mother, "it wouldn't be no worse than being married to a man that expectorates towards ladies and is such a fool in a checker game."

So I put my arm around her shoulder and she stroked my hand and I guess we got kind of spoony.

They was two days left of our stay in St. Petersburg and the next to the last day Mother introduced me to a Mrs. Kendall from Kingston, Rhode Island, who she had met at the chiropodist's.

Mrs. Kendall made us acquainted with her husband, who is in the grocery business. They have got two sons and five grandchildren and one great-grandchild. One of their sons lives in Providence and is way up in the Elks as well as a Rotarian.

We found them very congenial people and we played cards with them the last two nights we was there. They was both experts and I only wished we had met them sooner instead of running into the Hartsells. But the Kendalls will be there again next winter and we will see more of them, that is, if we decide to make the trip again.

We left the Sunshine City on the eleventh day of February, at 11 A.M. This give us a day trip through Florida and we seen all the country we had passed through at night on the way down.

We reached Jacksonville at 7 P.M. and pulled out of there at 8:10 P.M. We reached Fayetteville, North Carolina, at nine o'clock the following morning, and reached Washington, D. C., at 6:30 P.M., laying over there half an hour.

We reached Trenton at 11:01 P.M. and had wired ahead to my daughter and son-in-law and they met us at the train and we went to their house and they put us up for the night. John would of made us stay up all night, telling about our trip, but Edie said we must be tired and made us go to bed. That's my daughter.

The next day we took our train for home and arrived safe and sound, having been gone just one month and a day.

Here comes Mother, so I guess I better shut up.

PART FOUR

Little Tales of Suburbia

Who Dealt?

You know, this is the first time Tom and I have been with real friends since we were married. I suppose you'll think it's funny for me to call you *my* friends when we've never met before, but Tom has talked about you so much and how much he thought of you and how crazy he was to see you and everything—well, it's just as if I'd known you all my life, like he has.

We've got our little crowd out there, play bridge and dance with them; but of course we've only been there three months, at least I have, and people you've known that length of time, well, it isn't like knowing people all your life, like you and Tom. How often I've heard Tom say he'd give any amount of money to be with Arthur and Helen, and how bored he was out there with just poor little me and his new friends!

Arthur and Helen, Arthur and Helen—he talks about you so much that it's a wonder I'm not jealous; especially of you, Helen. You must have been his real pal when you were kids.

Nearly all of his kid books, they have your name in front—to Thomas Cannon from Helen Bird Strong. This is a wonderful treat for him to see you! And a treat for me, too. Just think, I've at last met the wonderful Helen and Arthur! You must forgive me calling you by your first names; that's how I always think of you and I simply can't say Mr. and Mrs. Gratz.

No, thank you, Arthur; no more. Two is my limit and I've already exceeded it, with two cocktails before dinner and now this. But it's a special occasion, meeting Tom's best friends. I bet Tom wishes he could celebrate too, don't you, dear? Of course he could if he wanted to, but when he once makes up his mind to a thing, there's nothing in the world can shake him. He's got the strongest will power of any person I ever saw.

I do think it's wonderful, him staying on the wagon this long, a man that used to—well, you know as well as I do; probably a whole lot better, because you were with him so much in the old days, and all I know is just what he's told me. He told me about once in Pittsburgh—— All right, Tommie; I won't say another word. But it's all over now, thank heavens! Not a drop since we've been married; three whole months! And he says it's forever, don't you, dear? Though I don't mind a person drinking if they do it in moderation. But you know Tom! He goes the limit in everything he does. Like he used to in athletics——

All right, dear; I won't make you blush. I know how you hate the limelight. It's terrible, though, not to be able to boast about your own husband; everything he does or ever has done seems so wonderful. But is that only because we've been married such a short time? Do you feel the same way about Arthur, Helen? You do? And you married him four years ago, isn't that right? And you eloped, didn't you? You see I know all about you.

Oh, are you waiting for me? Do we cut for partners? Why can't we play families? I don't feel so bad if I do something dumb when it's Tom I'm playing with. He never scolds, though he does give me some terrible looks. But not very often lately; I don't make the silly mistakes I used to. I'm pretty good now, aren't I, Tom? You better say so, because if I'm not, it's your fault. You know Tom had to teach me the game. I never played at all till we were engaged. Imagine! And I guess I was pretty awful at first, but Tom was a dear, so patient! I know he thought I never would learn, but I fooled you, didn't I, Tommie?

No, indeed, I'd rather play than do almost anything. But you'll sing for us, won't you, Helen? I mean after a while. Tom has raved to me about your voice and I'm dying to hear it.

What are we playing for? Yes, a penny's perfectly all right. Out there we generally play for half a cent a piece, a penny a family. But a penny apiece is all right. I guess we can afford it now, can't we, dear? Tom hasn't told you about his raise. He was—— All right, Tommie; I'll shut up. I know you hate to be talked about, but your wife can't help being just a teeny bit proud of you. And I think your best friends are interested in your affairs, aren't you, folks?

But Tom is the most secretive person I ever knew. I believe he even keeps things from me! Not very many, though. I can usually tell when he's hiding something and I keep after him till he confesses.

He often says I should have been a lawyer or a detective, the way I can worm things out of people. Don't you, Tom?

For instance, I never would have known about his experience with those horrid football people at Yale if I hadn't just made him tell me. Didn't you know about that? No, Tom, I'm going to tell Arthur even if you hate me for it. I know you'd be interested, Arthur, not only because you're Tom's friend, but on account of you being such a famous athlete yourself. Let me see, how was it, Tom? You must help me out. Well, if I don't get it right, you correct me.

Well, Tom's friends at Yale had heard what a wonderful football player he was in high school so they made him try for a place on the Yale nine. Tom had always played half-back. You have to be a fast runner to be a half-back and Tom could run awfully fast. He can yet. When we were engaged we used to run races and the prize was —— All right, Tommie, I won't give away our secrets. Anyway, he can beat me to pieces.

Well, he wanted to play half-back at Yale and he was getting along fine and the other men on the team said he would be a wonder and then one day they were having their practice and Tex Jones, no, Ted Jones—he's the main coach—he scolded Tom for having the signal wrong and Tom proved that Jones was wrong and he was right and Jones never forgave him. He made Tom quit playing half-back and put him tackle or end or some place like that where you can't do anything and being a fast runner doesn't count. So Tom saw that Jones had it in for him and he quit. Wasn't that it, Tom? Well, anyway, it was something.

Oh, are you waiting for me? I'm sorry, What did you bid, Helen? And you, Tom? You doubled her? And Arthur passed? Well, let's see. I wish I could remember what that means. I know that sometimes when he doubles he means one thing and sometimes another. But I always forget which is which. Let me see; it was two spades that he doubled, wasn't it? That means I'm to leave him in, I'm pretty sure. Well, I'll pass. Oh, I'm sorry, Tommie! I knew I'd get it wrong. Please forgive me. But maybe we'll set them anyway. Whose lead?

I'll stop talking now and try and keep my mind on the game. You needn't look that way, Tommie. I *can* stop talking if I try. It's kind of hard to concentrate though, when you're, well, excited. It's not only meeting you people, but I always get excited traveling. I was just terrible on our honeymoon, but then I guess a honeymoon's enough to make anybody nervous. I'll never forget when we went into the hotel in Chicago—— All right, Tommie, I won't. But I can tell about meeting the Bakers.

They're a couple about our age that I've known all my life. They were the last people in the world I wanted to see, but we ran into them on State Street and they insisted on us coming to their hotel for dinner and before dinner they took us up to their room and Ken—that's Mr. Baker—Ken made some cocktails, though I didn't want any and Tom was on the wagon. He said a honeymoon was a fine time to be on the wagon! Ken said.

"Don't tempt him, Ken," I said. "Tom isn't a drinker like you and Gertie and the rest of us. When he starts, he can't stop." Gertie is Mrs. Baker.

So Ken said why should he stop and I said there was good reason why he should because he had promised me he would and he told me the day we were married that if I ever saw him take another drink I would know that——

What did you make? Two odd? Well, thank heavens that isn't a game! Oh, that does make a game, doesn't it? Because Tom doubled and I left him in. Isn't that wicked! Oh, dearie, please forgive me and I'll promise to pay attention from now on! What do I do with these? Oh, yes, I make them for Arthur.

I was telling you about the Bakers. Finally Ken saw he couldn't make Tom take a drink, so he gave up in disgust. But imagine meeting them on our honeymoon, when we didn't want to see anybody! I don't suppose anybody does unless they're already tired of each other, and we certainly weren't, were we, Tommie? And aren't yet, are we, dear? And never will be. But I guess I better speak for myself.

There! I'm talking again! But you see it's the first time we've been with anybody we really cared about; I mean, you're Tom's best friends and it's so nice to get a chance to talk to somebody who's known him a long time. Out there the people we run around with are almost strangers and they don't talk about anything but themselves and how much money their husbands make. You never can talk to them about things that are worth while, like books. I'm wild about books, but I honestly don't believe half the women we know out there can read. Or at least they don't. If you mention some really worth while novel like, say, "Black Oxen," they think you're trying to put on the Ritz.

You said a no-trump, didn't you, Tom? And Arthur passed. Let me see; I wish I knew what to do. I haven't any five-card—it's terrible! Just a minute. I wish somebody could—I know I ought to take—but—well, I'll pass. Oh, Tom, this is the worst you ever saw, but I don't know what I could have done.

I do hold the most terrible cards! I certainly believe in the saying, "Unlucky at cards, lucky in love." Whoever made it up must have been thinking of me. I hate to lay them down, dear. I know you'll say I ought to have done something. Well, there they are! Let's see your hand, Helen. Oh, Tom, she's—but I mustn't tell, must I? Anyway, I'm dummy. That's one comfort. I can't make a mistake when I'm dummy. I believe Tom overbids lots of times so I'll be dummy and can't do anything ridiculous. But at that I'm much better than I used to be, aren't I, dear?

Helen, do you mind telling me where you got that gown? Crandall and Nelsons's? I've heard of them, but I heard they were terribly expensive. Of course a person can't expect to get a gown like that without paying for it. I've got to get some things while I'm here and I suppose that's where I better go, if their things aren't too horribly dear. I haven't had a thing new since I was married and I've worn this so much I'm sick of it.

Tom's always after me to buy clothes, but I can't seem to get used to spending somebody else's money, though it was dad's money I spent before I did Tom's, but that's different, don't you think so? And of course at first we didn't have very much to spend, did we, dear? But now that we've had our raise—— All right, Tommie, I won't say another word.

Oh, did you know they tried to get Tom to run for mayor? Tom is making faces at me to shut up, but I don't see any harm in telling it to his best friends. They know we're not the kind that brag, Tommie. I do think it was quite a tribute; he'd only lived there a little over a year. It came up one night when the Guthries were at our house, playing bridge. Mr. Guthrie—that's A. L. Guthrie—he's one of the big lumbermen out there. He owns—just what does he own, Tom? Oh, I'm sorry. Anyway, he's got millions. Well, at least thousands.

He and his wife were at our house playing bridge. She's the queerest woman! If you just saw her, you'd think she was a janitor or something; she wears the most hideous clothes. Why, that night she had on a—honestly you'd have sworn it was a maternity gown, and for no reason. And the first time I met her—well, I just can't describe it. And she's a graduate of Bryn Mawr and one of the oldest families in Philadelphia. You'd never believe it!

She and her husband are terribly funny in a bridge game. He doesn't think there ought to be any conventions; he says a person might just as well tell each other what they've got. So he won't pay any attention to what-do-you-call-'em, informatory, doubles and so forth. And she plays all the conventions, so you can imagine how they get along. Fight! Not really fight, you know, but argue. That is, he does. It's horribly embarrassing to whoever is playing with them. Honestly, if Tom ever spoke to me like Mr. Guthrie does to his wife, well—aren't they terrible, Tom? Oh, I'm sorry!

She was the first woman in Portland that called on me and I thought it was awfully nice of her, though when I saw her at the door I would have sworn she was a book agent or maybe a cook looking for work. She had on a—well, I can't describe it. But it was sweet of her to call, she being one of the real people there and me— well, that was before Tom was made a vice-president. What? Oh, I never dreamed he hadn't written you about that!

But Mrs. Guthrie acted just like it was a great honor for her to meet me, and I like people to act that way even when I know it's all apple sauce. Isn't that a funny expression, "apple sauce"? Some man said it in a vaudeville show in Portland the Monday night before we left. He was a comedian—Jack Brooks or Ned Frawley or something. It means—well, I don't know how to describe it. But we had a terrible time after the first few minutes. She is the silentest person I ever knew and I'm kind of bashful myself with strangers. What are you grinning about, Tommie? I am, too, bashful when I don't know people. Not exactly bashful, maybe, but, well, bashful.

It was one of the most embarrassing things I ever went through. Neither of us could say a word and I could hardly help from laughing at what she had on. But after you get to know her you don't mind her clothes, though it's a terrible temptation all the time not to tell her how much nicer—— And her hair! But she plays a dandy game of bridge, lots better than her husband. You know he won't play conventions. He says it's just like telling you what's in each other's hand. And they have awful arguments in a game. That is, he does. She's nice and quiet and it's a kind of mystery how they ever fell in love. Though there's a saying or a proverb or something, isn't there, about like not liking like? Or is it just the other way?

But I was going to tell you about them wanting Tom to be mayor. Oh, Tom, only two down? Why, I think you did splendidly! I gave you a miserable hand and Helen had—what didn't you have, Helen? You had the ace, king of clubs. No, Tom had the king. No, Tom had the queen. Or was it spades? And you had the ace of hearts. No, Tom had that. No, he didn't. What *did* you have, Tom? I don't exactly see what you bid on. Of course I was terrible, but—what's the difference anyway?

What was I saying? Oh, yes, about Mr. and Mrs. Guthrie. It's funny for a couple like that to get married when they are so different in every way. I never saw two people with such different tastes. For instance, Mr. Guthrie is keen about motoring and Mrs. Guthrie just hates it. She simply suffers all the time she's in a car. He likes a good time, dancing, golfing, fishing, shows, things like that. She isn't interested in anything but church work and bridge work.

"Bridge work." I meant bridge, not bridge work. That's funny, isn't it? And yet they get along awfully well; that is when they're not playing cards or doing something else together. But it does seem queer that they picked each other out. Still, I guess hardly any husband and wife agree on anything.

You take Tom and me, though, and you'd think we were made for each other. It seems like we feel just the same about everything. That is, almost everything. The things we don't agree on are little things that don't matter. Like music. Tom is wild about jazz and blues and dance music. He adores Irving Berlin and Gershwin and Jack Kearns. He's always after those kind of things on the radio and I just want serious, classical things like "Humoresque" and "Indian Love Lyrics." And then there's shows. Tom is crazy over Ed Wynn and I can't see anything in him. Just the way he laughs at his own jokes is enough to spoil him for me. If I'm going to spend time and money on a theater I want to see something worth while—"The Fool" or "Lightnin'."

And things to eat. Tom insists, or that is he did insist, on a great big breakfast—fruit, cereal, eggs, toast, and coffee. All I want is a little fruit and dry toast and coffee. I think it's a great deal better for a person. So that's one habit I broke Tom of, was big breakfasts. And another thing he did when we were first married was to take off his shoes as soon as he got home from the office and put on bedroom slippers. I believe a person ought not to get sloppy just because they're married.

But the worst of all was pajamas! What's the difference, Tommie? Helen and Arthur don't mind. And I think it's kind of funny, you being so old-fashioned. I mean Tom had always worn a nightgown till I made him give it up. And it was a struggle, believe me! I had to threaten to leave him if he didn't buy pajamas. He certainly hated it. And now he's mad at me for telling, aren't you, Tommie? I just couldn't help it. I think it's so funny in this day and age. I hope Arthur doesn't wear them; nightgowns, I mean. You don't, do you, Arthur? I knew you didn't.

Oh, are you waiting for me? What did you say, Arthur? Two diamonds? Let's see what that means. When Tom makes an original bid of two it means he hasn't got the tops. I wonder—but of course you couldn't have the—heavens! What am I saying! I guess I better just keep still and pass.

But what was I going to tell you? Something about—oh, did I tell you about Tom being an author? I had no idea he was talented that way till after we were married and I was unpacking his old papers and things and came across a poem he'd written, the saddest, mushiest poem! Of course it was a long time ago he wrote it; it was dated four years ago, long before he met me, so it didn't make me very jealous, though it was about some other girl. You didn't know I found it, did you, Tommie?

But that wasn't what I refer to. He's written a story, too, and he's sent it to four different magazines and they all sent it back. I tell him though, that that doesn't mean anything. When you see some of the things the magazines do print, why, it's an honor to have them *not* like yours. The only thing is that Tom worked so hard over it and sat up nights writing and rewriting, it's a kind of a disappointment to have them turn it down.

It's a story about two men and a girl and they were all brought up together and one of the men was awfully popular and well off and good-looking and a great athlete—a man like Arthur. There, Arthur! How is that for a T. L.? The other man was just an ordinary man with not much money, but the girl seemed to like him better and she promised to wait for him. Then this man worked hard and got money enough to see him through Yale.

The other man, the well-off one, went to Princeton and made a big hit as an athlete and everything and he was through college long before his friend because his friend had to earn the money first. And the well-off man kept after the girl to marry him. He didn't know she had promised the other one. Anyway she got tired waiting for the man she was engaged to and eloped with the other one. And the story ends up by the man she threw down welcoming the couple when they came home and pretending everything was all right, though his heart was broken.

What are you blushing about, Tommie? It's nothing to be ashamed of. I thought it was very well written and if the editors had any sense they'd have taken it.

Still, I don't believe the real editors see half the stories that are sent to them. In fact I know they don't. You've either got to have a name or a pull to get your things published. Or else pay the magazines to publish them. Of course if you are Robert Chambers or Irving R. Cobb, they will print whatever you write whether it's good or bad. But you haven't got a chance if you are an unknown like Tom. They just keep your story long enough so you will think they are considering it and then they send it back with a form letter saying it's not available for their magazine and they don't even tell why.

You remember, Tom, that Mr. Hastings we met at the Hammonds'. He's a writer and knows all about it. He was telling me of an experience he had with one of the magazines; I forget which one, but it was one of the big ones. He wrote a story and sent it to them and they sent it back and said they couldn't use it.

Well, some time after that Mr. Hastings was in a hotel in Chicago and a bell-boy went around the lobby paging Mr.—— I forget the name, but it was the name of the editor of this magazine that had sent back the story, Runkle, or Byers, or some such name. So the man, whatever his name was, he was really there and answered the page and afterwards Mr. Hastings went up to him and introduced himself and told the man about sending a story to his magazine and the man said he didn't remember anything about it. And he was the editor! Of course he'd never seen it. No wonder Tom's story keeps coming back!

He says he is through sending it and just the other day he was going to tear it up, but I made him keep it because we may meet somebody some time who knows the inside ropes and can get a hearing with some big editor. I'm sure it's just a question of pull. Some of the things that get into the magazines sound like they had been written by the editor's friends or relatives or somebody whom they didn't want to hurt their feelings. And Tom really can write!

I wish I could remember that poem of his I found. I memorized it once, but—wait! I believe I can still say it! Hush, Tommie! What hurt will it do anybody? Let me see; it goes:

> "I thought the sweetness of her song
> Would ever, ever more belong
> To me; I thought (O thought divine!)
> My bird was really mine!
> But promises are made, it seems,
> Just to be broken. All my dreams
> Fade out and leave me crushed, alone.
> My bird, alas, has flown!"

Isn't that pretty. He wrote it four years ago. Why, Helen, you revoked! And Tom, do you know that's Scotch you're drinking? You said—— *Why, Tom!*

Liberty Hall

My husband is in Atlantic City, where they are trying out "Dear Dora," the musical version of "David Copperfield." My husband wrote the score. He used to take me along for these out-of-town openings, but not any more.

He, of course, has to spend almost all his time in the theater and that leaves me alone in the hotel, and pretty soon people find out whose wife I am and introduce themselves, and the next thing you know they are inviting us for a week or a weekend at Dobbs Ferry or Oyster Bay. Then it is up to me to think of some legitimate-sounding reason why we can't come.

In lots of cases they say, "Well, if you can't make it the twenty-second, how about the twenty-ninth?" and so on till you simply have to accept. And Ben gets mad and stays mad for days.

He absolutely abhors visiting and thinks there ought to be a law against invitations that go beyond dinner and bridge. He doesn't mind hotels where there is a decent light for reading in bed and one for shaving, and where you can order meals, with coffee, any time you want them. But I really believe he would rather spend a week in the death house at Sing Sing than in somebody else's home.

Three or four years ago we went around quite a lot with a couple whom I will call the Buckleys. We liked them and they liked us. We had dinner together at least twice a week and after dinner we played bridge or went to a show or just sat and talked.

Ben never turned down their invitations and often actually called them up himself and suggested parties. Finally they moved to Albany on account of Mr. Buckley's business. We missed them a great deal, and when Mrs. Buckley wrote for us to come up there for the holidays we were tickled pink.

Well, their guest-room was terribly cold; it took hours to fill the bathtub; there was no reading-lamp by the bed; three reporters called to interview Ben, two of them kittenish young girls; the breakfasts were just fruit and cereal and toast; coffee was not served at luncheon; the faucets in the wash-basin were the kind that won't run unless you keep pressing them; four important keys on the piano were stuck and people were invited in every night to hear Ben play, and the Buckley family had been augmented by a tremendous police dog, who was "just a puppy and never growled or snapped at any-one he knew," but couldn't seem to remember that Ben was not an utter stranger.

On the fourth awful day Ben gave out the news—news to him and to me as well as to our host and hostess—that he had lost a filling which he would not trust any but his own New York dentist to re-place. We came home and we have never seen the Buckleys since. If we do see them it will be an accident. They will hardly ask us there unless we ask them here, and we won't ask them here for fear they would ask us there. And they were honestly the most congenial people we ever met.

It was after our visit to the Craigs at Stamford that Ben originated what he calls his "emergency exit." We had such a horrible time at the Craigs' and such a worse time getting away that Ben swore he would pay no more visits until he could think up a graceful method of curtailing them in the event they proved unbearable.

Here is the scheme he hit on: He would write himself a telegram and sign it with the name Ziegfeld or Gene Buck or Dillingham or George M. Cohan. The telegram would say that he must return to New York at once, and it would give a reason. Then, the day we started out, he would leave it with Irene, the girl at Harms', his publishers, with instructions to have it sent to him twenty-four hours later.

When it arrived at whatever town we were in, he would either have the host or hostess take it over the telephone or ask the telegraph company to deliver it so he could show it around. We would put on long faces and say how sorry we were, but of course business was business, so good-by and so forth. There was never a breath of suspicion even when the telegram was ridiculous, like the one Ben had sent to himself at Spring Lake, where we were staying with the Marshalls just after "Betty's Birthday" opened at the Globe. The Marshalls loved musical shows, but knew less than nothing about music and swallowed this one whole:

Shaw and Miss Miller both suffering from laryngitis Stop Entire score must be rewritten half tone lower Stop Come at once Stop.

C. B. Dillingham.

If, miraculously, Ben had ever happened to be enjoying himself, he would, of course, have kept the contents of his message a secret or else displayed it and remarked swaggeringly that he guessed he wasn't going to let any so-and-so theatrical producer spoil his fun.

Ben is in Atlantic City now and I have read every book in the house and am writing this just because there doesn't seem to be anything else to do. And also because we have a friend, Joe Frazier, who is a magazine editor and the other day I told him I would like to try my hand at a short story, but I was terrible at plots, and he said plots weren't essential; look at Ernest Hemingway; most of his stories have hardly any plot; it's his style that counts. And he—I mean Mr. Frazier—suggested that I write about our visit to Mr. and Mrs. Thayer in Lansdowne, outside of Philadelphia, which Mr. Frazier said, might be termed the visit that ended visits and which is the principal reason why I am here alone.

Well, it was a beautiful night a year ago last September. Ben was conducting the performance—"Step Lively"—and I was standing at the railing of the Boardwalk in front of the theater, watching the moonlight on the ocean. A couple whom I had noticed in the hotel dining-room stopped alongside of me and pretty soon the woman spoke to me, something about how pretty it was. Then came the old question, wasn't I Mrs. Ben Drake? I said I was, and the woman went on:

"My name is Mrs. Thayer—Hilda Thayer. And this is my husband. We are both simply crazy about Mr. Drake's music and just dying to meet him personally. We wondered if you and he would have supper with us after the performance tonight."

"Oh, I'm afraid that's impossible," I replied. "You see when they are having a tryout, he and the librettists and the lyric writers work all night every night until they get everything in shape for the New York opening. They never have time for more than a sandwich and they eat that right in the theater."

"Well, how about luncheon tomorrow?"

"He'll be rehearsing all day."

"How about dinner tomorrow evening?"

"Honestly, Mrs. Thayer, it's out of the question. Mr. Drake never makes engagements during a tryout week."

"And I guess he doesn't want to meet us anyway," put in Mr. Thayer. "What use would a genius like Ben Drake have for a couple of common-no-account admirers like Mrs. Thayer and myself! If we were 'somebody' too, it would be different!"

"Not at all!" said I. "Mr. Drake is perfectly human. He loves to have his music praised and I am sure he would be delighted to meet you if he weren't so terribly busy."

"Can you lunch with us yourself?"

"Tomorrow?"

"Any day."

Well, whatever Ben and other husbands may think, there is no decent way of turning down an invitation like that. And besides I was lonesome and the Thayers looked like awfully nice people.

I lunched with them and I dined with them, not only the next day but all the rest of the week. And on Friday I got Ben to lunch with them and he liked them, too; they were not half as gushing and silly as most of his "fans."

At dinner on Saturday night, they cross-examined me about our immediate plans. I told them that as soon as the show was "over" in New York, I was going to try to make Ben stay home and do nothing for a whole month.

"I should think," said Mrs. Thayer, "it would be very hard for him to rest there in the city, with the producers and publishers and phonograph people calling him up all the time."

I admitted that he was bothered a lot.

"Listen, dearie," said Mrs. Thayer. "Why don't you come to Landsdowne and spend a week with us? I'll promise you faithfully that you won't be disturbed at all. I won't let anyone know you are there and if any of our friends call on us I'll pretend we're not at home. I won't allow Mr. Drake to even touch the piano. If he wants exercise, there are miles of room in our yard to walk around in, and nobody can see him from the street. All day and all night, he can do nothing or anything, just as he pleases. It will be 'Liberty Hall' for you both. He needn't tell anybody where he is, but if some of his friends or business acquaintances find out and try to get in touch with him, I'll frighten them away. How does that sound?"

"It sounds wonderful," I said, "but——"

"It's settled then," said Mrs. Thayer, "and we'll expect you on Sunday, October eleventh."

"Oh, but the show may not be 'set' by that time," I remonstrated.

"How about the eighteenth?" said Mr. Thayer.

Well, it ended by my accepting for the week of the twenty-fifth and Ben took it quite cheerfully.

"If they stick to their promise to keep us under cover," he said, "it may be a lot better than staying in New York. I know that Buck and the Shuberts and Ziegfeld want me while I'm 'hot' and they wouldn't give me a minute's peace if they could find me. And of course if things aren't as good as they look, Irene's telegram will provide us with an easy out."

On the way over to Philadelphia he hummed me an awfully pretty melody which had been running through his head since we left the apartment. "I think it's sure fire," he said. "I'm crazy to get to a piano and fool with it."

"That isn't resting, dear."

"Well, you don't want me to throw away a perfectly good tune! They aren't so plentiful that I can afford to waste one. It won't take me five minutes at a piano to get it fixed in my mind."

The Thayers met us in an expensive-looking limousine.

"Ralph," said Mrs. Thayer to her husband, "you sit in one of the little seats and Mr. and Mrs. Drake will sit back here with me."

"I'd really prefer one of the little seats myself," said Ben and he meant it, for he hates to get his clothes mussed and being squeezed in beside two such substantial objects as our hostess and myself was bound to rumple him.

"No, sir!" said Mrs. Thayer positively. "You came to us for a rest and we're not going to start you off uncomfortable."

"But I'd honestly rather——"

It was no use. Ben was wedged between us and throughout the drive maintained a morose silence, unable to think of anything but how terrible his coat would look when he got out.

The Thayers had a very pretty home and the room assigned to us was close to perfection. There were comfortable twin beds with a small stand and convenient reading-lamp between; a big dresser and chiffonier; an ample closet with plenty of hangers; a bathroom with hot water that was hot, towels that were not too new and faucets that stayed on when turned on, and an ash-tray within reach of wherever you happened to be. If only we could have spent all our time in that guest-room, it would have been ideal.

But presently we were summoned downstairs to luncheon. I had warned Mrs. Thayer in advance and Ben was served with coffee. He drinks it black.

"Don't you take cream, Mr. Drake?"

"No. Never."

"But that's because you don't get good cream in New York."

"No. It's because I don't like cream in coffee."

"You would like our cream. We have our own cows and the cream is so rich that it's almost like butter. Won't you try just a little?"

"No, thanks."

"But just a little, to see how rich it is."

She poured about a tablespoon of cream into his coffee-cup and for a second I was afraid he was going to pick up the cup and throw it in her face. But he kept hold of himself, forced a smile and declined a second chop.

"You haven't tasted your coffee," said Mrs. Thayer.

"Yes, I have," lied Ben. "The cream is wonderful. I'm sorry it doesn't agree with me."

"I don't believe coffee agrees with anyone," said Mrs. Thayer. "While you are here, not doing any work, why don't you try to give it up?"

"I'd be so irritable you wouldn't have me in the house. Besides, it isn't plain coffee that disagrees with me; it's coffee with cream."

"Pure, rich cream like ours couldn't hurt you," said Mrs. Thayer, and Ben, defeated, refused to answer.

He started to light a Jaguar cigaret, the brand he had been smoking for years.

"Here! Wait a minute!" said Mr. Thayer. "Try one of mine."

"What are they?" asked Ben.

"Trumps," said our host, holding out his case. "They're mild and won't irritate the throat."

"I'll sample one later," said Ben.

"You've simply got to try one now," said Mrs. Thayer. "You may as well get used to them because you'll have to smoke them all the time you're here. We can't have guests providing their own cigarets." So Ben had to discard his Jaguar and smoke a Trump, and it was even worse than he had anticipated.

After luncheon we adjourned to the living-room and Ben went straight to the piano.

"Here! Here! None of that!" said Mrs. Thayer. "I haven't forgotten my promise."

"What promise?" asked Ben.

"Didn't your wife tell you? I promised her faithfully that if you visited us, you wouldn't be allowed to touch the piano."

"But I want to," said Ben. "There's a melody in my head that I'd like to try."

"Oh, yes, I know all about that," said Mrs. Thayer. "You just think you've got to entertain us! Nothing doing! We invited you here for yourself, not to enjoy your talent. I'd be a fine one to ask you to my home for a rest and then make you perform."

"You're not making me," said Ben. "Honestly I want to play for just five or ten minutes. I've got a tune that I might do something with and I'm anxious to run it over."

"I don't believe you, you naughty man!" said our hostess. "Your wife has told you how wild we are about your music and you're determined to be nice to us. But I'm just as stubborn as you are. Not one note do you play as long as you're our guest!"

Ben favored me with a stricken look, mumbled something about unpacking his suitcase—it was already unpacked—and went up to our room, where he stayed nearly an hour, jotting down his new tune, smoking Jaguar after Jaguar and wishing that black coffee flowed from bathtub faucets.

About a quarter of four Mr. Thayer insisted on taking him around the place and showing him the shrubbery, something that held in Ben's mind a place of equal importance to the grade of wire used in hairpins.

"I'll have to go to business tomorrow," said Mr. Thayer, "and you will be left to amuse yourself. I thought you might enjoy this planting more if you knew a little about it. Of course it's much prettier in the spring of the year."

"I can imagine so."

"You must come over next spring and see it."

"I'm usually busy in the spring," said Ben.

"Before we go in," said Mr. Thayer, "I'd like to ask you one question: Do tunes come into your mind and then you write them down, or do you just sit at the piano and improvise until you strike something good?"

"Sometimes one way and sometimes the other," said Ben.

"That's very interesting," said Mr. Thayer. "I've often wondered how it was done. And another question: Do you write the tunes first and then give them to the men who write the words, or do the men write the words first and then give them to you to make up the music to them?"

"Sometimes one way and sometimes the other," said Ben.

"That's very interesting," said Mr. Thayer. "It's something I'm glad to know. And now we'd better join the ladies or my wife will say I'm monopolizing you."

They joined us, much to my relief. I had just reached a point where I would either have had to tell "Hilda" exactly how much Ben earned per annum or that it was none of her business.

"Well!" said Mrs. Thayer to Ben. "I was afraid Ralph had kidnapped you."

"He was showing me the shrubbery," said Ben.

"What did you think of it?"

"It's great shrubbery," said Ben, striving to put some warmth into his voice.

"You must come and see it in the spring."

"I'm usually busy in the spring."

"Ralph and I are mighty proud of our shrubbery."

"You have a right to be."

Ben was taking a book out of the bookcase.

"What book is that?" asked Mrs. Thayer.

" 'The Great Gatsby,' " said Ben. "I've always wanted to read it but never got around to it."

"Heavens!" said Mrs. Thayer as she took it away from him. "That's old! You'll find the newest ones there on the table. We keep pretty well up to date. Ralph and I are both great readers. Just try any one of those books in that pile. They're all good."

Ben glanced them over and selected "Chevrons." He sat down and opened it.

"Man! Man!" exclaimed Mrs. Thayer. "You've picked the most uncomfortable chair in the house!"

"He likes straight chairs," I said.

"That's on the square," said Ben.

"But you mustn't sit there," said Mrs. Thayer. "It makes me uncomfortable just to look at you. Take this chair here. It's the softest, nicest chair you've ever sat in."

"I like hard straight chairs," said Ben, but he sank into the soft, nice one and again opened his book.

"Oh, you never can see there!" said Mrs. Thayer. "You'll ruin your eyes! Get up just a minute and let Ralph move your chair by that lamp."

"I can see perfectly well."

"I know better! Ralph, move his chair so he can see."

"I don't believe I want to read just now anyway," said Ben, and went to the phonograph. "Bess," he said, putting on a record, "here's that 'Oh! Miss Hannah!' by the Revelers."

Mrs. Thayer fairly leaped to his side, and herded Miss Hannah back into her stall.

"We've got lots later ones than that," she said. "Let me play you the new Gershwins."

It was at this juncture that I began to suspect our hostess of a lack of finesse. After all, Gershwin is a rival of my husband's and, in some folks' opinion, a worthy one. However, Ben had a word of praise for each record as it ended and did not even hint that any of the tunes were based on melodies of his own.

"Mr. Drake," said our host at length, "would you like a gin cocktail or a Bacardi?"

"I don't like Bacardi at all," said Ben.

"I'll bet you will like the kind I've got," said Mr. Thayer. "It was brought to me by a friend of mine who just got back from Cuba. It's the real stuff!"

"I don't like Bacardi," said Ben.

"Wait till you taste this," said Mr. Thayer.

Well, we had Bacardi cocktails. I drank mine and it wasn't so good. Ben took a sip of his and pretended it was all right. But he had told the truth when he said he didn't like Bacardi.

I won't go into details regarding the dinner except to relate that three separate items were highly flavored with cheese, and Ben despises cheese.

"Don't you care for cheese, Mr. Drake?" asked Mr. Thayer, noticing that Ben was not exactly bolting his food.

"No," replied the guest of honor.

"He's spoofing you, Ralph," said Mrs. Thayer. "Everybody likes cheese."

There was coffee, and Ben managed to guzzle a cup before it was desecrated with pure cream.

We sat down to bridge. "Do you like to play families or divide up?"

"Oh, we like to play together," said I.

"I'll bet you don't," said Mrs. Thayer. "Suppose Ralph and you play Mr. Drake and me. I think it's a mistake for husbands and wives to be partners. They're likely to criticize one another and say things that leave a scar."

Well, Mr. Thayer and I played against Ben and Mrs. Thayer and I lost sixty cents at a tenth of a cent a point. Long before the evening was over I could readily see why Mrs. Thayer thought it was a mistake to play with her husband and if it had been possible I'd have left him a complete set of scars.

Just as we were getting to sleep, Mrs. Thayer knocked on our door.

"I'm afraid you haven't covers enough," she called. "There are extra blankets on the shelf in your closet."

"Thanks," I said. "We're as warm as toast."

"I'm afraid you aren't," said Mrs. Thayer.

"Lock the door," said Ben, "before she comes in and feels our feet."

All through breakfast next morning we waited in vain for the telephone call that would yield Irene's message. The phone rang once and Mrs. Thayer answered, but we couldn't hear what she said. At noon Ben signalled me to meet him upstairs and there he stated grimly that I might do as I choose, but he was leaving Liberty Hall ere another sun had set.

"You haven't any excuse," I reminded him.

"I'm a genius," he said, "and geniuses are notoriously eccentric."

"Geniuses' wives sometimes get eccentric, too," said I, and began to pack up.

Mr. Thayer had gone to Philadelphia and we were alone with our hostess at luncheon.

"Mrs. Thayer," said Ben, "do you ever have premonitions or hunches?"

She looked frightened. "Why, no. Do you?"

"I had one not half an hour ago. Something told me that I positively must be in New York tonight. I don't know whether it's business or illness or what, but I've just got to be there!"

"That's the strangest thing I ever heard of," said Mrs. Thayer. "It scares me to death!"

"It's nothing you need be scared of," said Ben. "It only concerns me."

"Yes, but listen," said Mrs. Thayer. "A telegram came for you at breakfast time this morning. I wasn't going to tell you about it because I had promised that you wouldn't be disturbed. And it didn't seem so terribly important. But this hunch of yours puts the matter in a different light. I'm sorry now that I didn't give you the message when I got it, but I memorized it and can repeat it word for word: 'Mr. Ben Drake, care of Mr. Ralph Thayer, Lansdowne, Pennsylvania. In Nile song, second bar of refrain, bass drum part reads A flat which makes discord. Should it be A natural? Would appreciate your coming to theater tonight to straighten this out as harmony must be restored in orchestra if troupe is to be success. Regards, Gene Buck.' "

"It sounds silly, doesn't it?" said Ben. "And yet I have known productions to fail and lose hundreds of thousands of dollars just because an author or composer left town too soon. I can well understand that you considered the message trivial. At the same time I can thank my stars that this instinct, or divination, or whatever you want to call it, told me to go home."

Just as the trainmen were shouting "Board!" Mrs. Thayer said:

"I have one more confession to make. I answered Mr. Buck's telegram. I wired him. 'Mr. Ben Drake resting at my home. Must not be bothered. Suggest that you keep bass drums still for a week.' And I signed my name. Please forgive me if I have done something terrible. Remember, it was for you."

Small wonder that Ben was credited at the Lambs' Club with that month's most interesting bender.

Contract

When the Sheltons were settled in their new home in the pretty little suburb of Linden, Mrs. Shelton was afraid nobody would call on them. Her husband was afraid somebody would. For ages Mrs. Shelton had bravely pretended to share her husband's aversion to a social life; he hated parties that numbered more than four people and she had convincingly, so she thought, played the rôle of indifference while declining invitations she would have given her right eye to accept. Shelton had not been fooled much, but his dislike of "crowds" was so great that he seldom sought to relieve her martyrdom by insisting that they "go" somewhere.

This was during the first six years of their connubial existence, while it was necessary to live, rather economically, in town. Recently, however, Shelton's magazine had advanced him to a position as associate editor and he was able, with the assistance of a benignant bond and mortgage company, to move into a house in Linden. Mrs. Shelton was sure suburbanites would be less tedious and unattractive than people they had known in the city and that it would not be fatal to her spouse to get acquainted and play around a little; anyway she could make friends with other wives, if they were willing, and perhaps enjoy afternoons of contract bridge, a game she had learned to love in three lessons. At the same time Shelton resolved to turn over a new leaf for his wife's sake and give her to understand that he was open for engagements, secretly hoping, as I have hinted, that Linden's denizens would treat them as if they were quarantined.

Mrs. Shelton's fears were banished, and Shelton's resolution put to a test, on an evening of their second week in the new house. They were dropped in on by Mr. and Mrs. Robert French who lived three blocks away. Mrs. French was pretty and Shelton felt inclined to like her until she remarked how fascinating it must be to edit a magazine and meet Michael Arlen. French had little to say, being occupied most of the while in a petting party with his mustache.

Mrs. Shelton showed Mrs. French her seven hooked rugs. Mrs. French said, "Perfectly darling!" seven times, inquired where each of the seven had been procured and did not listen to the answers. Shelton served highballs of eighty dollar Scotch he had bought from a Linden bootlegger. French commented favorably on the Scotch. Shelton thought it was terrible himself and that French was a poor judge, or was being polite, or was deceived by some flavor lurking in the mustache. Mrs. Shelton ran out of hooked rugs and Mrs. French asked whether they played contract. Mrs. Shelton hesitated from habit. Shelton swallowed hard and replied that they did, and liked it very much.

"That's wonderful!" said Mrs. French. "Because the Wilsons have moved to Chicago. They were crazy about contract and we used to have a party every Wednesday night; two tables—the Wilsons, ourselves, and the Dittmars and Camerons. It would be just grand if you two would take the Wilsons' place. We have dinner at somebody's house and next Wednesday is our turn. Could you come?"

Mrs. Shelton again hesitated and Shelton (to quote O. O. McIntyre) once more took the bull by the horns.

"It sounds fine!" he said. "We haven't anything else on for that night, have we, dear?"

His wife uttered an astonished no and the Frenches left.

"What in the world has happened to you?" demanded Mrs. Shelton.

"Nothing at all. They seem like nice people and we've got to make friends here. Besides, it won't be bad playing cards."

"I don't know about contract," said Mrs. Shelton doubtfully. "You've got good card sense, and the only time you played it, you were all right. But I'm afraid I'll make hideous mistakes."

"Why should you? And even if you do, what of it?"

"These people are probably whizzes."

"I don't care if they're Lenz's mother-in-law."

"But you'll care if they criticise you."

"Of course I will. People, and especially strangers, have no more right to criticize your bridge playing than your clothes or your complexion."

"You know that's silly. Bridge is a game."

"Tennis is a game, too. But how often do you hear one tennis player say to another, 'You played that like an old fool!'?"

"You're not partners in tennis."

"You are in doubles. However, criticism in bridge is not confined to partners. I've made bonehead plays in bridge (I'll admit it), and been laughed at and scolded for them by opponents who ought to have kissed me. It's a conviction of most bridge players, and some golf players, that God sent them into the world to teach. At that, what they tell you isn't intended for your edification and future good. It's just a way of announcing 'I'm smart and you're a lunkhead.' And to my mind it's a revelation of bad manners and bad sportsmanship. If I asked somebody what I did wrong, that's different. But when they volunteer——"

It was an old argument and Mrs. Shelton did not care to continue it. She knew she couldn't win and she was sleepy. Moreover, she was so glad they were "going out" on her husband's own insistence that she felt quite kindly toward him. She did hope, though, that their new acquaintances would suppress their educational complex if any.

On Wednesday night this hope was knocked for a double row of early June peas. Mrs. Shelton was elected to play with French, Mrs. Cameron and Mr. Dittmar. Mrs. Cameron was what is referred to as a statuesque blonde, but until you were used to her you could think of nothing but her nostrils, where she might easily have carried two after dinner mints. Mr. Dittmar appeared to be continuing to enjoy his meal long after it was over. And French had to deal one-handed to be sure his mustache remained loyal. These details distracted Mrs. Shelton's mind to such an extent that she made a few errors and was called for them. But she didn't mind that and her greatest distraction was caused by words and phrases that came from the other table, where her husband was engaged with Mr. Cameron, Mrs. Dittmar and the hostess.

The French cocktails had been poured from an eye-dropper and Shelton maintained perfect control of his temper and tongue. His polite reception of each criticism was taken as a confession of ignorance and a willingness to learn, and his three table-mates were quick to assume the rôle of faculty, with him as the entire student-body. He was stepped on even when he was dummy, his partner at the time, Mrs. Dittmar, attributing the loss of a trick to the manner in which he had laid out his cards, the light striking the nine of diamonds in such a way as to make her think it was an honor.

Mrs. Dittmar had married a man much younger than herself and was trying to disguise that fact by acting much younger than he. An eight-year-old child who is kind of backward hardly ever plays contract bridge; otherwise, if you didn't look at Mrs. Dittmar and judged only by her antics and manner of speech, you would have thought Dittmar had spent the final hours of his courtship waiting outside the sub-primary to take her home. Mrs. French, when she was not picking flaws in Shelton's play, sought to make him feel at home by asking intelligent questions about his work—"Do the people who draw the illustrations read the stories first?" "Does H. C. Witwer talk Negro dialect all the time?" And "How old is Peter B. Kinney?" Cameron, from whom Work, Lenz, Whitehead and Shepard had plagiarized the game, was frankly uninterested in anything not connected with it. The stake was half a cent a point and the pains he took to see that his side's score was correct or better proved all the rumors about the two Scotchmen.

Mrs. Shelton was well aware that her husband was the politest man in the world when sober; yet he truly amazed her that evening by his smiling acquiescence to all that was said. From the snatches she overheard, she knew he must be afire inside and it was really wonderful of him not to show it.

There was a time when Mrs. Dittmar passed and he passed and Cameron bid two spades. Mrs. French passed and Mrs. Dittmar bid three hearts, a denial of her partner's spades if Shelton ever heard one. Shelton passed and Cameron went three hearts, which stood. Shelton held four spades to the nine, four diamonds to the king, two small hearts and the eight, six and five of clubs. He led the trey of diamonds. I am not broadcasting the battle play by play, but when it was over, "Oh, partner! Any other opening and we could have set them," said Mrs. French.

"My! My! My! My! Leading away from a king!" gurgled the child-wife.

"That lead was all that saved us," said Cameron.

They waited for Shelton to apologize and explain, all prepared to scrunch him if he did either.

"I guess I made a mistake," he said.

"Haven't you played much bridge?" asked Mrs. French.

"Evidently not enough," he replied.

"It's a game you can't learn in a minute," said Cameron.

"Never you mind!" said Mrs. Dittmar. "I've played contract ever since it came out, and Daddy still scolds me terribly for some of the things I do."

Shelton presumed that Daddy was her husband. Her father must be dead or at least too feeble to scold.

There was a time when a hand was passed around.

"Oh! A goulash!" crowed Mrs. Dittmar.

"Do you play them, Mr. Shelton?" asked his hostess.

"Yes," said Shelton.

"Mrs. Shelton," called Mrs. Dittmar to the other table, "does your big man play goulashes?"

"Oh, yes," said Mrs. Shelton.

"You're sure you know what they are," said Cameron to Shelton.

"I've played them often," said the latter.

"A goulash," said the hostess, "is where the hand is passed and then we all put our hands together like this and cut them and the dealer deals five around twice and then three. It makes crazy hands, but it's thrilling."

"And the bidding is different," said Mrs. Dittmar, his partner at this stage. "Big mans mustn't get too wild."

Shelton, who had dealt, looked at his hand and saw no temptation to get wild; at least, not any wilder than he was. He had the king, queen and jack of spades, four silly hearts, four very young clubs and two diamonds of no standing. He passed. Cameron bid three clubs and Mrs. Dittmar four diamonds. That was enough to make game (they already had thirty), and when Mrs. French went by, Shelton unhesitatingly did the same. So did Cameron. It developed that Mrs. Dittmar had the ace, king, jack, ten and another diamond. Cameron had none and Mrs. French reeked with them. The bidder was set two. Her honors counted one hundred and the opponents' net profit was two hundred, Mrs. Dittmar being vulnerable, or "venerable," as Mrs. French laughingly, but not very tactfully, called it.

Cameron lighted into Mrs. French for not doubling Mrs. Dittmar and Mrs. French observed that she guessed she knew what she was doing. Shelton hoped this would develop into a brawl, but it was forgotten when Mrs. Dittmar asked him querulously why he had not shown her his spades, a suit of which she had held the ace, ten to five.

"We're lucky, partner," said Mrs. French to Cameron. "They could have made four spades like a breeze."

"I'd have lost only the ace of hearts and queen of diamonds," said Mrs. Dittmar, doubtless figuring that the maid would have disposed of her two losing clubs when she swept next morning.

"In this game, everything depends on the bidding," said Mrs.

French to Shelton. "You *must* give your partner all the information you can."

"Don't coach him!" said Cameron with an exasperating laugh. "He's treating us pretty good."

"Maybe," said Mrs. French to Mrs. Dittmar, "he would have shown you his spades if you had bid three diamonds instead of four."

"But you see," said Mrs. Dittmar, "we needed four for game and I didn't know if he'd think of that."

And there was a time when Shelton bid a fair no trump and was raised to three by his partner, Cameron, who held king, queen, ten to five hearts and the ace of clubs for a re-entry. The outstanding hearts were bunched in Mrs. French's hand, Shelton himself having the lone ace. After he had taken a spade trick, led his ace of hearts and then a low club to make all of dummy's hearts good (which turned out to be impossible), he put over two deep sea finesses of the eight and nine of diamonds from the dummy hand, made four odd and heard Cameron murmur, "A fool for luck!"

"My! What a waste of good hearts!" said Mrs. Dittmar, ignoring the facts that they weren't good hearts, that if he had continued with them, Mrs. French would have taken the jack and led to her (Mrs. Dittmar's) four good spade tricks, and that with the ace of clubs gone, Shelton couldn't have got back in the dummy's hands with a pass from Judge Landis.

At the close of a perfect evening, the Sheltons were six dollars ahead and invited to the Dittmars' the following Wednesday. Mrs. Shelton expected an explosion on the way home, but was agreeably disappointed. Shelton seemed quite cheerful. He had a few jocose remarks to make about their new pals, but gave the impression that he had enjoyed himself. Knowing him as she did, she might have suspected that a plot was hatching in his mind. However, his behavior was disarming and she thought he had at last found a "crowd" he didn't object to, that they would now be neighborly and gregarious for the first time in their married life.

On the train from the city Friday afternoon, Shelton encountered Gale Bartlett, the writer, just returned from abroad. Bartlett was one of the star contributors to Shelton's magazine and it was he who had first suggested Linden when Shelton was considering a suburban home. He had a place there himself though most of his time was spent in Paris and he was back now for only a brief stay.

"How do you like it?" he asked.

"Fine," said Shelton.

"Whom have you met?"

"Three married couples, the Camerons, the Frenches and the Dittmars."

"God Lord!" said Bartlett. "I don't know the Dittmars but otherwise you're slumming. Cameron and French are new rich who probably made their money in a hotel washroom. I think they met their wives on an excursion to Far Rockaway. How did you happen to get acquainted?"

"The Frenches called on us, and Wednesday night we went to their house for dinner and bridge."

"Bridge!"

"Contract bridge at that."

"Well, maybe Dittmar's a contractor. But from what I've seen of the Frenches and Camerons, they couldn't even cut the cards without smearing them with shoe polish. You break loose from them before they forget themselves and hand you a towel."

"We're going to the Dittmars' next Wednesday night."

"Either call it off or keep it under your hat. I'll introduce you to people that are people! I happen to know them because my wife went to their sisters' boarding school. I'll see that you get the entree and then you can play bridge with bridge players."

Shelton brightened at the prospect. He knew his wife was too kind-hearted to wound the Camerons et al. by quitting them cold and it was part of his scheme, all of it in fact, to make them do the quitting. With the conviction that she would be more than compensated by the promised acquaintance of people they both could really like, he lost what few scruples he had against separating her from people who sooner or later would drive him to the electric chair. The thing must be done at the first opportunity, next Wednesday at the Dittmars'. It would be kind of fun, but unpleasant, too, the unpleasant part consisting in the mental anguish it would cause her and the subsequent days, not many he hoped, when she wouldn't be speaking to him at all.

Fate, in the form of one of Mrs. Shelton's two-day headaches, brought about the elimination of the unpleasant part. The ache began Wednesday afternoon and from past experience, she knew she would not be able to sit through a dinner or play cards that night. She telephoned her husband.

"Say we can't come," was his advice.

"But I hate to do that. They'll think we don't want to and they won't ask us again. I wish you'd go, and maybe they could ask somebody in to take my place. I don't suppose you'd consider that, would you?"

Shelton thought it over a moment and said yes, he would.

Before retiring to her darkened room and her bed, Mrs. Shelton called up Mrs. Dittmar. Mrs. Dittmar expressed her sympathy in baby talk and said it was all right for Mr. Shelton to come alone; it was more than all right, Mrs. Shelton gathered, because Mrs. Dittmar's brother was visiting her and they would be just eight.

Shelton, who had learned long ago that his wife did not want him around when her head was threatening to burst open, stayed in town until six o'clock, preparing himself for the evening's task with liberal doses of the business manager's week-old-rye. He was not going to be tortured by any drought such as he had endured at the Frenches'. He arrived at the party in grand shape and, to his surprise, was plied with cocktails potent enough to keep him on edge.

Mrs. Dittmar's brother (she called him her dreat, big B'udder) was an amateur jazz pianist. Or rather, peeanist). He was proving his amateur standing when Shelton got there and something in the way he treated "Rhapsody in Blue" made Shelton resolve to open fire at once. His eagerness was increased when, on the way to the dining room, Mrs. Dittmar observed that her b'udder had not played much contract "either" and she must be sure and not put them (Shelton and B'udder) at the same table, for they might draw each other as partners and that would hardly be fair.

Dinner began and so did Shelton.

"A week ago," he said, "you folks criticised my bridge playing."

The Camerons, Dittmars and Frenches looked queer.

"You didn't mind it, I hope," said Mrs. Dittmar. "We were just trying to teach you."

"I didn't mind it much," said Shelton. "But I was just wondering whether it was good manners for one person to point out another person's mistakes when the other person didn't ask to have them pointed out."

"Why," said Cameron, "when one person don't know as much about a thing as other people, it's their duty to correct him."

"You mean just in bridge," said Shelton.

"I mean in everything," said Cameron.

"And the person criticised or corrected has no right to resent it?" said Shelton.

"Certainly not!"

"Does everybody here agree with that?"

"Yes," "Of course," "Sure," came from the others.

"Well, then," said Shelton, "I think it's my duty to tell you, Mr. Cameron, that soup should be dipped away from you and not toward you."

There was a puzzled silence, then a laugh, to which Cameron contributed feebly.

"If that's right I'm glad to know it, and I certainly don't resent your telling me," he said.

"It looks like Mr. Shelton was out for revenge," said Mrs. Cameron.

"And I must inform you, Mrs. Cameron," said Shelton, "that 'like' is not a conjunction. 'It looks as if Mr. Shelton were out for revenge' would be the correct phrasing."

A smothered laugh at the expense of Mrs. Cameron, whose embarrassment showed itself in a terrifying distension of the nostrils. Shelton decided not to pick on her again.

"Let's change the subject," said Mrs. Dittmar. "Mr. Shelton's a mean, bad man and he'll make us cwy."

"That verb," said Shelton, "is cry, not cwy. It is spelled c-r-y."

"Tell a story, Bob," said Mrs. French to her husband.

"Well, let's see," said French. "I'll tell the one about the Scotchman and the Jew playing golf. Stop me if anybody's heard it."

"I have, for one," said Shelton.

"Maybe the others haven't," said French.

"They must have been unconscious for years," said Shelton. "But go ahead and tell it. I knew I couldn't stop you."

French went ahead and told it, and the others laughed as a rebuke to Shelton.

Cameron wanted things understood.

"You see," he said, "the reason we made a few little criticisms of your bridge game was because we judged you were a new beginner."

"I think 'beginner' is enough, without the 'new,' " said Shelton. "I don't know any old beginners excepting, perhaps, people old in years who are doing something or taking up something for the first time. But probably you judged I was a beginner at bridge because of mistakes I made, and you considered my apparent inexperience justified you in criticising me."

"Yes," said Cameron.

"Well," said Shelton, "I judge from observing Mrs. French eat her fish that she is a new beginner at eating and I take the liberty of stating that the fork ought never to be conveyed to the mouth with the left hand, even by a left-handed eater. To be sure, these forks are salad forks, not fish forks, as Mrs. Dittmar may believe. But even salad forks, substituting for fish forks, must not be carried mouthward by the left hand."

A storm was gathering and Mrs. Cameron sought to ward it off. She asked Mrs. Dittmar what had become of Peterson, a butler.

"He just up and left me last week," said Mrs. Dittmar. "He was getting too impudent, though, and you can bet I didn't object to him going."

" '*His* going,' " said Shelton. "A participle used as a substantive is modified in the possessive."

Everyone pretended not to hear him.

"This new one is grand!" said Mrs. Dittmar. "I didn't get up till nearly eleven o'clock this morning——"

"Eleven!" exclaimed Mrs. French.

"Yes. Imagine!" said Mrs. Dittmar. "The itta girl just overslept herself, that's all."

"Mrs. Dittmar," said Shelton, "I have no idea who the itta girl is, but I am interested in your statement that she overslept herself. Would it be possible for her, or any other itta girl, to oversleep somebody else? If it were a sleeping contest, I should think 'outsleep' would be preferable, but even so I can't understand how a girl of any size outsleeps herself."

The storm broke. Dittmar sprang to his feet.

"That's enough, Shelton!" he bellowed. "We've had enough of this nonsense! More than enough!"

"I think," said Shelton, "that the use of the word 'enough' three time in one short speech is more than enough. It grates on me to hear or read a word reiterated like that. I suggest as synonyms 'plenty,' 'a sufficiency,' 'an abundance,' 'a plethora.' "

"Shut your smart aleck mouth and get out!"

"Carl! Carl! Musn't lose temper!" said Mrs. Dittmar. "Lose temper and can't digest food. Daddy mustn't lose temper and be sick all nighty night."

"Shelton just thinks he's funny," said Cameron.

"He's drunk and he'll leave my house at once!" said Dittmar.

"If that's the way you feel about it," said Shelton.

He stopped on the way out to bid Mrs. Dittmar's brother good-night.

"Good-night, B'udder old boy," he said. "I'm glad to have met you, but sorry to learn you're deaf."

"Deaf! What makes you think I'm deaf?"

"I understood your sister to say you played the piano by ear."

Knowing his wife would have taken something to make her sleep, and therefore not afraid of disturbing her, Shelton went home, got out a bottle of Linden Scotch and put the finishing touches on his bender. In the morning Mrs. Shelton was a little better and came to the breakfast table where he was fighting an egg.

"Well, what kind of time did you have?"

"Glorious! Much more exciting than at the Frenches'. Mrs. Dittmar's brother is a piano playing fool."

"Oh, wasn't there any bridge then?"

"No. Just music and banter."

"Maybe the brother can't play contract and I spoiled the party by not going."

"Oh, no. *You* didn't spoil the party!"

"And do we go to the Camerons' next Wednesday?"

"I don't believe so. Nothing was said."

They did go next Wednesday night to the palatial home of E. M. Pardee, a friend of Gale Bartlett's and one of the real aristocrats of Linden. After dinner, Mrs. Pardee asked the Sheltons whether they played contract, and they said they did. The Pardees, not wishing to impoverish the young immigrants, refused to play "families." They insisted on cutting and Shelton cut Mrs. Pardee.

"Oh, Mr. Shevlin," she said at the end of the first hand, "why *didn't* you lead me a club? You *must* watch the discards!"

Author's Postcript: This story won't get me anything but the money I am paid for it. Even if it be read by those with whom I usually play—Mr. C., Mrs. W., Mr. T., Mrs. R. and the rest—they will think I mean two other fellows and tear into me like wolves next time I bid a slam and make one odd.

Old Folks' Christmas

Tom and Grace Carter sat in their living-room on Christmas Eve, sometimes talking, sometimes pretending to read and all the time thinking things they didn't want to think. Their two children, Junior, aged nineteen, and Grace, two years younger, had come home that day from their schools for the Christmas vacation. Junior was in his first year at the university and Grace attending a boarding-school that would fit her for college.

I won't call them Grace and Junior any more, though that is the way they had been christened. Junior had changed his name to Ted and Grace was now Caroline, and thus they insisted on being addressed, even by their parents. This was one of the things Tom and Grace the elder were thinking of as they sat in their living-room Christmas Eve.

Other university freshmen who had lived here had returned on the twenty-first, the day when the vacation was supposed to begin. Ted had telegraphed that he would be three days late owing to a special examination which, if he passed it, would lighten the terrific burden of the next term. He had arrived at home looking so pale, heavy-eyed and shaky that his mother doubted the wisdom of the concentrated mental effort, while his father secretly hoped the stuff had been non-poisonous and would not have lasting effects. Caroline, too, had been behind schedule, explaining that her laundry had gone astray and she had not dared trust others to trace it for her.

Grace and Tom had attempted, with fair success, to conceal their disappointment over this delayed home-coming and had continued with their preparations for a Christmas that would thrill their children and consequently themselves. They had bought an imposing lot of presents, costing twice or three times as much as had been Tom's father's annual income when Tom was Ted's age, or Tom's own income a year ago, before General Motors' acceptance of his new weather-proof paint had enabled him to buy this suburban home and luxuries such as his own parents and Grace's had never dreamed of, and to give Ted and Caroline advantages that he and Grace had perforce gone without.

Behind the closed door of the music-room was the elaborately decked tree. The piano and piano bench and the floor around the tree were covered with beribboned packages of all sizes, shapes and weights, one of them addressed to Tom, another to Grace, a few to the servants and the rest to Ted and Caroline. A huge box contained a sealskin coat for Caroline, a coat that had cost as much as the Carters had formerly paid a year for rent. Even more expensive was a "set" of jewelry consisting of an opal brooch, a bracelet of opals and gold filigree, and an opal ring surrounded by diamonds.

Grace always had preferred opals to any other stone, but now that she could afford them, some inhibition prevented her from buying them for herself; she could enjoy them much more adorning her pretty daughter. There were boxes of silk stockings, lingerie, gloves and handkerchiefs. And for Ted, a three-hundred-dollar watch, a de-luxe edition of Balzac, an expensive bag of shiny, new steel-shafted golf-clubs and the last word in portable phonographs.

But the big surprise for the boy was locked in the garage, a black Gorham sedan, a model more up to date and better-looking than Tom's own year-old car that stood beside it. Ted could use it during the vacation if the mild weather continued and could look forward to driving it around home next spring and summer, there being a rule at the university forbidding undergraduates the possession or use of private automobiles.

Every year for sixteen years, since Ted was three and Caroline one, it had been the Christmas Eve custom of the Carter's to hang up their children's stockings and fill them with inexpensive toys.

Tom and Grace had thought it would be fun to continue the custom this year; the contents of the stockings—a mechanical negro dancing doll, music-boxes, a kitten that meowed when you pressed a spot on her back, et cetera—would make the "kids" laugh. And one of Grace's first pronouncements to her returned offspring was that they must go to bed early so Santa Claus would not be frightened away.

But it seemed they couldn't promise to make it so terrible early. They both had long-standing dates in town. Caroline was going to dinner and a play with Beatrice Murdock and Beatrice's nineteen-year-old brother Paul. The latter would call for her in his car at half past six. Ted had accepted an invitation to see the hockey match with two classmates, Herb Castle and Bernard King. He wanted to take his father's Gorham, but Tom told him untruthfully that the foot-brake was not working; Ted must be kept out of the garage till tomorrow morning.

Ted and Caroline had taken naps in the afternoon and gone off together in Paul Murdock's stylish roadster, giving their word that they would be back by midnight or a little later and that tomorrow night they would stay home.

And now their mother and father were sitting up for them, because the stockings could not be filled and hung till they were safely in bed, and also because trying to go to sleep is a painful and hopeless business when you are kind of jumpy.

"What time is it?" asked Grace, looking up from the third page of a book that she had begun to "read" soon after dinner.

"Half past two," said her husband. (He had answered the same question every fifteen or twenty minutes since midnight.)

"You don't suppose anything could have happened?" said Grace.

"We'd have heard if there had," said Tom.

"It isn't likely, of course," said Grace, "but they might have had an accident some place where nobody was there to report it or telephone or anything. We don't know what kind of a driver the Murdock boy is."

"He's Ted's age. Boys that age may be inclined to drive too fast, but they drive pretty well."

"How do you know?"

"Well, I've watched some of them drive."

"Yes, but not all of them."

"I doubt whether anybody in the world has seen every nineteen-year-old boy drive."

"Boys these days seem so kind of irresponsible."

"Oh, don't worry! They probably met some of their young friends and stopped for a bite to eat or something." Tom got up and walked to the window with studied carelessness. "It's a pretty night," he said. "You can see every star in the sky."

But he wasn't looking at the stars. He was looking down the road for headlights. There were none in sight and after a few moments he returned to his chair.

"What time is it?" asked Grace.

"Twenty-two of," he said.

"Of what?"

"Of three."

"Your watch must have stopped. Nearly an hour ago you told me it was half past two."

"My watch is all right. You probably dozed off."

"I haven't closed my eyes."

"Well, it's time you did. Why don't you go to bed?"

"Why don't *you?*"

"I'm not sleepy."

"Neither am I. But honestly, Tom, it's silly for you to stay up. I'm just doing it so I can fix the stockings, and because I feel so wakeful. But there's no use of your losing your sleep."

"I couldn't sleep a wink till they're home."

"That's foolishness! There's nothing to worry about. They're just having a good time. You were young once yourself."

"That's just it! When I was young, I was young." He picked up his paper and tried to get interested in the shipping news.

"What time is it?" asked Grace.

"Five minutes of three."

"Maybe they're staying at the Murdocks' all night."

"They'd have let us know."

"They were afraid to wake us up, telephoning."

At three-twenty a car stopped at the front gate.

"There they are!"

"I told you there was nothing to worry about."

Tom went to the window. He could just discern the outlines of

the Murdock boy's roadster, whose lighting system seemed to have
broken down.

"He hasn't any lights," said Tom. "Maybe I'd better go out and
see if I can fix them."

"No, don't!" said Grace sharply. "He can fix them himself. He's
just saving them while he stands still."

"Why don't they come in?"

"They're probably making plans."

"They can make them in here. I'll go out and tell them we're
still up."

"No, don't!" said Grace as before, and Tom obediently remained
at the window.

It was nearly four when the car lights flashed on and the car
drove away. Caroline walked into the house and stared dazedly at
her parents.

"Heavens! What are you doing up?"

Tom was about to say something, but Grace forestalled him.

"We were talking over old Christmases," she said. "Is it very late?"

"I haven't any idea," said Caroline.

"Where is Ted?"

"Isn't he home? I haven't seen him since we dropped him at the
hockey place."

"Well, you go right to bed," said her mother. "You must be worn
out."

"I am, kind of. We danced after the play. What time is breakfast?"

"Eight o'clock."

"Oh, Mother, can't you make it nine?"

"I guess so. You used to want to get up early on Christmas."

"I know, but——"

"Who brought you home?" asked Tom.

"Why, Paul Murdock—and Beatrice."

"You look rumpled."

"They made me sit in the 'rumple' seat."

She laughed at her joke, said good night and went upstairs. She
had not come even within hand-shaking distance of her father and
mother.

"The Murdocks," said Tom, "must have great manners, making
their guest ride in that uncomfortable seat."

Grace was silent.

"You go to bed, too," said Tom. "I'll wait for Ted."

"You couldn't fix the stockings."

"I won't try. We'll have time for that in the morning; I mean, later in the morning."

"I'm not going to bed till you do," said Grace.

"All right, we'll both go. Ted ought not to be long now. I suppose his friends will bring him home. We'll hear him when he comes in."

There was no chance not to hear him when, at ten minutes before six, he came in. He had done his Christmas shopping late and brought home a package.

Grace was downstairs again at half past seven, telling the servants breakfast would be postponed till nine. She nailed the stockings beside the fireplace, went into the music-room to see that nothing had been disturbed and removed Ted's hat and overcoat from where he had carefully hung them on the hall floor.

Tom appeared a little before nine and suggested that the children ought to be awakened.

"I'll wake them," said Grace, and went upstairs. She opened Ted's door, looked, and softly closed it again. She entered her daughter's room and found Caroline semiconscious.

"Do I have to get up now? Honestly I can't eat anything. If you could just have Molla bring me some coffee. Ted and I are both invited to the Murdock's for breakfast at half past twelve, and I could sleep for another hour or two."

"But dearie, don't you know we have Christmas dinner at one?"

"It's a shame, Mother, but I thought of course our dinner would be at night."

"Don't you want to see your presents?"

"Certainly I do, but can't they wait?"

Grace was about to go to the kitchen to tell the cook that dinner would be at seven instead of one, but she remembered having promised Signe the afternoon and evening off, as a cold, light supper would be all anyone wanted after the heavy midday meal.

Tom and Grace breakfasted alone and once more sat in the living-room, talking, thinking and pretending to read.

"You ought to speak to Caroline," said Tom.

"I will, but not today. It's Christmas."

"And I intend to say a few words to Ted."

"Yes, dear, you must. But not today."

"I suppose they'll be out again tonight."

"No, they promised to stay home. We'll have a nice cozy evening."

"Don't bet too much on that," said Tom.

At noon the "children" made their entrance and responded to their parents' salutations with almost the proper warmth. Ted declined a cup of coffee and he and Caroline apologized for making a "breakfast" date at the Murdocks'.

"Sis and I both thought you'd be having dinner at seven, as usual."

"We've always had it at one o'clock on Christmas," said Tom.

"I'd forgotten it was Christmas," said Ted.

"Well, those stockings ought to remind you."

Ted and Caroline looked at the bulging stockings.

"Isn't there a tree?" asked Caroline.

"Of course," said her mother. "But the stockings come first."

"We've only a little time," said Caroline. "We'll be terribly late as it is. So can't we see the tree now?"

"I guess so," said Grace, and led the way into the music-room.

The servants were summoned and the tree stared at and admired.

"You must open your presents," said Grace to her daughter.

"I can't open them all now," said Caroline. "Tell me which is special."

The cover was removed from the huge box and Grace held up the coat.

"Oh, Mother!" said Caroline. "A sealskin coat!"

"Put it on," said her father.

"Not now. We haven't time."

"Then look at this!" said Grace, and opened the case of jewels.

"Oh, Mother! Opals!" said Caroline.

"They're my favorite stone," said Grace quietly.

"If nobody minds," said Ted, "I'll postpone my personal investigation till we get back. I know I'll like everything you've given me. But if we have no car in working order, I've got to call a taxi and catch a train."

"You can drive in," said his father.

"Did you fix the brake?"

"I think it's all right. Come up to the garage and we'll see."

Ted got his hat and coat and kissed his mother good-by.

"Mother," he said, "I know you'll forgive me for not having any presents for you and Dad. I was so rushed the last three days at school. And I thought I'd have time to shop a little when we got in yesterday, but I was in too much of a hurry to be home. Last night, everything was closed."

"Don't worry," said Grace. "Christmas is for young people. Dad and I have everything we want."

The servants had found their gifts and disappeared, expressing effusive Scandinavian thanks.

Caroline and her mother were left alone.

"Mother, where did the coat come from?"

"Lloyd and Henry's."

"They keep all kinds of furs, don't they?"

"Yes."

"Would you mind horribly if I exchanged this?"

"Certainly not, dear. You pick out anything you like, and if it's a little more expensive, it won't make any difference. We can go in town tomorrow or next day. But don't you want to wear your opals to the Murdocks'?"

"I don't believe so. They might get lost or something. And I'm not—well, I'm not so crazy about——"

"I think they can be exchanged, too," said Grace. "You run along now and get ready to start."

Caroline obeyed with alacrity, and Grace spent a welcome moment by herself.

Tom opened the garage door.

"Why, you've got two cars!" said Ted.

"The new one isn't mine," said Tom.

"Whose is it?"

"Yours. It's the new model."

"Dad, that's wonderful! But it looks just like the old one."

"Well, the old one's pretty good. Just the same, yours is better. You'll find that out when you drive it. Hop in and get started. I had her filled with gas."

"I think I'd rather drive the old one."

"Why?"

"Well, what I really wanted, Dad, was a Barnes sport roadster, something like Paul Murdock's, only a different color scheme. And if I don't drive this Gorham at all, maybe you could get them to take it back or make some kind of a deal with the Barnes people."

Tom didn't speak till he was sure of his voice. Then: "All right, son. Take my car and I'll see what can be done about yours."

Caroline, waiting for Ted, remembered something and called to her mother. "Here's what I got for you and Dad," she said. "It's two tickets to 'Jolly Jane,' the play I saw last night. You'll love it!"

"When are they for?" asked Grace.

"Tonight," said Caroline.

"But dearie," said her mother, "we don't want to go out tonight, when you promised to stay home."

"We'll keep our promise," said Caroline, "but the Murdocks may drop in and bring some friends and we'll dance and there'll be music. And Ted and I both thought you'd rather be away somewhere so our noise wouldn't disturb you."

"It was sweet of you to do this," said her mother, "but your father and I don't mind noise as long as you're enjoying yourselves."

"It's time anyway that you and Dad had a treat."

"The real treat," said Grace, "would be to spend a quiet evening here with just you two."

"The Murdocks practically invited themselves and I couldn't say no after they'd been so nice to me. And honestly, Mother, you'll love this play!"

"Will you be home for supper?"

"I'm pretty sure we will, but if we're a little late, don't you and Dad wait for us. Take the seven-twenty so you won't miss anything. The first act is really the best. We probably won't be hungry, but have Signe leave something out for us in case we are."

Tom and Grace sat down to the elaborate Christmas dinner and didn't make much impression on it. Even if they had had any appetite, the sixteen-pound turkey would have looked almost like new when they had eaten their fill. Conversation was intermittent and related chiefly to Signe's excellence as a cook and the mildness of the weather. Children and Christmas were barely touched on.

Tom merely suggested that on account of its being a holiday and their having theatre tickets, they ought to take the six-ten and eat supper at the Metropole. His wife said no; Ted and Caroline might come home and be disappointed at not finding them. Tom seemed about to make some remark, but changed his mind.

The afternoon was the longest Grace had ever known. The children were still absent at seven and she and Tom taxied to the train. Neither talked much on the way to town. As for the play, which Grace was sure to love, it turned out to be a rehash of "Cradle Snatchers" and "Sex," retaining the worst features of each.

When it was over, Tom said: "Now I'm inviting you to the Cove Club. You didn't eat any breakfast or dinner or supper and I can't have you starving to death on a feast-day. Besides, I'm thirsty as well as hungry."

They ordered the special *table d'hôte* and struggled hard to get away with it. Tom drank six high-balls, but they failed to produce the usual effect of making him jovial. Grace had one high-ball and some kind of cordial that gave her a warm, contented feeling for a moment. But the warmth and contentment left her before the train was half way home.

The living-room looked as if Von Kluck's army had just passed through. Ted and Caroline had kept their promise up to a certain point. They had spent part of the evening at home, and the Murdocks must have brought all their own friends and everybody else's, judging from the results. The tables and floors were strewn with empty glasses, ashes and cigaret stubs. The stockings had been torn off their nails and the wrecked contents were all over the place. Two sizable holes had been burnt in Grace's favorite rug.

Tom took his wife by the arm and led her into the music-room.

"You never took the trouble to open your own present," he said.

"And I think there's one for you, too," said Grace. "They didn't come in here," she added, "so I guess there wasn't much dancing or music."

Tom found his gift from Grace, a set of diamond studs and cuff buttons for festive wear. Grace's present from him was an opal ring.

"Oh, Tom!" she said.

"We'll have to go out somewhere tomorrow night, so I can break these in," said Tom.

"Well, if we do that, we'd better get a good night's rest."

"I'll beat you upstairs," said Tom.

Ex Parte

Most always when a man leaves his wife, there's no excuse in the world for him. She may have made whoop-whoop-whoopee with the whole ten commandments, but if he shows his disapproval to the extent of walking out on her, he will thereafter be a total stranger to all his friends excepting the two or three bums who will tour the night clubs with him so long as he sticks to his habits of paying for everything.

When a woman leaves her husband, she must have good and sufficient reasons. He drinks all the time, or he runs around, or he doesn't give her any money, or he uses her as the heavy bag in his home gymnasium work. No more is he invited to his former playmates' houses for dinner and bridge. He is an outcast just the same as if he had done the deserting. Whichever way it happens, it's his fault. He can state his side of the case if he wants to, but there is nobody around listening.

Now I claim to have a little chivalry in me, as well as a little pride. So in spite of the fact that Florence has broadcast her grievances over the red and blue network both, I intend to keep mine to myself till death do me part.

But after I'm gone, I want some of my old pals to know that this thing wasn't as lopsided as she has made out, so I will write the true story, put it in an envelope with my will and appoint Ed Osborne executor. He used to be my best friend and would be yet if his wife would let him. He'll have to read all my papers, including this, and he'll tell everybody else about it and maybe they'll be a little sorry that they treated me like an open manhole.

(Ed, please don't consider this an attempt to be literary. You know I haven't written for publication since our days on "The Crimson and White," and I wasn't so hot then. Just look on it as a statement of facts. If I were still alive, I'd take a bible oath that nothing herein is exaggerated. And whatever else may have been my imperfections, I never lied save to shield a woman or myself.)

Well, a year ago last May I had to go to New York. I called up Joe Paxton and he asked me out to dinner. I went, and met Florence. She and Marjorie Paxton had been at school together and she was there for a visit. We fell in love with each other and got engaged. I stopped off in Chicago on the way home, to see her people. They liked me all right, but they hated to have Florence marry a man who lived so far away. They wanted to postpone her leaving home as long as possible and they made us wait till April this year.

I had a room at the Belden and Florence and I agreed that when we were married, we would stay there awhile and take our time about picking out a house. But the last day of March, two weeks before the date of our wedding, I ran into Jeff Cooper and he told me his news, that the Standard Oil was sending him to China in some big job that looked permanent.

"I'm perfectly willing to go," he said. "So is Bess. It's a lot more money and we think it will be an interesting experience. But here I am with a brand-new place on my hands that cost me $45,000, including the furniture, and no chance to sell it in a hurry except at a loss. We were just beginning to feel settled. Otherwise we would have no regrets about leaving this town. Bess hasn't any real friends here and you're the only one I can claim."

"How much would you take for your house, furniture and all?" I asked him.

"I'd take a loss of $5,000," he said. "I'd take $40,000 with the buyer assuming my mortgage of $15,000, held by the Phillips Trust and Mortgage Company in Seattle."

I asked him if he would show me the place. They had only been living there a month and I hadn't had time to call. He said, what did I want to look at it for and I told him I would buy it if it looked o. k. Then I confessed that I was going to be married; you know I had kept it a secret around here.

Well, he took me home with him and he and Bess showed me everything, all new and shiny and a bargain if you ever saw one. In the first place, there's the location, on the best residential street in town, handy to my office and yet with a whole acre of ground, and a bed of cannas coming up in the front yard that Bess had planted when they bought the property last fall. As for the house, I always liked stucco, and this one is *built!* You could depend on old Jeff to see to that.

But the furniture was what decided me. Jeff had done the smart thing and ordered the whole works from Wolfe Brothers, taking their advice on most of the stuff, as neither he nor Bess knew much about it. Their total bill, furnishing the entire place, rugs, beds, tables, chairs, everything, was only $8,500, including a mahogany upright player-piano that they ordered from Seattle. I had my mother's old mahogany piano in storage and I kind of hoped Jeff wouldn't want me to buy this, but it was all or nothing, and with a bargain like that staring me in the face, I didn't stop to argue, not when I looked over the rest of the furniture and saw what I was getting.

The living-room had, and still has, three big easy chairs and a couch, all over-stuffed, as they call it, to say nothing of an Oriental rug that alone had cost $500. There was a long mahogany table behind the couch, with lamps at both ends in case you wanted to lie down and read. The dining-room set was solid mahogany—a table and eight chairs that had separated Jeff from $1,000.

The floors downstairs were all oak parquet. Also he had blown himself to an oak mantelpiece and oak woodwork that must have run into heavy dough. Jeff told me what it cost him extra, but I don't recall the amount.

The Coopers were strong for mahogany and wanted another set for their bedroom, but Jake Wolfe told them it would get monotonous if there was too much of it. So he sold them five pieces—a bed, two chairs, a chiffonier and a dresser—of some kind of wood tinted green, with flowers painted on it. This was $1,000 more, but it certainly was worth it. You never saw anything prettier than that bed when the lace spreads were on.

Well, we closed the deal and at first I thought I wouldn't tell Florence, but would let her believe we were going to live at the Belden and then give her a surprise by taking her right from the train to our own home. When I got to Chicago, though, I couldn't keep my mouth shut. I gave it away and it was I, not she, that had the surprise.

Instead of acting tickled to death, as I figured she would, she just looked kind of funny and said she hoped I had as good taste in houses as I had in clothes. She tried to make me describe the house and the furniture to her, but I wouldn't do it. To appreciate a layout like that, you have to see it for yourself.

We were married and stopped in Yellowstone for a week on our way here. That was the only really happy week we had together. From the minute we arrived home till she left for good, she was a different woman than the one I thought I knew. She never smiled and several times I caught her crying. She wouldn't tell me what ailed her and when I asked if she was just homesick, she said no and choked up and cried some more.

You can imagine that things were not as I expected they would be. In New York and in Chicago and Yellowstone, she had had more *life* than any girl I ever met. Now she acted all the while as if she were playing the title rôle at a funeral.

One night late in May the telephone rang. It was Mrs. Dwan and she wanted Florence. If I had known what this was going to mean, I would have slapped the receiver back on the hook and let her keep on wanting.

I had met Dwan a couple of times and had heard about their place out on the Turnpike. But I had never seen it or his wife either.

Well, it developed that Mildred Dwan had gone to school with Florence and Marjorie Paxton, and she had just learned from Marjorie that Florence was my wife and living here. She said she and her husband would be in town and call on us the next Sunday afternoon.

Florence didn't seem to like the idea and kind of discouraged it. She said we would drive out and call on them instead. Mrs. Dwan said no, that Florence was the newcomer and it was her (Mrs. Dwan's) first move. So Florence gave in.

They came and they hadn't been in the house more than a minute when Florence began to cry. Mrs. Dwan cried, too, and Dwan and I stood there first on one foot and then the other, trying to pretend we didn't know the girls were crying. Finally, to relieve the tension, I invited him to come and see the rest of the place. I showed him all over and he was quite enthusiastic. When we returned to the living-room, the girls had dried their eyes and were back in school together.

Florence accepted an invitation for one-o'clock dinner a week from that day. I told her, after they had left, that I would go along only on condition that she and our hostess would both control their tear-ducts. I was so accustomed to solo sobbing that I didn't mind it any more, but I couldn't stand a duet of it either in harmony or unison.

Well, when we got out there and had driven down their private lane through the trees and caught a glimpse of their house, which people around town had been talking about as something wonderful, I laughed harder than any time since I was single. It looked just like what it was, a reorganized barn. Florence asked me what was funny, and when I told her, she pulled even a longer face than usual.

"I think it's beautiful," she said.

Tie that!

I insisted on her going up the steps alone. I was afraid if the two of us stood on the porch at once, we'd fall through and maybe founder before help came. I warned her not to smack the knocker too hard or the door might crash in and frighten the horses.

"If you make jokes like that in front of the Dwans," she said, "I'll never speak to you again."

"I'd forgotten you ever did," said I.

I was expecting a hostler to let us in, but Mrs. Dwan came in person.

"Are we late?" said Florence.

"A little," said Mrs. Dwan, "but so is dinner. Helga didn't get home from church till half past twelve."

"I'm glad of it," said Florence. "I want you to take me all through this beautiful, beautiful house right this minute."

Mrs. Dwan called her husband and insisted that he stop in the middle of mixing a cocktail so he could join us in a tour of the beautiful, beautiful house.

"You wouldn't guess it," said Mrs. Dwan, "but it used to be a barn."

I was going to say I had guessed it. Florence gave me a look that changed my mind.

"When Jim and I first came here," said Mrs. Dwan, "we lived in an ugly little rented house on Oliver Street. It was only temporary, of course; we were just waiting till we found what we really wanted. We used to drive around the country Saturday afternoons and Sundays, hoping we would run across the right sort of thing. It was in the late fall when we first say this place. The leaves were off the trees and it was visible from the Turnpike.

" 'Oh, Jim!' I exclaimed. 'Look at that simply gorgeous old barn! With those wide shingles! And I'll bet you it's got hand-hewn beams in that middle, main section.' Jim bet me I was wrong, so we left the car, walked up the driveway, found the door open and came brazenly in. I won my bet as you can see."

She pointed to some dirty old rotten beams that ran across the living-room ceiling and looked as if five or six generations of rats had used them for gnawing practise.

"They're beautiful!" said Florence.

"The instant I saw them," said Mrs. Dwan, "I knew this was going to be our home!"

"I can imagine!" said Florence.

"We made inquiries and learned that the place belonged to a family named Taylor," said Mrs. Dwan. "The house had burned down and they had moved away. It was suspected that they had started the fire themselves, as they were terribly hard up and it was insured. Jim wrote to old Mr. Taylor in Seattle and asked him to set a price on the barn and the land, which is about four acres. They exchanged several letters and finally Mr. Taylor accepted Jim's offer. We got it for a song."

"Wonderful!" said Florence.

"And then, of course," Mrs. Dwan continued, "we engaged a house-wrecking company to tear down the other four sections of the barn—the stalls, the cow-shed, the tool-shed, and so forth—and take them away, leaving us just this one room. We had a man from Seattle come and put in these old pine walls and the flooring, and plaster the ceiling. He was recommended by a friend of Jim's and he certainly knew his business."

"I can see he did," said Florence.

"He made the hay-loft over for us, too, and we got the wings built by day-labor, with Jim and me supervising. It was so much fun that I was honestly sorry when it was finished."

"I can imagine!" said Florence.

Well, I am not very well up in Early American, which was the name they had for pretty nearly everything in the place, but for the benefit of those who are not on terms with the Dwans I will try and describe from memory the *objets d'art* they bragged of the most and which brought forth the loudest squeals from Florence.

The living-room walls were brown bare boards without a picture or scrap of wall-paper. On the floor were two or three "hooked rugs," whatever that means, but they needed five or six more of them, or one big carpet, to cover up all the knots in the wood. There was a maple "low-boy"; a "dough-trough" table they didn't have space for in the kitchen; a pine "stretcher" table with sticks connecting the four legs near the bottom so you couldn't put your feet anywhere; a "Dutch" chest that looked as if it had been ordered from the undertaker by one of Singer's Midgets, but he got well; and some "Windsor" chairs in which the only position you could get comfortable was to stand up behind them and lean your elbows on their back.

Not one piece that matched another, and not one piece of mahogany anywhere. And the ceiling, between the beams, had apparently been plastered by a workman who was that way, too.

"Some day soon I hope to have a piano," said Mrs. Dwan. "I can't live much longer without one. But so far I haven't been able to find one that would fit in."

"Listen," I said. "I've got a piano in storage that belonged to my mother. It's a mahogany upright and not so big that it wouldn't fit in this room, especially when you get that 'trough' table out. It isn't doing me any good and I'll sell it to you for $250. Mother paid $1,250 for it new."

"Oh, I couldn't think of taking it!" said Mrs. Dwan.

"I'll make it $200 even just because you're a friend of Florence's," I said.

"Really, I couldn't!" said Mrs. Dwan.

"You wouldn't have to pay for it all at once," I said.

"Don't you see," said Florence, "that a mahogany upright piano would be a perfect horror in here? Mildred wouldn't have it as a gift, let alone buy it. It isn't in the period."

"She could get it tuned," I said.

The answer to this was, "I'll show you the up-stairs now and we can look at the dining-room later on."

We were led to the guest-chamber. The bed was a maple four-poster, with pineapple posts, and a "tester" running from pillar to post. You would think a "tester" might be a man that went around trying out beds, but it's really a kind of frame that holds a canopy over the bed in case it rains and the roof leaks. There was a quilt made by Mrs. Dwan's great-grandmother, Mrs. Anthony Adams, in 1859, at Lowell, Mass. How is that for a memory?

"This used to be the hay-loft," said Mrs. Dwan.

"You ought to have left some of the hay so the guests could hit it," I said.

The dressers, or chests of drawers, and the chairs were all made of maple. And the same in the Dwans' own room; everything maple.

"If you had maple in one room and mahogany in the other," I said, "people wouldn't get confused when you told them that so and so was up in Maple's room."

Dwan laughed, but the women didn't.

The maid hollered up that dinner was ready.

"The cocktails aren't ready," said Dwan.

"You will have to go without them," said Mrs. Dwan. "The soup will be cold."

This put me in a great mood to admire the "sawbuck" table and the "slat back" chairs, which were evidently the *chef-d'œuvre* and the *pièce de résistance* of the *chez Dwan*.

"It came all the way from Pennsylvania," said Mildred, when Florence's outcries, brought on by her first look at the table, had died down. "Mother picked it up at a little place near Stroudsburg and sent it to me. It only cost $550, and the chairs were $45 apiece."

"How reasonable!" exclaimed Florence.

That was before she had sat in one of them. Only one thing was more unreasonable than the chairs, and that was the table itself, consisting of big planks nailed together and laid onto a railroad tie, supported underneath by a whole forest of cross-pieces and beams. The surface was as smooth on top as the trip to Catalina Island and all around the edges, great big divots had been taken out with some blunt instrument, probably a bayonet. There were stains and scorch marks that Florence fairly crowed over, but when I tried to add to the general ensemble by laying a lighted cigaret right down beside my soup-plate, she and both the Dwans yelled murder and made me take it off.

They planted me in an end seat, a location just right for a man who had stretched himself across a railway track and had both legs cut off at the abdomen. Not being that kind of man, I had to sit so far back that very few of my comestibles carried more than half-way to their target.

After dinner I was all ready to go home and get something to eat, but it had been darkening up outdoors for half an hour and now such a storm broke that I knew it was useless trying to persuade Florence to make a start.

"We'll play some bridge," said Dwan, and to my surprise he produced a card-table that was nowhere near "in the period."

At my house there was a big center chandelier that lighted up a bridge game no matter in what part of the room the table was put. But here we had to waste forty minutes moving lamps and wires and stands and when they were all fixed, you could tell a red suit from a black suit, but not a spade from a club. Aside from that and the granite-bottomed "Windsor" chairs and the fact that we played "families" for a cent a point and Florence and I won $12 and didn't get paid, it was one of the pleasantest afternoons I ever spent gambling.

The rain stopped at five o'clock and as we splashed through the puddles of Dwan's driveway, I remarked to Florence that I had never known she was such a kidder.

"What do you mean?" she asked me.

"Why, your pretending to admire all that junk," I said.

"Junk!" said Florence. "That is one of the most beautifully furnished homes I have ever seen!"

And so far as I can recall, that was her last utterance in my presence for six nights and five days.

At lunch on Saturday I said: "You know I like the silent drama one evening a week, but not twenty-four hours a day every day. What's the matter with you? If it's laryngitis, you might write me notes."

"I'll tell you what's the matter!" she burst out. "I hate this house and everything in it! It's too new! Everything shines! I loathe new things! I want a home like Mildred's, with things in it that I can look at without blushing for shame. I can't invite anyone here. It's

too hideous. And I'll never be happy here a single minute as long
as I live!"

Well, I don't mind telling that this kind of got under my skin. As
if I hadn't intended to give her a pleasant surprise! As if Wolfe
Brothers, in business thirty years, didn't know how to furnish a
home complete! I was pretty badly hurt, but I choked it down and
said, as calmly as I could:

"If you'll be a little patient, I'll try to sell this house and its contents for what I paid for it and them. It oughtn't to be much trouble;
there are plenty of people around who know a bargain. But it's too
bad you didn't confess your barn complex to me long ago. Only
last February, old Ken Garrett had to sell his establishment and the
men who bought it turned it into a garage. It was a livery-stable
which I could have got for the introduction of a song, or maybe just
the vamp. And we wouldn't have had to spend a nickel to make it as
nice and comfortable and homey as your friend Mildred's dump."

Florence was on her way upstairs before I had finished my speech.

I went down to Earl Benham's to see if my new suit was ready. It
was and I put it on and left the old one to be cleaned and pressed.

On the street I met Harry Cross.

"Come up to my office," he said. "There's something in my desk
that may interest you."

I accepted his invitation and from three different drawers he
pulled out three different quart bottles of Early American rye.

Just before six o'clock I dropped in Kane's store and bought
myself a pair of shears, a blow torch and an ax. I started home, but
stopped among the trees inside my front gate and cut big holes in
my coat and trousers. Alongside the path to the house was a sizable
mud puddle. I waded in it. And I bathed my gray felt hat.

Florence was sitting on the floor of the living-room, reading. She
seemed a little upset by my appearance.

"Good heavens! What's happened?"

"Nothing much," said I. "I just didn't want to look too new."

"What are those things you're carrying?"

"Just a pair of shears, a blow torch and an ax. I'm going to try
and antique this place and I think I'll begin on the dining-room
table."

Florence went into her scream, dashed upstairs and locked herself in. I went about my work and had the dinner-table looking pretty Early when the maid smelled fire and rushed in. She rushed out again and came back with a pitcher of water. But using my vest as a snuffer, I had had the flames under control all the while and there was nothing for her to do.

"I'll just nick it up a little with this ax," I told her, "and by the time I'm through, dinner ought to be ready."

"It will never be ready as far as I'm concerned," she said. "I'm leaving just as soon as I can pack."

And Florence had the same idea—vindicating the old adage about great minds.

I heard the front door slam and the back door slam, and I felt kind of tired and sleepy, so I knocked off work and went up to bed.

That's my side of the story, Eddie, and it's true so help me my bootlegger. Which reminds me that the man who sold Harry the rye makes this town once a week, or did when this was written. He's at the Belden every Tuesday from nine to six and his name is Mike Farrell.

The Young Immigrunts

PREFACE

The person whose name is signed to this novel was born on the nineteenth day of August, 1915, and was therefore four years and three months old when the manuscript was found, late in November, 1919. The narrative is substantially true, with the following exceptions:

1. "My Father," the leading character in the work, is depicted as a man of short temper, whereas the person from whom the character was drawn is in reality as pleasant a fellow as one would care to meet and seldom has a cross word for any one, let alone women and children.

2. The witty speeches accredited to "My Father" have, possibly

owing to the limitations of a child's memory, been so garbled and twisted that they do not look half so good in print as they sounded in the open air.

3. More stops for gas were made than are mentioned in the story.

As the original manuscript was written on a typewriter with a rather frayed ribbon, and as certain words were marked out and others handwritten in, I have taken the liberty of copying the entire work with a fresh ribbon and the inclusion of the changes which the author indicated in pencil in the first draft. Otherwise the story is presented to the reader exactly as it was first set down.

THE FATHER.

Chapter 1

MY PARENTS

My parents are both married and ½ of them are very good looking. The balance is tall and skiny and has a swarty complexion with moles but you hardily ever notice them on account of your gaze being rapped up in his feet which would be funny if brevvity wasnt the soul of wit. Everybody says I have his eyes and I am glad it didnt half to be something else tho Rollie Zeider the ball player calls him owl eyes for a nick name but if I was Rollie Zeider and his nose I wouldnt pick on somebodys else features.

He wears pretty shirts which he bought off of another old ball player Artie Hofman to attrack tension off of his feet and must of payed a big price for them I heard my ant tell my uncle when they thorght I was a sleep down to the lake tho I guess he pays even more for his shoes if they sell them by the frunt foot.

I was born in a hospittle in Chicago 4 years ago and liked it very much and had no idear we were going to move till 1 day last summer I heard my mother arsk our nurse did she think she could get along O. K. with myself and 3 brothers John Jimmie and David for 10 days wilst she and my old man went east to look for a costly home.

Well yes said our nurse barshfully.

I may as well exclaim to the reader that John is 7 and Jimmie is 5 and I am 4 and David is almost nothing as yet you might say and tho I was named for my father they call me Bill thank God.

The conversation amungst my mother and our nurse took place right after my father came back from Toledo where Jack Dempsey knocked Jessie Willard for a gool tho my father liked the big fellow and bet on him.

David was in his bath at the time and my mother and our nurse and myself and 2 elder brothers was standing around admireing him tho I notice that when the rest of the family takes their bath they dont make open house of the occassion.

Well my parents went east and dureing their absents myself and brothers razed hell with David on the night shift but when they come back my mother said to the nurse were they good boys.

Fine replid our nurse lamely and where are you going to live.

Connecticut said my mother.

Our nurse forced a tired smile.

Here we will leave my parents to unpack and end this chapter.

Chapter 2

STARTING GAILY

We spent the rest of the summer on my granmother in Indiana and my father finley went to the worst series to write it up as he has followed sports of all sorts for years and is a expert so he bet on the wite sox and when he come home he acted rarther cross.

Well said my mother simperingly I suppose we can start east now.

We will start east when we get good and ready said my father with a lordly sneeze.

The next thing was how was we going to make the trip as my father had boughten a new car that the cheepest way to get it there was drive it besides carrying a grate deal of our costly bagage but if all of us went in it they would be no room left for our costly bagage and besides 2 of my brothers always acts like devils incarnite when they get in a car so my mother said to our nurse.

If you think you can manage the 2 older boys and David on the train myself and husband will take Bill in the car said my mother to our nurse.

Fine replid our nurse with a gastly look witch my mother did not see.

Myself and parents left Goshen Indiana on a fine Monday morning leaving our nurse and brothers to come latter in the weak on the railway. Our plans was to reach Detroit that night and stop with my uncle and ant and the next evening take the boat to Buffalo and thence to Connecticut by motor so the first town we past through was Middlebury.

Elmer Flick the old ball player use to live here said my father modestly.

My mother forced a smile and soon we were acrost the Michigan line and my mother made the remark that she was thirsty.

We will stop at Coldwater for lunch said my father with a strate face as he pulls most of his lines without changeing expressions.

Sure enough we puled up to 1 side of the road just after leaveing Coldwater and had our costly viands of frid chicken and doughnuts and milk fernished by my grate ant and of witch I partook freely.

We will stop at Ypsilanti for supper said my father in calm tones that is where they have the state normal school.

I was glad to hear this and hoped we would get there before dark as I had always wanted to come in contack with normal peaple and see what they are like and just at dusk we entered a large size town and drove past a large size football field.

Heavens said my mother this must be a abnormal school to have such a large football field.

My father wore a qeer look.

This is not Ypsilanti this is Ann Arbor he crid.

But I thorght you said we would go south of Ann Arbor and direct to Ypsilanti said my mother with a smirk.

I did say that but I thorght I would surprise you by comeing into Ann Arbor replid my father with a corse jesture.

Personly I think the surprise was unanimous.

Well now we are here said my mother we might as well look up Bill.

Bill is my uncle Bill so we stoped at the Alfa Delt house and got him and took him down to the hotel for supper and my old man called up Mr. Yost the football coach of the Michigan football team and he come down and visited with us.

What kind of a team have you got coach said my father lamely.

I have got a determined team replid Mr. Yost they are determined to not play football.

At this junction my unlucky mother changed the subjeck to the league of nations and it was 10 o'clock before Mr. Yost come to a semi colon so we could resume our journey and by the time we past through Ypsilanti the peaple was not only subnormal but unconsius. It was nerly midnight when we puled up in frunt of my ants and uncles house in Detroit that had been seting up since 7 expecting us.

Were sorry to be so late said my mother bruskly.

Were awfully glad you could come at all replid my ant with a ill consealed yawn.

We will now leave my relitives to get some sleep and end this chapter.

Chapter 3

ERIE LAKE

The boat leaves Detroit every afternoon at 5 oclock and reachs Buffalo the next morning at 9 tho I would better exclaim to my readers that when it is 9 oclock in Buffalo it is only 8 oclock in Goshen for instants as Buffalo peaple are qeer.

Well said my father the next morning at brekfus I wander what time we half to get the car on the board of the boat.

I will find out down town and call up and let you know replid my uncle who is a engineer and digs soors or something.

Sure enough he called up dureing the fornoon and said the car must be on the board of the boat at 3 oclock so my father left the house at 2 oclock and drove down to the worf tho he had never drove a car in Detroit before but has nerves of steal. Latter my uncle come out to his home and took myself and mother and ant down to the worf where my old man was waiting for us haveing put the car on the board.

What have you been doing ever since 3 oclock arsked my mother as it was now nerly 5.

Haveing a high ball my father replid.

I thorght Detroit was dry said my mother shyly.

Did you said my father with a rye smile and as it was now nerly time for the boat to leave we said good by to my uncle and ant and went on the boat. A messenger took our costly bagage and put it away wilst myself and parents went out on the porch and set looking

at the peaple on the worf. Suddenly they was a grate hub bub on
the worf and a young man and lady started up the gangs plank wilst
a big crowd throwed rice and old shoes at them and made a up roar.

Bride and glum going to Niagara Falls said my father who is well
travelled and seams to know everything.

Instantly the boat give a blarst on the wistle and I started with
suprise.

Did that scare you Bill said my father and seamed to enjoy it and
I supose he would of laughed out right had I fell overboard and
been drowned in the narsty river water.

Soon we were steeming up the river on the city of Detroit 3.

That is Canada over there is it not said my mother.

What did you think it was the Austrian Tyrol replid my father
explodcing a cough. Dureing our progress up the river I noticed
sevral funny things flotting in the water with lanterns hanging on
them and was wandering what they could be when my mother said
they seam to have plenty of boys.

They have got nothing on us replid my father quick as a flarsh.

A little latter who should come out on the porch and set themselfs ner us but the bride and glum.

Oh I said to myself I hope they will talk so as I can hear them as I
have always wandered what newlyweds talk about on their way to
Niagara Falls and soon my wishs was realized.

Some night said the young glum are you warm enough.

I am perfectly comfertible replid the fare bride tho her looks belid
her words what time do we arive in Buffalo.

9 oclock said the lordly glum are you warm enough.

I am perfectly comfertible replid the fare bride what time do we
arive in Buffalo.

9 oclock said the lordly glum I am afrade it is too cold for you out
here.

Well maybe it is replid the fare bride and without farther adieu
they went in the spacius parlers.

I wander will he be arsking her 8 years from now is she warm
enough said my mother with a faint grimace.

The weather may change before then replid my father.

Are you warm enough said my father after a slite pause.

No was my mothers catchy reply.

Well said my father we arive in Buffalo at 9 oclock and with that we all went inside as it was now pitch dark and had our supper and retired and when we rose the next morning and drest and had brekfus we puled up to the worf in Buffalo and it was 9 oclock so I will leave the city of Detroit 3 tide to the worf and end this chapter.

Chapter 4

BUFFALO TO ROCHESTER 76.4

As we was leaveing the boat who should I see right along side of us but the fare bride and the lordly glum.

We are right on the dot said the glum looking at his costly watch it is just 9 oclock and so they past out of my life.

We had to wait qite a wile wilst the old man dug up his bill of loading and got the costly moter.

We will half to get some gas he said I wonder where they is a garage.

No sooner had the words fell from his lips when a man with a flagrant Adams apple handed him a card with the name of a garage on it.

Go up Genesee st 5 blks and turn to the left or something said the man with the apple.

Soon we reached the garage and had the gas tank filled with gas it was 27 cents in Buffalo and soon we was on our way to Rochester. Well these are certainly grate roads said my father barshfully.

They have lots better roads in the east than out west replid my mother with a knowing wink.

The roads all through the east are better than out west remarked my father at lenth.

These are wonderfull replid my mother smuggleing me vs her arm.

The time past quickly with my parents in so jocular a mood and all most before I knew it we was on the outer skirts of Batavia.

What town is this quired my mother in a tolerant voice.

Batavia husked my father sloughing down to 15 miles per hour.

Well maybe we would better stop and have lunch here said my mother coyly.

We will have lunch in Rochester replid my father with a loud cough.

My mother forced a smile and it was about ½ past 12 when we arived in Rochester and soon we was on Genesee st and finley stoped in front of a elegant hotel and shared a costly lunch.

Chapter 5

MY FATHER'S IDEAR

Wilst participateing in the lordly viands my father halled out his map and give it the up and down.

Look at here he said at lenth they seams to be a choice of 2 main roads between here and Syracuse but 1 of them gos way up north to Oswego wilst the other gos way south to Geneva where as Syracuse is strate east from here you might say so it looks to me like we would save both millage and time if we was to drive strate east through Lyons the way the railway gos.

Well I dont want to ride on the ties said my mother with a loud cough.

Well you dont half to because they seams to be a little road that gos strate through replid my father removeing a flys cadaver from the costly farina.

Well you would better stick to the main roads said my mother tacklessly.

Well you would better stick to your own business replid my father with a pungent glance.

Soon my father had payed the check and gave the waiter a lordly bribe and once more we sprang into the machine and was on our way. The lease said about the results of my fathers grate idear the soonest mended in a word it turned out to be a holycost of the first water as after we had covered miles and miles of ribald roads we suddenly come to a abrupt conclusion vs the side of a stagnant freight train that was stone deef to honks. My father set there for nerly ½ a hour reciteing the 4 Horses of the Apoplex in a under tone but finely my mother mustard up her curage and said affectedly why dont we turn around and go back somewheres. I cant spell what my father replid.

At lenth my old man decided that Lyons wouldnt never come to

Mahomet if we set it out on the same lines all winter so we backed up and turned around and retraced 4 miles of shell holes and finely reached our objective by way of Detour.

Puling up in front of a garage my father beckoned to a dirty mechanic.

How do we get to Syracuse from her arsked my father blushing furiously.

Go strate south to Geneva and then east to Syracuse replid the dirty mechanic with a loud cough.

Isnt there no short cut arsked my father.

Go strate south to Geneva and then east to Syracuse replid the dirty mechanic.

You see daddy we go to Geneva after all I said brokenly but luckly for my piece of mind my father dont beleive in corporeal punishment a specially in front of Lyons peaple.

Soon we was on a fine road and nothing more hapened till we puled into Syracuse at 7 that evening and as for the conversation that changed hands in the car between Lyons and Syracuse you could stick it in a day message and send it for 30 cents.

Chapter 6

SYRACUSE TO HUDSON 183.2

Soon we was on Genesee st in Syracuse but soon turned off a blk or 2 and puled up in front of a hotel that I cant ether spell or pronounce besides witch they must of been a convention of cheese sculpters or something stoping there and any way it took the old man a hour to weedle a parler bed room and bath out of the clerk and put up a cot for me.

Wilst we was enjoying a late and futile supper in the hotel dinning room a man named Duffy reckonized my father and came to our table and arsked him to go to some boxing matchs in Syracuse that night.

Thanks very much said my father with a slite sneeze but you see what I have got on my hands besides witch I have been driveing all day and half to start out again erly in the morning so I guess not.

Between you and I dear reader my old man has been oposed to pugilisms since the 4 of July holycost.

Who is that man arsked my mother when that man had gone away.

Mr. Duffy replid my father shove the ketchup over this way.

Yes I know he is Mr. Duffy but where did you meet him insisted my mother quaintly.

In Boston my father replid where would a person meet a man named Duffy.

When we got up the next morning it was 6 o'clock and purring rain but we eat a costly brekfus and my father said we would save time if we would all walk down to the garage where he had horded the car witch he stated was only 2 short blks away from the hotel. Well if it was only 2 short blks why peaple that lives next door to each other in Syracuse are by no means neighbors and when we got there the entire party was soping wet and rarther rabid.

We will all catch our death of cold chuckled my mother.

What of it explained my old man with a dirty look at the sky.

Maybe we would better put up the curtains sugested my mother smirking.

Maybe we wouldnt too said my father cordialy.

Well maybe it will clear up said my mother convulsively.

Maybe it wont too replid my father as he capered into the drivers seat.

My father is charming company wilst driveing on strange roads through a purring rain and even when we past through Oneida and he pronounced it like it was a biscuit neither myself or my mother ventured to correct him but finely we reached Utica when we got to witch we puled up along side the kerb and got out and rang ourselfs out to a small extent when suddenly a closed car sored past us on the left.

Why that was Mrs. Heywood in that car explained my mother with a fierce jesture. By this time it was not raining and we got back into the car and presently over took the closed car witch stoped when they reckonized us.

And witch boy is this quired Mrs. Heywood when the usual compliments had been changed.

This is the third he is named for his father replid my mother forceing a smile.

He has his eyes was the comment.

Bill dont you remember Mrs. Heywood said my mother turning on me she use to live in Riverside and Dr. Heywood tended to you that time you had that slite atack of obesity.

Well yes I replid with a slite accent but did not add how rotten the medicine tasted that time and soon we was on Genesee st on our way out of Utica.

I wander why they dont name some of their sts Genesee in these eastren towns said my father for the sun was now shining but no sooner had we reached Herkimer when the clouds bersed with re-nude vigger and I think my old man was about to say we will stop here and have lunch when my mother sugested it herself.

No replid my father with a corse jesture we will go on to Little Falls.

It was raining cats and dogs when we arived at Little Falls and my father droped a quaint remark.

If Falls is a verb he said the man that baptized this town was a practicle joker.

We will half to change our close replid my mother steping into a mud peddle in front of the hotel with a informal look.

When we had done so we partook of a meger lunch and as it was now only drooling resumed our jurney.

They soked me 5 for that room said my father but what is a extra sokeing or 2 on a day like this.

I didnt mean for you to get a room said my mother violently.

Where did you want us to change our close on the register said my old man turning pail.

Wasnt it funny that we should happen to see Mrs. Heywood in Utica said my mother at lenth.

They live there dont they my father replid.

Why yes my mother replid.

Well then my father replid the real joke would of been if we had of happened to see her in Auburn.

A little wile latter we past a grate many signs reading dine at the Big Nose Mountain Inn.

Rollie Zeider never told me they had named a mountain after him crid my father and soon we past through Fonda.

Soon we past through Amsterdam and I guess I must of dosed off at lease I cant remember anything between there and Schenectady and I must apologize to my readers for my laps as I am unable to ether describe the scenery or report anything that may of been said between these 2 points but I recall that as we entered Albany a remark was adrest to me for the first time since lunch.

Bill said my mother with a ½ smirk this is Albany the capital of New York state.

So this is Albany I thorght to myself.

Who is governor of New York now arsked my mother to my father.

Smith replid my father who seams to know everything.

Queer name said my mother sulkily.

Soon we puled up along side a policeman who my father arsked how de we get acrost the river to the New York road and if Albany pays their policemans by the word I'll say we were in the presents of a rich man and by the time he got through it was dark and still drooling and my old man didnt know the road and under those conditions I will not repete the conversation that transpired between Albany and Hudson but will end my chapter at the city limits of the last named settlemunt.

Chapter 7

HUDSON

We were turing gaily down the main st of Hudson when a man of 12 years capered out from the side walk and hoped on the runing board.

Do you want a good garage he arsked with a dirty look.

Why yes my good man replid my father tenderly but first where is the best hotel.

I will take you there said the man.

I must be a grate favorite in Hudson my father wispered at my mother.

Soon folling the mans directions we puled up in front of a hotel but when my father went at the register the clerk said I am full tonight.

Where do you get it around here arsked my father tenderly.

We have no rooms replid the senile clerk paying no tension to my old mans remark but there is a woman acrost the st that takes loggers.

Not to excess I hope replid my father but soon we went acrost the st and the woman agrede to hord us for the night so myself and mother went to our apartmunts wilst my father and the 12 year old besought the garage. When we finley got reunited and went back to the hotel for supper it was past 8 oclock as a person could of told from the viands. Latter in front of our loggings we again met the young man who had welcomed us to Hudson and called my father to 1 side.

There is a sailer going to spend the night here he said in a horse wisper witch has walked all the way from his home Schenectady and he has got to report on his ship in New York tomorrow afternoon and has got no money so if he dont get a free ride he will be up vs it.

He can ride with us replid my father with a hiccup if tomorrow is anything like today a sailer will not feel out of place in my costly moter.

I will tell him replid the man with a corse jesture.

Will you call us at ½ past 5 my mother reqested to our lanlady as we entered our Hudson barracks.

I will if I am awake she replid useing her handkerchief to some extent.

Latter we wandered how anybody could help from being awake in that hot bed of mones and grones and cat calls and caterwauls and gulish screaks of all kinds and tho we had rose erly at Syracuse and had a day of retchedness we was all more than ready to get up when she wraped on our door long ere day brake.

Where is that sailer that stoped here last night quired my father as we was about to make a lordly outburst.

He wouldnt pay his bill and razed hell so I kicked him out replid the lanlady in her bear feet.

Without farther adieu my father payed his bill and we walked into the dismul st so I will end this chapter by leaveing the fare lanlady flaping in the door way in her sredded night gown.

Chapter 8

HUDSON TO YONKERS 106.5

It was raining a little so my father bad my mother and I stand in the st wilst he went to the garage and retained the costly moter. He returned ½ a hour latter with the story that the garage had been locked and he had to go to the props house and roust him out.

How did you know where he lived quired my mother barshfully.

I used the brains god gave me was my fathers posthumous reply.

Soon we rumpled into Rhinebeck and as it was now day light and the rain had siezed we puled up in front of the Beekman arms for brekfus.

It says this is the oldest hotel in America said my mother reading the programme.

The eggs tastes all right replid my father with a corse jesture.

What is the next town quired my mother when we again set sale.

Pokippsie was my father's reply.

Thats where Vassar is said my mother as my old man stiffled a yawn I wonder if there is a store there that would have a koop for David.

I doubt it they ever heard of him said my father dryly how much do they cost.

Well I dont know.

We entered Pokippsie at lenth and turned to the left up the main st and puled up in front of a big store where myself and mother went in and purchased a koop for my little brother and a kap for me witch only took a ½ hour dureing witch my father lost his temper and when we finley immerged he was barking like a dog and giveing the Vassar yell. 2 men come out of the store with us and tost the koop with the rest of the junk in the back seat and away we went.

Doesnt this look cute on him said my mother in regards to my new kap.

What of it replid my father with a grimace and with that we puled into Garrison.

Isnt this right acrost the river from West Point said my mother with a gastly look.

What of it replid my father tenderly and soon we found ourselfs in Peekskill.

This is where that young girl cousin of mine gos to school said my father from Philadelphia.

What of it said my mother with a loud cough and presently we stoped and bought 15 gals of gas.

I have got a fund of usefull information about every town we come to said my father admireingly for instants this is Harmon where they take off the steem engines and put on the electric bull-gines.

My mother looked at him with ill consealed admiration.

And what do you know about this town she arsked as we frisked into Ossining.

Why this is Ossining where they take off the hair and put on the stripes replid my father qick as a flarsh and the next place is Tarrytown where John D. Rockefeller has a estate.

What is the name of the estate quired my mother breathlessly.

Socony I supose was the sires reply.

With that we honked into Yonkers and up the funny looking main st.

What a funny looking st said my mother and I always thorght it was the home of well to do peaple.

Well yes replid my father it is the home of the ruling class at lease Bill Klem the umpire and Bill Langford the referee lives here.

I will end my chapter on that one.

Chapter 9

THE BUREAU OF MANHATTAN

Isn't it about time said my mother as we past Spuyten Duyvil and entered the Bureau of Manhattan that we made our plans.

What plans said my father all my plans is all ready made.

Well then you might make me your confident sugested my mother with a quaint smirk.

Well then heres the dope uttered my father in a vage tone I am going to drop you at the 125 st station where you will only half to wait 2 hours and a ½ for the rest of the family as the train from the west is do at 350 at 125 st in the meen wile I will drive out to Grenitch with Bill and see if the house is ready and etc and if the other peaples train is on time you can catch the 4 4 and I an Bill will meet you at the Grenitch station.

If you have time get a qt of milk for David said my mother with a pail look.

What kind of milk arsked my dad.

Oh sour milk my mother screened.

As she was now in a pretty bad temper we will leave her to cool off for 2 hours and a ½ in the 125 st station and end this chapter.

Chapter 10

N. Y. TO GRENITCH 500.0

The lease said about my and my fathers trip from the Bureau of Manhattan to our new home the soonest mended. In some way ether I or he got balled up on the grand concorpse and next thing you know we was thretning to swoop down on Pittsfield.

Are you lost daddy I arsked tenderly.

Shut up he explained.

At lenth we doubled on our tracks and done much better as we finley hit New Rochelle and puled up along side a policeman with falling archs.

What road do I take for Grenitch Conn quired my father with poping eyes.

Take the Boston post replid the policeman.

I have all ready subscribed to one out of town paper said my father and steped on the gas so we will leave the flat foot gaping after us like a prune fed calf and end this chapter.

Chapter 11

HOW IT ENDED

True to our promise we were at the station in Grenitch when the costly train puled in from 125 st. Myself and father hoped out of the lordly moter and helped the bulk of the famly off of the train and I aloud our nurse and my 3 brothers to kiss me tho David left me rarther moist.

Did you have a hard trip my father arsked to our nurse shyly.

Why no she replid with a slite stager.

She did too said my mother they all acted like little devils.

Did you get Davids milk she said turning on my father.

Why no does he like milk my father replid with a gastly smirk.

We got lost mudder I said brokenly.

We did not screened my father and accidently cracked me in the shins with a stray foot.

To change the subjeck I turned my tensions on my brother Jimmie who is nerest my age.

I've seen our house Jimmie I said brokenly I got here first.

Yes but I slept all night on a train and you didnt replid Jimmie with a dirty look.

Nether did you said my brother John to Jimmie you was awake all night.

Were awake said my mother.

Me and David was awake all night and crid said my brother John.

But I only crid once the whole time said my brother Jimmie.

But I didnt cry at all did I I arsked to my mother.

So she replid with a loud cough Bill was a very very good boy.

So now we will say fare well to the characters in this book.

Symptoms of Being 35

The other night one of my friends whose name is Legion got me on the telephone some way another and wanted I should come over and call, but that is all I done the last 3 or 4 times I had went over there and it costs a lot of money even in a 4 bit limit. So I said no that I was busy on a book which I had promised my publisher I would write it.

"What is it about" says Legion.

So I told him "How it feels to be 35."

"That guy must think you got a good memory" says Legion and hung up on me.

Well friends 35 is how young I am no matter how old I look, but I am so use to haveing smart Alex make wise cracks when I tell them my age that it don't have no more effect on me now than the 6 day bicycle race. Only I can't figure why they think I would lie about it like I was trying to pose as a boy chess marvel or something. When a man has got a legal wife and 4 and no one hundredths children what does he care if he is 35 or double that amt. Besides which they claim that 35 is about the average of all the grown ups in the world.

If I was above the average would I keep it a secret? Don't be silly.

And don't judge a person by their hair gents. Many a man that can remember the first Ford has got more foliage on their egg than myself and also I know several ball players in the big league to-day that is anywheres from 5 to 30 yrs. younger than the present writer that when the fish applauds them for makeing a 2 handed catch with 1 hand, you wonder why they don't take off their cap. Personly I am not sensitive about my plummage. When my features got to the decision that one of them would half to retract all I done was thank God they picked the forehead and not the chin. The only hardship connected with pyorrhea of the scalp is trying to act supprised when the barber says you are looseing your hair.

But I guess it ain't only the loss of a few ebony ringlets that makes me look senile. It seems like I was over estimated long before I begin to molt. For inst. I can recall when I was 16 and had a thatch on my dome like a virtuoso and I used to pal around with a boy who we will call Geo. Dougan because that was his name and Geo. was going on 21. Well this was in Niles, Mich., in the days when they sold 6⅞ beer in vases and for $.20 you could get enough to patrol 4th St. serenading true music lovers of the opposing sex. In them hellcyon days 1 of the few things that was vs. the law was selling it to minors and 2 or 3 of the retail mchts. around town was pretty strick and time and again I and Geo. would be out shopping and go in a store and order 2 vats and Dave or Punk or who ever it happened to be would set one up for me to knock over and then give Geo. a wise cracking smile and ask him would he like a bottle of white pop. Incidentally I had a taste of that lucius ambrosia at a ball game once and if the penalty for selling honest old beer to minors was a $100 fine why 2 to 14 yrs in a meat grinder would be mild for a guy that sells white pop on the theory that its a drink.

Well Geo. would say "Aw come on Dave I am older than him." But you couldn't fool Dave and the result was that we would half to take our custom down to Pigeon's where everybody that had a dime was the same age and the only minors was the boys that tried to start a charge acct.

I must hand it to Geo. for one thing. No matter how sore it made him to get turned down he never told them the truth about me. And they wouldn't of believed him if he had of. No more than you birds believe me now.

But now in regards to this book: When the publisher asked me to write it up I said I didn't see how more than only a few people would be interested because they was only a few that is this old. So he told me that as a matter of fact pretty near everybody in the world that can read is either 35 or a few mos. one way or the other and if I didn't think that was so to go and look it up in a book. So I looked up in the encyclopedia and they was nothing in there like he said but I found out a whole lot of other things that was news to me and maybe the reader don't know them neither so I will write them down.

In the 1st. place it says that most people dies when they are 1 yr. old and the 1st. 10 yrs. is the most fatalist. But if they's a 100 thousand people that can manage to get to be 10 yrs. old why then 749 of them is pretty libel to die the next yr. After that the older you get the longer you live, up to when you are 59 and then you can just about count on liveing 14 and seven-tenths yrs. more. In other wds. if you ain't one of the 749 that crokes between 10 and 11 why you are safe till about June of the yr. when you are 73. So a person is a sucker to try and take care of themself at my age and from now on I am going to be a loose fish and run wild.

Out in Benton Harbor, Mich. however, near where I use to live, they have got a sex that calls themselfs the Holy Terrors or something that claims you live as long as you are good and as soon as you do wrong you die. But I notice that they all wear a beard so as the encyclopedia can't tell if they are 73 or 21.

Another thing it says in the book is that figures compiled in Norway and Sweden shows the death rate amongst bachelors is a lot more than amongst married men even includeing murder. So anybody that is between 11 and 73 yrs. old and got a wife is practically death proof especially if you are a Swede.

But all that is either here or there. The idear is to tell how it feels to be my age and I may as well get to it. Well in the 1st. place I am speaking for myself only. I don't know how the other 35 yr. olders feels about it and don't care. Probably the most of them don't feel near as old as the writer. Laughter is supposed to keep a man young but if its forced laughter it works the opp. When a guy is named

Ring W. and is expected to split their sides when ever somebody asks if your middle name is Worm which is an average of 365 times per annum over a period of 35 annums, why it can't help from telling on you. Or it don't lighten the wgt. of the yrs. none to half to snicker every time they say Ring give me a ring or Ring why ain't you a ring master in Ringling Bros. And yet a number of birds has asked me if that was my real name or did I assume it. They would probably ask the kaiser if he moved to Holland to be near the tulips.

I suppose that on the morning of their 21st birthday the right kind of a American citizen wakes up full of excitement and says to themself "Now I am of age and can vote and everything." And when they come to what I often call the 35th. mile stone they are even more smoked up with the thought that now they are eligible to be President and go around all day stoop shouldered with the new responsibility.

Well I don't recall how I woke up the day I was 21 if at all but my last birthday is still green and sour in my memory. I spent the most of it in Mineola signing mortgages and if I thought of the White House it was just to wonder if it would do any good to write and tell President Wilson about the Long Island R. R.

At the present writeing I have got so use to being 35 that I don't know if it feels any different from 34 or 33. But I can at lease state that being 35 don't feel nothing like being under 30. For inst. when the telephone rings now days I am scared to death that its somebody asking us to go somewheres for dinner or somewheres. Six yrs. ago I was afraid it wasn't. At 29 home was like they say on the vaudeville stage, a place to go when all the other joints was closed up. At 35 its a place you never leave without a loud squawk.

A man don't appreciate their home till you are up around par for 9 holes. Under 30 you think of it as a dump where you can't pick out what you want to eat like roast Vt. turkey or a filet mignon or some of that prune fed muskrat a la Biltmore. If Kathleen decides in the A. M. that you are going to crave spare ribs at night why you can either crave spare ribs at night or put on a hunger strike that won't get you no more sympathy than the hiccups.

In them ribald days home is just a kind of a pest where you half to choke down breakfast or they will think something ails you and talk about sending for a Dr. And 1 or 2 evenings per wk. when you can't think of no reason to go out, its where you half to set around and wait for 9 o'clock so as you begin to talk about going to bed and sometimes things gets so desperate that you half to read a book or something.

But at 35 you spell it with a big H. Its where you can take off your shoes. Its where you can have more soup. Its where you don't half to say nothing when they's nothing to say. Its where they don't wait till the meal is all over and then give you a eye dropper full of coffee raw. Its where you don't half to listen. Its where they don't smear everything with cheese dressing. Its where you can pan everybody without it going no further. Its where they know you like doughnuts and what you think about a banana.

When you was 29 you didn't care for the band to play Home sweet Home. It was old stuff and a rotten tune any way. Now you hope they won't play it neither. Its a pretty tune but it makes you bust out crying.

Bud Kelland that lives over to Port Washington wrote a piece for a magazine a wile ago where he said in it that it kind of shocked him to find out that young people didn't act like he was one of them no more. Well he ain't but it took the old gaffer a long time to find it out. Here he is pretty near 39 and I guess the old Methuselum wants folks to hide I Mary Mac Lane when he comes in the rm.

Well it was 5 or 6 yrs. ago when I realized that I was past my nonages as they say. It come to me all of a sudden that the only compliments I had for a long wile was what a pretty tie you got or something. Nothing about my natural charms no more. It was an egg's age since anybody had called me to 1 side and whispered "I got a T. L. for you. Gertie thinks your ears is immense."

I seen then that I wasn't no longer a larva and I guess maybe it hurt at first. But its like falling hair or the telephone service or anything else. When you have lived with it a wile you don't mind. Which is just as well because they ain't a wk. passes when you wouldn't get touched on the raw if they was any raw left.

Like for inst. a few wks. back I was up in Boston where I got a young and beautiful sister in law. When it come time to part from she and her husband she kissed me 6 times which was suppose to be once for me and once apiece for the Mrs. and 4 kiddies. Well I thought it was pretty nice and got kind of excited about it till I looked at her husband to see how he took it. He took it without batting an eye. To him it was like as if she was kissing an old cab horse on a bet for the benefit of the Red Cross. And when I had left and they was alone together, instead of lepping at her throat with a terrible curse he probably says "Janey, you're a good game gal," and she gave him a kiss that meant something.

Now an incidence like this would of spoilt my whole trip if I didn't look at it in a sensible way which is to say to yourself, "Well if I wasn't in the Sears and yellow I wouldn't of got them 6 kisses. And 6 kisses is ½ a dozen kisses in any language."

Or for inst. out on the golf course. Suppose I and Grant Rice is playing with some young whipper snapper like say Jack Wheeler and they's only 1 caddy for the 3 of us. "Take them two" says Jack pointing to my and Grant's bags but the caddy has all ready took them any way as soon as he found out which ones belonged to which. Or when one of my young brother in laws is around the house and I come in the rm. and they are setting in the easy chair, why they jump up like food shot from guns and say "Here take this chair."

All and all when you get hardened to it they's many advantages in reaching your dottage. When they's 7 passengers for a 7 passenger car its never you that has to take one of them little torture seats. When your brother in law is here on a visit and the Mrs. thinks it would be nice to have a fire in the fire place, you ain't the one that has got to ruin his clothes. Yes friends the benefits is many fold but if them ½ dozen kisses and a few stray others pretty near as good was all, why you could still think to yourself Youth may get good service, but 35 ain't makeing no complaints to the management neither.

As for the gen. symptoms of 35 and vicinity as I have found them and not speaking for nobody only myself you understand, the following points may interest science:

1. The patient sometimes finds himself and one lady the only people left at the table and all the others is danceing. They seems to be nothing for it but to get up and dance. You start and the music stops and the young buddies on the flr. claps their hands for a en- core. The patient claps his hands too but not very loud and he hopes to high heaven the leader will take it in a jokeing way.

2. For some reason another its necessary to find some old papers

and in going through the trunk the patient runs acrost a bunch of souvenirs and keep sakes like a note a gal wrote him in high school, a picture of himself in a dirty football suit, a program of the 1907 May festival in South Bend and etc. "Why keep this junk" he says and dumps them all in the waste basket.

3. The case develops nausea in the presents of all story tellers except maybe Irvin Cobb and Riley Wilson and Bert Williams. Any others has to work pretty fast to get him cornered. Violent chills attends the sound of those saddest wds. of tongue or pen "I don't know if you heard this one or not but it struck me funny. It seems they was a woman went in a drygoods store in Detroit to buy some towels. Stop me if you heard it before." You couldn't stop them with big Bertha. The best funny storys is Balzac's because they are in a book and you don't half to buy it. But when you get up vs. one of these here voluntary stag entertainers you either got to listen and laugh or they put you down as a dumb bell.

4. The invalid goes to a ball game and along comes the last ½ of the 14th. innings and the score is 1 and 1 and the 1st. guy up makes a base hit. The patient happens to look at his watch and it says 11 minutes to 6 and if he leaves the park right away he can make the 6:27 home where as if he waits a few min. he will half to take the 6:54. Without no hesitation he leaves the park right away and makes the 6:27.

5. The subject is woke up at 3 A. M. by the fire whistle. He sniffles but can't smell no smoke. He thinks well it ain't our house and goes back to sleep.

6. He sets down after breakfast to read the paper. The mail man comes and brings him 3 letters. One of them looks like it was a gal's writeing. He reads the paper.

7. He buys a magazine in April and reads the first instalment of a misery serial. The instalment winds up with the servants finding their master's body in bed and his head in the ash tray. Everything pts. to the young wife. Our patient forgets to buy the May number.

8. Somebody calls up and says they are giveing a party Thursday night for Mabel Normand and can you come. Our hero says he is sorry but he will be in Washington on business. He hasn't no more business in Washington than Gov. Cox.

9. They's a show in town that you got to see like Frank Craven

or "Mecca." "It's a dandy night" says the Mrs. "Shall we drive in or take the train?" "We will take the train" says our hero.

These is a few of the symptoms as I have observed them and as I say I am speaking for just myself and maybe I am a peculiar case. They may not be another 35 yr. older in the world that is affected the same way and in fact I know several suffers about that age which I am as different than as day and night. Take Jess Willard for inst. He was somewheres around 35 in July 1919 and Dempsey knocked him down 7 times in one rd. He wouldn't do that to me, not 7 times he wouldn't. Or look at Ty Cobb. Do you think they would get me to play center field and manage a ball club for $30,000? Or would Jim Thorpe's brother in law look on him as too frail to hobble down in the basement and get a few sticks of wood?

On the other hand they might be 2 or 3 brother eagles in the mediocer 30s that is even more mildewed than me, but I am afraid they's a whole lot more of them feels like a colt. They take care of themselfs. When they get up in the A. M. they take a cold plunge and then hang by their eye teeth on a hook in the closet while they count 50 in Squinch. And noons when they come back from their lunch of hot milk and ferns, they roll over on the office rug 10 times without bending their shin.

I can't compete with these babies. I slice a few golf balls in season but bet. Nov. and May the only exercise I get or want to get is twice a wk. when I take the buttons out of shirt A and stick them in shirt B.

They's still another crowd yet that renews their youth by going back every yr. to commencement or a class reunion or something. Well I don't know if I want to renew my youth or not. Leave bad enough alone is my slogum. And in the 2d. place I don't half to go nowheres to a class reunion. I could hold it in the bath tub. I was the only one that graduated when I did as it was in March of my freshman yr. and they didn't seem to be haveing no commencement exercises for nobody else. I guess I must have been one of these here infantile proteges like that 11 mos. old junior they got up to Columbia.

No book of this kind would be complete without shooting a few wds. of unwanted advice at my youngers and betters. For inst. John D. tells the boys how to build up a fortune and John Jones tells them how to rise from a white wings to a steeple jack. So it looks like it was up to me to tell them how to get to be what I am, 35 yrs. old.

Well my lads they's 4 rules that I made and have stuck to them and I think you will find they'll bring you the same results. The 1st. rule is don't die the 1st. yr. The 2d. rule is don't be one of the 749 that dies when they are 11. The 3d. rule is don't pick a quarrel with a man like Dempsey. And the 4th. and last rule is marry a girl like Sue.

In explanations of that last rule I will say that the one I married ain't Sue but the name don't make no differents if she is the right kind of a gal. And the reason I say that is because its customary in these intimate capital I talks to throw in a paragraph of blurb about the little woman. What ever success a man has had he has got to pretend he owes it to Her. So if they's any glory to be gleaned out of my success in reaching 35 and looking even older why she can have it.

Dinner

Harry Barton was thirty-three years old, unmarried and good-looking. Young matrons liked him as a filler-in at dinner parties, but he hated dinner parties unless they promised an evening of contract. So it was with a heavy heart that he heard Grace Halpern's voice on the telephone.

"You've just got to do this for me! I know you'll hate it. There won't be any bridge. But Frank backed out at the last minute and I can't get anybody else. I honestly tried. I tried Bill; I even tried Lester Graham, but neither of them can come. And I must have two bachelors because there are going to be two girls from out of town, girls who were in my class in boarding school. They really are peaches and I can't disappoint them. Please say——"

Harry was a bad liar and, besides, he liked Grace. He had had lots of good times at her house. He said yes and wished all the rest of the day that he hadn't.

He arrived late at the Halperns', too late to get half enough cock-tails. He knew everybody there excepting the two peaches, a Miss Coakley and a Miss Rell. They were strikingly pretty, Miss Coakley a pony brunette and Miss Rell a rather tall, slender blonde. Harry thought maybe it wouldn't be so bad after all.

His hostess drew him aside before dinner was announced.

"I'm going to reward you for this. I'm going to let you sit between them at dinner. And remember, they're both free."

"What do you mean, free?"

"Not engaged or anything. And I think it's about time you were settling down."

The other bachelor, Dave Wallace, sat on Miss Coakley's left, with Harry, as Grace had promised, between Miss Coakley and Miss Rell.

"Grace tells me you're a great bridge player," Miss Rell said.

"No, but I like——"

"Which do you consider the greatest authority, Lenz or Works or Whitehall? I don't know anything about it myself, but I hear people arguing about it at home, I mean I live in Chicago. I belong to a bridge club there and I was just getting so the others didn't laugh at me when somebody introduced this horrible contract and I simply gave up. That's the game, you know, where you don't bid anything but slams and I just haven't the nerve, I mean in bridge. I don't want you to think I'm a coward in everything."

"I——"

"Because I'm not, I made a flight with Lindbergh in Washington. It was arranged through Congressman Burleigh. He's a great friend of my father's. You know, Burleigh the paint people in South Chicago. Oh, it was too thrilling for words! But I felt just as safe as if I'd been in a car, safer because once I was in a terrible smash-up out in Lake Forest and the doctor said I was lucky to escape without at least a few broken ribs.

"I was a little bit scared when we first started, but then I thought to myself this is the man who flew from Detroit to Paris and why should anybody be frightened just flying twenty minutes over Washington with him at the wheel. Have you ever been up?"

"Yes, I——"

"Then you don't know what a real thrill is. Honestly, it just makes you gasp, like the first time you dive in Lake Michigan. I really dive and I swim awfully well and some of the men say I swim awfully well for a girl. There's one man in Chicago, Lee Roberts— he and his wife are our best friends, I mean my brother's and mine —Lee calls me Gertrude Ederle; you know she's the girl who swam across the English Channel and back.

"Of course he says it just joking because naturally I'm not in her class. She's quite fat, isn't she? Or haven't you ever seen her? She looks fat in her pictures. But then you can't always tell from pictures. There was a picture of me in the rotogravure section that made me look simply hideous."

Mr. Halpern, on Miss Rell's right, spoke to her and Harry found himself attacked by Miss Coakley.

"Mr. Burton, I was just telling Mr. Walters about—— I don't know whether you'd be interested or not—maybe you don't—but still everybody I've told, they think—it's probably——"

"I'm sure I'd like to hear it," said Harry.

"I hate to bore people with—you know how it is—you'd be too polite to—and this is so awfully—well, it isn't a thing that—it's just interesting if you happen—people in Baltimore—though we've only lived here a few——"

"If," said Harry to himself, "she doesn't complete a sentence in the next two minutes, I'm going to ask Grace for a high-ball."

"——it was some people who lived—well, our apartment was just two buildings—they were people you wouldn't want—but it was in a kind of secluded—not many apartments—it's a neighborhood that's just—and my sister's little boy goes to the same school as——"

"Grace," said Harry, "am I an old enough customer here to ask for a drink?"

"Whatever you like," said his hostess.

"I'd like a high-ball. I had a pretty tough day."

Miss Rell turned on him.

"Oh, are you in the Street? That's what they call Wall Street, isn't it? I should think it would be just thrilling! But I suppose it is hard work, too. You stand there all day and shout at other men, don't you, and they shout back at you? It must ruin your voice. Why, I know we went to the Illinois-Chicago game last fall and I got excited and yelled so for Illinois that I couldn't talk for a week."

"That must have——"

"Do you have football here in the East? Oh, certainly you do! I'd forgotten—Yale and Harvard. And which are the Giants? I never can keep them straight. My father and Lou—that's my brother; we're great pals—he and Father read the sporting page religiously every day. I tease them about it and they tease me about reading the society news and the movies. We have great tiffs over it, all in fun of course.

"Father is a great golfer, I mean really. He's fifty-four years old and he plays the Onwentsia course in sixty, or maybe it's a hundred and sixty. Which would be right? He wanted me to take it up and begged and begged till finally one day I went out and played nine holes with him.

"I made some wonderful shots, I mean I really did, and he said I had a perfect natural swing and if I would take lessons from the professor it wouldn't be long before I could be playing in tournaments, just for women I mean. Wouldn't that be exciting! But I just couldn't do it; I'd die!

"And besides, it seems to me that girls who win things in sports are always queer looking, at least most of them, and what chance would—I mean it would be almost unheard of if—— Well, I just don't believe I could ever be a champion of anything. Do you play golf?"

"Yes."

"You ought to try it. It's lots of fun, especially for a man. I mean men seem to have such good times playing together, the nineteenth hole and all that. And I should think it would be such wonderful relaxation for you over the weekend after that Wall Street grind."

"I'm not in Wall Street."

"Oh, now I've got an expert here, I wish you'd tell me what are bulls and what are bears? Father's tried to explain it to me, but I can't get it straight."

"Well, a bull is——"

"Have you ever been to bull-fights, I mean in Spain or Mexico? They say they are terribly thrilling, but terribly cruel. I mean about the horses. You know what they do, don't you?"

"No. I never heard of them."

"Well, they bring out three or four old horses into the ring and men with spears spear the bull and get him mad at the horses and he goes after them and kills them and the blood makes him mad at everybody and then the man comes out and kills him. They call them toreadors."

"Who?"

"The man that fights the bull. Haven't you ever heard 'Carmen,' I mean the opera? There's a toreador in that. He sings a song; it goes, '*Toreador, en garde.*' That's the French. It's a French opera. Carmen is the girl; she works in a cigaret factory. First she falls in love with a soldier and then this toreador wins her away from him, but the soldier kills himself and her.

"I haven't heard it for years; I like to go to ones I haven't heard so much. We've got a simply gorgeous opera company in Chicago. Everybody says it's better than the Metropolitan. And Rosa Raisa is the greatest dramatic soprano I ever heard. She's Ruffo's wife. No, I guess she's Rimini's. Anyway, they're both barytones."

Again Mr. Halpern intervened and Harry took on Miss Coakley for another round.

"Mr. Walters and I were just—— Don't you like Nassau better than—I mean for climate—and the different colors of the water—and it's ideal bathing, hardly any surf—of course lots of people prefer heavy surf—but for people like me who can't—and I think the crowd that goes there—and the tennis. Then there's that lovely garden, with the orchestra.

"Three of us girls—I think it was four winters—it was three winters ago. One night we went—it's the Holy Rollers—honestly they do the craziest—a man told us they were just—but I couldn't believe it, they were so—I think—— Have you ever been there, Mr. Burton?"

"No."

"We went by land to—and then from Miami—when you wake up—it's the most beautiful—with the sun just rising over the islands —it's simply heavenly—it's just—— Well, you have no idea!"

"Yes, I have," said Harry to himself, and aloud: "Grace, I'd like a high-ball. I had a tough day."

"The days are getting shorter," said his hostess.

"I imagine every day must be pretty hard for you men in the Street," said Miss Rell.

"I'm not in any street," said Harry. "Not even a path."

"I know how secretive you Wall Street men are," said Miss Rell, "but I wonder if you would do me a favor. Just before I left home, I heard Father talking about some stock that I think he said he had a tip on—he's got a lot of influential friends that tell him things like that, but of course nobody like you who is right in Wall Street. Now it would be perfectly wonderful if you would tell me whether this stock is any good or not and then when I go home, I can tell Father what you said and who you are and he'll think his child isn't so dumb after all. Will you?"

"What's the stock?"

"Isn't it marvelous that I remember the name of it? It's General Motors."

"General Motors! Well, listen, if you'll keep this under your hat——"

"Oh, that reminds me, I saw your Mayor Jimmy Walker in the parade today and I told Grace I thought he was the only man in the world who could wear a high hat without looking silly. Do you know him? I'll bet he's fascinating to know. He's cute! I wish we had a cute mayor. I suppose you New Yorkers must think our town is a regular wild West show. It really isn't as bad as all that.

"Lou—that's my brother—he said the funniest thing the night before I came away. No, it was Wednesday night he said it and I didn't leave till Friday noon on the Century. What was I saying? Oh, yes, Father and Lou and I were waiting for dinner—you know we live on the North Side, just a block south of the park—and anyway there were some noises out on the street that sounded just like pistol-shots and Father hurried to the window and looked out and announced that it was just back-fire from a truck.

"Then Lou said, 'Well, I'm glad they're beginning to defend themselves.' He meant the trucks were firing back at whoever was shooting at them. Or would it be whomever? I never can get who and whom straight. But Lou is awfully witty; I mean he really is. He has had two or three things in 'College Humor.' What was your college?"

"The Electoral College."

"Oh, you're an engineer! And what are you doing on Wall Street? I suppose you gave up your profession 'for gold.' You ought to be ashamed of yourself! You might be accomplishing big things like building bridges. Which reminds me, do you play bridge?"

"Yes."

"You ought to, honestly. I'm not very good, but it's lots of fun. I belong to a club and we just have a circus. The other girls used to laugh at me, I was so dumb, but this last winter I got good; I mean really not bad at all. And then, just when I was doing so well, they decided to play this contract and I can't get it at all. You don't bid anything but slams and I just can't do that. I simply haven't the nerve."

"Have you ever been up with Lindbergh?" asked Harry.

"Yes. I'm not joking. I really mean it. It was while he was in Washington. My father arranged it through Congressman Burleigh. That's the Burleigh Paint Company in South Chicago. Mr. Burleigh is a congressman and one of Father's closest friends. It was the most thrilling experience I ever had in my life. And I wasn't frightened at all, only a little bit, like when you go in swimming and dive for the first time."

"Can you dive?"

"You ought to see me! Honestly, not boasting, I'm a regular Gertrude Ederle; you know, the girl that swam across the English Channel so many times. I wouldn't want to swim that Channel, though. It's bad enough in a boat. I'm a pretty good sailor, but the last time my brother and I crossed from Calais to Dover, well, 'it happens in the best of families,' as Briggs says, or is it Mutt and Jeff?"

"Do you read the funny pages? I suppose I oughtn't to confess it, but I read them religiously. Father often jokes me about it and pretends the money he spent sending me to college was all wasted because all I got out of it was a taste for 'the funnies.' I answer him back by saying he went to college, too, and all he cares anything about now is golf. It's all joking of course. Father and I are the best friends and chums! What was your college?"

'The War College."

"Oh, West Point! I'd just love to go up there and watch them drill sometime! I've seen it across the river going by on the train and it looks lovely. And fall before last, Father and Lou and I went to the big football game between West Point and the Annapolis Navy. You know they had it in Chicago, at Soldiers' Field, in Grant Park. It's an enormous place and lots of people couldn't see the game at all, but our seats were grand. Father got them through Congressman Burleigh."

"Is that," asked Harry, "the Burleigh who's in the paint business in South Chicago?"

"Do you know him?"

"I bought a can of paint from him once when I was redecorating my garage."

"Why, he's one of Father's best friends. He's in Congress. How funny that you should really know him!"

"You can meet congressmen if you go at it the right way."

Miss Coakley was talking.

"Oh, Mr. Buckley, will you——? Mr. Walsh and I—— Just what was it you said, Mr.——?"

"I don't remember saying anything," replied Dave Wallace on her left.

"Why, you—— He did, too, Mr.—— He said the Mauretania was the—— And I said the Paris or the Majestic, or the Berengaria—— Now we want you to give us your honest——"

"I never crossed on anything but the Santa Maria," said Harry.

"Oh, Italy, how I love it! I could simply—— There's no other country—it just seems as if—— If it weren't for my sister in Baltimore—maybe some day—— But a girl is foolish——"

"Grace," said Harry, "how's the Scotch holding out?"

"The whole week must have been tough," said Grace.

"I don't see how you men live through it," said Miss Rell, "standing there on the floor of the Exchange all day, shouting at each other. Why, it simply kills me just to stand and wait five minutes in a shop! To have to do it all day, I'd perish! How do you endure it?"

"Well, you know those little stools that golf fans carry around with them. I never go on the floor without one," said Harry.

"My father is the greatest golf fan in the world; I mean I really believe he is, without exception. He never plays less than four times a week and he's a fine player, I mean for a man his age. He's fifty-four years old and he goes around Onwentsia in a hundred and twenty. Can that be right?"

"Easily."

Dinner was over and they went into the living-room. Harry and Dave Wallace were together a moment.

"I notice you didn't talk much," remarked Dave.

"But what I said made a big impression."

"I'd have traded you Coakley for your dame. Your gal just goes

along as if she were speaking into a mike, but Miss Coakley is a per-
petual missing-word contest and it's impossible to keep out of it—
every little while you feel as if you just had to guess what's left out."

"She called me Burton and Buckley."

"She called me everything from Welling to Wolheim."

Harry tried to hide behind the piano, but Miss Rell soon found
him.

"If we could get two more, don't you think Grace would let us
play bridge?"

"I don't know the game," said Harry.

"But I'd just love to teach you. I can teach you regular auction,
but not this new contract, where you just bid and bid till you're
dizzy."

"I haven't any card sense and besides, I think that liquor Grace
gave me was bad."

"Oh, truly?"

"I'm going to ask her where she got it."

"I know a man, or at least my father does, who gets the real thing
straight from Canada. Only he's out in Chicago."

Harry peremptorily summoned Grace into the hall.

"Grace, that's terrible Scotch you've got. It's given me the first
headache I've had in years."

"I understand, and I'll tell them you were sick and had to go
home. You were a darling to come and I'll never forget it."

"Neither will I."

At the door he said:

"Remember, old girl, I've left your schoolmates just as I found
them. They're still free."

There Are Smiles

At the busy corner of Fifth Avenue and Forty-sixth Street there
was, last summer, a traffic policeman who made you feel that he
didn't have such a terrible job after all. Lots of traffic policemen
seem to enjoy abusing you, sadistic complex induced by exposure

to bad weather and worse drivers, and, possibly, brutal wives. But Ben Collins just naturally appeared to be having a good time whether he was scolding you or not; his large freckled face fairly beamed with joviality and refused to cloud up even under the most trying conditions.

It heartened you to look at him. It amused you to hear him talk. If what he said wasn't always so bright, the way he said it was.

Ben was around thirty years old. He was six feet four inches tall and weighed two hundred and eighteen pounds. This describes about eighty per cent of all the traffic officers between Thirty-second Street and the Park. But Ben was distinguished from the rest by his habitual good humor and—well, I guess you'd have to call it his subtlety.

For example, where Noonan or Wurtz or Carmody was content with the stock "Hey! Get over where you belong!" or "Where the hell do you think you're going?" Ben was wont to finesse.

"How are you, Barney?" he would say to a victim halted at the curb.

"My name isn't Barney."

"I beg your pardon. The way you was stepping along, I figured you must be Barney Oldfield."

Or, "I suppose you didn't see that red light."

"No."

"Well, what did you think the other cars was stopped for? Did you think they'd all ran out of gas at once?"

Or, "What business are you in?"

"I'm a contractor."

"Well, that's a good, honorable business and, if I was you, I wouldn't be ashamed of it. I'd quit trying to make people believe I was in the fire department."

Or, "How do you like London?"

"Me? I've never been there."

"I thought that's where you got the habit of driving on the wrong side of the street."

Transgressions at Ben's corner, unless they resulted seriously, were seldom punished beyond these sly rebukes, which were delivered in such a nice way that you were kind of glad you had done wrong.

Off duty he was "a big good-natured boy," willing to take Grace to a picture, or go over to the Arnolds' and play cards, or just stay at home and do nothing.

And then one morning in September, a dazzling new Cadillac roadster, blue with yellow trimmings, flashed down from the north, violating all the laws of common sense and of the State and City of New York. Shouts and whistles from Carmody and Noonan, at Forty-eighth and Forty-seventh, failed to check its crazy career, but Ben, first planting his huge bulk directly in its path, giving the driver the choice of slackening speed or running into him, and then, with an alertness surprising in one so massive, sidestepping and jumping onto the running-board, succeeded in forcing a surrender at the curb half-way between his post and Forty-fifth Street.

He was almost mad and about to speak his mind in words beginning with capitals when he got his first look at the miscreant's face. It was the prettiest face he had ever seen and it wore a most impudent, ill-timed, irresistible smile, a smile that spoiled other smiles for you once for all.

"Well—" Ben began falteringly; then recovering something of his stage presence: "Where's your helmet?"

She made no reply, but continued to smile.

"If you're in the fire department," said Ben, "you ought to wear a helmet and a badge. Or paint your car red and get a sireen."

Still no reply.

"Maybe I look like a bobby. Maybe you thought you was in London where they drive on the left side of the street."

"You're cute," she said, and her voice was as thrilling as her smile. "I could stay here all morning and listen to you. That is I could, but I can't. I've got a date down on Eighth Street and I'm late for it now. And I know you're busy, too. So we mustn't keep each other any longer now. But I'd like to hear your whole line some day."

"Oh, you would!"

"Where do you live?"

"At home."

"That isn't very polite, is it? I was thinking you might live in the Bronx——"

"I do."

"—and that's on the way to Rye, where I live, so I might drive you."

"Thanks. When I die, I want to die of old age."

"Oh, I'm not a bad driver, really. I do like to go fast, but I'm careful. In Buffalo, where we lived before, the policemen all knew I was careful and they generally let me go as fast as I wanted to."

"This ain't Buffalo. And this ain't no speedway. If you want to go fast, stay off Fifth Avenue."

The girl looked him right in the eye. "Would you like that?"

"No," said Ben.

She smiled at him again. "What time are you through?"

"Four o'clock," said Ben.

"Well," said the girl, "some afternoon I may be going home about then——"

"I told you I wasn't ready to die."

"I'd be extra careful."

Ben suddenly realized that they were playing to a large staring audience and that, for once, he was not the star.

"Drive on!" he said in his gruffest tone. "I'm letting you go because you're a stranger, but you won't get off so easy next time."

"I'm very, very grateful," said the girl. "Just the same I don't like being a stranger and I hope you won't excuse me on that ground again."

Which remark, accompanied by her radiant smile, caused Mr. Collins, hitherto only a bathroom singer, to hum quite loudly all the rest of his working day snatches of a gay Ohman and Arden record that his wife had played over and over the night before.

His relief, Tim Martin, appeared promptly at four, but Ben seemed in no hurry to go home. He pretended to listen to two new ones Tim had heard on the way in from Flushing, one about a Scotchman and some hotel towels and one about two Heebs in a night club. He managed to laugh in the right place, but his attention was on the northbound traffic, which was now none of his business.

At twenty minutes past four he said good-by to Martin and walked slowly south on the east side of the street. He walked as far as Thirty-sixth, in vain. Usually he caught a ride home with some Bronx or north suburban motorist, but now he was late and had to pay for his folly by hurrying to Grand Central and standing up in a subway express.

"I was a sucker!" he thought. "She probably drove up some other street on purpose to miss me. Or she might have come in on one of them cross streets after I'd walked past it. I ought to stuck or Forty-fourth a while longer. Or maybe some other fella done his duty and had her locked up. Not if she smiled at him, though."

But she wouldn't smile like that at everybody. She had smiled at him because she liked him, because she really thought he was cute. Yes, she did! That was her regular line. That was how she had worked on them Buffalo fellas. "Cute!" A fine word to use on a human Woolworth Building. She was kidding. No, she wasn't; not entirely. She'd liked his looks as plenty other gals had, and maybe that stuff about the fire department and London had tickled her.

Anyway, he had seen the most wonderful smile in the world and he still felt warm from it when he got home, so warm that he kissed his wife with a fervor that surprised her.

When Ben was on the day shift, he sometimes entertained Grace at supper with an amusing incident or two of his work. Sometimes his stories were pure fiction and she suspected as much, but what difference did it make? They were things that ought to have happened even if they hadn't.

On this occasion he was wild to talk about the girl from Rye, but he had learned that his wife did not care much for anecdotes concerning pretty women. So he recounted one-sided arguments with bungling drivers of his own sex which had very little foundation in fact.

"There was a fella coming south in a 1922 Buick and the light changed and when it was time to go again, he thought he was starting in second, and it was reverse instead, and he backed into a big Pierce from Greenwich. He didn't do no damage to the Pierce and only bent himself a little. But they'd have held up the parade ten minutes talking it over if I hadn't bore down.

"I got the Buick fella over to the curb and I said to him, 'What's the matter? Are you homesick?' So he said what did I mean, home-sick, and I said, 'Well, you was so anxious to get back to wherever you come from that you couldn't even wait to turn around.'

"Then he tried to explain what was the matter, just like I didn't know. He said this was his first trip in a Buick and he was used to a regular gear shift.

"I said, 'That's fine, but this ain't no training-camp. The place to practice driving is four blocks farther down, at Forty-second. You'll find more automobiles there and twicet as many pedestrians and policemen, and besides, they've got street-cars and a tower to back into.'

"I said, 'You won't never learn nothing in a desert like this.' You ought to heard the people laugh."

"I can imagine!" said Grace.

"Then there was a Jordan, an old guy with a gray beard. He was going to park right in front of Kaskel's. He said he wouldn't be more than half an hour. I said, "Oh, that's too bad! I wished you could spend the weekend.' I said, 'If you'd let us knew you was coming, we'd have arranged some parties for you.' So he said, 'I've got a notion to report you for being too fresh.'

"So I said, 'If you do that, I'll have you arrested for driving without your parents' consent.' You ought to have heard them laugh. I said, 'Roll, Jordan, roll!' You ought to have heard them."

"I'll bet!" said Grace.

Ben fell into a long, unaccustomed silence.

"What are you thinking about?"

It came out against his better judgment. "There was a gal in a blue Cadillac."

"Oh! There was! What about her?"

"Nothing. Only she acted like it was her Avenue and I give her hell."

"What did you say to her?"

"I forget."

"Was she pretty?"

"I didn't notice. I was sore."

"You!"

"She all but knocked me for a corpse."

"And you probably just smiled at her."

"No. She done the smiling. She smiled——" He broke off and rose from the table. "Come on, babe. Let's go to the Franklin. Joe Frisco's there. And a Chaplin picture."

Ben saw nothing of the blue Cadillac or its mistress the rest of that week, but in all his polemics he was rehearsing lines aimed to strengthen her belief in his "cuteness." When she suddenly appeared, however, late on the following Tuesday afternoon, he was too excited to do anything but stare, and he would have lost an opportunity of hearing her enchanting voice if she hadn't taken the initiative. Northbound, she stopped at the curb a few feet above his corner and beckoned to him.

"It's after four," she said. "Can't I drive you home?"

What a break! It was his week on the late shift.

"I just come to work. I won't be off till midnight."

"You're mean! You didn't tell me you were going to change."

"I change every week. Last week, eight to four; this week, four to twelve."

"And next week eight to four?"

"Yes'm."

"Well, I'll just have to wait."

He couldn't say a word.

"Next Monday?"

He made an effort. "If you live."

She smiled that smile. "I'll live," she said. "There's an incentive."

She was on her way and Ben returned to his station, dizzy.

"Incentive, incentive, incentive," he repeated to himself, memorizing it, but when he got home at half past one, he couldn't find it in Grace's abridged Webster; he thought it was spelled with an *s*.

The longest week in history ended. A little before noon on Monday the Cadillac whizzed past him going south and he caught the word "later." At quitting time, while Tim Martin was still in the midst of his first new one about two or more Heebs, Ben was all at once aware that she had stopped right beside him, was blocking the traffic, waiting for him.

Then he was in her car, constricting his huge bulk to fit it and laughing like a child at Tim's indelicate ejaculation of surprise.

"What are you laughing at?"

"Nothing. I just feel good."

"Are you glad to be through?"

"Yes. Today."

"Not always?"

"I don't generally care much."

"I don't believe you do. I believe you enjoy your job. And I don't see how you can because it seems to me such a hard job. I'm going to make you tell me all about it as soon as we get out of this jam."

A red light stopped them at Fifty-first Street and she turned and looked at him amusedly.

"It's a good thing the top is down," she said. "You'd have been hideously uncomfortable in one more fold."

"When I get a car of my own," said Ben, "it'll have to be a Mack, and even then I'll have to hire a man to drive it."

"Why a man?"

"Men ain't all crazy."

"Honestly, I'm not crazy. Have I come near hitting anything?"

"You've just missed everything. You drive too fast and you take too many chances. But I knew it before I got in, so I can't kick."

"There isn't room for you to, anyway. Do you want to get out?"

"No."

"I doubt if you could. Where do you live?"

"Hundred and sixty-fourth, near the Concourse," said Ben.

"How do you usually go home?"

"Like this."

"And I thought I was saving you from a tiresome subway ride or something. I ought to have known you'd never lack invitations. Do you?"

"Hardly ever."

"Do the people ask you all kinds of questions?"

"Yes."

"I'm sorry. Because I wanted to and now I can't."

"Why not?"

"You must be tired of answering."

"I don't always answer the same."

"Do you mean you lie to people, to amuse yourself?"

"Sometimes."

"Oh, that's grand! Come on, lie to me! I'll ask you questions, probably the same questions they all ask, and you answer them as if I were a fool. Will you?"

"I'll try."

"Well, let's see. What shall I ask first? Oh, yes. Don't you get terribly cold in winter?"

He repeated a reply he had first made to an elderly lady, obviously a visitor in the city, whose curiosity had prompted her to cross-examine him for over twenty minutes on one of the busiest days he had ever known.

"No. When I feel chilly, I stop a car and lean against the radiator."

His present interviewer rewarded him with more laughter than was deserved.

"That's wonderful!" she said. "And I suppose when your ears are cold, you stop another car and borrow its hood."

"I'll remember that one."

"Now what next? Do you ever get hit?"

"Right along, but only glancing blows. I very seldom get knocked down and run over."

"Doesn't it almost kill you, standing on your feet all day?"

"It ain't near as bad as if it was my hands. Seriously, Madam, I get so used to it that I sleep that way nights."

"Don't the gasoline fumes make you sick?"

"They did at first, but now I can't live without them. I have an apartment near a public garage so I can run over there any time and re-fume myself."

"How tall are you?"

"Six feet ten."

"Not really!"

"You know better, don't you? I'm six feet four, but when women ask me, I tell them anything from six feet eight to seven feet two. And they always say, 'Heavens!' "

"Which do you have the most trouble with, men drivers or women drivers?"

"Men drivers."

"Honestly?"

"Sure. There's fifty times as many of them."

"Do lots of people ask you questions?"

"No. You're the first one."

"Were you mad at me for calling you cute the other day?"

"I couldn't be mad at you."

A silence of many blocks followed. The girl certainly did drive fast and Ben might have been more nervous if he had looked ahead, but mostly his eyes were on her profile which was only a little less alluring than her smile.

"Look where we are!" she exclaimed as they approached Fordham Road. "And you live at a Hundred and sixty-fourth! Why didn't you tell me?"

"I didn't notice."

"Don't get out. I'll drive you back."

"No, you won't. I'll catch a ride. There's a fella up this way I want to see."

"You were nice to take a chance with me and not to act scared. Will you do it again?"

"Whenever you say."

"I drive in once a week. I go down to Greenwich Village to visit my sister. Generally on Mondays."

"Next Monday I'll be on the late shift."

"Let's make it the Monday after."

"That's a long ways off."

"The time will pass. It always does."

It did, but so haltingly! And the day arrived with such a threat of rain that Ben was afraid she wouldn't come in. Later on, when the threat was fulfilled and the perils of motoring trebled by a steady drizzle and slippery pavements, he was afraid she would. Prudence, he knew, was not in her make-up and if she had an engagement with her sister, nothing short of a flood would prevent her keeping it.

Just before his luncheon time, the Cadillac passed, going south. Its top was up and its squeegee flying back and forth across the front glass.

Through the rain he saw the girl smile and wave at him briefly. Traffic was thick and treacherous and both must keep their minds on it.

It was still drizzling when she reappeared and stopped for him at four.

"Isn't this a terrible day?" she said.

"Not now!"

She smiled, and in an instant he forgot all the annoyance and discomfort of the preceding hours.

"If we leave the top up, you'll get stoop-shouldered, and if we take it down, we'll be drowned."

"Leave it up. I'm all right."

"Do you mind if we don't talk much? I feel quiet."

He didn't answer and nothing more was said until they turned east at Mount Morris Park. Then:

"I could find out your name," she said, "by remembering your number and having somebody look it up. But you can save me the trouble by telling me."

"My name is Ben Collins. And I could learn yours by demanding to see your driver's license."

"Heavens! Don't do that! I haven't any. But my name is Edith Dole."

"Edith Dole. Edith Dole," said Ben.

"Do you like it?"

"It's pretty."

"It's a funny combination. Edith means happiness and Dole means grief."

"Well," said Ben, "you'll have plenty of grief if you drive without a license. You'll have it anyway if you drive fast on these kind of streets. There's nothing skiddier than car-tracks when it's raining."

They were on upper Madison and the going was dangerous. But that was not the only reason he wanted her to slow down.

Silence again until they were on the Concourse.

"Are you married?" she asked him suddenly.

"No," he lied. "Are you?"

"I will be soon."

"Who to?"

"A man in Buffalo."

"Are you stuck on him?"

"I don't know. But he wants me and my father wants him to have me."

"Will you live in Buffalo?"

"No. He's coming here to be my father's partner."

"And yours."

"Yes. Oh, dear! Here's a Hundred and sixty-fourth and I musn't take you past it today, not in this weather. Do you think you can extricate yourself?"

He managed it with some difficulty.

"I don't suppose I'll see you again for two weeks."

"I'm afraid not," she said.

He choked down the words that wanted to come out. "Miss Dole," he said, "take my advice and don't try for no records getting home. Just loaf along and you'll be there an hour before your supper's ready. Will you? For that guy's sake in Buffalo?"

"Yes."

"And my sake, too."

Gosh! What a smile to remember!

He must walk slow and give himself a chance to calm down before he saw Grace. Why had he told the girl he wasn't married? What did she care?

Grace's greeting was a sharp command. "Take a hot bath right away! And wear your bath-robe afterwards. We won't be going anywhere tonight."

She and Mary Arnold had been in Mount Vernon at a card-party. They had got soaked coming home. She talked about it all through supper, thank the Lord!

After supper he tried to read, but couldn't. He listened awhile to the Ohman and Arden record which his wife couldn't get enough of. He went to bed, wishing he could sleep and dream, wishing he could sleep two weeks.

He was up early, early enough to look at the paper before breakfast. "Woman Motorist Killed By Street-Car in Bronx." His eyes felt funny as he read: "Miss Edith Dole, twenty-two, of Rye, was instantly killed when the automobile she was driving skidded and struck a street-car at the corner of Fordham Road and Webster Avenue, the Bronx, shortly after four-thirty yesterday afternoon.

"Grace," he said in a voice that was not his own, "I forgot. I'm supposed to be on the job at seven this morning. There's some kind of a parade."

Out of the house, alone, he talked aloud to himself for the first time since he was a kid.

"I can't feel as bad as I think I do. I only seen her four or five times. I can't really feel this bad."

Well, on an afternoon two or three weeks later, a man named Hughes from White Plains, driving a Studebaker, started across

Forty-sixth Street out of turn and obeyed a stern order to pull over to the curb.

"What's your hurry?" demanded the grim-faced traffic policeman. "Where the hell do you think you're going? What's the matter with you, you so-and-so!"

"I forgot myself for a minute. I'm sorry," said Mr. Hughes. "If you'll overlook it, I'll pick you up on my way home and take you to the Bronx. Remember, I give you a ride home last month? Remember? That is, it was a fella that looked like you. That is, he looked something like you. I can see now it wasn't you. It was a different fella."

Say It with Oil

The Editor of this hardy perennial asked me would I write a article on my impressions in regards to wives.

"Well," I says, "I have only got the one wife, and wile I admit she has made quite an impression, still and all it seems to me like you ought to get a hold of a husband with more experience."

So he says:

"Yes, I know you have only got one yourself, but you must be acquainted with a whole lot of them."

"I suppose I am," I said, blushing furiously; "I guess I am personly acquainted with practally every A-No. 1 wife around N. Y. City except Nina Wilcox Putnam."

The Editor jumped as if stang by a bee.

"That is almost uncanny you mentioning her name," he said. "She is the lady who has wrote up a article in regards to husbands, and what I am asking you to write is a kind of a reply to what she wrote. Because I would not be loyal to my sex was I to print her scatheing arrangement of the male gender and not give no space to our defense."

"All right," I said; "but I can't conduct no defense without knowing what is the charges, so before I reply to her article I would better see it first."

So he showed me the article, and I read it, and you can read it for yourselfs as it is printed elsewheres in this issue* under the dainty *nom de plume* of "Say It With Bricks," only I suppose the proof-readers has kind of fixed it up since I seen it, as it struck me that the lady in question has studied husbands at the expense of grammar and spelling.

But before dealing with her article, and wile still cool, I would like to state the cold facts which the gen. public is well aware of same, but for one reason and another don't care to confess it even to themselfs. One fact is that a man defending husbands vs. wives, or men vs. women has got about as much chance as a traffic policeman trying to stop a mad dog by blowing 2 whistles. Another fact is that, with all the recent jokeing about give us equal rights and etc. the wives has got the husbands licked to a pulp and has had them licked for hundreds of yrs., and same can be proved by consulting the works of any writer young or old that touches on the subject.

We will take for inst. the dictionary, and what does it say about a husband? The 1st. definition is a husbandman, which don't mean nothing. The 2d. definition is a frugal person, an economist. The 3d. definition is a man who has a wife. In other wds. Mr. Webster realized that his book wouldn't have no sale unless it tickled the women-folks, so before he dast come out and say that a husband is a man with a wife, he had to call him a tightwad.

Now what is the definition of a wife? Well, he says she is the lawful consort of a man, and it don't require no Shylock Holmes to figure out that what he meant to say, but was scared to say, was *awful* consort.

Back toward the end of the same book you will run across the wd. uxorcide which means the murder of a wife by her husband. But nowheres in the book will you find a wd. that means the murder of a husband by a wife. Unless it's the wd. congratulations.

In this connection it might be well to point out the fine bunch of equal rights with which the happy pair embarks on the matrimonial seas. If either one of them ain't satisfied with the other, why they have got equal rights to shoot. But if it's the wife that gets bumped off, the husband has got exclusive rights to a seat in the electric chair, or strap hanging by his Adam's apple, or spending the rest of

---

* *The American Magazine,* November, 1922.

his life in a bird cage. If, however, the husband was the target, why the worst that can happen to mother is that she will half to poll the jury with kisses, which can't be such a hardship even granting that statistics is accurate, and that 10 out of every 12 good men and true is kindly disposed toward eating-tobacco.

But to return to the writers, why you can't find more than a couple of them great or small but what has came out in print or in speeches before the Rotary Club to the effect that their success and everybody else's was due to their wives or sweethearts. They know a whole lot better, but don't dast say so. The prominent exceptions to this rule is Francis Bacon and Rudyard Kipling. Mr. Bacon made the remark that "he that hath wife and children hath given hostages to fortune, for they are impediments to great enterprises, either of virtue or mischief." And Mr. Kipling wrote one about a good man married being a good man marred, and another one to the effect that he travels the fastest who travels alone.

Some nerve these two babies had, but where did it land them? Mr. Bacon is quite dead and Mr. Kipling wasn't even invited to Princess Mary's wedding.

The writers of the present day has learnt better than take chances like that, and you can't read a story or tend the theatre now days without getting a fresh sample of log rolling in favor of the squalling sex. Like for inst. take the play "To the Ladies" where Marc Connelly and Geo. Kaufman has their leading female character say a line something like "No man that wasn't married ever made a name for himself." Well they was a whole lot of us guys in the audience with our wives, and when the line was sprang why we just kind of giggled and smirked as much as to say "How true that is." Where as if we had of dared to be nasty we would of rose up on our legs and said "What about H. L. Mencken and Tris Speaker and Geo. Ade?"

Even the authors of the marriage ceremony has woke up to the situation and agreed to rewrite same and fix themselfs right with the ladies by leaving out the wd. obey. This is just another public recognition of how bad we are licked. As a matter of fact the obey rule got obsolete along about the same time as 1st. bounce is out. And another thing the boys is going to eliminate is the giving of a woman in marriage, because the gals don't like to have it even hinted that anybody has got the right to give them away like they was a cut glass gold fish bowl or a pen wipper. So instead of "Who giveth this dame to this guy," why from now on they are going to can those lines and substitute a hymn or anthem which will probably be some song like O what a gal was Mary.

So much for Man's position in the Standing of the Clubs and the fat chance I or any other male has got to defend ourself vs. attacks by Mrs. Putnam or any other member of her lodge. But when I undertake to do a job why I am one of these here he-blooded Americans that never quits till they are counted out which can't possibly happen till I been in the arena 10 seconds. In this case however I expect to last longer than that for one little reason. The wife I have got don't read my stuff. Incidently that just about describes her. But any way the knowledge that she don't read my stuff gives me courage to say a few wds. about wives and what they are that I wouldn't dast say if I thought she was going to read it.

Well then here is some of my idears about wives as I have studied them at home and abroad.

Wives is people that thinks you ought to eat at 8 o'clock, one o'clock, and 7 o'clock. If you express yourself as having an appetite for turkey at midnight they think you are crazy.

Wives is people that always wants to go home when you don't and vice versa.

Wives is people that ain't never satisfied as they are always too fat or too thin. Of all the wives I ever talked to I never run acrost one yet that was just right.

Wives is people that thinks 2 ash trays should ought to be plenty for a 12 rm. house.

Wives is people that asks you what time the 12:55 train gets to New York. "At 1:37," you tell them. "How do you know?" they ask.

Wives is people that sets on the right side of the front seat in their husband's costly motor and when he turns down a street to the left they tell him he ought to of kept straight ahead.

They are people that you ask them to go to a ball game and they act tickled to death. So along about the 7th. innings you look at them and they are fast asleep and you remind them with a delicate punch in the ribs that they are supposed to be excited. "Oh, yes," they say. "I love it." So you ask them what is the score and they say "St. Louis is ahead ain't they?" "Well," you say, "I don't know if St.

Louis is ahead or ain't ahead, but the game you are watching is between Boston and New York."

That reminds me of one time I took the little woman (I can't always remember her first name) to a game in old Chi and it was Cleveland vs. the White Sox and it was a close game something like 2 to 1 in favor of somebody and along come the 8th. innings, and Mother, which is how I sometimes think of her, was sleeping pretty and all of a sudden they was a big jam down around 1st. base between a citizen named Tris Speaker, mentioned before in this article and now mentioned again, and Chick Gandil of blessed memory. As they was taking the shirtless remains of Chick off of the field I nudged Mamma in the jaw and said: "Did you see that? It looked to me like Graney took a wallop at him for good measure." "Who is ahead?" says the little gal.

Wives is people who you make an outlay of $50, so as they can set somewheres in New Jersey during the so-called Dempsey-Carpentier fight and when it is over, you meet them and ask them how they liked it and they say Oh, they was thrilled. "Did you see that last punch?" you ask them. "No," they say. "I was watching Irma Goldberg." Who of course is worth watching even at $50.

They are people who you get invited out somewheres with them and you ask them if they think you ought to shave and they say no, you look all right. But when you get to wherever you are going they ask everybody to please forgive Lute as he didn't have time to shave.

They are people that kid you because when the morning paper comes the first thing you look at is the sporting sheet. You leave the paper home and buy another one to read on the way downtown. When you get home that evening, in trying to make conversation you remark that it was kind of sad, the Kaiser's wife dying in exile. "I didn't know she was dead," says Ma. "Well," you tell her, "it was in the morning paper." "I didn't notice it," she says. "It must of been on the front page."

They are people that never have nothing that is fit to wear.

They are people that think when the telephone bell rings it is against the law to not answer it.

They are people whose watch is always a ¼ of a hr. off either one way or the other. But they wouldn't have no idear what time it was any way as this daylight savings gets them all balled up.

The above observations is made without resentment as I have no complaint vs. wives in gen. or anybody's wife in particular. Personly I get along fine with whatever her name is and am perfectly satisfied with my home, which I often call my castle. I also refer to it sometimes as jail, but only in a joking way.

But here I am in jail and supposed to be defending my sex vs. the opponents and as I said before what a fat chance. However I promised the old boy that I would answer Mrs. Putnam's article, and a promise is a promise especially when you get paid for it.

So will point out in the beginning that Mrs. Putnam denies all through her article that it is a article and she certainly hit the nail on the hammer that time. What it reads like to me is pure ficton. Like for inst. she gives you the impression that whenever she seen her husbands before she married them, they always had on a dress suit. Well friends I think you will find the fact is that when a kid is 16 or 17 yrs. of age he gets a dress suit and by the time he is 19 yrs. of age he couldn't get it on with a shoe horn, and from that age to when he gets married he don't have no more dress suit than Robinson Crusoe and he wouldn't never have no more dress suit as long as he lived if she didn't insist on him joining the Rotarians.

The lady's complaint is that after being used to him in nothing but dress suits wile he was doing the alleged courting, why it is a kind of a blow to see him walking around the rm. in his shaving uniform with his suspenders drapped over his hips. In reply to that will say that the lady shouldn't ought to of had no trouble picking out a husband with something on his hip besides suspenders.

Another complaint is how much noise a husband makes with his tooth brush. Well if a man is at all musical they's no instrument he won't attempt to play on and besides what good is brushing your teeth if you are going to keep it a secret.

And another complaint is that husbands prefers toothpicks to any other form of dessert. I don't think this is entirely fair because they's some desserts that you get in hotels and restaurants that a person would really relish more than a toothpick, whereas they's desserts that is served in some private homes than whom a person would not only rather have toothpicks but sulphur matches if necessary.

The lady says it is husbands that is always delaying the game and when they are told that dinner is ready dear, why it is then and then only that they start to wash their hands and brush their hair. Our reply to that is that when the little woman says dinner is ready you can generally always figure on anywheres from 10 minutes to a ½ hr. before they's anything on the table but flies.

As for husbands causing the missing of the first act, judgeing from the most of the plays I seen lately she should ought to be grateful for that and if he is even slower and makes her miss the whole show she ought to kiss him.

Now then along toward the finish of her story the lady says something which I will half to quote as it is such a pretty sentiment namely, "Any complaint you can make about husbands and marriage would be a true one. And only one thing about them (meaning husbands) has got me buffaloed. Would I be willing to do without them? And the answer to that is 'No.' "

Well friends it is hard to bear ill will toward a writer that kind of softens her tirade with such a neat little compliment as that and it looks to me like it would be no more than gentlemanly on my part to reply to same in kind. For inst.

"Pretty near any complaint you make about wives, why it is true though they will probably resent it. But I often ask myself the question could I get along without them? And the answer to that is that I got along without none for twenty-five yrs. and never felt better in my life. Believe you me."

Marriage Made Easy

Every once in so often old Doc Crane breaks loose with a article in regards to one thing another, and one time he asked a lot of questions about one thing another, and unlest a man could answer them all without looking it up in the seed catalogue, why you was supposed to be a moron poor and simple, and the questions the Doc asked was so tough that a whole lot of our smartest Alex took just one look and then went to the county cuckoo cage and gave themselfs up and couldn't get out to vote.

Well it didn't do so much harm to get all them people out of the way, but since the Doc has came acrost with 20 rules on how to be a happy marriage and they are even tougher than the cuckoo test, but it wouldn't make no differents to me as I have all ready got the proposition mastered without no doctor's prescription, but still and all this country is full of young upstarts that may of been just getting ready to assume the connubial yokel and all of a sudden they run acrost the Doc's dope and say it can't be done and they decide to remain celebrates and then what is to become of them 2 grand American institutions, the home and the rent for same.

So in order to perpetrate same by not allowing our young single-tons to discourage themselfs with the Doc's dope, I have wrote out a set of 10 simple rules instead of 20 tough ones witch means it won't only take ½ as long to be a happy marriage and twice as easy.

1

The marital twain should ought to be opp. sex if possible and somewheres near the other one's age. For inst. when a man of 15 gets marred to a gal of 45 why it may pan out all right for the time being but don't never forget that when a groom is nearing the century mark and wants to know where they's a clean bath towel, why he can't find out without leaveing Thurston the magician into the secret.

2

The ideal marred life is for the 2 belligerents to live in the same town so as when they feel like a brawl they won't be no toll charges.

3

The bride should ought to have at lease as much money as the groom and a salary of her own so as when she feels like she has got to buy something she don't want she will know that it's her money being throwed away. All women hates to feel like they was sponge-ing off of their husbands but the most of them is such a good actress that you wouldn't never guess how it hurts them.

4

If the union is crowned with a offspring, the offspring should be crowned at intervals by the father. Otherwise the mother should have exclusive rights as care taker as even a baby don't like to change horses in the middle of the night and wile the old adage says that everybody ought to have 8 hrs. sleep, why it amounts to the same thing if a couple splits 16 hrs. between them, the husband getting the winners share of 80 per cent. and $\frac{1}{2}$ the picture rights.

5

As Doc Crane says, it ain't right to find fault with the other on no grounds and the best way is to pertend like you are tickled to death with everything she does. Like for inst. if you are $\frac{1}{2}$ way home on the train and she shreaks that she has forgot her pocket book, lean over and give her a good loud kiss.

6

Both partys should try and talk about subjects that the other is interested in it. They ain't no husband cares a d—mn if the wash woman that is comeing next wk. goes to a different church than the one that was here last wk. and they's very few wifes cares the same amt. whether Max Baer is going to be the next heavyweight champion, so the idear is that when supper is over and the loveing pair sets down in the liveing rm. to wait till its polite to go to bed, the husband should ought to insist that they won't be no conversation unlest its about the wash woman and the wife should ought to insist that they won't be no conversation unlest its about the next heavyweight champ and if the both of them insist hard enough they won't be no conversation at all witch boarders on the ideal.

7

In most familys its too cold to set up late but when the partys retires the wife wants to go right to sleep like a horse or something wile the husband wants to read, but the wife can't sleep if he reads a wile. This can be overcome by a unselfish spirit on both sides. Let the wife keep saying, "I don't want you to not read on my acct." and keep turning the light on and the husband keep saying, "I don't want you to not sleep on my acct. or you will crab about it all day tomorrow" and every time she turns the light on he turns it off and in this way its morning before you know it and both sides a winner.

8

Marred life is a job just the same as like a telegraph operator or a embalmer and every employ is entitled to 2 wks. vacation per annum and if the husband takes a 2 wks. vacation trip every summer and vice versa, why they will get so as they won't miss their regular jobs ½ as much as if they was on it all the wile. For inst. I knew a couple where the husband use to go South for a mo. every Winter and one time he didn't come home at all and all of his relic's friends was feeling sorry for her where as she didn't know he was still missing till one night in August when a bat got in the house and she screamed and nobody told her to shut up.

9

Doc Crane advises marred couples to not both get mad at the same time, the old spoil sport. That was the trouble with Sharkey and Schmeling over in Long's Island because Schmeling didn't lose his temper though the boys tell me he had even more reason than the saps that paid $55 for a ringside seat. They's no fun playing tennis unlest the guy on the other side of the net has got a racket and the same goes for a connubial quarl and my advice is for the husband to call up home just before he leaves the office and ask the spouse if she is feeling brutal this evening and if she ain't she better be, because by the time he gets the right number they won't be nobody half to wait till dog days to see him froth at the mouth.

10

Finely, try and forget once in a wile that you are marred and go out somewheres together for a good time. Don't go to a dance or a card party or a good show or the opera, but pick out something that the both of you can enjoy, like for inst. a 3 cushion billiard match or a cock fight or to watch the high school football five practice. Remember always that you swore at each other at the altar that each was taking the other from bad to worse and may the best man win.

Table Manners

We are now bordering on the head end of the convention season and the hotel owners in Detroit and Atlantic City where practically all the conventions is held are prepareing for some by hireing extra house detectives and putting a padlock on their soap and towels.

Well I don't belong to nothing and don't expect to tend none of the conventions already scheduled, but will take the opportunity to tell my friends and admires that I would gladly be a delegate to a convention where something would be accomplished in addition to getting boiled, namely a convention to disgust and alter the code of etiquette as now practiced and a specially the rules that govern table manners besides a couple that governs the attitude of man to what is laughingly referred to as the fair sex.

If they's enough people thinks like I do along these lines I do not see no reason why we cannot all get together either at the City of Straits or America's playground as I have dubbed them and fix up a new code with some sense to it and do away with some of the regulations which is not only silly but border on the ridiculous and is rapidly makeing residents of the earth the laughing stalk of the solar system.

Let's take table manners and I will state some of my idears in regards to needed changes and one of the first that comes to mind is the Soup Rule which has been appealed to the Soupreme Court without getting a rumble and the rules I refer to is the rules which makes it a perennial offense to tip up your soup dish so as to get all the soup.

They ain't no man or woman liveing that can pick up all their soup from a flat lie useing only a spoon and the result is that from 1/10 to a ½ an inch is always left laying in the bottom of the dish which is plane waste as the most economical Jap in the world cannot do nothing with left over soup only throw it in the ash can.

A convention of right thinking Americans would specialize on the Soup Rule and make it permissible to tip the dish to any safe and reasonable angle so as to satisfy a legal thirst for a good sound non alcoholic beverage.

The next rule that is in dire need of alterations is the rule in regards to bread and butter. According to the code in usages in exclusive Great Neck homes it is O.K. to take a whole chunk of toast and smear it with butter or any good substitute but when it comes to plain bread why then you half to break it in a couple pieces and lay the pieces on your bread and butter plate which is generally always a full arm's length away and smear them while they lay there, but you mustn't smear the both of them at once but just the piece which you pick out to start in on.

The theory in back of this rule is that maybe you won't want only the one piece and if you leave the other one unbuttered why it can be salvaged and maybe used the following week in the kid's pudding.

That is the theory and all guests recognizes it, but when they follow it out it is just like say to the house wife you are a cheap skate and further and more while a person may get through with one buttering operation unscathed, it is too much to expect to do it twice and keep your sleeves their natural color.

The convention would give this rule the air and advocate the free and unlimited smearing of whole pieces of bread either held in the hand or laid on the table which ever makes the greatest appeal.

The convention would ask for waivers on the finger bowl which ain't proved no case and should be throwed out of court. In the first place when the hostess allows finger bowls to be passed around she as much as tells you outright that you have been fondling a chicken bone with the bare hands or that they's a relict of mushroom sauce on the lower lip.

A man with a drop of red he-blood in their veins resents this and personly my fingers has yet to sully themselfs by straying into a finger bowl and will state without bragging that I always leave the table with hands practically as clean as when I set down unlest of course they was corn or steam clams or something and in the last named case nothing short of a bath tub will relieve the situation.

Under the present regime mine hostess, without I yes or no from the guests, takes it for granted that a man can get along on a $\frac{1}{2}$ demitasse of coffe and wait till a $\frac{1}{2}$ after 9 for same.

The convention would compel all hostesses to find out at the start of the meal if they's any real coffee stews amongst her guests and treat them accordingly.

Personly when I get a invitation to dinner, unles it comes from some right minded hostess like Katie Hollis, for inst., why I reply with a well modulated but firm No as I do not enjoy a evening of bridge with headache for a partner.

This will maybe exclaim why I refuse so many invitations and perhaps cause many a broken heart.

Now in regards to a couple of rules governing man and woman. To state the matter briefly on acct. of the lateness of the hr. I would ask the convention to change the following rules:

1. The rule which compels a perfect gent to get up and give a lady a seat on a subway or elevated train or st. car. A great many perfect gentlemen is floor walkers and barbers, a job where you half to be on your ft. all day. A great many ladys is stenographers and very few of them does their typewriting standing up. More gentlemen than ladys deserves a seat and the rule should ought to be fixed so as when a dame gets on a car she must state the nature of her employment. If she has got a setting down job let her ride home on a strap. This amendment would be more than justice on the grounds that if it was not for men everybody would half to walk home, at least I have never heard of a traction system being built by the hands that rocks a cradle.

2. The rule which forbids a gentleman from hanging up the receiver till the lady says goodbye. All that is ever nessary for a gentleman and lady to say to each other can certainly be said in 3 minutes at the outside but the way it is now the average telephone conversation between the 2 sexes lasts from 30 minutes to a ½ hr. because the lady in question ain't got nothing else to do and hates to give in and the only party that benefits by the rule is the telephone company, and the last I heard about them, they didn't need no benefits.

* * *

Some weeks ago I had a few words to say in regards to formal dinner partys and what kind of a table to set for same and since then I been beseiged with letters from readers beseiging me to devote more articles to social etiquette and as more than one of these letters makes special mention of introductions I may as well devote this article to that subject.

One reader enclosed me a copy of a article on this subject by Mrs. Julia Hoyt of N.Y. city who is supposed to be the last word in decorums of all kinds but the article in question left many pts. to be cleared up at lease in the opinion of the party who sent it in and the last named wanted I should clarify these matters and also state what changes if any has been made in the code since Mrs. Hoyt's article seen print.

One pt. for inst. which the lady didn't even touch on was the matter of introduceing two people to each other when you don't now neither one's name.

This used to happen a lot more in the old days when people done their drinking standing up but they is still plenty of occasions when this embarrassing situation arises a specially in Pullman wash rooms or at a national convention of the moose.

I always kind of laugh it off and say something to the effect that you 2 boys knows each other of course and they generally tells one another what their name is which also gives me a clew.

Mrs. Hoyt gives it as a general rule that when you are makeing a plain introduction you just say "Mrs. Reed, Mrs. Wallace" unlest of course their names happens to be Mrs. Pinkney and Mrs. Welsh. But she says that when one woman is a young woman and the other one ain't so young, why the young one should ought to be presented to the older one, so if Mrs. Wallace is older than Mrs. Reed you half got to say "Mrs. Wallace, Mrs. Reed."

Now days however what with the beauty parlor and funny clothes it ain't always possible to be sure and a person would be a sucker to go ahead with the introductions without first asking the 2 dames which is the oldest.

According to Mrs. Hoyt's article when a man and woman is introduced the woman ain't required to shake hands unlest the guy sticks out his hand, but if he does so it is very rude for the woman to not grab a hold of it.

Personly however I have been introduced to many a dame that must have thought I was holding out my hand so as she could admire the callouses or something and I been humiliated so many times along these lines that now days when they's a dame being introduced to me I always pretend like I was unloosening my belt or looking through my vest pockets for a tooth pick.

It is well to remember then when the party who is makeing the introduction says "Mr. Bolling, shake hands with Mrs. Gavin," that don't neserally mean that you got to shake hands. The introducer ain't any authority to designate the mode of caress and irregardless of whatever he says you are free to put your arm around Mrs. Gavin or slap her face or ignore her entirely.

The reader who sent me Mrs. Hoyt's article marked one paragraph which she says has got her all up in the air, namely the paragraph where it says that if you are presenting your married daughter to a older man you have got to say "My daughter, Mrs. Reed."

She says that since reading the article she has had numerable occasions to introduce her daughter to old galoots and when she springs that "Mrs. Reed" they all think she is ginny as it is a notorious fact that the name of the man her daughter married is Eyclesheimer. Of course in cases like this you have to use your own judgement and as far as I am conserned I would be a whole lot more libel to think that a woman was ½ seas over if she told me her daughter's name was Mrs. Eyclesheimer.

Mrs. Hoyt's article goes on to say that when you present anybody to the President you are supposed to say "Mr. President, I have the honor to present Mr. Burke of San Francisco." But when you introduce him to a Cardinal, you must say "Your Eminence, may I present Mr. Burke?"

My reader don't think it's hardly fair to tell the President where Mr. Burke is from but to keep it a secret from the Cardinal, but personly it looks to me like this was makeing a mt. out of a mole hill because if Mr. Burke is really from San Francisco, the dialogue ain't libel to continue more than 2 or 3 hrs. before the Cardinal might of suspects same.

It is the worst kind of form to ask the introducer to say a name over when you don't catch it the first time but they's a way to get around this. Like for inst. suppose you are introduced to a pretty gal and you ain't got no idear what the man said her name was, why all as you have to do is say, "I am certainly pleased to meet you

Miss Gourmand" or some such name and she will say "My name is Andrews please."

In closeing up her article Mrs. Hoyt gives a list of don'ts in introductions and amongst them she says don't ask any personal questions the moment after you have been introduced. A great many people might have different ideas in regards to what is a personal question as used in this connection and no doubt some poor hicks will draw the line too fine and refrain from asking questions which might of been regarded as too personal in the old days but would be OK now.

Maybe I better wind up this article of mine by giveing a couple examples of what kind of questions not to ask and what kind is perfectly permissable.

Well then we will pretend like you have just been introduced to a man named Harley. Don't say to him "Glad to meet you, Mr. Harley. Do you and your wife get along all right?" Or "Glad to know you Mr. Harley. What makes you limp?"

But do say if you feel like it, "Pleased to meet you Mr. Harley. Got anything on the hip?"

Dogs

Every little wile you hear people talking about a man that they don't nobody seem to have much use for him on acct. of him not paying his debts or beating his wife or something and everybody takes a rap at him about this and that until finely one of the party speaks up and says they must be some good in him because he likes animals.

"A man can't be all bad when he is so kind to dogs." That is what they generally always say and that is the reason you see so many men stop on the st. when they see a dog and pet it because they figure that may be somebody will be looking at them do it, and the next time they are getting panned, why who ever seen it will speak up and say:

"He can't be all bad because he likes dogs."

Well friends when you come right down to cases they's about as much sence to this as a good many other delusions that we got here in this country, like for inst. the one about nobody wanting to win the first pot and the one about the whole lot of authors not being able to do their best work unlest they are ½ pickled.

But if liking animals ain't a virtue in itself I don't see how it proves that a man has got any virtues, and personly if I had a daughter and she wanted to get marred and I asked her what kind of a bird the guy was and she said she don't know nothing about him except that one day she seen him kiss a leopard, why I would hold up my blessing till a few of the missing precincts was heard from.

But as long as our best people has got it in their skull that a friendly feeling toward dumb brutes takes the curse off of a bad egg, why I or nobody else is going to be a sucker enough to come out and admit that all the horses, rams, and oxen in the world could drop dead tomorrow morning without us batting an eye.

Pretty near everybody wants to be well thought of and if liking dogs or sheep is a helping along these lines, why even if I don't like them, I wouldn't never loose a opportunity to be seen in their company and act as if I was haveing the time of my life.

But while I was raised in a kennel, you might say, and some of my most intimate childhood friends was of the canine gender, still in all I believe dogs is better in some climates than others, the same as oysters, and I don't think it should ought to be held against a man if he don't feel the same towards N.Y. dogs as he felt towards Michigan dogs, and I am free to confess that the 4 dogs who I have grew to know personly here on Long Island has failed to arouse tender yearnings anyways near similar to those inspired by the flea bearers of my youth.

And in case they should be any tendency on the part of my readers to denounce me for failing to respond whole heartily to the wiles of the Long Island breed let me present a brief sketch of some so as true lovers of the canine tribe can judge for themselfs if the fault is all mind.

NO. 1

This was the dainty boy that belonged to Gene Buck and it was a bull dog no bigger than a 2 car garage and it wouldn't harm a hair of nobody's head only other animals and people. Children were as safe with this pet as walking in the Pittsburgh freight yards and he wouldn't think of no more wronging a cat than scratching himself.

In fairness to Mr. Buck I'll state that a pal of his give him the dog as a present without no comment. Well they wasn't no trouble till Gene had the dog pretty near $\frac{1}{2}$ hr. when they let him out. He was gone 10 minutes during which Gene received a couple of phone calls announcing more in anger than in sorrow the sudden deaths of 2 adjacent cats of noble berth so when the dog come back Gene spanked him and give him a terrible scolding and after that he didn't kill no more cats except when he got outdoors.

But the next day De Wolf Hopper come over to call and brought his kid which the dog thought would look better with one leg and it took 5 people to get him not to operate, so after that Gene called up the supt. of a dogs reform school and the man said he would take him and cure him of the cat habit by trying one of his victims around his neck and leaving it there for a wk. but he didn't know how to cure the taste for young Hoppers unlest De Wolf could spare the kid the wk. after they was finished with the cat.

This proposition fell through but anyway Gene sent the dog to the reformatory and is still paying board for same.

NO. 2

The people that lived 3 houses from the undersigned decided to move to England where it seems like you can't take dogs no more so they asked us did we want the dog as it was very nice around children and we took it and sure enough it was OK in regards to children but it shared this new owners feeling towards motorcycles and every time one went past the house the dog would run out and spill the contents, and on Sundays when the traffic was heavy they would sometimes be as many as 4 or 5 motorcycle jehus standing on their heads in the middle of the road.

One of them finely took offence and told on the dog and the justice of the peace called me up and said I would have to kill it within 24 hrs. and the only way I could think of to do same was drown it in the bath tub and if you done that, why the bath tub wouldn't be no good no more because it was a good sized dog and no matter how often you pulled the stopper it would still be there.

NO. 3

The next-door neighbors has a pro-German police dog that win a blue ribbon once but now it acts as body guard for the lady of the house and one day we was over there and the host says to slap his Mrs. on the arm and see what happened so I slapped her on the arm and I can still show you what happened.

When you dance with mine hostess this sweet little pet dances right along with you and watches your step and if you tred on my ladys toe he fines you a mouth full and if you and her is partners in a bridge game he lays under the table and you either bid right and play right or you get nipped.

NO. 4

This is our present incumbrance which we didn't ask for him and nobody give him to us but here he is and he has got the insomnia and he has picked a spot outside my window to enjoy it but not only that but he has learnt that if you jump at a screen often enough it will finely give way and the result is that they ain't a door or window on the first floor that you couldn't drive a rhinoceros through it and all the bugs that didn't already live in the house is moveing in and bringing their family.

That is a true record of the dogs who I have met since takeing up my abode in Nassau county so when people ask me do I like dogs I say I'm crazy about them and I think they are all right in their place but it ain't Long Island.

PART FIVE

The Popular Arts

Alibi Ike

His right name was Frank X. Farrell, and I guess the X stood for "Excuse me." Because he never pulled a play, good or bad, on or off the field, without apologizin' for it.

"Alibi Ike" was the name Carey wished on him the first day he reported down South. O' course we all cut out the "Alibi" part of it right away for the fear he would overhear it and bust somebody. But we called him "Ike" right to his face and the rest of it was understood by everybody on the club except Ike himself.

He ast me one time, he says:

"What do you all call me Ike for? I ain't no Yid."

"Carey give you the name," I says. "It's his nickname for everybody he takes a likin' to."

"He mustn't have only a few friends then," says Ike. "I never heard him say 'Ike' to nobody else."

But I was goin' to tell you about Carey namin' him. We'd been workin' out two weeks and the pitchers was showin' somethin' when this bird joined us. His first day out he stood up there so good and took such a reef at the old pill that he had everyone lookin'. Then him and Carey was together in left field, catchin' fungoes, and it was after we was through for the day that Carey told me about him.

"What do you think of Alibi Ike?" ast Carey.

"Who's that?" I says.

"This here Farrell in the outfield," says Carey.

"He looks like he could hit," I says.

"Yes," says Carey, "but he can't hit near as good as he can apologize."

Then Carey went on to tell me what Ike had been pullin' out there. He'd dropped the first fly ball that was hit to him and told Carey his glove wasn't broke in good yet, and Carey says the glove could easy of been Kid Gleason's gran'father. He made a whale of a catch out o' the next one and Carey says "Nice work!" or somethin' like that, but Ike says he could of caught the ball with his back turned only he slipped when he started after it and, besides that, the air currents fooled him.

"I thought you done well to get to the ball," says Carey.

"I ought to been settin' under it," says Ike.

"What did you hit last year?" Carey ast him.

"I had malaria most o' the season," says Ike. "I wound up with .356."

"Where would I have to go to get malaria?" says Carey, but Ike didn't wise up.

I and Carey and him set at the same table together for supper. It took him half an hour longer'n us to eat because he had to excuse himself every time he lifted his fork.

"Doctor told me I needed starch," he'd say, and then toss a shovelful o' potatoes into him. Or, "They ain't much meat on one o' these chops," he'd tell us, and grab another one. Or he'd say: "Nothin' like onions for a cold," and then he'd dip into the perfumery.

"Better try that apple sauce," says Carey. "It'll help your malaria."

"Whose malaria?" says Ike. He'd forgot already why he didn't only hit .356 last year.

I and Carey begin to lead him on.

"Whereabouts did you say your home was?" I ast him.

"I live with my folks," he says. "We live in Kansas City—not right down in the business part—outside a ways."

"How's that come?" says Carey. "I should think you'd get rooms in the post office."

But Ike was too busy curin' his cold to get that one.

"Are you married?" I ast him.

"No," he says. "I never run around much with girls, except to shows onct in a wile and parties and dances and roller skatin'."

"Never take 'em to the prize fights, eh?" says Carey.

"We don't have no real good bouts," says Ike. "Just bush stuff. And I never figured a boxin' match was a place for the ladies."

Well, after supper he pulled a cigar out and lit it. I was just goin' to ask him what he done it for, but he beat me to it.

"Kind o' rests a man to smoke after a good work-out," he says. "Kind o' settles a man's supper, too."

"Looks like a pretty good cigar," says Carey.

"Yes," says Ike. " A friend o' mine give it to me—a fella in Kansas City that runs a billiard room."

"Do you play billiards?" I ast him.

"I used to play a fair game," he says. "I'm all out o' practice now —can't hardly make a shot."

We coaxed him into a four-handed battle, him and Carey against Jack Mack and I. Say, he couldn't play billiards as good as Willie Hoppe; not quite. But to hear him tell it, he didn't make a good shot all evenin'. I'd leave him an awful-lookin' layout and he'd gather 'em up in one try and then run a couple o' hundred, and between every carom he'd say he'd put too much stuff on the ball, or the English didn't take, or the table wasn't true, or his stick was crooked, or somethin'. And all the time he had the balls actin' like they was Dutch soldiers and him Kaiser William. We started out to play fifty points, but we had to make it a thousand so as I and Jack and Carcy could try the table.

The four of us set round the lobby a wile after we was through playin', and when it got along toward bedtime Carey whispered to me and says:

"Ike'd like to go to bed, but he can't think up no excuse."

Carey hadn't hardly finished whisperin' when Ike got up and pulled it:

"Well, good night, boys," he says. "I ain't sleepy, but I got some gravel in my shoes and it's killin' my feet."

We knowed he hadn't never left the hotel since we'd came in from the grounds and changed our clo'es. So Carey says:

"I should think they'd take them gravel pits out o' the billiard room."

But Ike was already on his way to the elevator, limpin'.

"He's got the world beat," says Carey to Jack and I. "I've knew lots o' guys that had an alibi for every mistake they made; I've heard pitchers say that the ball slipped when somebody cracked one off'n 'em; I've heard infielders complain of a sore arm after heavin' one into the stand, and I've saw outfielders tooken sick with a dizzy spell when they've misjudged a fly ball. But this baby can't even go to bed without apologizin', and I bet he excuses himself to the razor when he gets ready to shave."

"And at that," says Jack, "he's goin' to make us a good man."

"Yes," says Carey, "unless rheumatism keeps his battin' average down to .400."

Well, sir, Ike kept whalin' away at the ball all through the trip till everybody knowed he'd won a job. Cap had him in there regular the last few exhibition games and told the newspaper boys a week before the season opened that he was goin' to start him in Kane's place.

"You're there, kid," says Carey to Ike, the night Cap made the 'nnouncement. "They ain't many boys that wins a big league berth their third year out."

"I'd of been up here a year ago," says Ike, "only I was bent over all season with lumbago."

II

It rained down in Cincinnati one day and somebody organized a little game o' cards. They was shy two men to make six and ast I and Carey to play.

"I'm with you if you get Ike and make it seven-handed," says Carey.

So they got a hold of Ike and we went up to Smitty's room.

"I pretty near forgot how many you deal," says Ike. "It's been a long wile since I played."

I and Carey give each other the wink, and sure enough, he was just as ig'orant about poker as billiards. About the second hand, the pot was opened two or three ahead of him, and they was three in when it come his turn. It cost a buck, and he throwed in two.

"It's raised, boys," somebody says.

"Gosh, that's right, I did raise it," says Ike.

"Take out a buck if you didn't mean to tilt her," says Carey.

"No," says Ike, "I'll leave it go."

Well, it was raised back at him and then he made another mistake and raised again. They was only three left in when the draw come. Smitty'd opened with a pair o' kings and he didn't help 'em. Ike stood pat. The guy that'd raised him back was flushin' and he didn't fill. So Smitty checked and Ike bet and didn't get no call. He tossed his hand away, but I grabbed it and give it a look. He had king, queen, jack and two tens. Alibi Ike he must have seen me peekin', for he leaned over and whispered to me.

"I overlooked my hand," he says. "I thought all the wile it was a straight."

"Yes," I says, "that's why you raised twice by mistake."

They was another pot that he come into with tens and fours. It was tilted a couple o' times and two o' the strong fellas drawed ahead of Ike. They each drawed one. So Ike throwed away his little pair and come out with four tens. And they was four treys against him. Carey'd looked at Ike's discards and then he says:

"This lucky bum busted two pair."

"No, no, I didn't," says Ike.

"Yes, yes, you did," says Carey, and showed us the two fours.

"What do you know about that?" says Ike. "I'd of swore one was a five spot."

Well, we hadn't had no pay day yet, and after a wile everybody except Ike was goin' shy. I could see him gettin' restless and I was wonderin' how he'd make the get-away. He tried two or three times. "I got to buy some collars before supper," he says.

"No hurry," says Smitty. "The stores here keeps open all night in April."

After a minute he opened up again.

"My uncle out in Nebraska ain't expected to live," he says. "I ought to send a telegram."

"Would that save him?" says Carey.

"No, it sure wouldn't," says Ike, "but I ought to leave my old man know where I'm at."

"When did you hear about your uncle?" says Carey.

"Just this mornin'," says Ike.

"Who told you?" ast Carey.

"I got a wire from my old man," says Ike.

"Well," says Carey, "your old man knows you're still here yet this afternoon if you was here this mornin'. Trains leavin' Cincinnati in the middle o' the day don't carry no ball clubs."

"Yes," says Ike, "that's true. But he don't know where I'm goin' to be next week."

"Ain't he got no schedule?" ast Carey.

"I sent him one openin' day," says Ike, "but it takes mail a long time to get to Idaho."

"I thought your old man lived in Kansas City," says Carey.

"He does when he's home," says Ike.

"But now," says Carey, "I s'pose he's went to Idaho so as he can be near your sick uncle in Nebraska."

"He's visitin' my other uncle in Idaho."

"Then how does he keep posted about your sick uncle?" ast Carey.

"He don't," says Ike. "He don't even know my other uncle's sick. That's why I ought to wire and tell him."

"Good night!" says Carey.

"What town in Idaho is your old man at?" I says.

Ike thought it over.

"No town at all," he says. "But he's near a town."

"Near what town?" I says.

"Yuma," says Ike.

Well, by this time he'd lost two or three pots and he was desperate. We was playin' just as fast as we could, because we seen we couldn't hold him much longer. But he was tryin' so hard to frame an escape that he couldn't pay no attention to the cards, and it looked like we'd get his whole pile away from him if we could make him stick.

The telephone saved him. The minute it begun to ring, five of us jumped for it. But Ike was there first.

"Yes," he says, answerin' it. "This is him. I'll come right down."

And he slammed up the receiver and beat it out o' the door without even sayin' good-by.

"Smitty'd ought to locked the door," says Carey.

"What did he win?" ast Carey.

We figured it up—sixty-odd bucks.

"And the next time we ask him to play," says Carey, "his fingers will be so stiff he can't hold the cards."

Well, we set round a wile talkin' it over, and pretty soon the telephone rung again. Smitty answered it. It was a friend of his'n from Hamilton and he wanted to know why Smitty didn't hurry down. He was the one that had called before and Ike had told him he was Smitty.

"Ike'd ought to split with Smitty's friend," says Carey.

"No," I says, "he'll need all he won. It costs money to buy collars and to send telegrams from Cincinnati to your old man in Texas and keep him posted on the health o' your uncle in Cedar Rapids, D. C."

III

And you ought to heard him out there on that field! They wasn't
a day when he didn't pull six or seven, and it didn't make no difference whether he was goin' good or bad. If he popped up in the
pinch he should of made a base hit and the reason he didn't was
so-and-so. And if he cracked one for three bases he ought to had a
home run, only the ball wasn't lively, or the wind brought it back,
or he tripped on a lump o' dirt, roundin' first base.

They was one afternoon in New York when he beat all records.
Big Marquard was workin' against us and he was good.

In the first innin' Ike hit one clear over that right field stand, but
it was a few feet foul. Then he got another foul and then the count
come to two and two. Then Rube slipped one acrost on him and he
was called out.

"What do you know about that!" he says afterward on the bench.
"I lost count. I thought it was three and one, and I took a strike."

"You took a strike all right," says Carey. "Even the umps knowed
it was a strike."

"Yes," says Ike, "but you can bet I wouldn't of took it if I'd knew
it was the third one. The score board had it wrong."

"That score board ain't for you to look at," says Cap. "It's for you
to hit that old pill against."

"Well," says Ike, "I could of hit that one over the score board if
I'd knew it was the third."

"Was it a good ball?" I says.

"Well, no, it wasn't," says Ike. "It was inside."

"How far inside?" says Carey.

"Oh, two or three inches or half a foot," says Ike.

"I guess you wouldn't of threatened the score board with it then,"
says Cap.

"I'd of pulled it down the right foul line if I hadn't thought he'd
call it a ball," says Ike.

Well, in New York's part o' the innin' Doyle cracked one and Ike
run back a mile and a half and caught it with one hand. We was all
sayin' what a whale of a play it was, but he had to apologize just the
same as for gettin' struck out.

"That stand's so high," he says, "that a man don't never see a ball till it's right on top o' you."

"Didn't you see that one?" ast Cap.

"Not at first," says Ike; "not till it raised up above the roof o' the stand."

"Then why did you start back as soon as the ball was hit?" says Cap.

"I knowed by the sound that he'd got a good hold of it," says Ike.

"Yes," says Cap, "but how'd you know what direction to run in?"

"Doyle usually hits 'em that way, the way I run," says Ike.

"Why don't you play blindfolded?" says Carey.

"Might as well, with that big high stand to bother a man," says Ike. "If I could of saw the ball all the time I'd of got it in my hip pocket."

Along in the fifth we was one run to the bad and Ike got on with one out. On the first ball throwed to Smitty, Ike went down. The ball was outside and Meyers throwed Ike out by ten feet.

You could see Ike's lips movin' all the way to the bench and when he got there he had his piece learned.

"Why didn't he swing?" he says.

"Why didn't you wait for his sign?" says Cap.

"He give me his sign," says Ike.

"What is his sign with you?" says Cap.

"Pickin' up some dirt with his right hand," says Ike.

"Well, I didn't see him do it," Cap says.

"He done it all right," says Ike.

Well, Smitty went out and they wasn't no more argument till they come in for the next innin'. Then Cap opened it up.

"You fellas better get your signs straight," he says.

"Do you mean me?" says Smitty.

"Yes," Cap says. "What's your sign with Ike?"

"Slidin my left hand up to the end o' the bat and back," says Smitty.

"Do you hear that, Ike?" ast Cap.

"What of it?" says Ike.

"You says his sign was pickin' up dirt and he says it's slidin his hand. Which is right?"

"I'm right," says Smitty. "But if you're arguin' about him goin' last innin', I didn't give him no sign."

"You pulled your cap down with your right hand, didn't you?" ast Ike.

"Well, s'pose I did," says Smitty. "That don't mean nothin'. I never told you to take that for a sign, did I?"

"I thought maybe you meant to tell me and forgot," says Ike.

They couldn't none of us answer that and they wouldn't of been no more said if Ike had of shut up. But wile we was settin' there Carey got on with two out and stole second clean.

"There!" says Ike. "That's what I was tryin' to do and I'd of got away with it if Smitty'd swang and bothered the Indian."

"Oh!" says Smitty. "You was tryin' to steal then, was you? I thought you claimed I give you the hit and run."

"I didn't claim no such a thing," says Ike. "I thought maybe you might of gave me a sign, but I was goin' anyway because I thought I had a good start."

Cap prob'ly would of hit him with a bat, only just about that time Doyle booted one on Hayes and Carey come acrost with the run that tied.

Well, we go into the ninth finally, one and one, and Marquard walks McDonald with nobody out.

"Lay it down," says Cap to Ike.

And Ike goes up there with orders to bunt and cracks the first ball into that right-field stand! It was fair this time, and we're two ahead, but I didn't think about that at the time. I was too busy watchin' Cap's face. First he turned pale and then he got red as fire and then he got blue and purple, and finally he just laid back and busted out laughin'. So we wasn't afraid to laugh ourselfs when we seen him doin' it, and when Ike come in everybody on the bench was in hysterics.

But instead o' takin' advantage, Ike had to try and excuse himself. His play was to shut up and he didn't know how to make it.

"Well," he says, "if I hadn't hit quite so quick at that one I bet it'd of cleared the center-field fence."

Cap stopped laughin'.

"It'll cost you plain fifty," he says.

"What for?" says Ike.

"When I say 'bunt' I mean 'bunt,'" says Cap.

"You didn't say 'bunt,'" says Ike.

"I says 'Lay it down,' " says Cap. "If that don't mean 'bunt,' what does it mean?"

" 'Lay it down' means 'bunt' all right," says Ike, "but I understood you to say 'Lay on it.' "

"All right," says Cap, "and the little misunderstandin' will cost you fifty."

Ike didn't say nothin' for a few minutes. Then he had another bright idear.

"I was just kiddin' about misunderstandin' you," he says. "I knowed you wanted me to bunt."

"Well, then, why didn't you bunt?" ast Cap.

"I was goin' to on the next ball," says Ike. "But I thought if I took a good wallop I'd have 'em all fooled. So I walloped at the first one to fool 'em, and I didn't have no intention o' hittin' it."

"You tried to miss it, did you?" says Cap.

"Yes," says Ike.

"How'd you happen to hit it?" ast Cap.

"Well," Ike says, "I was lookin' for him to throw me a fast one and I was goin' to swing under it. But he come with a hook and I met it right square where I was swingin' to go under the fast one."

"Great!" says Cap. "Boys," he says, "Ike's learned how to hit Marquard's curve. Pretend a fast one's comin' and then try to miss it. It's a good thing to know and Ike'd ought to be willin' to pay for the lesson. So I'm goin' to make it a hundred instead o' fifty."

The game wound up 3 to 1. The fine didn't go, because Ike hit like a wild man all through that trip and we made pretty near a clean-up. The night we went to Philly I got him cornered in the car and I says to him:

"Forget them alibis for a wile and tell me somethin'. What'd you do that for, swing that time against Marquard when you was told to bunt?"

"I'll tell you," he says. "That ball he threwed me looked just like the one I struck out on in the first innin' and I wanted to show Cap what I could of done to that other one if I'd knew it was the third strike."

"But," I says, "the one you struck out on in the first innin' was a fast ball."

"So was the one I cracked in the ninth," says Ike.

IV

You've saw Cap's wife, o' course. Well, her sister's about twict as good-lookin' as her, and that's goin' some.

Cap took his missus down to St. Louis the second trip and the other one come down from St. Joe to visit her. Her name is Dolly, and some doll is right.

Well, Cap was goin' to take the two sisters to a show and he wanted a beau for Dolly. He left it to her and she picked Ike. He'd hit three on the nose that afternoon—off'n Sallee, too.

They fell for each other that first evenin'. Cap told us how it come off. She begin flatterin' Ike for the star game he'd played and o' course he begin excusin' himself for not doin' better. So she thought he was modest and it went strong with her. And she believed everything he said and that made her solid with him—that and her make-up. They was together every mornin' and evenin' for the five days we was there. In the afternoons Ike played the grandest ball you ever see, hittin' and runnin' the bases like a fool and catchin' everything that stayed in the park.

I told Cap, I says: "You'd ought to keep the doll with us and he'd make Cobb's figures look sick."

But Dolly had to go back to St. Joe and we come home for a long serious.

Well, for the next three weeks Ike had a letter to read every day and he'd set in the clubhouse readin' it till mornin' practice was half over. Cap didn't say nothin' to him, because he was goin' so good. But I and Carey wasted a lot of our time tryin' to get him to own up who the letters was from. Fine chanct!

"What are you readin'?" Carey'd say. "A bill?"

"No," Ike'd say, "not exactly a bill. It's a letter from a fella I used to go to school with."

"High school or college?" I'd ask him.

"College," he'd say.

"What college?" I'd say.

Then he'd stall a wile and then he'd say:

"I didn't go to the college myself, but my friend went there."

"How did it happen you didn't go?" Carey'd ask him.

"Well," he'd say, "they wasn't no colleges near where I lived."

"Didn't you live in Kansas City?" I'd say to him.

One time he'd say he did and another time he didn't. One time he says he lived in Michigan.

"Where at?" says Carey.

"Near Detroit," he says.

"Well," I says, "Detroit's near Ann Arbor and that's where they got the university."

"Yes," says Ike, "they got it there now, but they didn't have it there then."

"I come pretty near goin' to Syracuse," I says, "only they wasn't no railroads runnin' through there in them days."

"Where'd this friend o' yours go to college?" says Carey.

"I forget now," says Ike.

"Was it Carlisle?" ast Carey.

"No," says Ike, "his folks wasn't very well off."

"That's what barred me from Smith," I says.

"I was goin' to tackle Cornell's," says Carey, "but the doctor told me I'd have hay fever if I didn't stay up North."

"Your friend writes long letters," I says.

"Yes," says Ike; "he's tellin' me about a ball player."

"Where does he play?" ast Carey.

"Down in the Texas League—Fort Wayne," says Ike.

"It looks like a girl's writin'," Carey says.

"A girl wrote it," says Ike. "That's my friend's sister, writin' for him."

"Didn't they teach writin' at this here college where he went?" says Carey.

"Sure," Ike says, "they taught writin', but he got his hand cut off in a railroad wreck."

"How long ago?" I says.

"Right after he got out o' college," says Ike.

"Well," I says, "I should think he'd of learned to write with his left hand by this time."

"It's his left hand that was cut off," says Ike; "and he was left-handed."

"You get a letter every day," says Carey. "They're all the same writin'. Is he tellin' you about a different ball player every time he writes?"

"No," Ike says. "It's the same ball player. He just tells me what he does every day."

"From the size o' the letters, they don't play nothin' but double-headers down there," says Carey.

We figured that Ike spent most of his evenin's answerin' the letters from his "friend's sister," so we kept tryin' to date him up for shows and parties to see how he'd duck out of 'em. He was bugs over spaghetti, so we told him one day that they was goin' to be a big feed of it over to Joe's that night and he was invited.

"How long'll it last?" he says.

"Well," we says, "we're goin' right over there after the game and stay till they close up."

"I can't go," he says, "unless they leave me come home at eight bells."

"Nothin' doin'," says Carey. "Joe'd get sore."

"I can't go then," says Ike.

"Why not?" I ast him.

"Well," he says, "my landlady locks up the house at eight and I left my key home."

"You can come and stay with me," says Carey.

"No," he says, "I can't sleep in a strange bed."

"How do you get along when we're on the road?" says I.

"I don't never sleep the first night anywheres," he says. "After that I'm all right."

"You'll have time to chase home and get your key right after the game," I told him.

"The key ain't home," says Ike. "I lent it to one o' the other fellas and he's went out o' town and took it with him."

"Couldn't you borry another key off'n the landlady?" Carey ast him.

"No," he says, "that's the only one they is."

Well, the day before we started East again, Ike come into the clubhouse all smiles.

"Your birthday?" I ast him.

"No," he says.

"What do you feel so good about?" I says.

"Got a letter from my old man," he says. "My uncle's goin' to get well."

"Is that the one in Nebraska?" says I.

"Not right in Nebraska," says Ike. "Near there."

But afterwards we got the right dope from Cap. Dolly'd blew in from Missouri and was goin' to make the trip with her sister.

V

Well, I want to alibi Carey and I for what come off in Boston. If we'd of had any idear what we was doin', we'd never did it. They wasn't nobody outside o' maybe Ike and the dame that felt worse over it than I and Carey.

The first two days we didn't see nothin' of Ike and her except out to the park. The rest o' the time they was sight-seein' over to Cambridge and down to Revere and out to Brook-a-line and all the other places where the rubes go.

But when we come into the beanery after the third game Cap's wife called us over.

"If you want to see somethin' pretty," she says, "look at the third finger on Sis's left hand."

Well, o' course we knowed before we looked that it wasn't goin' to be no hangnail. Nobody was su'prised when Dolly blew into the dinin' room with it—a rock that Ike'd bought off'n Diamond Joe the first trip to New York. Only o' course it'd been set into a lady's-size ring instead o' the automobile tire he'd been wearin'.

Cap and his missus and Ike and Dolly ett supper together, only Ike didn't eat nothin', but just set there blushin' and spillin' things on the tablecloth. I heard him excusin' himself for not havin' no appetite. He says he couldn't never eat when he was clost to the ocean. He'd forgot about them sixty-five oysters he destroyed the first night o' the trip before.

He was goin' to take her to a show, so after supper he went upstairs to change his collar. She had to doll up, too, and o' course Ike was through long before her.

If you remember the hotel in Boston, they's a little parlor where the piano's at and then they's another little parlor openin' off o' that. Well, when Ike come down Smitty was playin' a few chords and I and Carey was harmonizin'. We seen Ike go up to the desk to leave his key and we called him in. He tried to duck away, but we wouldn't stand for it.

We ast him what he was all duded up for and he says he was goin'
to the theayter.

"Goin' alone?" says Carey.

"No," he says, "a friend o' mine's goin' with me."

"What do you say if we go along?" says Carey.

"I ain't only got two tickets," he says.

"Well," says Carey, "we can go down there with you and buy our
own seats; maybe we can all get together."

"No," says Ike. "They ain't no more seats. They're all sold out."

"We can buy some off'n the scalpers," says Carey.

"I wouldn't if I was you," says Ike. "They say the show's rotten."

"What are you goin' for, then?" I ast.

"I didn't hear about it bein' rotten till I got the tickets," he says.

"Well," I says, "if you don't want to go I'll buy the tickets from
you."

"No," says Ike, "I wouldn't want to cheat you. I'm stung and I'll
just have to stand for it."

"What are you goin' to do with the girl, leave her here at the
hotel?" I says.

"What girl?" says Ike.

"The girl you ett supper with," I says.

"Oh," he says, "we just happened to go into the dinin' room together, that's all. Cap wanted I should set down with 'em."

"I noticed," says Carey, "that she happened to be wearin' that
rock you bought off'n Diamond Joe."

"Yes," says Ike. "I lent it to her for a wile."

"Did you lend her the new ring that goes with it?" I says.

"She had that already," says Ike. "She lost the set out of it."

"I wouldn't trust no strange girl with a rock o' mine," says Carey.

"Oh, I guess she's all right," Ike says. "Besides, I was tired o' the
stone. When a girl asks you for somethin', what are you goin' to do?"

He started out toward the desk, but we flagged him.

"Wait a minute!" Carey says. "I got a bet with Sam here, and it's
up to you to settle it."

"Well," says Ike, "make it snappy. My friend'll be here any
minute."

"I bet," says Carey, "that you and that girl was engaged to be
married."

"Nothin' to it," says Ike.

"Now look here," says Carey, "this is goin' to cost me real money if I lose. Cut out the alibi stuff and give it to us straight. Cap's wife just as good as told us you was roped."

Ike blushed like a kid.

"Well, boys," he says, "I may as well own up. You win, Carey."

"Yatta boy!" says Carey. "Congratulations!"

"You got a swell girl, Ike," I says.

"She's a peach," says Smitty.

"Well, I guess she's O. K.," says Ike. "I don't know much about girls."

"Didn't you never run round with 'em?" I says.

"Oh, yes, plenty of 'em," says Ike. "But I never seen none I'd fall for."

"That is, till you seen this one," says Carey.

"Well," says Ike, "this one's O. K., but I wasn't thinkin' about gettin' married yet a wile."

"Who done the askin'—her?" says Carey.

"Oh, no," says Ike, "but sometimes a man don't know what he's gettin' into. Take a good-lookin' girl, and a man gen'ally almost always does about what she wants him to."

"They couldn't no girl lasso me unless I wanted to be lassoed," says Smitty.

"Oh, I don't know," says Ike. "When a fella gets to feelin' sorry for one of 'em it's all off."

Well, we left him go after shakin' hands all round. But he didn't take Dolly to no show that night. Some time wile we was talkin' she'd came into that other parlor and she'd stood there and heard us. I don't know how much she heard. But it was enough. Dolly and Cap's missus took the midnight train for New York. And from there Cap's wife sent her on her way back to Missouri.

She'd left the ring and a note for Ike with the clerk. But we didn't ask Ike if the note was from his friend in Fort Wayne, Texas.

VI

When we'd came to Boston Ike was hittin' plain .397. When we got back home he'd fell off to pretty near nothin'. He hadn't drove one out o' the infield in any o' them other Eastern parks, and he didn't even give no excuse for it.

To show you how bad he was, he struck out three times in Brooklyn one day and never opened his trap when Cap ast him what was the matter. Before, if he'd whiffed oncet in a game he'd of wrote a book tellin' why.

Well, we dropped from first place to fifth in four weeks and we was still goin' down. I and Carey was about the only ones in the club that spoke to each other, and all as we did was remind ourself o' what a boner we'd pulled.

"It's goin' to beat us out o' the big money," says Carey.

"Yes," I says. "I don't want to knock my own ball club, but it looks like a one-man team, and when that one man's dauber's down we couldn't trim our whiskers."

"We ought to knew better," says Carey.

"Yes," I says, "but why should a man pull an alibi for bein' engaged to such a bearcat as she was?"

"He shouldn't," says Carey. "But I and you knowed he would or we'd never started talkin' to him about it. He wasn't no more ashamed o' the girl than I am of a regular base hit. But he just can't come clean on no subjec'."

Cap had the whole story, and I and Carey was as pop'lar with him as an umpire.

"What do you want me to do, Cap?" Carey'd say to him before goin' up to hit.

"Use your own judgment," Cap'd tell him. "We want to lose another game."

But finally, one night in Pittsburgh, Cap had a letter from his missus and he come to us with it.

"You fellas," he says, "is the ones that put us on the bum, and if you're sorry I think they's a chancet for you to make good. The old lady's out to St. Joe and she's been tryin' her hardest to fix things up. She's explained that Ike don't mean nothin' with his talk; I've wrote and explained that to Dolly, too. But the old lady says that Dolly says that she can't believe it. But Dolly's still stuck on this baby, and she's pinin' away just the same as Ike. And the old lady says she thinks if you two fellas would write to the girl and explain how you was always kiddin' with Ike and leadin' him on, and how the ball club was all shot to pieces since Ike quit hittin', and how he acted like he was goin' to kill himself, and this and that, she'd fall for it and maybe soften down. Dolly, the old lady says, would believe you before she'd believe I and the old lady, because she thinks it's her we're sorry for, and not him."

Well, I and Carey was only too glad to try and see what we could do. But it wasn't no snap. We wrote about eight letters before we got one that looked good. Then we give it to the stenographer and had it wrote out on a typewriter and both of us signed it.

It was Carey's idear that made the letter good. He stuck in some-thin' about the world's serious money that our wives wasn't goin' to spend unless she took pity on a "boy who was so shy and modest that he was afraid to come right out and say that he had asked such a beautiful and handsome girl to become his bride."

That's prob'ly what got her, or maybe she couldn't of held out much longer anyway. It was four days after we sent the letter that Cap heard from his missus again. We was in Cincinnati.

"We've won," he says to us. "The old lady says that Dolly says she'll give him another chancet. But the old lady says it won't do no good for Ike to write a letter. He'll have to go out there."

"Send him to-night," says Carey.

"I'll pay half his fare," I says.

"I'll pay the other half," says Carey.

"No," says Cap, "the club'll pay his expenses. I'll send him scoutin'."

"Are you goin' to send him to-night?"

"Sure," says Cap. "But I'm goin' to break the news to him right now. It's time we win a ball game."

So in the clubhouse, just before the game, Cap told him. And I certainly felt sorry for Rube Benton and Red Ames that afternoon! I and Carey was standin' in front o' the hotel that night when Ike come out with his suitcase.

"Sent home?" I says to him.

"No," he says, "I'm goin' scoutin'."

"Where to?" I says. "Fort Wayne?"

"No, not exactly," he says.

"Well," says Carey, "have a good time."

"I ain't lookin' for no good time," says Ike. "I says I was goin' scoutin'."

"Well, then," says Carey, "I hope you see somebody you like."

"And you better have a drink before you go," I says.

"Well," says Ike, "they claim it helps a cold."

My Roomy

I

No—I ain't signed for next year; but there won't be no trouble about that. The dough part of it is all fixed up. John and me talked it over and I'll sign as soon as they send me a contract. All I told him was that he'd have to let me pick my own roommate after this and not sic no wild man on to me.

You know I didn't hit much the last two months o' the season. Some o' the boys, I notice, wrote some stuff about me gettin' old and losin' my battin' eye. That's all bunk! The reason I didn't hit was because I wasn't gettin' enough sleep. And the reason for that was Mr. Elliott.

He wasn't with us after the last part o' May, but I roomed with him long enough to get the insomny. I was the only guy in the club game enough to stand for him; but I was sorry afterward that I done it, because it sure did put a crimp in my little old average.

And do you know where he is now? I got a letter today and I'll read it to you. No—I guess I better tell you somethin' about him first. You fellers never got acquainted with him and you ought to hear the dope to understand the letter. I'll make it as short as I can.

He didn't play in no league last year. He was with some semi-pros over in Michigan and somebody writes John about him. So John sends Needham over to look at him. Tom stayed there Saturday and Sunday, and seen him work twice. He was playin' the outfield, but as luck would have it they wasn't a fly ball hit in his direction in both games. A base hit was made out his way and he booted it, and that's the only report Tom could get on his fieldin'. But he wallops two over the wall in one day and they catch two line drives off him. The next day he gets four blows and two o' them is triples.

So Tom comes back and tells John the guy is a whale of a hitter and fast as Cobb, but he don't know nothin' about his fieldin'. Then John signs him to a contract—twelve hundred or somethin' like that. We'd been in Tampa a week before he showed up. Then he comes to the hotel and just sits round all day, without tellin' nobody who he was. Finally the bellhops was going to chase him out and he says he's one o' the ballplayers. Then the clerk gets John to go over and talk to him. He tells John his name and says he hasn't had nothin' to eat for three days, because he was broke. John told me afterward that he'd drew about three hundred in advance—last winter sometime. Well, they took him in the dinin' room and they tell me he inhaled about four meals at once. That night they roomed him with Heine.

Next mornin' Heine and me walks out to the grounds together and Heine tells me about him. He says:

"Don't never call me a bug again. They got me roomin' with the champion o' the world."

"Who is he?" I says.

"I don't know and I don't want to know," says Heine; "but if they stick him in there with me again I'll jump to the Federals. To start with, he ain't got no baggage. I ast him where his trunk was and he says he didn't have none. Then I ast him if he didn't have no suitcase, and he says: 'No. What do you care?' I was goin' to lend him some pajamas, but he put on the shirt o' the uniform John give him last night and slept in that. He was asleep when I got up this mornin'. I seen his collar layin' on the dresser and it looked like he had wore it in Pittsburgh every day for a year. So I throwed it out the window and he comes down to breakfast with no collar. I ast him what size collar he wore and he says he didn't want none, because he wasn't goin' out nowheres. After breakfast he beat it up to the room again and put on his uniform. When I got up there he was lookin' in the glass at himself, and he done it all the time I was dressin'."

When we got out to the park I got my first look at him. Pretty good-lookin' guy, too, in his unie—big shoulders and well put together; built somethin' like Heine himself. He was talkin' to John when I come up.

"What position do you play?" John was askin' him.

"I play anywheres," says Elliott.

"You're the kind I'm lookin' for," says John. Then he says: "You was an outfielder up there in Michigan, wasn't you?"

"I don't care where I play," says Elliott.

John sends him to the outfield and forgets all about him for a while. Pretty soon Miller comes in and says:

"I ain't goin' to shag for no bush outfielder!"

John ast him what was the matter, and Miller tells him that Elliott ain't doin' nothin' but just standin' out there; that he ain't makin' no attemp' to catch the fungoes, and that he won't even chase 'em. Then John starts watchin' him, and it was just like Miller said. Larry hit one pretty near in his lap and he stepped out o' the way. John calls him in and ast him:

"Why don't you go after them fly balls?"

"Because I don't want 'em," says Elliott.

John gets sarcastic and says:

"What do you want? Of course we'll see that you get anythin' you want!"

"Give me a ticket back home," says Elliott.

"Don't you want to stick with the club?" says John, and the busher tells him, no, he certainly did not. Then John tells him he'll have to pay his own fare home and Elliott don't get sore at all. He just says:

"Well, I'll have to stick, then—because I'm broke."

We was havin' battin' practice and John tells him to go up and hit a few. And you ought to of seen him bust 'em!

Lavender was in there workin' and he'd been pitchin' a little all winter, so he was in pretty good shape. He lobbed one up to Elliott, and he hit it 'way up in some trees outside the fence—about a mile, I guess. Then John tells Jimmy to put somethin' on the ball. Jim comes through with one of his fast ones and the kid slams it agin the right-fieldwall on a line.

"Give him your spitter!" yells John, and Jim handed him one. He pulled it over first base so fast that Bert, who was standin' down there, couldn't hardly duck in time. If it'd hit him it'd killed him.

Well, he kep' on hittin' everythin' Jim give him—and Jim had somethin' too. Finally John gets Pierce warmed up and sends him out to pitch, tellin' him to hand Elliott a flock o' curve balls. He wanted to see if lefthanders was goin' to bother him. But he slammed 'em right along, and I don't b'lieve he hit more'n two the whole mornin' that wouldn't of been base hits in a game.

They sent him out to the outfield again in the afternoon, and after a lot o' coaxin' Leach got him to go after fly balls; but that's all he did do—just go after 'em. One hit him on the bean and another on the shoulder. He run back after the short ones and 'way in after the ones that went over his head. He catched just one—a line drive that he couldn't get out o' the way of; and then he acted like it hurt his hands.

I come back to the hotel with John. He ast me what I thought of Elliott.

"Well," I says, "he'd be the greatest ballplayer in the world if he could just play ball. He sure can bust 'em."

John says he was afraid he couldn't never make an outfielder out o' him. He says:

"I'll try him on the infield to-morrow. They must be some place he can play. I never seen a lefthand hitter that looked so good agin lefthand pitchin'—and he's got a great arm; but he acts like he'd never saw a fly ball."

Well, he was just as bad on the infield. They put him at short and he was like a sieve. You could of drove a hearse between him and second base without him gettin' near it. He'd stoop over for a ground ball about the time it was bouncin' up agin the fence; and when he'd try to cover the bag on a peg he'd trip over it.

They tried him at first base and sometimes he'd run 'way over in the coachers' box and sometimes out in right field lookin' for the bag. Once Heine shot one acrost at him on a line and he never touched it with his hands. It went bam! right in the pit of his stomach—and the lunch he'd ate didn't do him no good.

Finally John just give up and says he'd have to keep him on the bench and let him earn his pay by bustin' 'em a couple o' times a week or so. We all agreed with John that this bird would be a whale of a pinch hitter—and we was right too. He was hittin' 'way over five hundred when the blowoff come, along about the last o' May.

II

Before the trainin' trip was over, Elliott had roomed with pretty near everybody in the club. Heine raised an awful holler after the second night down there and John put the bug in with Needham. Tom stood him for three nights. Then he doubled up with Archer, and Schulte, and Miller, and Leach, and Saier—and the whole bunch in turn, averagin' about two nights with each one before they put up a kick. Then John tried him with some o' the youngsters, but they wouldn't stand for him no more'n the others. They all said he was crazy and they was afraid he'd get violent some night and stick a knife in 'em.

He always insisted on havin' the water run in the bathtub all night, because he said it reminded him of the sound of the dam near his home. The fellers might get up four or five times a night and shut off the faucet, but he'd get right up after 'em and turn it on again. Carter, a big bush pitcher from Georgia, started a fight with him about it one night, and Elliott pretty near killed him. So the rest o' the bunch, when they'd saw Carter's map next mornin', didn't have the nerve to do nothin' when it come their turn.

Another o' his habits was the thing that scared 'em, though. He'd brought a razor with him—in his pocket, I guess—and he used to do his shavin' in the middle o' the night. Instead o' doin' it in the bathroom he'd lather his face and then come out and stand in front o' the lookin'-glass on the dresser. Of course he'd have all the lights turned on, and that was bad enough when a feller wanted to sleep; but the worst of it was that he'd stop shavin' every little while and turn round and stare at the guy who was makin' a failure o' tryin' to sleep. Then he'd wave his razor round in the air and laugh, and begin shavin' agin. You can imagine how comf'table his roomies felt!

John had bought him a suitcase and some clothes and things, and charged 'em up to him. He'd drew so much dough in advance that he didn't have nothin' comin' till about June. He never thanked John and he'd wear one shirt and one collar till some one throwed 'em away.

Well, we finally gets to Indianapolis, and we was goin' from there to Cincy to open. The last day in Indianapolis John come and ast me how I'd like to change roomies. I says I was perfectly satisfied with Larry. Then John says:

"I wisht you'd try Elliott. The other boys all kicks on him, but he seems to hang round you a lot and I b'lieve you could get along all right."

"Why don't you room him alone?" I ast.

"The boss or the hotels won't stand for us roomin' alone," says John. "You go ahead and try it, and see how you make out. If he's too much for you let me know; but he likes you and I think he'll be diff'rent with a guy who can talk to him like you can."

So I says I'd tackle it, because I didn't want to throw John down. When we got to Cincy they stuck Elliott and me in one room, and we was together till he quit us.

III

I went to the room early that night, because we was goin' to open next day and I wanted to feel like somethin'. First thing I done when I got undressed was turn on both faucets in the bathtub. They was makin' an awful racket when Elliott finally come in about midnight. I was layin' awake and I opened right up on him. I says:

"Don't shut off that water, because I like to hear it run."

Then I turned over and pretended to be asleep. The bug got his clothes off, and then what did he do but go in the bathroom and shut off the water! Then he come back in the room and says:

"I guess no one's goin' to tell me what to do in here."

But I kep' right on pretendin' to sleep and didn't pay no attention. When he'd got into his bed I jumped out o' mine and turned on all the lights and begun stroppin' my razor. He says:

"What's comin' off?"

"Some o' my whiskers," I says. "I always shave along about this time."

"No, you don't!" he says. "I was in your room one mornin' down in Louisville and I seen you shavin' then."

"Well," I says, "the boys tell me you shave in the middle o' the night; and I thought if I done all the things you do mebbe I'd get so's I could hit like you."

"You must be superstitious!" he says. And I told him I was. "I'm a good hitter," he says, "and I'd be a good hitter if I never shaved at all. That don't make no diff'rence."

"Yes, it does," I says. "You prob'ly hit good because you shave at night; but you'd be a better fielder if you shaved in the mornin'."

You see, I was tryin' to be just as crazy as him—though that wasn't hardly possible.

"If that's right," says he, "I'll do my shavin' in the mornin'—because I seen in the papers where the boys says that if I could play the outfield like I can hit I'd be as good as Cobb. They tell me Cobb gets twenty thousand a year."

"No," I says; "he don't get that much—but he gets about ten times as much as you do."

"Well," he says, "I'm goin' to be as good as him, because I need the money."

"What do you want with money?" I says.

He just laughed and didn't say nothin'; but from that time on the water didn't run in the bathtub nights and he done his shavin' after breakfast. I didn't notice, though, that he looked any better in fieldin' practice.

IV

It rained one day in Cincy and they trimmed us two out o' the other three; but it wasn't Elliott's fault.

They had Larry beat four to one in the ninth innin' o' the first game. Archer gets on with two out, and John sends my roomy up to hit—though Benton, a lefthander, is workin' for them. The first thing Benton serves up there Elliott cracks it a mile over Hobby's head. It would of been good for three easy—only Archer—playin' safe, o' course—pulls up at third base. Tommy couldn't do nothin' and we was licked.

The next day he hits one out o' the park off the Indian; but we was 'way behind and they was nobody on at the time. We copped the last one without usin' no pinch hitters.

I didn't have no trouble with him nights durin' the whole series. He come to bed pretty late while we was there and I told him he'd better not let John catch him at it.

"What would he do?" he says.

"Fine you fifty," I says.

"He can't fine me a dime," he says, "because I ain't got it."

Then I told him he'd be fined all he had comin' if he didn't get in the hotel before midnight; but he just laughed and says he didn't think John had a kick comin' so long as he kep' bustin' the ball.

"Some day you'll go up there and you won't bust it," I says.

"That'll be an accident," he says.

That stopped me and I didn't say nothin'. What could you say to a guy who hated himself like that?

The "accident" happened in St. Louis the first day. We needed two runs in the eighth and Saier and Brid was on, with two out. John tells Elliott to go up in Pierce's place. The bug goes up and Griner gives him two bad balls—'way outside. I thought they was goin' to walk him—and it looked like good judgment, because they'd heard what he done in Cincy. But no! Griner comes back with a fast one right over and Elliott pulls it down the right foul line, about two foot foul. He hit it so hard you'd of thought they'd sure walk him then; but Griner gives him another fast one. He slammed it again just as hard, but foul. Then Griner gives him one 'way outside and it's two and three. John says, on the bench:

"If they don't walk him now he'll bust that fence down."

I thought the same and I was sure Griner wouldn't give him nothin' to hit; but he come with a curve and Rigler calls Elliott out. From where we sat the last one looked low, and I thought Elliott'd make a kick. He come back to the bench smilin'.

John starts for his position, but stopped and ast the bug what was the matter with that one. Any busher I ever knowed would of said, "It was too low," or "It was outside," or "It was inside." Elliott says:

"Nothin' at all. It was right over the middle."

"Why didn't you bust it, then?" says John.

"I was afraid I'd kill somebody," says Elliott, and laughed like a big boob.

John was pretty near chokin'.

"What are you laughin' at?" he says.

"I was thinkin' of a nickel show I seen in Cincinnati," says the bug.

"Well," says John, so mad he couldn't hardly see, "that show and that laugh'll cost you fifty."

We got beat, and I wouldn't of blamed John if he'd fined him his whole season's pay.

Up'n the room that night I told him he'd better cut out that laughin' stuff when we was gettin' trimmed or he never would have no pay day. Then he got confidential.

"Pay day wouldn't do me no good," he says. "When I'm all squared up with the club and begin to have a pay day I'll only get a hundred bucks at a time, and I'll owe that to some o' you fellers. I wisht we could win the pennant and get in on that World's Series dough. Then I'd get a bunch at once."

"What would you do with a bunch o' dough?" I ast him.

"Don't tell nobody, sport," he says; "but if I ever get five hundred at once I'm goin' to get married."

"Oh!" I says. "And who's the lucky girl?"

"She's a girl up in Muskegon," says Elliott; "and you're right when you call her lucky."

"You don't like yourself much, do you?" I says.

"I got reason to like myself," says he. "You'd like yourself, too, if you could hit 'em like me."

"Well," I says, "you didn't show me no hittin' to-day."

"I couldn't hit because I was laughin' too hard," says Elliott.

"What was it you was laughin' at?" I says.

"I was laughin' at that pitcher," he says. "He thought he had somethin' and he didn't have nothin'."

"He had enough to whiff you with," I says.

"He didn't have nothin'!" says he again. "I was afraid if I busted one off him they'd can him, and then I couldn't never hit agin him no more."

Naturally I didn't have no comeback to that. I just sort o' gasped and got ready to go to sleep; but he wasn't through.

"I wisht you could see this bird!" he says.

"What bird?" I says.

"This dame that's nuts about me," he says.

"Good-looker?" I ast.

"No," he says; "she ain't no bear for looks. They ain't nothin' about her for a guy to rave over till you hear her sing. She sure can holler some."

"What kind o' voice has she got?" I ast.

"A bear," says he.

"No," I says; "I mean is she a barytone or an air?"

"I don't know," he says; "but she's got the loudest voice I ever hear on a woman. She's pretty near got me beat."

"Can you sing?" I says; and I was sorry right afterward that I ast him that question.

I guess it must of been bad enough to have the water runnin' night after night and to have him wavin' that razor round; but that couldn't of been nothin' to his singin'. Just as soon as I'd pulled that boner he says, "Listen to me?" and starts in on 'Silver Threads Among the Gold.' Mind you, it was after midnight and they was guests all round us tryin' to sleep!

They used to be noise enough in our club when we had Hofman and Sheckard and Richie harmonizin'; but this bug's voice was louder'n all o' theirn combined. We once had a pitcher named Martin Walsh—brother o' Big Ed's—and I thought he could drownd out the Subway; but this guy made a boiler factory sound like Dummy Taylor. If the whole hotel wasn't awake when he'd howled the first line it's a pipe they was when he cut loose, which he done when he come to "Always young and fair to me." Them words could of been heard easy in East St. Louis.

He didn't get no encore from me, but he goes right through it again—or starts to. I knowed somethin' was goin' to happen before he finished—and somethin' did. The night clerk and the house detective come bangin' at the door. I let 'em in and they had plenty to say. If we made another sound the whole club'd be canned out o' the hotel. I tried to salve 'em, and I says:

"He won't sing no more."

But Elliott swelled up like a poisoned pup.

"Won't I?" he says. "I'll sing all I want to."

"You won't sing in here," says the clerk.

"They ain't room for my voice in here anyways," he says. "I'll go outdoors and sing."

And he puts his clothes on and ducks out. I didn't make no attemp' to stop him. I heard him bellowin' 'Silver Threads' down the corridor and down the stairs, with the clerk and the dick chasin' him all the way and tellin' him to shut up.

Well, the guests make a holler the next mornin'; and the hotel people tells Charlie Williams that he'll either have to let Elliott stay somewheres else or the whole club'll have to move. Charlie tells John, and John was thinkin' o' settlin' the question by releasin' Elliott.

I guess he'd about made up his mind to do it; but that afternoon they had us three to one in the ninth, and we got the bases full, with two down and Larry's turn to hit. Elliott had been sittin' on the bench sayin' nothin'.

"Do you think you can hit one today?" says John.

"I can hit one any day," says Elliott.

"Go up and hit that lefthander, then," says John, "and remember there's nothin' to laugh at."

Sallee was workin'—and workin' good; but that didn't bother the bug. He cut into one, and it went between Oakes and Whitted like a shot. He come into third standin' up and we was a run to the good. Sallee was so sore he kind o' forgot himself and took pretty near his full wind-up pitchin' to Tommy. And what did Elliott do but steal home and get away with it clean!

Well, you couldn't can him after that, could you? Charlie gets him a room somewheres and I was relieved of his company that night. The next evenin' we beat it for Chi to play about two weeks at home. He didn't tell nobody where he roomed there and I didn't see nothin' of him, 'cep' out to the park. I ast him what he did with himself nights and he says:

"Same as I do on the road—borrow some dough some place and go to the nickel shows."

"You must be stuck on 'em," I says.

"Yes," he says; "I like the ones where they kill people—because I want to learn how to do it. I may have that job some day."

"Don't pick on me," I says.

"Oh," says the bug, "you never can tell who I'll pick on."

It seemed as if he just couldn't learn nothin' about fieldin', and finally John told him to keep out o' the practice.

"A ball might hit him in the temple and croak him," says John.

But he busted up a couple o' games for us at home, beatin' Pittsburgh once and Cincy once.

V

They give me a great big room at the hotel in Pittsburgh; so the fellers picked it out for the poker game. We was playin' along about ten o'clock one night when in come Elliott—the earliest he'd showed up since we'd been roomin' together. They was only five of us playin' and Tom ast him to sit in.

"I'm busted," he says.

"Can you play poker?" I ast him.

"They's nothin' I can't do!" he says. "Slip me a couple o' bucks and I'll show you."

So I slipped him a couple o' bucks and honestly hoped he'd win, because I knowed he never had no dough. Well, Tom dealt him a hand and he picks it up and says:

"I only got five cards."

"How many do you want?" I says.

"Oh," he says, "if that's all I get I'll try to make 'em do."

The pot was cracked and raised, and he stood the raise. I says to myself: "There goes my two bucks!" But no—he comes out with three queens and won the dough. It was only about seven bucks; but you'd of thought it was a million to see him grab it. He laughed like a kid.

"Guess I can't play this game!" he says; and he had me fooled for a minute—I thought he must of been kiddin' when he complained of only havin' five cards.

He copped another pot right afterward and was sittin' there with about eleven bucks in front of him when Jim opens a roodle pot for a buck. I stays and so does Elliott. Him and Jim both drawed one card and I took three. I had kings or queens—I forget which. I didn't help 'em none; so when Jim bets a buck I throws my hand away.

"How much can I bet?" says the bug.

"You can raise Jim a buck if you want to," I says.

So he bets two dollars. Jim comes back at him. He comes right back at Jim. Jim raises him again and he tilts Jim right back. Well, when he'd boosted Jim with the last buck he had, Jim says:

"I'm ready to call. I guess you got me beat. What have you got?"

"I know what I've got, all right," says Elliott. "I've got a straight." And he throws his hand down. Sure enough, it was a straight, eight high. Jim pretty near fainted and so did I.

The bug had started pullin' in the dough when Jim stops him.

"Here! Wait a minute!" says Jim. "I thought you had somethin'. I filled up." Then Jim lays down his nine full.

"You beat me, I guess," says Elliott, and he looked like he'd lost his last friend.

"Beat you?" says Jim. "Of course I beat you! What did you think I had?"

"Well," says the bug, "I thought you might have a small flush or somethin'."

When I regained consciousness he was beggin' for two more bucks.

"What for?" I says. "To play poker with? You're barred from the game for life!"

"Well," he says, "if I can't play no more I want to go to sleep, and you fellers will have to get out o' this room."

Did you ever hear o' nerve like that? This was the first night he'd came in before twelve and he orders the bunch out so's he can sleep! We politely suggested to him to go to Brooklyn.

Without sayin' a word he starts in on his 'Silver Threads'; and it wasn't two minutes till the game was busted up and the bunch—all but me—was out o' there. I'd of beat it too, only he stopped yellin' as soon as they'd went.

"You're some buster!" I says. "You bust up ball games in the afternoon and poker games at night."

"Yes," he says; "that's my business—bustin' things."

And before I knowed what he was about he picked up the pitcher of ice-water that was on the floor and throwed it out the window—through the glass and all.

Right then I give him a plain talkin' to. I tells him how near he come to gettin' canned down in St. Louis because he raised so much Cain singin' in the hotel.

"But I had to keep my voice in shape," he says. "If I ever get dough enough to get married the girl and me'll go out singin' together."

"Out where?" I ast.

"Out on the vaudeville circuit," says Elliott.

"Well," I says, "if her voice is like yours you'll be wastin' money if you travel round. Just stay up in Muskegon and we'll hear you, all right!"

I told him he wouldn't never get no dough if he didn't behave himself. That, even if we got in the World's Series, he wouldn't be with us—unless he cut out the foolishness.

"We ain't goin' to get in no World's Series," he says, "and I won't never get a bunch o' money at once; so it looks like I couldn't get married this fall."

Then I told him we played a city series every fall. He'd never thought o' that and it tickled him to death. I told him the losers always got about five hundred apiece and that we were about due to win it and get about eight hundred. "But," I says, "we still got a good chance for the old pennant; and if I was you I wouldn't give up hope o' that yet—not where John can hear you, anyway."

"No," he says, "we won't win no pennant, because he won't let me play reg'lar; but I don't care so long as we're sure o' that city-series dough."

"You ain't sure of it if you don't behave," I says.

"Well," says he, very serious, "I guess I'll behave." And he did— till we made our first Eastern trip.

VI

We went to Boston first, and that crazy bunch goes out and piles up a three-run lead on us in seven innin's the first day. It was the pitcher's turn to lead off in the eighth, so up goes Elliott to bat for him. He kisses the first thing they hands him for three bases; and we says, on the bench: "Now we'll get 'em!"—because, you know, a three-run lead wasn't nothin' in Boston.

"Stay right on that bag!" John hollers to Elliott.

Mebbe if John hadn't said nothin' to him everythin' would of been all right; but when Perdue starts to pitch the first ball to Tommy, Elliott starts to steal home. He's out as far as from here to Seattle.

If I'd been carryin' a gun I'd of shot him right through the heart. As it was, I thought John'd kill him with a bat, because he was standin' there with a couple of 'em, waitin' for his turn; but I guess John was too stunned to move. He didn't even seem to see Elliott when he went to the bench. After I'd cooled off a little I says:

"Beat it and get into your clothes before John comes in. Then go to the hotel and keep out o' sight."

When I got up in the room afterward, there was Elliott, lookin' as innocent and happy as though he'd won fifty bucks with a pair o' treys.

"I thought you might of killed yourself," I says.

"What for?" he says.

"For that swell play you made," says I.

"What was the matter with the play?" ast Elliott, surprised. "It was all right when I done it in St. Louis."

"Yes," I says; "but they was two out in St. Louis and we wasn't no three runs behind."

"Well," he says, "if it was all right in St. Louis I don't see why it was wrong here."

"It's a diff'rent climate here," I says, too disgusted to argue with him.

"I wonder if they'd let me sing in this climate?" says Elliott.

"No," I says. "Don't sing in this hotel, because we don't want to get fired out o' here—the eats is too good."

"All right," he says. "I won't sing." But when I starts down to supper he says: "I'm li'ble to do somethin' worse'n sing."

He didn't show up in the dinin' room and John went to the boxin' show after supper; so it looked like him and Elliott wouldn't run into each other till the murder had left John's heart. I was glad o' that—because a Mass'chusetts jury might not consider it justifiable hommercide if one guy croaked another for givin' the Boston club a game.

I went down to the corner and had a couple o' beers; and then I come straight back, intendin' to hit the hay. The elevator boy had went for a drink or somethin', and they was two old ladies already waitin' in the car when I stepped in. Right along after me comes Elliott.

"Where's the boy that's supposed to run this car?" he says. I told him the boy'd be right back; but he says: "I can't wait. I'm much too sleepy."

And before I could stop him he'd slammed the door and him and I and the poor old ladies was shootin' up.

"Let us off at the third floor, please!" says one o' the ladies, her voice kind o' shakin'.

"Sorry, madam," says the bug; "but this is a express and we don't stop at no third floor."

I grabbed his arm and tried to get him away from the machinery; but he was as strong as a ox and he throwed me agin the side o' the car like I was a baby. We went to the top faster'n I ever rode in an elevator before. And then we shot down to the bottom, hittin' the bumper down there so hard I thought we'd be smashed to splinters.

The ladies was too scared to make a sound durin' the first trip; but while we was goin' up and down the second time—even faster'n the first—they begun to scream. I was hollerin' my head off at him to quit and he was makin' more noise than the three of us—pretendin' he was the locomotive and the whole crew o' the train.

Don't never ask me how many times we went up and down! The women fainted on the third trip and I guess I was about as near it as I'll ever get. The elevator boy and the bellhops and the waiters and the night clerk and everybody was jumpin' round the lobby screamin'; but no one seemed to know how to stop us.

Finally—on about the tenth trip, I guess—he slowed down and stopped at the fifth floor, where we was roomin'. He opened the door and beat it for the room, while I, though I was tremblin' like a leaf, run the car down to the bottom.

The night clerk knowed me pretty well and knowed I wouldn't do nothin' like that; so him and I didn't argue, but just got to work together to bring the old women to. While we was doin' that Elliott must of run down the stairs and slipped out o' the hotel, because when they sent the officers up to the room after him he'd blowed.

They was goin' to fire the club out; but Charlie had a good stand-in with Amos, the proprietor, and he fixed it up to let us stay—providin' Elliott kep' away. The bug didn't show up at the ball park next day and we didn't see no more of him till we got on the rattler for New York. Charlie and John both bawled him, but they give him a berth—an upper—and we pulled into the Grand Central Station without him havin' made no effort to wreck the train.

VII

I'd studied the thing pretty careful, but hadn't come to no conclusion. I was sure he wasn't no stew, because none o' the boys had ever saw him even take a glass o' beer, and I couldn't never detect the odor o' booze on him. And if he'd been a dope I'd of knew about it —roomin' with him.

There wouldn't of been no mystery about it if he'd been a left-hand pitcher—but he wasn't. He wasn't nothin' but a whale of a hitter and he throwed with his right arm. He hit lefthanded, a' course; but so did Saier and Brid and Schulte and me, and John himself; and none of us was violent. I guessed he must of been just a plain nut and li'ble to break out any time.

They was a letter waitin' for him at New York, and I took it, intendin' to give it to him at the park, because I didn't think they'd let him room at the hotel; but after breakfast he come up to the room, with his suitcase. It seems he'd promised John and Charlie to be good, and made it so strong they b'lieved him.

I give him his letter, which was addressed in a girl's writin' and come from Muskegon.

"From the girl?" I says.

"Yes," he says; and, without openin' it, he tore it up and throwed it out the window.

"Had a quarrel?" I ast.

"No, no," he says; "but she can't tell me nothin' I don't know already. Girls always writes the same junk. I got one from her in Pittsburgh, but I didn't read it."

"I guess you ain't so stuck on her," I says.

He swells up and says:

"Of course I'm stuck on her! If I wasn't, do you think I'd be goin' round with this bunch and gettin' insulted all the time? I'm stickin' here because o' that series dough, so's I can get hooked."

"Do you think you'd settle down if you was married?" I ast him.

"Settle down?" he says. "Sure, I'd settle down. I'd be so happy that I wouldn't have to look for no excitement."

Nothin' special happened that night 'cep' that he come in the room about one o'clock and woke me up by pickin' up the foot o' the bed and droppin' it on the floor, sudden-like.

"Give me a key to the room," he says.

"You must of had a key," I says, "or you couldn't of got in."

"That's right!" he says, and beat it to bed.

One o' the reporters must of told Elliott that John had ast for waivers on him and New York had refused to waive, because next mornin' he come to me with that dope.

"New York's goin' to win this pennant!" he says.

"Well," I says, "they will if some one else don't. But what of it?"

"I'm goin' to play with New York," he says, "so's I can get the World's Series dough."

"How you goin' to get away from this club?" I ast.

"Just watch me!" he says. "I'll be with New York before this series is over."

Well, the way he goes after the job was original, anyway. Rube'd

had one of his good days the day before and we'd got a trimmin';
but this second day the score was tied up at two runs apiece in the
tenth, and Big Jeff'd been wabblin' for two or three innin's.

Well, he walks Saier and me, with one out, and Mac sends for
Matty, who was warmed up and ready. John sticks Elliott in in
Brid's place and the bug pulls one into the right-field stand.

It's a cinch McGraw thinks well of him then, and might of went
after him if he hadn't went crazy the next afternoon. We're tied up
in the ninth and Matty's workin'. John sends Elliott up with the
bases choked; but he doesn't go right up to the plate. He walks over
to their bench and calls McGraw out. Mac tells us about it afterward.

"I can bust up this game right here!" says Elliott.

"Go ahead," says Mac; "but be careful he don't whiff you."

Then the bug pulls it.

"If I whiff," he says, "will you get me on your club?"

"Sure!" says Mac, just as anybody would.

By this time Bill Koem was hollerin' about the delay; so up goes
Elliott and gives the worst burlesque on tryin' to hit that you ever
see. Matty throws one a mile outside and high, and the bug swings
like it was right over the heart. Then Matty throws one at him and
he ducks out o' the way—but swings just the same. Matty must of
been wise by this time, for he pitches one so far outside that the
Chief almost has to go to the coachers' box after it. Elliott takes his
third healthy and runs through the field down to the clubhouse.

We got beat in the eleventh; and when we went in to dress he has
his street clothes on. Soon as he seen John comin' he says: "I got to
see McGraw!" And he beat it.

John was goin' to the fights that night; but before he leaves the
hotel he had waivers on Elliott from everybody and had sold him
to Atlanta.

"And," says John, "I don't care if they pay for him or not."

My roomy blows in about nine and got the letter from John out
of his box. He was goin' to tear it up, but I told him they was news
in it. He opens it and reads where he's sold. I was still sore at him;
so I says:

"Thought you was goin' to get on the New York club?"

"No," he says. "I got turned down cold. McGraw says he wouldn't have me in his club. He says he'd had Charlie Faust—and that was enough for him."

He had a kind o' crazy look in his eyes; so when he starts up to the room I follows him.

"What are you goin' to do now?" I says.

"I'm goin' to sell this ticket to Atlanta," he says, "and go back to Muskegon, where I belong."

"I'll help you pack," I says.

"No," says the bug. "I come into this league with this suit o'clothes and a collar. They can have the rest of it." Then he sits down on the bed and begins to cry like a baby. "No series dough for me," he blubbers, "and no weddin' bells! My girl'll die when she hears about it!"

Of course that made me feel kind o' rotten, and I says:

"Brace up, boy! The best thing you can do is go to Atlanta and try hard. You'll be up here again next year."

"You can't tell me where to go!" he says, and he wasn't cryin' no more. "I'll go where I please—and I'm li'ble to take you with me."

I didn't want no argument, so I kep' still. Pretty soon he goes up to the lookin'-glass and stares at himself for five minutes. Then, all of a sudden, he hauls off and takes a wallop at his reflection in the glass. Naturally he smashed the glass all to pieces and he cut his hand somethin' awful.

Without lookin' at it he come over to me and says: "Well, good-by, sport!"—and holds out his other hand to shake. When I starts to shake with him he smears his bloody hand all over my map. Then he laughed like a wild man and run out o' the room and out o' the hotel.

VIII

Well, boys, my sleep was broke up for the rest o' the season. It might of been because I was used to sleepin' in all kinds o' racket and excitement, and couldn't stand for the quiet after he'd went—or it might of been because I kep' thinkin' about him and feelin' sorry for him.

I of'en wondered if he'd settle down and be somethin' if he could get married; and finally I got to b'lievin' he would. So when we was dividin' the city series dough I was thinkin' of him and the girl. Our share o' the money—the losers', as usual—was twelve thousand seven hundred sixty bucks or somethin' like that. They was twenty-one of us and that meant six hundred seven bucks apiece. We was just goin' to cut it up that way when I says:

"Why not give a divvy to poor old Elliott?"

About fifteen of 'em at once told me that I was crazy. You see, when he got canned he owed everybody in the club. I guess he'd stuck me for the most—about seventy bucks—but I didn't care nothin' about that. I knowed he hadn't never reported to Atlanta, and I thought he was prob'ly busted and a bunch o' money might make things all right for him and the other songbird.

I made quite a speech to the fellers, tellin' 'em how he'd cried when he left us and how his heart'd been set on gettin' married on the series dough. I made it so strong that they finally fell for it. Our shares was cut to five hundred eighty apiece, and John sent him a check for a full share.

For a while I was kind o' worried about what I'd did. I didn't know if I was doin' right by the girl to give him the chance to marry her.

He'd told me she was stuck on him, and that's the only excuse I had for tryin' to fix it up between 'em; but, b'lieve me, if she was my sister or a friend o' mine I'd just as soon of had her manage the Cincinnati Club as marry that bird. I thought to myself:

"If she's all right she'll take acid in a month—and it'll be my fault; but if she's really stuck on him they must be somethin' wrong with her too, so what's the diff'rence?"

Then along comes this letter that I told you about. It's from some friend of hisn up there—and they's a note from him. I'll read 'em to you and then I got to beat it for the station:

DEAR SIR: They have got poor Elliott locked up and they are goin' to take him to the asylum at Kalamazoo. He thanks you for the check, and we will use the money to see that he is made comf'table.

When the poor boy come back here he found that his girl was married to Joe Bishop, who runs a soda fountain. She had wrote to him about it, but he did not read her letters. The news drove him crazy—poor boy—and he went to the place where they was livin' with a baseball bat and very near killed 'em both. Then he marched down the street singin' 'Silver Threads Among the Gold' at the top of his voice. They was goin' to send him to prison for assault with intent to kill, but the jury decided he was crazy.

He wants to thank you again for the money.

Yours truly,

Jim——

I can't make out his last name—but it don't make no diff'rence. Now I'll read you his note:

OLD ROOMY: I was at bat twice and made two hits; but I guess I did not meet 'em square. They tell me they are both alive yet, which I did not mean 'em to be. I hope they got good curve-ball pitchers where I am goin'. I sure can bust them curves—can't I, sport?

Yours,

B. ELLIOTT.

P. S.—The B stands for Buster.

That's all of it, fellers; and you can see I had some excuse for not hittin'. You can also see why I ain't never goin' to room with no bug again—not for John or nobody else!

Hurry Kane

It says here: "Another great race may be expected in the American League, for Philadelphia and New York have evidently added enough strength to give them a fighting chance with the White Sox and Yankees. But if the fans are looking for as 'nervous' a finish as last year's, with a climax such as the Chicago and New York clubs staged on the memorable first day of October, they are doubtless in for a disappointment. That was a regular Webster 'thrill that comes once in a lifetime,' and no oftener."

"Thrill" is right, but they don't know the half of it. Nobody knows the whole of it only myself, not even the fella that told me. I mean the big sap, Kane, who you might call him, I suppose, the hero of the story, but he's too dumb to have realized all that went on, and besides, I got some of the angles from other sources and seen a few things with my own eyes.

If you wasn't the closest-mouthed bird I ever run acrost, I wouldn't spill this to you. But I know it won't go no further and I think it may give you a kick.

Well, the year before last, it didn't take no witch to figure out what was going to happen to our club if Dave couldn't land a pitcher or two to help out Carney and Olds. Jake Lewis hurt his arm and was never no good after that and the rest of the staff belonged in the Soldiers' Home. Their aim was perfect, but they were always shooting at the pressbox or somebody's bat. On hot days I often felt like leaving my mask and protector in the clubhouse; what those fellas were throwing up there was either eighty feet over my head or else the outfielders had to chase it. I could have caught naked except on the days when Olds and Carney worked.

In the fall—that's a year and a half ago—Dave pulled the trade with Boston and St. Louis that brought us Frank Miller and Lefty Glaze in exchange for Robinson, Bullard and Roy Smith. The three he gave away weren't worth a dime to us or to the clubs that got them, and that made it just an even thing, as Miller showed up in the spring with a waistline that was eight laps to the mile and kept getting bigger and bigger till it took half the Atlantic cable to hold up his baseball pants, while Glaze wanted more money than Landis and didn't report till the middle of June, and then tried to condition himself on wood alcohol. When the deal was made, it looked like Dave had all the best of it, but as it turned out, him and the other two clubs might as well have exchanged photographs of their kids in Girl Scout uniforms.

But Dave never lost no sleep over Glaze or Miller. We hadn't been in Florida three days before him and everybody on the ball club was absolutely nuts about big Kane. Here was a twenty-year-old boy that had only pitched half a season in Waco and we had put in a draft for him on the recommendation of an old friend of Dave's, Billy Moore. Billy was just a fan and didn't know much baseball, but he had made some money for Dave in Texas oil leases and Dave took this tip on Kane more because he didn't want to hurt Billy's feelings than out of respect for his judgment. So when the big sapper showed up at Fort Gregg, he didn't get much of a welcome. What he did get was a laugh. You couldn't look at him and not laugh; anyway, not till you got kind of used to him.

You've probably seen lots of pictures of him in a uniform, but they can't give you no idear of the sight he was the first day he blew in the hotel, after that clean, restful little train ride all the way from Yuma. Standing six foot three in what was left of his stockings, he was wearing a suit of Arizona store clothes that would have been a fair fit for Singer's youngest Midget and looked like he had pressed it with a tractor that had been parked on a river bottom.

He had used up both the collars that he figured would see him through his first year in the big league. This left you a clear view of his Adam's apple, which would make half a dozen pies. You'd have thought from his shoes that he had just managed to grab hold of the rail on the back platform of his train and been dragged from Yuma to Jacksonville. But when you seen his shirt, you wondered if he hadn't rode in the cab and loaned it to the fireman for a wash-cloth. He had a brown paper suitcase held together by bandages. Some of them had slipped and the raw wounds was exposed. But if the whole thing had fell to pieces, he could have packed the contents in two of his vest pockets without bulging them much.

One of the funniest things about him was his walk and I'll never forget the first time we seen him go out to take his turn pitching to the batters. He acted like he was barefooted and afraid of step-ping on burrs. He'd lift one dog and hold it in the air a minute till he could locate a safe place to put it down. Then he'd do the same thing with the other, and it would seem about a half-hour from the time he left the bench till he got to his position. Of course Dave soon had him pretty well cured of that, or that is, Dave didn't, but Kid Farrell did. For a whole week, the Kid followed him every step he took and if he wasn't going fast enough, he either got spiked in the heel or kicked in the calf of his hind leg. People think he walks slow yet, but he's a shooting star now compared with when he broke in.

Well, everybody was in hysterics watching him make that first trip and he looked so silly that we didn't expect him to be any good to us except as a kind of a show. But we were in for a big surprise.

Before he threw a ball, Dave said to him: "Now, go easy. Don't cut loose and take a chance till you're in shape."

"All right," says Kane.

And all of a sudden, without no warning, he whammed a fast

ball acrost that old plate that blew Tierney's cap off and pretty near knocked me down. Tierney hollered murder and ran for the bench. All of us were pop-eyed and it was quite a while before Dave could speak. Then he said:

"Boy, your fast one *is* a fast one! But I just got through telling you not to cut loose. The other fellas ain't ready for it and neither are you. I don't want nobody killed this time of year."

So Kane said: "I didn't cut loose. I can send them through there twice as fast as that. I'm scared to yet, because I ain't sure of my control. I'll show you something in a couple more days."

Well when he said "twice as fast," he was making it a little strong. But his real fast one was faster than that first one he threw, and before the week was over we looked at speed that made it seem like Johnson had never pitched nothing but toy balloons. What had us all puzzled was why none of the other clubs had tried to grab him. I found out by asking him one night at supper. I asked him if he'd been just as good the year before as he was now.

"I had the same stuff," he said, "but I never showed it, except once."

I asked him why he hadn't showed it. He said:

"Because I was always scared they would be a big league scout in the stand and I didn't want to go 'up.' "

Then I said why not, and he told me he was stuck on a gal in Waco and wanted to be near her.

"Yes," I said, "but your home town, Yuma, is a long ways from Waco and you couldn't see much of her winters even if you stayed in the Texas League."

"I got a gal in Yuma for winters," he says. "This other gal was just for during the season."

"How about that one time you showed your stuff?" I asked him. "How did you happen to do it?"

"Well," he said, "the Dallas club was playing a series in Waco and I went to a picture show and seen the gal with Fred Kruger. He's Dallas's manager. So the next day I made a monkey out of his ball club. I struck out fifteen of them and give them one hit—a fly ball that Smitty could have caught in a hollow tooth if he hadn't drunk his lunch."

Of course that was the game Dave's friend seen him pitch and we were lucky he happened to be in Waco just then. And it was Kane's last game in that league. Him and his "during the season" gal had a brawl and he played sick and got himself sent home.

Well, everybody knows now what a whale of a pitcher he turned out to be. He had a good, fast-breaking curve and Carney learned him how to throw a slow ball. Old Kid Farrell worked like a horse with him and got him so he could move around and field his position. At first he seemed to think he was moored out there. And another cute habit that had to be cured was his full wind-up with men on bases. The Kid starved him out of this.

Maybe I didn't tell you what an eater he was. Before Dave caught on to it, he was ordering one breakfast in his room and having another downstairs, and besides pretty near choking himself to death at lunch and supper, he'd sneak out to some lunch-room before bedtime, put away a Hamburger steak and eggs and bring back three or four sandwiches to snap at during the night.

He was rooming at the start with Joe Bonham and Joe finally told on him, thinking it was funny. But it wasn't funny to Dave and he named the Kid and Johnny Abbott a committee of two to see that Kane didn't explode. The Kid watched over him at table and Johnny succeeded Bonham as his roommate. And the way the Kid got him to cut out his wind-up was by telling him, "Now if you forget yourself and use it with a man on, your supper's going to be two olives and a finger-bowl, but if you hold up those runners, you can eat the chef."

As I say, the whole world knows what he is now. But they don't know how hard we worked with him, they don't know how close we came to losing him altogether, and they don't know the real story of that final game last year, which I'll tell you in a little while.

First, about pretty near losing him: As soon as Dave seen his possibilities and his value to us, he warned the boys not to ride him or play too many jokes on him because he was simple enough to take everything in dead earnest, and if he ever found out we were laughing at him, he might either lay down and quit trying or blow us entirely. Dave's dope was good, but you can't no more prevent a bunch of ball players from kidding a goofer like Kane than you can stop the Century at Herkimer by hollering "Whoa!"

He was always saying things and doing things that left him wide open and the gang took full advantage, especially Bull Wade.

I remember one night everybody was sitting on the porch and Bull was on the railing, right in front of Kane's chair.

"What's your first name, Steve?" Bull asked him.

"Well," says Kane, "It ain't Steve at all. It's Elmer."

"It would be!" says Bull. "It fits you like your suit. And that reminds me, I was going to inquire where you got that suit."

"In Yuma," said Kane. "In a store."

"A store!" says Bull.

"A clothing store," says Kane. "They sell all kinds of clothes."

"I see they do," said Bull.

"If you want a suit like it, I'll write and find out if they've got another one," says Kane.

"They couldn't be two of them," says Bull, "and if they was, I'll bet Ed Wynn's bought the other. But anyway, I've already got a suit, and what I wanted to ask you was what the boys out West call you. I mean, what's your nickname?"

" 'Hurry,' " says the sap. " 'Hurry' Kane. Lefty Condon named me that."

"He seen you on your way to the dining-room," said Bull.

Kane didn't get it.

"No," he said. "It ain't nothing to do with a dining-room. A hurricane is a kind of a storm. My last name is Kane, so Lefty called me 'Hurry' Kane. It's a kind of a storm."

"A brainstorm," says Bull.

"No," said Kane. "A hurricane is a big wind-storm."

"Does it blow up all of a sudden?" asked Bull.

"Yeah, that's it," says Kane.

"We had three or four of them on this club last year," said Bull. "All pitchers, too. Dave got rid of them and he must be figuring on you to take their place."

"Do you mean you had four pitchers named Kane?" says the big busher.

"No," said Bull. "I mean we had four pitchers that could blow up all of a sudden. It was their hobby. Dave used to work them in turn, the same afternoon; on days when Olds and Carney needed a rest. Each one of the four would pitch an innings and a half."

Kane thought quite a while and then said: "But if they was four of them, and they pitched an innings and a half apiece, that's only six innings. Who pitched the other three?"

"Nobody," says Bull. "It was always too dark. By the way what innings is your favorite? I mean, to blow in?"

"I don't blow," says the sap.

"Then," said Bull, "why was it that fella called you 'Hurry' Kane?"

"It was Lefty Condon called me 'Hurry,' " says the sap. "My last name is Kane, and a hurricane is a big wind."

"Don't a wind blow?" says Bull.

And so on. I swear they kept it up for two hours, Kane trying to explain his nickname and Bull leading him on, and Joe Bonham said that Kane asked him up in the room who that was he had been talking to, and when Joe told him it was Wade, one of the smartest ball players in the league, Hurry said: "Well, then, he must be either stewed or else this is a damn sight dumber league than the one I came from."

Bull and some of the rest of the boys pulled all the old gags on him that's been in baseball since the days when you couldn't get on a club unless you had a walrus mustache. And Kane never disappointed them.

They made him go to the club-house after the key to the batter's box; they wrote him mash notes with fake names signed to them and had him spending half his evenings on some corner, waiting to meet gals that never lived; when he held Florida University to two hits in five innings, they sent him telegrams of congratulation from Coolidge and Al Smith, and he showed the telegrams to everybody in the hotel; they had him report at the ball park at six-thirty one morning for a secret "pitchers' conference"; they told him the Ritz was where all the unmarried ball players on the club lived while we were home, and they got him to write and ask for a parlor, bedroom and bath for the whole season. They was nothing he wouldn't fall for till Dave finally tipped him off that he was being kidded, and even then he didn't half believe it.

Now I never could figure how a man can fool themselves about their own looks, but this bird was certain that he and Tommy Meighan were practically twins. Of course the boys soon found this out and strung him along. They advised him to quit baseball and go into pictures. They sat around his room and had him strike different poses and fix his hair different ways to see how he could show off his beauty to the best advantage. Johnny Abbott told me, after he began rooming with him, that for an hour before he went to bed and when he got up, Kane would stand in front of the mirror staring at himself and practising smiles and scowls and all kinds of silly faces, while Johnny pretended he was asleep.

Well, it wasn't hard to kid a fella like that into believing the dames were mad about him and when Bull Wade said that Evelyn Corey had asked who he was, his chest broke right through his shirt.

I know more about Evelyn now, but I didn't know nothing than except that she was a beautiful gal who had been in Broadway shows a couple of seasons and didn't have to be in them no more. Her room was two doors down the hall from Johnny's and Kane's. She was in Florida all alone, probably because her man friend, whoever he was at that time, had had to go abroad or somewheres with the family. All the ball players were willing to meet her, but she wasn't thrilled over the idear of getting acquainted with a bunch of guys who hadn't had a pay day in four or five months. Bull got Kane to write her a note; then Bull stole the note and wrote an answer, asking him to call. Hurry went and knocked at her door. She opened it and slammed it in his face.

"It was kind of dark," he said to Johnny, "and I guess she failed to recognize me." But he didn't have the nerve to call again.

He showed Johnny a picture of his gal in Yuma, a gal named Minnie Olson, who looked like she patronized the same store where Kane had bought his suit. He said she was wild about him and would marry him the minute he said the word and probably she was crying her eyes out right now, wishing he was home. He asked if Johnny had a gal and Johnny loosened up and showed him the picture of the gal he was engaged to. (Johnny married her last November.) She's a peach, but all Kane would say was, "Kind of skinny, ain't she?" Johnny laughed and said most gals liked to be that way.

"Not if they want me," says Kane.

"Well," said Johnny, "I don't think this one does. But how about your friend, that Miss Corey? You certainly can't call her plump, yet you're anxious to meet her."

"She's got class!" said Kane.

Johnny laughed that off, too. This gal of his, that he's married to now, she's so far ahead of Corey as far as class is concerned—well, they ain't no comparison. Johnny, you know, went to Cornell a couple of years and his wife is a college gal he met at a big house-party. If you put her and Evelyn beside of each other you wouldn't have no trouble telling which of them belonged on Park Avenue and which Broadway.

Kane kept on moaning more and more about his gal out West and acting glummer and glummer. Johnny did his best to cheer him up, as he seen what was liable to happen. But they wasn't no use. The big rube "lost" his fast ball and told Dave he had strained his arm and probably wouldn't be no good all season. Dave bawled him out and accused him of stalling. Kane stalled just the same. Then Dave soft-soaped him, told him how he'd burn up the league and how we were all depending on him to put us in the race and keep us there. But he might as well have been talking to a mounted policeman.

Finally, one day during the last week at Fort Gregg, Johnny Abbott got homesick himself and put in a long-distance call for his gal in New York. It was a rainy day and him and Kane had been just laying around the room. Before the call went through Johnny hinted that he would like to be alone while he talked. Kane paid no attention and began undressing to take a nap. So Johnny had to speak before an audience and not only that, but as soon as Kane heard him say "Darling" or "Sweetheart," or whatever he called her, he moved right over close to the phone where he wouldn't miss nothing. Johnny was kind of embarrassed and hung up before he was ready to; then he gave Kane a dirty look and went to the window and stared out at the rain, dreaming about the gal he'd just talked with.

Kane laid down on his bed, but he didn't go to sleep. In four or five minutes he was at the phone asking the operator to get Minnie Olson in Yuma. Then he laid down again and tossed a while, and then he sat up on the edge of the bed.

"Johnny," he says, "how far is it from here to New York?"

"About a thousand miles," said Johnny.

"And how far to Yuma?" said Kane.

"Oh," says Johnny, "that must be three thousand miles at least."

"How much did that New York call cost you?" asked Kane.

"I don't know yet," said Johnny. "I suppose it was around seven bucks."

Kane went to the writing table and done a little arithmetic. From there he went back to the phone.

"Listen, girlie," he said to the operator, "you can cancel that Yuma call. I just happened to remember that the party I wanted won't be home. She's taking her mandolin lesson, way the other side of town."

Johnny told me afterwards that he didn't know whether to laugh or cry. Before he had a chance to do either, Kane says to him:

"This is my last day on this ball club."

"What do you mean?" said Johnny.

"I mean I'm through; I'm going home," says Kane.

"Don't be a fool!" says Johnny. "Don't throw away the chance of a lifetime just because you're a little lonesome. If you stay in this league and pitch like you can pitch, you'll be getting the big money next year and you can marry that gal and bring her East with you. You may not have to wait till next year. You may pitch us into the world's series and grab a chunk of dough this fall."

"We won't be in no world's series," says Kane.

"What makes you think so?" said Johnny.

"I can't work every day," says Kane.

"You'll have help," says Johnny. "With you and Carney and Olds taking turns, we can be right up in that old fight. Without you, we can't even finish in the league. If you won't do it for yourself or for Dave, do it for me, your roomy. You just seen me spend seven or eight bucks on a phone call, but that's no sign I'm reeking with jack. I spent that money because I'd have died if I hadn't. I've got none to throw away and if we don't win the pennant, I can't marry this year and maybe not next year or the year after."

"I've got to look out for myself," says Kane. "I tell you I'm through and that's all there is to it. I'm going home where my gal is, where they ain't no smart Alecks kidding me all the while, and where I can eat without no assistant manager holding me down to a sprig of parsley, and a thimbleful of soup. For your sake, Johnny," he says, "I'd like to see this club finsh on top, but I can't stick it out and I'm afraid your only hope is for the other seven clubs to all be riding on the same train and hit an open bridge."

Well, of course Johnny didn't lose no time getting to Dave with the bad news, and Dave and Kid Farrell rushed to the sapper's room. They threatened him and they coaxed him. The promised him he could eat all he wanted. They swore that anybody who tried to play jokes on him would either be fined or fired off the club. They reminded him that it cost a lot of money to go from Florida to Yuma, and he would have to pay his own way. They offered him a new contract with a five-hundred-dollar raise if he would stay. They argued and pleaded with him from four in the afternoon till midnight. When they finally quit, they were just where they'd been when they started. He was through.

"All right!" Dave hollered. "Be through and go to hell! If you ain't out of here by tomorrow noon, I'll have you chased out! And don't forget that you'll never pitch in organized baseball again!"

"That suits me," says Kane, and went to bed.

When Johnny Abbott woke up about seven the next morning, Hurry was putting his extra collar and comb in the leaky suitcase. He said:

"I'm going to grab the eleven-something train for Jacksonville. I got money enough to take me from here to New Orleans and I know a fella there that will see me the rest of the way—if I can find him and he ain't broke."

Well, Johnny couldn't stand for that and he got up and dressed and was starting out to borrow two hundred dollars from me to lend to Kane, when the phone rang loud and long. Kane took off the receiver, listened a second, and then said "Uh-huh" and hung up.

"Who was it!" asked Johnny.

"Nobody," says Kane. "Just one of Bull Wade's gags."

"What did he say?" Johnny asked him.

"It was a gal, probably the telephone operator," said Kane. "She said the hotel was on fire and not to get excited, but that we better move out."

"You fool!" yelled Johnny and run to the phone.

They was no gag about it. The hotel had really caught fire in the basement and everybody was being warned to take the air. Johnny tossed some of his stuff in a bag and started out, telling Kane to follow him quick. Hurry got out in the hall and then remembered that he had left his gal's picture on the dresser and went back after it. Just as he turned towards the door again, in dashed a dame with a kimono throwed over her nightgown. It was Evelyn Corey herself, almost in the flesh.

"Oh, please!" she said, or screamed. "Come and help me carry my things!"

Well, here was once that the name "Hurry" was on the square. He dropped his own suitcase and was in her room in nothing and no-fifths. He grabbed her four pieces of hand baggage and was staggering to the hall with them when a bellhop bounced in and told them the danger was over, the fire was out.

This seemed to be more of a disappointment than Evelyn could stand. Anyway, she fainted—onto a couch—and for a few minutes she was too unconscious to do anything but ask Kane to pour her a drink. He also poured himself one and settled down in the easy chair like he was there for the day. But by now she had come to and got a good look at him.

"I thank you very much," she said, "and I'm so exhausted with all this excitement that I think I'll go back to bed."

Kane took his hint and got up.

"But ain't I going to see you again?" he asked her.

"I'm afraid not," says Evelyn. "I'm leaving here this evening and I'll be getting ready from now till then."

"Where are you headed for?" Kane asked her.

"For home, New York," she said.

"Can't I have your address?" said Kane.

"Why, yes," said Evelyn without batting an eye. "I live at the Ritz."

"The Ritz!" says Kane. "That's where I'm going to live, if they ain't filled up."

"How wonderful!" said Evelyn. "Then we'll probably see each other every day."

Kane beat it down to the dining-room and straight to Dave's table.

"Boss," he said, "I've changed my mind."

"Your what!" says Dave.

"My mind," says Kane. "I've decided to stick."

It was all Dave could do not to kiss him. But he thought it was best to act calm.

"That's fine, Hurry!" he said. "And I'll see that you get that extra five hundred bucks."

"What five hundred bucks?" says Kane.

"The five hundred I promised you if you'd stay," says Dave.

"I hadn't heard about it," said Kane. "But as long as I ain't going home, I'm in no rush for money. Though I'm liable to need it," he says, "as soon as we hit New York."

And he smiled the silliest smile you ever seen.

I don't have to tell you that he didn't live at the Ritz. Or that Evelyn Corey didn't live there neither. He found out she hadn't never lived there, but he figured she'd intended to and had to give it up because they didn't have a suite good enough for her.

I got him a room in my boarding-house in the Bronx and for the first few days he spent all his spare time looking through city directories and different telephone directories and bothering the life out of Information, trying to locate his lost lady. It was when he had practically give up hope that he told me his secret and asked for help.

"She's all I came here for," he said, "and if I can't find her, I ain't going to stay."

Well, of course if you went at it the right way, you wouldn't have much trouble tracing her. Pretty near anybody in the theatrical business, or the people that run the big night clubs, or the head waiters at the hotels and restaurants—they could have put you on the right track. The thing was that it would be worse to get a hold of her than not to, because she'd have give him the air so strong that he would have caught his death of cold.

So I just said that they was no question but what she had gone away somewheres, maybe to Europe, and he would hear from her as soon as she got back. I had to repeat this over and over and make it strong or he'd have left us flatter than his own feet before he pitched two games. As it was, we held him till the end of May without being obliged to try any tricks, but you could see he was getting more impatient and restless all the while and the situation got desperate just as we were starting on our first trip West. He asked me when would we hit St. Louis and I told him the date and said:

"What do you want to know for?"

"Because," he says, "I'm going home from there."

I repeated this sweet news to Dave and Kid Farrell. We finally called in Bull Wade and it was him that saved the day. You remember Bull had faked up a note from Evelyn to Kane down at Fort Gregg; now he suggested that he write some more notes, say one every two or three weeks, sign her name to them, send them to Bull's brother in Montreal and have the brother mail them from there. It was a kind of a dirty, mean thing to do, but it worked. The notes all read about the same——

"Dear Mr. Kane:—I am keeping track of your wonderful pitching and looking forward to seeing you when I return to New York, which will be early in the fall. I hope you haven't forgotten me."

And so on, signed "Your friend and admirer, Evelyn Corey."

Hurry didn't answer only about half of them as it was a real chore for him to write. He addressed his answers in care of Mr. Harry Wade, such and such a street number, Montreal, and when Bull's brother got them, he forwarded them to Bull, so he'd know if they was anything special he ought to reply to.

The boys took turns entertaining Kane evenings, playing cards with him and staking him to picture shows. Johnny Abbott done more than his share. You see the pennant meant more to Johnny than to anybody else; it meant the world's series money and a fall wedding, instead of a couple of years' wait. And Johnny's gal, Helen Kerslake, worked, too. She had him to her house to supper—when her folks were out—and made him feel like he was even handsomer and more important than he thought. She went so far as to try and get some of her gal friends to play with him, but he always wanted to pet and that was a little too much.

Well, if Kane hadn't stuck with us and turned out to be the marvel he is, the White Sox would have been so far ahead by the Fourth of July that they could have sat in the stand the rest of the season and let the Bloomer Girls play in their place. But Hurry had their number from the first time he faced them till the finish. Out of eleven games he worked against them all last year, he won ten and the other was a nothing to nothing tie. And look at the rest of his record! As I recall it, he took part in fifty-eight games. He pitched forty-three full games, winning thirty-six, losing five and tying two. And God knows how many games he saved! He had that free, easy side-arm motion that didn't take much out of him and he could pitch every third day and be at his best.

But don't let me forget to credit myself with an assist. Late in August, Kane told me he couldn't stand it no longer to just get short notes from the Corey gal and never see her, and when we started on our September trip West, he was going to steal a week off and run up to Montreal; he would join us later, but he must see Evelyn. Well, for once in my life I had an idear hit me right between the eyes.

The Yuma gal, Minnie Olson, had been writing to him once a week and though he hardly ever wrote to her and seemed to only be thinking of Corey, still I noticed that he could hardly help from crying when Minnie's letters came. So I suggested to Dave that he telegraph Minnie to come East and visit with all her expenses paid, wire her money for her transportation, tell her it would be doing Kane a big favor as well as the rest of us, and ask her to send Kane a telegram, saying when she would reach New York, but to be sure and never mention that she wasn't doing it on her own hook.

Two days after Dave's message was sent, Kane got a wire from El Paso. She was on her way and would he meet her at the Pennsylvania Station on such and such a date. I never seen a man as happy as Hurry was when he read that telegram.

"I knew she was stuck on me," he said, "but I didn't know it was that strong. She must have worked in a store or something since spring to save up money for this trip."

You would have thought he'd never heard of or seen a gal by the name of Evelyn Corey.

Minnie arrived and was just what we expected: a plain, honest, good-hearted, small-town gal, dressed for a masquerade. We had supper with her and Kane her first night in town—I and Johnny and Helen. She was trembling like a leaf, partly from excitement over being in New York and amongst strangers, but mostly on account of seeing the big sap again. He wasn't no sap to her and I wished they was some dame would look at me the way she kept looking at Hurry.

The next morning Helen took her on a shopping tour and got her fixed up so cute that you couldn't hardly recognize her. In the afternoon she went to the ball game and seen Kane shut the Detroit club out with two hits.

When Hurry got a glimpse of her in her Fifth Avenue clothes, he was as proud as if he had bought them himself and it didn't seem to occur to him that they must have cost more than she could have paid.

Well, with Kane happy and no danger of him walking out on us, all we had to worry about was that the White Sox still led us by three games, with less than twenty left to play. And the schedule was different than usual—we had to wind up with a Western trip and play our last thirteen games on the road. I and Johnny and Dave was talking it over one day and the three of us agreed that we would be suckers not to insist on Miss Olson going along. But Dave wondered if she wouldn't feel funny, being the only girl.

"I'll make my gal go, too," said Johnny.

And that's the way it was fixed.

We opened in St. Louis and beat them two out of three. Olds was trimmed, but Carney and Kane both won. We didn't gain no ground, because the White Sox grabbed two out of three from Washington. We made a sweep of our four games in Detroit, while the Sox was winning three from Philadelphia. That moved us up to two and a half games from first place. We beat Cleveland three straight, Kane licking them 6 to 1 and holding Carney's one run lead through the eighth and ninth innings of another game. At the same time, Chicago took three from Boston.

So we finally struck old Chi, where the fans was already counting the pennant won, two and a half games behind and three to go— meaning we had to win all three or be sunk.

I told you how Kane had the Chicago club's number. But I didn't tell you how Eddie Brainard had been making a monkey of us. He had only worked against us six times and had beat us five. His other game was the nothing to nothing tie with Hurry. Eddie is one sweet pitcher and if he had been the horse for work that Kane was, that last series wouldn't have got us nowheres. But Eddie needs his full rest and it was a cinch he wouldn't be in there for more than one game and maybe part of another.

In Brainard's six games against us, he had give us a total of four runs, shutting us out three times and trimming us 3 to 2, 4 to 1 and 2 to 1. As the White Sox only needed one game, it was a cinch that they wouldn't start Eddie against Kane, who was so tough for them, but would save him for Carney or Olds, whichever one worked first.

Carney hadn't been able to finish a game with Chicago and Olds' record wasn't much better.

Well, we was having breakfast in our hotel the morning we got in from Cleveland, and Kane sent for Dave to come to the table where him and Johnny Abbott and the two gals was eating.

"Boss," he says, "I'm thinking of getting married and so is Johnny here, but they ain't neither of us can do it, not now anyway, unless we grab some of that world's series jack. And we can't get into the series without we win these three games. So if I was managing this ball club, I'd figure on that and know just how to work my pitchers."

"Maybe I've thought about it a little myself," says Dave. "But I'd like to listen to your idears."

"All right," says Kane. "I'd start Kane today, and I'd start Kane tomorrow, and I'd start Kane the day after that."

"My plan is a little different," said Dave. "Of course you start today, and if you win, why, I want to play a joke on them tomorrow. I intend to start Olds so they'll start Brainard. And if the game is anywheres near close at the end of the third or fourth innings, you're going in. It will be too late for them to take Brainard out and expect him to be as good the third day. And if we win that second game, why, you won't have to beg me to pitch the last one."

You'll think I'm getting long-winded, but they ain't much more to tell. You probably heard the details of those first two games even if you was on the Other Side. Hurry beat them the first one, 7 to 1, and their one run was my fault. Claymore was on second base with two men out in the sixth innings. King hit a foul ball right straight up and I dropped it. And then he pulled a base-hit inside of Bull, and Claymore scored. Olds and Brainard started the second game and at the end of our half of the fourth innings, the score was one and one. Hurry had been warming up easy right along, but it certainly was a big surprise to the Chicago club and pretty near everybody else when Dave motioned him to a relieve Olds. The White Sox never came close to another run and we got to Brainard for one in the eighth, just enough to beat him.

Eddie had pitched his head off and it was a tough one for him to lose. But the best part of it was, he was through and out of the way.

Well, Johnny and Kane had their usual date with the two gals for supper. Johnny was in his bathroom, washing up, when the phone rang. Kane answered it, but he talked kind of low and Johnny didn't hear what he was saying. But when Hurry had hung up, he acted kind of nervous and Johnny asked him what was the matter.

"It's hard luck," said Kane. "They's a friend of mine from Yuma here, and he's in trouble and I've got to go over on the North Side and see him. Will you take both the gals to supper yourself? Because I may not be back till late. And don't tell Min who I'm going to see."

"How could I tell her when you ain't told me?" said Johnny.

"Well," said Kane, "just tell her I'm wore out from working so hard two days in a row and I went right to bed so I'd be all right for tomorrow."

Johnny was kind of worried and tried to coax him not to go. But Kane ducked out and didn't come in till midnight. Johnny tried to find out where he'd been and what had happened, but he said he was too sleepy to talk. Just the same, Johnny says, he tossed around and moaned all night like he was having a nightmare, and he usually slept like a corpse.

Kane got up early and went down to breakfast before Johnny was dressed. But Johnny was still worried, and hustled up and caught him before he was out of the dining-room. He was hoping Hurry would explain his getting in late and not sleeping. Kane wouldn't talk, though, and still acted nervous. So Johnny finally said:

"Hurry, you know what this game today means to me and you ought to know what it means to you. If we get trimmed, a lot of people besides ourselves will be disappointed, but they won't nobody be as disappointed as me. I wished you'd have had a good sleep last night and if you'll take my advice, you'll go up in the room and rest till it's time to go to the ball yard. If you're anywheres near yourself, this Chicago club is licked. And for heaven's sakes, be yourself, or your roomy is liable to walk out into Lake Michigan tonight so far that I can't get back!"

"I'm myself," says Kane and got up and left the table, but not quick enough so that Johnny didn't see tears in his eyes.

That afternoon's crowd beat all records and I was tickled to death to see it, because Hurry had always done his best work in front of crowds that was pulling against him. He warmed up fine and they wasn't nobody on our club, nobody but Kane himself and two others, who didn't feel perfectly confident that we were "in."

The White Sox were starting Sam Bonner and while he had beat us three or four times, we'd always got runs off him, and they'd always been lucky to score at all against Kane.

Bonner went through the first innings without no trouble. And then we got the shock of our lives. The first ball Hurry pitched was high and outside and it felt funny when I caught it. I was used to that old "zip" and I could have caught this one in my bare hand. Claymore took a cut at the next one and hit it a mile to left center for three bases. King hit for two bases, Welsh was safe when Digman three a ground ball into the seats, and Kramer slapped one out of the park for a homer. Four runs. The crowd was wild and we were wilder.

You ought to have heard us on that bench. "Yellow so-and-so" was the mildest name Hurry got called. Dave couldn't do nothing but just mumble and shake his fists at Kane. We was all raving and asking each other what in hell was going on. Hurry stood in front facing us, but he was looking up in the stand and he acted like he didn't hear one word of the sweet remarks meant for his ears.

Johnny Abbott pulled me aside.

"Listen," he says. "This kid ain't yellow and he ain't wore out. They's something wrong here."

By this time Dave had found his voice and he yelled at Kane: "You so-and-so so-and-so! You're going to stay right in there and pitch till this game is over! And if you don't pitch like you can pitch, I'll shoot you dead tonight just as sure as you're a yellow, quitting——!"

We'd forgot it was our turn to bat and Hildebrand was threatening to forfeit the game before he could get Bull Wade to go up there. Kane still stood in front of us, staring. But pretty soon Dave told young Topping to run out to the bull pen and warn Carney and Olds to both be ready. I seen Topping stop a minute alongside of Kane and look up in the stand where Kane was looking. I seen Topping say something to Kane and I heard Kane call him a liar. Then Topping said something more and Hurry turned white as a sheet and pretty near fell into the dugout. I noticed his hand shake as he took a drink of water. And then he went over to Dave and I heard him say:

"I'm sorry, Boss. I had a bad inning. But I'll be all right from now on."

"You'd better!" says Dave.

"Get me some runs is all I ask," says Kane.

And the words wasn't no sooner out of his mouth when Bull smacked one a mile over Claymore's head and came into the plate standing up. They was another tune on the bench now. We were yelling for blood, and we got it. Before they relieved Bonner, we'd got to him for three singles and a double—mine, if you must know —and the score was tied.

Say, if you think you ever seen pitching, you ought to have watched Kane cut them through there the rest of that day. Fourteen strike-outs in the last eight innings! And the only man to reach first base was Kramer, when Stout dropped an easy fly ball in the fifth.

Well, to shorten it up, Bull and Johnny Abbott and myself had some luck against Pierce in the seventh innings. Bull and Johnny scored and we licked them, 6 to 4.

In the club-house, Dave went to Hurry and said:

"Have you got anything to tell me, any explanation of the way you looked at the start of that game?"

"Boss," said Kane, "I didn't sleep good last night. Johnny will be a witness to that. I felt terrible in that first innings. I seemed to have lost my 'fast.' In the second innings it came back and I was all right."

And that's all he would say.

You know how we went ahead and took the big series, four games out of five, and how Hurry gave them one run in the three games he pitched. And now you're going to know what I promised to tell you when we first sat down, and I hope I ain't keeping you from a date with that gal from St. Joe.

The world's series ended in St. Louis and naturally I didn't come back East when it was over. Neither did Kane, because he was going home to Yuma, along with his Minnie. Well, they were leaving the next night, though most of the other boys had ducked out right after the final game. Hurry called me up at my house three or four hours before his train was due to leave and asked me would I come and see him and give him some advice. So I went to the hotel and he got me in his room and locked the door.

Here is what he had to say:

On the night before that last game in Chi, a gal called him up and it was nobody but our old friend Evelyn Corey. She asked him

to come out to a certain hotel on the North Side and have supper
with her. He went because he felt kind of sorry for her. But when
he seen her, he lost his head and was just as nuts about her as he'd
been at Fort Gregg. She encouraged him and strung him along till
he forgot all about poor Minnie. Evelyn told him she knew he could
have his pick of a hundred gals and she was broken-hearted because
they was no chance for her. He asked her what made her think that,
and she put her handkerchief to her eyes and pretended she was
crying and that drove him wild and he said he wouldn't marry nobody but her.

Then she told him they had better forget it, that she was broke
now, but had been used to luxury, and he promised he would work
hard and save up till he had three or four thousand dollars and
that would be enough for a start.

"Four thousand dollars!" she says. "Why, that wouldn't buy the
runs in my stockings! I wouldn't think of marrying a man who had
less than twenty thousand. I would want a honeymoon in Europe
and we'd buy a car over there and tour the whole continent, and
then come home and settle down in some nice suburb of New York.
And so," she says, "I am going to get up and leave you right now
because I see that my dream won't never come true."

She left him sitting in the restaurant and he was the only person
there outside of the waiters. But after he'd sat a little while—he was
waiting till the first shock of his disappointment had wore off—a
black-haired bird with a waxed mustache came up to him and asked
if he wasn't Hurry Kane, the great pitcher. Then he said: "I suppose
you'll pitch again tomorrow," and Kane said yes.

"I haven't nothing against you," says the stranger, "but I hope
you lose. It will cost me a lot of money if you win."

"How much?" said Kane.

"So much," says the stranger, "that I will give you twenty thousand dollars if you get beat."

"I can't throw my pals," said Kane.

"Well," said the stranger, "two of your pals has already agreed to
throw you."

Kane asked him who he referred to, but he wouldn't tell. Kane
don't know yet, but I do. It was Dignan and Stout, our shortstopper

and first baseman, and you'll notice they ain't with our club no more.

Hurry held out as long as he could, but he thought of Evelyn and that honeymoon in Europe broke him down. He took five thousand dollars' advance and was to come to the same place and get the balance right after the game.

He said that after Johnny Abbott had give him that talk at the breakfast table, he went out and rode around in a taxi so he could cry without being seen.

Well, I've told you about that terrible first innings. And I've told you about young Topping talking to him before he went down to the bull pen to deliver Dave's message to Carney and Olds. Topping asked him what he was staring at and Hurry pointed Evelyn out to him and said she was his gal.

"Your gal's grandmother!" said Topping. "That's Evelyn Corey and she belongs to Sam Morris, the bookie. If I was you, I'd lay off. You needn't tell Dave, but I was in Ike Bloom's at one o'clock this morning, and Sam and she were there, too. And one of the waiters told me that Sam had bet twenty thousand dollars on the White Sox way last spring and had got six to one for his money."

Hurry quit talking and I started to bawl him out. But I couldn't stay mad at him, especially when I realized that they was a fifty-three-hundred-dollar check in my pocket which I'd never have had only for him. Besides, they ain't nothing crooked about him. He's just a bone-headed sap.

"I won't tell Dave on you," I said, and I got up to go.

"Wait a minute," says Kane. "I confessed so I could ask you a question. I've still got that five thousand which Morris paid me in advance. With that dough and the fifty-three hundred from the series, I and Min could buy ourself a nice little home in Yuma. But do you think I should ought to give it back to that crook?"

"No," said I. "What you ought to do is split it with young Topping. He was your good luck!"

I run acrost Topping right here in town not long ago. And the first thing he said was, "What do you think of that goofey Kane? I had a letter from him and a check. He said the check was what he owed me."

"Twenty-five hundred dollars?" I says.

"Two hundred," said Topping, "and if I ever lent him two hundred or two cents, I'll roll a hoop from here to Yuma."

Nora

"Mr. Hazlett, shake hands with Jerry Morris and Frank Moon. I guess you've heard of the both of them."

The speaker was Louie Brock, producer of musical shows, who had cleared over half a million dollars in two years through the popularity of "Jersey Jane," tunes by Morris and lyrics by Moon.

They were in Brock's inner office, the walls of which were adorned with autographed pictures of six or seven of the more celebrated musical comedy stars and a too-perfect likeness of Brock's wife, whom he had evidently married in a dense fog.

"Mr. Hazlett," continued Brock, "has got a book which he wrote as a straight play, but it struck me right off that it was great material for a musical, especially with you two fellas to do the numbers. It's a brand-new idear, entirely opposite from most of these here musical comedy books that's all the same thing and the public must be getting sick of them by this time. Don't you think so, Jerry?"

"I certainly do," the tunesmith replied. "Give us a good novelty story, and with what I and Frank can throw in there to jazz it up, we'll run till the theatre falls down."

"Well, Mr. Hazlett," said Brock, "suppose you read us the book and we'll see what the boys thinks of it."

Hazlett was quite nervous in spite of Brock's approval of his work and the fact that friends to whom he had shown it had given it high praise and congratulated him on his good fortune in getting a chance to collaborate with Morris and Moon—Morris, who had set a new style in melodies and rhythms and whose tunes made up sixty percent of all dance programs, and Moon, the ideal lyricist who could fit Jerry's fast triplets with such cute-sounding three-syllable rhymes that no one ever went to the considerable trouble of trying to find out what they meant.

"I've tried to stay away from the stereotyped Cinderella theme," said Hazlett. "In my story, the girl starts out just moderately well off and winds up poor. She sacrifices everything for love and the end finds her alone with her lover, impoverished but happy. She——"

"Let's hear the book," said the producer.

Hazlett, with trembling fingers, opened to the first page of his script.

"Well," he began, "the title is 'Nora' and the first scene——"

"Excuse me a minute," Morris interrupted. "I promised a fella that I'd come over and look at a big second-hand Trinidad Twelve. Only eight grand and a bargain if there ever was one, hey, Frank?"

"I'll say it's a bargain," Moon agreed.

"The fella is going to hold it for me till half-past three and its nearly three o'clock now. So if you don't mind, Mr. Hazlett, I wish that instead of reading the book clear through, you'd kind of give us a kind of a synopsis and it will save time and we can tell just as good, hey, Frank?"

"Just as good," said Moon.

"All right, Mr. Hazlett," Brock put in. "Suppose you tell the story in your own way, with just the main idear and the situations."

"Well," said Hazlett, "of course, as a straight play, I wrote it in three acts, but when Mr. Brock suggested that I make a musical show out of it, I cut it to two. To start with, the old man, the girl's uncle, is an Irishman who came to this country when he was about twenty years old. He worked hard and he was thrifty and finally he got into the building business for himself. He's pretty well-to-do, but he's avaricious and not satisfied with the three or four hundred thousand he's saved up. He meets another Irish immigrant about his own age, a politician who has a lot to say about the letting of big city building contracts. This man, Collins, had a handsome young son, John, twenty-three or twenty-four.

"The old man, the girl's uncle—their name is Crowley—he tries his hardest to get in strong with old Collins so Collins will land him some of the city contracts, but Collins, though he's very friendly all the while, he doesn't do Crowley a bit of good in a business way.

"Well, Crowley gives a party at his house for a crowd of his Irish friends in New York, young people and people his own age, and during the party young John Collins sees a picture of Crowley's beautiful niece, Nora. She's still in Ireland and has never been to this country. Young Collins asks Crowley who it is and he tells him and young Collins says she is the only girl he will ever marry.

"Crowley then figures to himself that if he can connect up with the Collinses by having his niece marry young John, he can land just about all the good contracts there are. So he cables for Nora to come over and pay him a visit. She comes and things happen just as Crowley planned—John and Nora fall in love.

"Now there's a big dinner and dance in honor of the Mayor and one of the guests is Dick Percival, a transplanted Englishman who has made fifty million dollars in the sugar business. He also falls in love with Nora and confesses it to her uncle. Old Crowley has always hated Englishmen, but his avarice is so strong that he decides Nora must get rid of John and marry Dick. Nora refuses to do this, saying John is 'her man' and that she will marry him or nobody.

"Crowley forbids her to see John, but she meets him whenever she can get out. The uncle and niece had a long, stubborn battle of wills, neither yielding an inch. Finally John's father, old Collins, is caught red-handed in a big bribery scandal and sent to the penitentiary. It is also found out that he has gambled away all his money and John is left without a dime.

"Crowley, of course, thinks this settles the argument, that Nora won't have anything more to do with a man whose father is a crook and broke besides, and he gets up a party to announce the engagement between her and Dick. Nora doesn't interfere at all, but insists that young John Collins be invited. When the announcement is made, Nora says her uncle has got the name of her fiancé wrong; she has been engaged to John Collins since the first day she came to the United States, and if he will still have her, she is his. Then she and John walk out alone into the world, leaving Dick disappointed and Crowley in a good old-fashioned Irish rage."

"Well, boys," said Brock, after a pause, "what do you think of it?"
The "boys" were silent.

"You see," said Brock, "for natural ensembles, you got the first party at What's-his-name's, the scene on the pier when the gal lands from Ireland, the Mayor's party at some hotel maybe, and another party at What's-his-name's, only this time it's outdoors at his country place. You can have the boy sing a love-song to the picture before he ever sees the gal; you can make that the melody you want to carry clear through. You can have love duets between she and the boy and she and the Englishman. You can write a song like 'East Side, West Side' for the Mayor's party.

"You can write a corking good number for the pier scene, where the people of all nationalities are meeting their relatives and friends. And you can run wild with all the good Irish tunes in the world."

"Where's your comic?" inquired Morris.

"Mr. Hazlett forgot to mention the comic," Brock said. "He's an old Irishman, a pal of What's-his-name's, a kind of a Jiggs."

"People don't want an Irish comic these days," said Morris. "Can't you make him a Wop or a Heeb?"

"I'd have to rewrite the part," said Hazlett.

"No you wouldn't," said Morris. "Give him the same lines with a different twist to them."

"It really would be better," Brock put in, "if you could change him to a Heeb or even a Dutchman. I've got to have a spot for Joe Stein and he'd be a terrible flop as a Turkey."

"And listen," said Morris. "What are you going to do with Enriqueta?"

"Gosh! I'd forgot her entirely!" said Brock. "Of course we'll have to make room for her."

"Who is she?" Hazlett inquired.

"The best gal in Spain," said Brock. "I brought her over here and I'm paying her two thousand dollars every week, with nothing for her to do. You'll have to write in a part for her."

"Write in a part!" exclaimed Morris. "She'll play the lead or she won't play."

"But how is a Spanish girl going to play Nora Crowley?" asked Hazlett.

"Why does your dame have to be Nora Crowley?" Morris retorted. "Why does she have to be Irish at all?"

"Because her uncle is Irish."

"Make him a Spaniard, too."

"Yes, and listen," said Moon. "While you're making the gal and her uncle Spaniards, make your boy a wop. If you do that, I and Jerry have got a number that'll put your troupe over with a bang! Play it for them, Jerry."

Morris went to the piano and played some introductory chords. "This is a great break of luck," said Moon, "to have a number already written that fits right into the picture. Of course, I'll polish the lyric up a little more and I want to explain that the boy sings part of the lines, the gal the rest. But here's about how it is. Let's go, Jerry!"

Morris repeated his introduction and Moon began to sing:

> "Somewhere in the old world
> You and I belong.
> It will be a gold world,
> Full of light and song.
> Why not let's divide our time
> Between your native land and mine?
> Move from Italy to Spain,
> Then back to Italy again?

> "In sunny Italy,
> My Spanish queen,
> You'll fit so prettily
> In that glorious scene.
> You will sing me 'La Paloma';
> I will sing you 'Cara Roma';
> We will build a little home, a
> Bungalow serene.
> Then in the Pyrenees,
> Somewhere in Spain,
> We'll rest our weary knees
> Down in Lovers' Lane,
> And when the breakers roll a-
> Cross the azure sea,
> Espanola, Gorgonzola;
> Spain and Italy."

"A wow!" cried Brock. "Congratulations, Jerry! You, too, Frank! What do you think of that one, Mr. Hazlett?"

"Very nice," said Hazlett. "The tune sounds like 'Sole Mio' and 'La Paloma.'"

"It sounds like them both and it's better than either," said the composer.

"That one number makes our troupe, Jerry," said Brock. "You don't need anything else."

"But we've got something else, hey, Frank?"

"You mean 'Montgomery'?" said Moon.

"Yeh."

"Let's hear it," requested Brock.

"It'll take a dinge comic to sing it."

"Well, Joe Stein can do a dinge."

"I'll say he can! I like him best in blackface. And he's just the boy to put over a number like this."

Morris played another introduction, strains that Hazlett was sure he had heard a hundred times before, and Moon was off again:

"I want to go to Alabam'.
That's where my lovin' sweetheart am,
And won't she shout and dance for joy
To see once more her lovin' boy!
I've got enough saved up, I guess,
To buy her shoes and a bran'-new dress.
She's black as coal, and yet I think
When I walk in, she'll be tickled pink.

"Take me to Montgomery
Where it's always summery.
New York's just a mummery.
Give me life that's real.
New York fields are rotten fields.
Give me those forgotten fields;
I mean those there cotton fields,
Selma and Mobile.
I done been away so long;
Never thought I'd stay so long.
Train, you'd better race along
To my honey lamb.
Train, you make it snappy till
('Cause I won't be happy till)
I am in the capital,
Montgomery, Alabam'."

"Another knock-out!" said Brock enthusiastically. "Boys, either one of those numbers are better than anything in 'Jersey Jane.' Either one of them will put our troupe over. And the two of them together in one show! Well, it's in!"

Hazlett mustered all his courage.

"They're a couple of mighty good songs," he said. "But I don't exactly see how they'll fit."

"Mr. Hazlett," said Jerry Morris. "I understand this is your first experience with a musical comedy. I've had five successes in four years and could have had five more if I wanted to work that hard. I know the game backwards and I hope you won't take offense if I tell you a little something about it."

"I'm always glad to learn," said Hazlett.

"Well, then," said Morris, "you've got a great book there, with a good novelty idear, but it won't go without a few changes, changes that you can make in a half-hour and not detract anything from the novelty. In fact, they will add to it. While you were telling your story, I was thinking of it from the practical angle, the angle of show business, and I believe I can put my finger right on the spots that have got to be fixed.

"In the first place, as Louie has told you, he's got a contract with Enriqueta and she won't play any secondary parts. That means your heroine must be Spanish. Well, why not make her uncle her father and have him a Spaniard, running a Spanish restaurant somewhere down-town? It's a small restaurant and he just gets by. He has to use her as cashier and she sits in the window where the people going past can see her.

"One day the boy, who is really an Italian count—we'll call him Count Pizzola—he is riding alone in a taxi and he happens to look in the window and see the gal. He falls in love with her at first sight, orders the driver to stop and gets out and goes in the restaurant. He sits down and has his lunch, and while he is eating we can put in a novelty dance number with the boys and gals from the offices that are also lunching in this place.

"When the number is over, I'd have a comedy scene between Stein, who plays a dinge waiter, and, say, a German customer who isn't satisfied with the food or the check or something. Louie, who would you suggest for that part?"

"How about Charlie Williams?" said Brock.

"Great!" said Morris. "Well, they have this argument and the dinge throws the waiter out. The scrap amuses Pizzola and the gal, too, and they both laugh and that brings them together. He doesn't tell her he is a count, but she likes him pretty near as well as he likes her. They gab a while and then go into the Spanish number I just played for you.

"Now, in your story, you've got a boat scene where the gal is landing from Ireland. You'd better forget that scene. There was a boat scene in 'Sunny' and a boat scene in 'Hit the Deck,' and a lot of other troupes. We don't wan't anything that isn't our own. But Pizzola is anxious to take the gal out somewhere and let's see— Frank, where can he take her?"

"Why not a yacht?" suggested Moon.

"Great! He invites her out on a yacht, but he's got to pretend it isn't his own yacht. He borrowed it from a friend. She refuses at first, saying she hasn't anything to wear. She's poor, see? So he tells her his sister has got some sport clothes that will fit her. He gets the clothes for her and then we have a scene in her room where she is putting them on with a bunch of girl friends helping her. We'll write a number for that.

"Now the clothes he gave her are really his sister's clothes and the sister has carelessly left a beautiful brooch pinned in them. We go to the yacht and the Spanish dame knocks everybody dead. They put on an amateur show. That will give Enriqueta a chance for a couple more numbers. She and Pizzola are getting more and more stuck on each other and they repeat the Spanish song on the yacht, in the moonlight.

"There's a Frenchman along on the party who is greatly attracted by Enriqueta's looks. The Frenchman hates Pizzola. He has found out in some way that Enriqueta is wearing Pizzola's sister's clothes and he notices the diamond brooch. He figures that if he can steal it off of her, why, suspicion will be cast on the gal herself on account of her being poor, and Pizzola, thinking her a thief, won't have anything more to do with her and he, the Frenchman, can have her. So, during a dance, he manages to steal the brooch and he puts it in his pocket.

"Of course Pizzola's sister is also on the yachting party. All of a sudden she misses her brooch. She recalls having left it in the clothes she lent to Enriqueta. She goes to Enriqueta and asks her for it and the poor Spanish dame can't find it. Then Pizzola's sister calls her a thief and Pizzola himself can't help thinking she is one.

"They demand that she be searched, but rather than submit to that indignity, she bribes a sailor to take her off the yacht in a small launch and the last we see of her she's climbing overboard to get into the launch while the rest of the party are all abusing her. That's your first act curtain.

"I'd open the second act with a paddock scene at the Saratoga race-track. We'll write a jockey number and have about eight boys and maybe twenty-four gals in jockey suits. Enriqueta's father has gone broke in the restaurant business and he's up here looking for a job as assistant trainer or something. He used to train horses for the bull-fights in Spain.

"The gal is along with him and they run into the Frenchman that stole the brooch. The Frenchman tries to make love to the gal, but she won't have anything to do with him. While they are talking, who should come up but Pizzola! He is willing to make up with Enriqueta even though he still thinks her a thief. She won't meet his advances.

"He asks the Frenchman for a light. The Frenchman has a patent lighter and in pulling it out of his pocket, he pulls the brooch out, too. Then Pizzola realizes what an injustice he has done the gal and he pretty near goes down on his knees to her, but she has been badly hurt and won't forgive him yet.

"Now we have a scene in the café in the club-house and Stein is one of the waiters there. He sings the Montgomery number with a chorus of waiters and lunchers and at the end of the number he and the Spanish gal are alone on the stage.

"She asks him if he is really going to Montgomery and he says yes, and she says she and her father will go with him. She is anxious to go some place where there is no danger of running into the Frenchman or Pizzola.

"The third scene in the second act ought to be a plantation in Alabama. Stein is working there and the negroes are having a celebration or revival of some kind. Louie, you can get a male quartet to sing us some spirituals.

"Enriqueta's father has landed a job as cook at the plantation and she is helping with the housework. Pizzola and his sister follow her to Montgomery and come out to see her at the plantation.

"They are about to go up on the porch and inquire for her when they hear her singing the Spanish number. This proves to Pizzola that she still loves him and he finally gets his sister to plead with her for forgiveness. She forgives him. He tells her who he really is and how much dough he's got. And that pretty near washes us up."

"But how about our Japanese number?" said Moon.

"That's right," Morris said. "We'll have to send them to Japan before we end it. I've got a cherry-blossom number that must have the right setting. But that's easy to fix. You make these few changes I've suggested, Mr. Hazlett, and I feel that we've got a hit.

"And I want to say that your book is a whole lot better than most of the books they hand us. About the fella falling in love with the gal's picture—that's a novelty idear."

Hazlett said good-by to his producer and collaborators, went home by taxi and called up his bootlegger.

"Harry," he said, "what kind of whiskey have you got?"

"Well, Mr. Hazlett, I can sell you some good Scotch, but I ain't so sure of the rye. In fact, I'm kind of scared of it."

"How soon can you bring me a case?"

"Right off quick. It's the Scotch you want, ain't it?"

"No," said Hazlett. "I want the rye."

Rhythm

This story is slightly immoral, but so, I guess, are all stories based on truth. It concerns, principally, Harry Hart, whose frankness and naturalness were the traits that endeared him to fellow members of the Friars' Club and all red-blooded she-girls who met him in and out of show business. Music writers have never been noted for self-loathing and Harry was a refreshing exception to the general run. That was before "Upsy Daisy" began its year's tenancy of the Casino.

You can judge what sort of person he was by listening in on a talk he had at the club one night with Sam Rose, lyricist of "Nora's Nightie," "Sheila's Shirt" and a hundred popular songs. They were sitting alone at the table nearest the senile piano.

"Sam," said Harry, "I was wondering if they's a chance of you and I getting together."

"What's happened to Kane?" asked Sam.

"It's off between he and I," Harry replied. "That dame ruined him. I guess she married him to make an honest man of him. Anyways, he got so honest that I couldn't stand it no more. You know how I am, Sam—live and let live. I don't question nobody's ethics or whatever you call them, as long as they don't question mine. We're all trying to get along; that's the way I look at it. At that, I've heard better lyrics than he wrote for those two rhythm numbers of mine in 'Lottie'; in fact, between you and I, I thought he made a bum out of those two numbers. They sold like hymns, so I was really able to bear up when we reached the parting of the ways.

"But I'll tell you the climax just to show you how silly a guy can get. You remember our 'Yes, Yes, Eulalie.' Well, they was a spot for a swell love duet near the end of the first act and I had a tune for it that was a smash. You know I'm not bragging when I say that; I don't claim it as my tune, but it was and is a smash. I mean the 'Catch Me' number."

"I'll say it's a smash!" agreed Sam.

"But a smash in spite of the words," said Harry.

"You're right," said Sam.

"Well, the first time I played this tune for him, he went nuts over it and I gave him a lead sheet and he showed it to his wife. It seems she plays piano a little and she played this melody and she told him I had stole it from some opera; she thought it was 'Gioconda,' but she wasn't sure. So the next day Kane spoke to me about it and I told him it wasn't 'Gioconda'; it was Donizetti's 'Linda di Chamounix.' Well, he said he didn't feel like it was right to work on a melody that had been swiped from somewhere. So I said, 'Ain't it kind of late for you to be having all those scruples?' So he said, 'Maybe it is, but better late than never.' So I said, 'Listen, Benny— this is your wife talking, not you.' And he said, 'Let's leave her out of this,' and I said, 'I wished to heaven we could.'

"I said, 'Benny, you'll admit that's a pretty melody,' and he said yes, he admitted it. So I said: 'Well, how many of the dumb-bells that goes to our shows has ever heard "Linda di Chamounix" or ever will hear it? When I put this melody in our troupe I'm doing a million people a favor; I'm giving them a chance to hear a beautiful piece of music that they wouldn't never hear otherwise. Not only that, but they'll hear it at its best because I've improved it.' So Benny said, 'The first four bars is exactly the same and that's where people will notice.'

"So then I said: 'Now listen here, Benny—up to the present you haven't never criticized my music and I haven't criticized your lyrics. But now you say I'm a tune thief. I don't deny it, but if I wasn't, you'd of had a sweet time making a living for yourself, let alone get married. However, laying that to one side, I was over to my sister's house the other night and she had a soprano singer there and she sung a song something about "I love you, I love you; 'tis all my heart can say." It was a mighty pretty song and it come out about twenty or thirty years ago."

"So then Benny said, 'What of it?' So I said, 'Just this: I can recall four or five lyrics of yours where "I love you" comes in and I bet you've used the words "heart" and "say" and "all" at least twice apiece during your remarkable career as a song writer. Well, did you make those words up or did you hear them somewhere?' That's what I said to him and of course he was stopped. But his ethics was ravaged just the same and it was understood we'd split up right after 'Eulalie.' And as I say, his words wasn't no help to my Donizetti number; they'd of slayed it if it could of been slayed."

"Well?" said Sam.

"Well," said Harry, "Conrad Green wired me yesterday to come and see him, so I was up there today. He's so dumb that he thinks I'm better than Friml. And he's got a book by Jack Prendergast that he wanted Kane and I to work on. So I told him I wouldn't work with Kane and he said to get who I wanted. So that's why I gave you a ring."

"It sounds good to me," said Sam. "How is the book?"

"I only skimmed it through, but I guess it's all right. It's based on 'Cinderella,' so what with that idear combined with your lyrics and my tunes, it looks like we ought to give the public a novelty at least."

"Have you got any new tunes?"

"New?" Hart laughed. "I'm dirty with them." He sat down at the piano. "Get this rhythm number. If it ain't a smash, I'm Gatti-Casazza!"

He played it, beautifully, first in F sharp—a catchy refrain that seemed to be waltz time in the right hand and two-four in the left.

"It's pretty down here, too," he said, and played it again, just as surely, in B natural, a key whose mere mention is henbane to the average pianist.

"A wow!" enthused Sam Rose. "What is it?"

"Don't you know?"

"The Volga boat song."

"No," said Hart. "It's part of Aïda's number when she finds out the fella is going to war. And nobody that comes to our shows will spot it except maybe Deems Taylor and Alma Gluck."

"It's so pretty," said Sam, "that it's a wonder it never goes popular."

"The answer is that Verdi didn't know rhythm!" said Hart.

Or go back and observe our hero at the Bucks' house on Long Island. Several of the boys and girls were there and thrilled to hear that Harry Hart was coming. He hardly had time to taste his first cocktail before they were after him to play something.

"Something of your own!" pleaded the enraptured Helen Morse.

"If you mean something I made up," he replied with engaging frankness, "why, that's impossible; not exactly impossible, but it would be the homeliest tune you ever listened to. However, my name is signed to some mighty pretty things and I'll play you one or two of those."

Thus, without the conventional show of reluctance, Harry played the two "rhythm numbers" and the love-song that were making Conrad Green's "Upsy Daisy" the hit of the season. And he was starting in on another, a thing his informal audience did not recognize, when he overheard his hostess introducing somebody to Mr. Rudolph Friml.

"Good night!" exclaimed Hart. "Let somebody play that can play!" And he resigned his seat at the piano to the newcomer and moved to a far corner of the room.

"I hope Friml didn't hear me," he confided to a Miss Silloh. "I was playing a thing he wrote himself and letting you people believe it was mine."

Or catch him in the old days at a football game with Rita Marlowe of Goldwyn. One of the college bands was playing "Yes, Sir! That's My Baby!"

"Walter Donaldson. There's the boy that can write the hits!" said Hart.

"Just as if you couldn't!" said his companion.

"I don't class with him," replied her modest escort.

Later on, Rita remarked that he must have been recognized by people in the crowd. Many had stared.

"Let's not kid ourselves, girlie," he said. "They're staring at you, not me."

Still later, on the way home from the game, he told her he had saved over $25,000 and expected to average at least $40,000 a year income while his vogue lasted.

"I'm good as long as I don't run out of pretty tunes," he said, "and they's no reason why I should with all those old masters to draw from. I'm telling you my financial status because—well, I guess you know why."

Rita did know, and it was the general opinion, shared by the two principals, that she and Harry were engaged.

When "Upsy Daisy" had been running two months and its hit numbers were being sung, played, and whistled almost to cloyment, Hart was discovered by Spencer Deal. That he was the pioneer in a new American jazz, that his rhythms would revolutionize our music —these things and many more were set forth by Deal in a four-thousand-word article called "Harry Hart, Harbinger," printed by the erudite Webster's Weekly. And Harry ate it up, though some of the words nearly choked him.

Interesting people were wont to grace Peggy Leech's drawing-room on Sunday afternoons. Max Reinhardt had been there. Reinald Werrenrath had been there. So had Heifetz and Jeritza and Michael Arlen, and Noel Coward and Dudley Malone. And Charlie Chaplin, and Gene Tunney. In fact, Peggy's Sunday afternoons could be spoken of as salons and her apartment as a hotbed of culture.

It was to Peggy's that Spencer Deal escorted Hart a few weeks after the appearance of the article in Webster's. Deal, in presenting him, announced that he was at work on a "blue" symphony that would make George Gershwin's ultra rhythms and near dissonants sound like the doxology. "Oh!" exclaimed pretty Myra Hampton. "Will he play some of it for us?"

"Play, play, play!" said Hart querulously. "Don't you think I ever want a rest! Last night it was a party at Broun's and they kept after me and wouldn't take 'No' and finally I played just as rotten as I could, to learn them a lesson. But they didn't even know it was rotten. What do you do for a living?"

"I'm an actress," confessed the embarrassed young lady.

"Well, would you like it if, every time you went anywhere socially, people asked you to act?"

"Yes," she answered, but he had moved away.

He seemed to be seeking seclusion; sat down as far as possible from the crowd and looked hurt. He accepted a highball proffered by his hostess, but neglected to thank her. Not a bit discouraged, she brought him Signor Parelli of the Metropolitan.

"Mr. Hart," she said, "this is Mr. Parelli, one of the Metropolitan's conductors."

"Yay?" said Hart.

"Perhaps some day Mr. Parelli will conduct one of your operas."

"I hope so," said the polite Parelli.

"Do you?" said Hart. "Well, if I ever write an opera, I'll conduct it myself, or at least I won't take no chance of having it ruined by a foreigner."

The late war increased people's capacity for punishment and in about twenty minutes Peggy's guests began to act as if they would live in spite of Harry's refusal to perform. In fact, one of them, Roy Lattimer, full of Scotch courage and not so full of musical ability, went to the piano himself and began to play.

"Began" is all, for he had not completed four bars before Hart plunged across the room and jostled him off the bench.

"I hope you don't call yourself a pianist!" he said, pronouncing it as if it meant a cultivator of, or dealer in, peonies. And for two hours, during which everybody but Spencer Deal and the unfortunate hostess walked out on him, Harry played and played and played. Nor in all that time did he play anything by Kern, Gershwin, Stephen Jones, or Isham Jones, Samuels, Youmans, Friml, Stamper, Tours, Berlin, Tierney, Hubbell, Hein, or Gitz-Rice.

It was during this epoch that Harry had occasion one day to walk up Fifth Avenue from Forty-fifth Street to the Plaza. He noticed that almost everyone he passed on the line of march gazed at him intently. He recalled that his picture had been in two rotogravure sections the previous Sunday. It must have been a better likeness than he had thought.

New York was burning soft coal that winter and when Hart arrived in the Plaza wash-room he discovered a smudge on the left side of his upper lip. It made him look as if he had had a mustache, had decided to get it removed and then had changed his mind when the barber was half through.

Harry's date at the Plaza was with Rita Marlowe. He had put it off as long as he could. If the girl had any pride or sense, she'd have taken a hint. Why should he waste his time on a second-rate picture actress when he was hobnobbing with women like Elinor Deal and Thelma Warren and was promised an introduction to Mrs. Wallace Gerard? Girls ought to know that when a fella who has been taking them out three and four times a week and giving them a ring every morning, night and noon between whiles—they ought to know that when a fella stops calling them up and taking them out and won't even talk to them when they call up, there is only one possible answer. Yet this dame insists on you meeting her and probably having a scene. Well, she'll get a scene. No, she won't. No use being brutal. Just make it apparent in a nice way that things ain't like they used to be and get it over as quick as possible.

"Where can we go?" asked Rita. "I mean, to talk."

"Nowheres that'll take much time," said Harry. "I've got a date with Paul Whiteman to look over part of my symphony."

"I don't want to interrupt your work," said Rita. "Maybe it would be better if you came up to the house tonight."

"I can't tonight," he told her.

"When can you?"

"I'll give you a ring. It's hard to get away. You see——"

"I think I do," said Rita, and left him.

"About time," said Harry to himself.

His symphony went over fairly "big." The critics seemed less impressed than with the modern compositions of Gershwin and Deems Taylor. "But then," Harry reflected, "Gershwin was ahead of me and of course Taylor has friends on the paper."

A party instigated by Spencer Deal followed the concert and

Harry met Mrs. Wallace Gerard, who took a great interest in young composers and had been known to give them substantial aid. Hart accepted an invitation to play to her at her Park Avenue apartment. He made the mistake of thinking she wanted to be petted, not played to, and his first visit was his last.

He had been engaged by Conrad Green to do the music for a new show, with a book by Guy Bolton. He balked at working again with Sam Rose, whose lyrics were hopelessly proletarian. Green told him to pick his own lyricist and Harry chose Spencer Deal. The result of the collaboration was a score that required a new signature at the beginning of each bar, and a collection of six-syllable rhymes that has as much chance of being unriddled, let alone sung, by chorus girls as a pandect on biotaxy by Ernest Boyd.

"Terrible!" was Green's comment on advice of his musical adviser, Frank Tours.

"You're a fine judge!" said Hart. "But it don't make no difference what you think. Our contract with you is to write music and lyrics for this show and that's what we've done. If you don't like it, you can talk to my lawyer."

"Your lawyer is probably one of mine, too," replied Green. "He must be if he practises in New York. But that is neither here or there. If you think you can compel me to accept a score which Tours tells me that if it was orchestrated, Stokowski himself couldn't even read the triangle part, to say nothing of lyrics which you would have to ring up every night at seven o'clock to get the words in the opening chorus all pronounced in time for Bayside people to catch the one-twenty train—well, Hart, go along home now, because you and I are going to see each other in court every day for the next forty years."

A year or so later, Harry's total cash on hand and in bank amounted to $214.60, including the $56 he had cleaned up on the sale of sheet music and mechanical records of his symphony. He read in the Sunday papers that Otto Harbach had undertaken a book for Willis Merwin and the latter was looking around for a composer. Merwin was one of the younger producers and had been a pal of Harry's at the Friars'. Hart sought him there. He found Merwin and came to the point at once.

"It's too late," said the young entrepreneur. "I did consider you at first, but—well, I didn't think you were interested now in anything short of oratorio. The stuff you used to write would have been great, but this piece couldn't stand the ponderous junk you've been turning out lately. It needs light treatment and I've signed Donaldson and Gus Kahn."

"Maybe I could interpolate——" Harry began.

"I don't believe so," Merwin interrupted. "I don't recall a spot where we could use either a fugue or a dirge."

On his way out, Hart saw Benny Kane, his collaborator of other years. Benny made as if to get up and greet him, but changed his mind and sank back in his sequestered chair.

"He don't look as cocky as he used to," thought Harry, and wished that Kane had been more cordial. "What I'll have to do is turn out a hit song, just to tide me over. Of course I can write the words myself, but Benny had good idears once in a while."

Hart stopped in at his old publishers' where, in the halcyon days, he had been as welcome as more beer at the Pastry Cooks' Ball. He had left them for a more esthetic firm at the suggestion of Spencer Deal.

"Well, Harry," said Max Wise, one of the partners, "you're quite a stranger. We don't hear much of you lately."

"Maybe you will again," said Hart. "What would you say if I was to write another smash?"

"I'd say," replied Wise, "that it wasn't any too soon."

"How would you like to have me back here?"

"With a smash, yes. Go get one and you'll find the door wide open. Who are you working with?"

"I haven't nobody."

"You could do a lot worse," said Wise, "than team up again with Benny Kane. You and him parting company was like separating Baltimore and Ohio or pork and beans."

"He hasn't done nothing since he left me," said Hart.

"No," replied Wise, "but you can't hardly claim to have been glutting the country with sensations yourself!"

Hart went back to his hotel and wished there was no such thing as pride. He'd like to give Benny a ring.

He answered the telephone and recognized Benny's voice.

"I seen you at the Friars' today," said Benny, "and it reminded me of an idear. Where could we get together?"

"At the club," Harry replied. "I'll be there in a half-hour."

"I was thinking," said Benny, when they were seated at the table near the piano, "that nobody has wrote a rhythm song lately about 'I love you'; that is, not in the last two or three months. And one time you was telling me about being over to your sister's and they was a soprano there that sung a song that went 'I love you, I love you; 'tis all my heart can say.'"

"What of it?"

"Well," said Benny, "let's take that song and I'll just fix up the words a little and you can take the tune and put it into your rhythm and we're all set. That is, if the tune's o. k. What is it like?"

"Oh, 'Arcady' and 'Marcheta' and maybe that 'Buzz Around' song of Dave Stamper's. But then, what ain't?"

"Well, let's go to it."

"Where is your ethics?"

"Listen," said Benny Kane—"I and Rae was talking this afternoon, and we didn't disgust ethics. She was just saying she thought that all God's children had shoes except her."

"All right," said Hart. "I can remember enough of the tune. But I'll look the song up tomorrow and give it to you and you can rewrite the words."

"Fine! And now how about putting on the feed bag?"

"No," said Harry. "I promised to call up a dame."

Whereupon he kept his ancient promise.

"You've got a lot of nerve," said Rita at the other end of the wire, "imagining a girl would wait for you this long. And I'd say 'No' and say it good and loud, except that my piano has just been tuned and you've never played me your symphony."

"I ain't going to, neither," said Harry. "But I want to try out a new rhythm number that ought to be a smash. It starts off 'I love you, I love you.'"

"It sounds wonderful!" said Rita.

Tips on Horses

Once in every so often the undersized receives a circular from the Horse Breeders assn. of America or something along with a request to give same all possible publicity to the end that peoples' interest in horses will be revived and roused up and not allow the genus equine to become extinct in our land from lack of attention. And just as often as one of these literary broadsides hits my happy home just so often do I feel it incumbrance upon myself to come out flat-footed and open and above the boards and state my attitude towards what is known in exclusive livery stable circles as his highness le Horse.

Children, dogs and horses is regarded in this country as sacred items and it is considered pretty close to a felony to even make a face when any of the 3 is mentioned. Well, I am fond of children, well at least 4 of them and can tolerate a few dogs provided they can keep their mouth shut and ain't over a ft. high. But irregardless and less majesty and the deuce with same, I can't help from admitting at this junction that the bear mention of a horse has the same effect on me like red flags to a bull or ginger ale to a Elk.

A horse is the most overestimated animal in the world with the possible exception of a police dog. For every incidence where a horse has saved a human life I can dig you up a 100 incidents where they have killed people by falling off them or trampling them down or both. Personly, the only horse who I ever set on their back throwed me off on my bosom before I had road him 20 ft. and did the horse wait to see if I was hurt, no.

Devotees of horse flesh is wont to point out that King Richard III once offered his kingdom for one of them, but in the first place he was not the kind of a person who I would pin any faith on his judgment of values and in the second place the kingdom had been acquired by a couple of mild little murders and it was a case of easy come, easy go.

A study of some of the expressions in usage at the present day will serve to throw light on the real personality of the horse. Take for example the phrase "eat like a horse." The picture you get from these phrases is the picture of anybody eating without no regard to ethics or good manners, the picture of a person who you would as leaf have at the table as they.

Or take "horse laugh." This indicates the coarsest, roughest kind of a laugh and a person of breeding and refinement would pretty near as soon have their friends give them a head cold as the horse laugh. Or "horse play." How often do you hear theatre-goers complain that such and such a comedy has got too much horse play or observe parents order their kiddies to cut out the horse play. The answer is that a horse can't play nice like kittens or oxen or even wolfs, but has got to be ribald and rough in their sports as in everything else.

Defenders of le Horse will no doubt point to the term "good, common horse sense," or the simile "work like a horse," as being proof of the beast's virtues, but if a horse has got such good common sense, why do they always have to have a jockey show them the way round a fenced in race track where you couldn't possible go wrong unless you was dumb as for working like a horse, I never met a horse who worked because he thought it was funny. They work for the same reason the rest of us works.

I will pass over to what different horses has done to me in places like Saratoga, Belmont, Havana and New Orleans. Suffice it to say that none of them ever lived up to what I had been led to believe. And one day just last month I had to walk across 34th street in N. Y. city and dodged my way amongst taxi cabs, motor trucks, and street cars and was just congratulating myself on making the trip unscathed when a horse reached out and snapped at me, a stranger.

Horses ain't been no good in battle since trench warfare come into its own and besides you never heard of a horse volunteering for a army. And do you think Paul Revere even would of looked at a horse if all the taxis hadn't been engaged with the theatre crowds that night?

Last but not lease, have you ever been bit by a horse fly, which never would of been thought of only for his highness le Horse.

How Winners Quit Winners

One of the toughest problems faced by the people that indulges in the so-called games of chance like craps, poker, bridge whist, chemin de fer, and kindred ilks is the problem of how to quit when winner and still give the losers the impression that you wished to he—ll you didn't half to quit.

Personly I ain't hardly ever been bothered by this problem but have seen it faced numerable times by partys that is blessed with horseshoes which the under-signed certainly is not oweing to a all wise Providence system of giveing one person luck, another beauty another brains and etc.

And the methods employed by the lucky ones to try and create the above named impression is so crude that they would seem funny if they did not occur at a time when they didn't seem funny.

Like for inst. I was amongst the heavy sugar men in a so-called friendly stud game 2 or 3 weeks ago and one of the other boys was also behind and I was setting almost opp. him and I never seen nobody so wide awake and finely he win 5 pots in succession and was more winner than he had been loser and all of a sudden he was ceased with a attack of sleeping sickness though it could not of been more than 4 o'clock and when he yawned you could of thrown a basketball down his throat and they had to dash ice-water in his face when it was his turn to deal.

So he had to cash in and go to bed and the only wonder was that he could make such a accurate count of his checks wile practally unconscious.

About a ½ hr. later another member of the winning team begin to groan with indigestion and when we ast him did he want to quit he would say no but he said it in tones like the death whinnies of poisoned tweel and the game finely broke up in a wave of sympathy.

Another time honored method that ain't quite so crude is prepared for in advance. This is to have the Mrs. stay home and call you up ever so often and sooner or later one of her calls is libel to coincide with the time you are ready to quit and then you go back to the table and tell the rest of the boys that you got to get home right away as the baby has swallowed some sheet music.

The trouble with this system is that a good many wifes won't stay home and if they do stay home they seem to have a kind of a prejudice vs. getting up to telephone between 3 and 4 in the A. M.

So much for the crude messages in gen. usages and now I am going to tell you about a friend of mine that has originated some methods of his own and so far they ain't been nobody suspected him. This is a man named Elva Waffle and dureing day times he is a tree tickler by trade but makes his heavy dough nights at the gameing board.

Well Elva lives in a suburb which is right near 5 other suburbs and each of the 6 suburbs has got at lease one fire house so they ain't hardly a ½ hr. passes day or night when you can't hear a fire whistle blowing.

So Elva bought himself a badge that says on it the Ever Ready fire department and he always wears this badge where you can't help from seeing it.

Well we will say one of the fire whistles blows and if Elva is a big winner he shoves his checks at the banker, says he has got to go to the fire and dashes out of the house willy nilly.

If he is a loser when the siren sounds and one of the other guests asks him why don't he go to the fire, he says, you poor sap don't you know the difference between the Ever Ready whistle and the Qui Vive whistle.

But Elva ain't a sucker enough to always pull the same stuff in the same joint. He has got another scheme which is said to of been thought up by Ed Reulbach when the last named was pitching for the Cubs.

Ed was loseing a game vs. Brooklyn and between innings he says to Mgr. Chance I tell you what I will do. I'll eat some soap and when I get out there next inning I will have a fit and froth at the mouth and the crowd will go into a panic and swarm down on the field and the umpire will have to forfeit the game to Chicago.

Well Elva always has a tube of shaveing cream in his pocket and when he sees it's getting time for him to quit he secretly takes a swig out of the tube and the next minute he begins to froth at the mouth and makeing funny noises and as a rule the game breaks up instantum as very few people even losers cares to play in a game with a man that is conducive to fits.

Another one of Elva's tricks is to go to a poker party with a bag of chocolates and passes them around but they won't nobody take one as they look terrible.

So Elva eats them himself and gets his hands all smeared up an it ain't long before they ain't a deck of cards left in the house that decent people would play with.

Those is only 3 of Elva's little stock of ingenuities and he has ast me to not reveal no more of them but make people do their own thinking and planning like he done and I will say for Elva that he has been so successful with his schemes that he plans to soon give up card playing entirely and devote all his time to tree tickling which acts on him like a drug.

Salt Water Fishing

A few wks. ago the writer was prevailed on to give readers my hints and views in regards to the sport of fishing and what tackle to use for the different members of the Finny tribe and where to find them and etc. and since writeing same my mail has been swamped from nimrods all over the country thanking me for the article and how it helped them and etc.

They have also been a swarm of letters from men and women of both sexes complaining that my advice and instruction was all confined to fishing in streams, lakes and etc. and nothing in regards to deep sea fishing which of course is the grandest of all sports for folks who can afford same which these irated correspondents felt like they are as they pointed out that it wouldn't be no more than fair for me to do so much for them as I done for the small scale nimrods.

So it looks like I better devote a few spicy paragraphs to the sport of salt water fishing lest the followers of same accuse me of favorism.

Well friends, salt water fishing depends on the season of the year in regards to different kinds of fish. Like for inst. salt mackerel runs in the Fall and not in the Winter and Spring. Pickled eel can be caught in tropic waters in Winter and goes to Newport for the Summer. Tripe runs only dureing Winter months and walks the rest of the time. Cross-eyed hoke bites freely in the Spring and then lives the balance of the yr. on their own fat.

So it will be seen that with all the different fish haveing different habits, why only a few gen. suggestions can be given in this limited space.

Probably the greatest fishing that can be enjoyed by residents of this continent is gullet fishing dureing Winter months off the coast of Iowa.

Liver-lipped gullets weighs from ½ to 2 tons and is one of the gamest of mollusks. They will bite freely at a electric iron or swinging doors but once they have struck, the game is only started and sometimes it is a full 6 months between the first nibble and the time when Mr. Gullet lays on the bottom of your dingy.

I have even knew anglers who have claimed to of fought a yr. with a gullet and had their boat dragged by same from the Boone County fishing grounds to the Michigan fruit belt.

These fishermen was probably working on the old theory that the way to land a fish this size was to give him full play and leave him wear himself out but some fishers maintains that they's no use wasteing ½ a yr. or any part of same on a liver-lipped gullet and the right way to handle them is drag them to the surface and give them a bust on the jaw.

In still water fishing for liver-lipped gullets use a Biloxi fly on a No. 26 barbed wire line.

The lap-eared smike runs in schools off the coast of eastern Pittsburgh and is caught with live bait like a horse or a canteloupe. Use a No. 12 hook and a E string. The smike is one of the gamest of deep sea fish and also one of the hardest to conquer as they don't confine their battle to the water as they is libel to swim ashore and give you a merry chase across country.

The wise smike fisherman equips himself with a fast touring car as well as a boat so as to be able to keep up with the whims of the smike once she gets ashore.

Two yrs. ago a lop-eared friend of mine named Bob Poodle was smike fishing off Binghamton and got a bite with a quarter of beef. After eating all the well done meat the smike waded for shore and started for Omaha.

Mr. Poodle who is a well to do epileptic engaged a taxi and offered the driver a soldier's bonus of $100 if he would not loose sight of the smike. The last named finally wearied of the chase and was caught in a tree near Waukesha, Wisconsin, but without the means of hireing a taxi Mr. Poodle would of been obliged to go sans smike.

The snub-nosed jonah runs in prep schools off the Long Island coast from September to May. They will nibble at waffles and veal loaf but are caught mostly with live bait such as stoats or mangy kittens.

I recall an interesting personal experience with a snub-nosed jonah. I was fishing with the President off the coast of Lafayette, Indiana, and for 3 wks. neither of us had a nibble and was getting tired of each other when suddenly I seen my bobber move and felt the unmistakeable nibble of a snub-nosed jonah.

By 4 o'clock the next morning there could be no question but what it was a fish and suspicion was turned into certainty when the mollusk's features appeared on the surface of the water bound for Omaha.

The chase of the next 10 days would take the pen of a Jack Dempsey to describe it. The jonah had reservations on the St. Paul but a friendly porter put me up in the wash rm. of the next car.

Final battle in the yards of Omaha defys description. Sufficient to say that the little woman invited our friends the next week end to a snub-nosed jonah roast.

For Winter salt water fishing there's nothing so savory and full of fight as the pigeon-toed wham. These little fellows is found off the coast of Little Rock and will bite at live bait only.

A friend of mine named Orville Chow found out this fact by a queer accident. He was boating one day with his wife on the smooth waters of the Yazoo when she suddenly fainted from something she had eat.

Orville promptly throwed her overboard forgetting that he had tied a rope around her neck earlier in the day. In a instant he felt a strike and hauling in the rope, landed a 1200 pound pigeon-toed wham which was clinging to the madam's wrist watch.

Naturally my friend stayed in the vicinity for several days and landed all told a doz. when useing the Mrs. as bait.

The Origin of Football

From now till next October it seems like it would be a good time for different people to study up on football and what it's like and its history and etc. as they will be plenty of coaches meetings and changeing the rules and etc. as many ignorant people like the foreign immigrants and our women folks appears to have a great ignorants of football and nothing strikes me as more pitiful for instants than a member of the fair sex tending a football game at some suckers expense and when she gets there she don't know whether the object of the game is to match up all your cards or to get 3 men out.

Percy Haughten, the former manager of the Harvard football nine, once wrote a book called How to Understand Football where he tells what it's all about and even a woman can understand it if they keep their mind on what they are reading and not let their mind stray off the subject on to one of the tropics, which is nearest their heart, food or drink.

The writer advices men and women of both sexes to read this book and they will enjoy future games so much the more from have-ing a better understanding of what is going on and female readers especially will maybe learn enough to not give vent to screeks of happiness when their escort's team is getting murdered.

But there is nothing in Mr. Haughten's book regarding the true origin of American football and where it comes from and etc. and it looks like a few words on the subject from the undersigned wouldn't go amiss. So will say at the outset that our American game of foot-ball was borrowed from England is the bunkerino and where we really got a hold of our game was from the far flung fields of Galicia.

To be sure the English has got a game called Rugby, or Rounders, but it is a game which is generally played outdoors on a field faceing both ways. Rugby, or Rounders, is similar to the game played with the ft. in Brazil called Rigby, or Rinders, and something like the Dutch game called Roogby. The last named, however, is played with a walrus shaped ball and with a 1000 men on a side. A crowd of 20 spectators is nothing at a Roogby match in Wabash, Holland, and the Netherlands is dirty with lonely women and children whose fathers and husbands respy. spend the week end in various football vats.

Another game resembling the English Rugby, or Rounders, is called Ragby, or Randers, and is played by the Swedes on a crokinole board. In Ragby, however, the game is played by both sexes with a manager or referee acting as pastor or umpire and 4000 people on a side. In Nashville, Sweden, it is nothing to see a dozen Ragby fans watching a Ragby match or bolero.

But the daddy of our American football is the Galician game, Ruggles.

There is only 11 men on a college Ruggles team but sometimes as many as 13 comes out to try for the team and what to do with the 2 extra men is a neat problem for the coach. Some coaches has these 2 busy bodies "framed" for some imaginary violation of the law and "sent up the river" or jugged as the Galicians calls it while other more humane coaches merely allows them to hang around the field and watch the practice but don't speak to them or give them any encouragement.

Most of the college coaches takes off from Sunday till Thursday and it is on these wild junkets that they visit surrounding towns and encounter the coaches in rival colleges and make up a ruggles match for the following Saturday.

Then is when the fun starts to see if a field can be hired to play on and get up nicknames for the 2 rival colleges and etc. If all other matters is arranged satisfactory why on Friday nights the 2 coaches meets in a saloon and pick out the officials for the following days game. The officials consists of a referee, an umpire, and 2 bat men each carrying a book of the latest rules and fol de rols.

The morning of the game the officials, coaches and principle players of both sides meets in a obscure rabbit hutch and runs through each others signals, then run to the seen of the game in squads of 4.

Each college has its colors and just before the game there is a mad scramble to get the various officials to wear the colors of this team or that team as whoever colors the officials is wearing, he is supposed to give that team a shade the best of it.

At a few minutes before 2 o'clock the 2 bat men blows a buggle and the game is on. The captains of the 2 rival nines then draws straws and the longest straw kicks the flyskin to some member of the opposeing team usually a defensive rare back. The last named then tries to reach the ghoul in 4 downs but if he does it in one less it is called a birdie. If he is throwed back it is called a decisive set back and the 2 bat men cuts up antics on the side lines.

As soon as one team scores a ghoul or a set back the 1st ½ is considered practally over and some of the more easy satisfied players goes back to the rabbit hutch to gargle. From then on it is just a question of holding off and the one that holds off the longest is called the Touch me not which counts 3 points.

There are as many as 3 Ruggles matches played every Saturday in Galicia and the Azoores, but the big match of the season is the one which takes place at Omaha, Galicia, the first Friday after Thanksgiving. This is generally always between the Airedales and the flee bitten Poms and it is certainly inspireing to hear the rival cheering sections resound every great play of the rival dog teams with their college yells.

The followers of the Airedales will shout:

> My mission is wishing
> For upper Galician
> Airedales, rah, rah, rah.

And then hear the Pom section shout back:

> Pom, Pom, the Piper's son
> Stole the ball and away he run
> With a tiger!

That is the true spirit of Ruggles in Galicia and that is where we get our American football and not from the English game Rugby, or Rounders.

New Golf Accessories

Nearly every body now days is playing golf or at lease thinking about it and this is the best time in the yr. to try and decide what is the matter with your game and how to improve same and wile I don't make no pretences of knowing nothing about form, style and etc. still I am going to give my readers a few suggestions in regards to new accessorys which it looks to me like they are worth a trial at lease and they don't none of them cost much money so if they work good so much the better and vica versa.

I suppose my readers will think that they can't possibly be no accessorys that ain't been thought of before because golf has all ready got more accessorys than anything except those little automobiles that grows wild in Detroit, and the last one I heard about seemed like they had reached the limit, namely a stroke register which you fastened on to your arm and every time you swung at the ball the stroke was recorded on the register and when you had played around you would just half to look at the register and it would tell you whether you had made a 80 or 110 or what not.

This one don't seem to of had much of a sale though it certainly should ought to, on acct. of there being so many of the boys who can't seem to recall how many strokes they have had on one hole let alone a complete rd. but of course they was one trouble with it, namely that it registered practice swings the same like when you was in ernest and I guess I'm about the only golfer in the world that don't use at lease 18 practice swings per rd. and the reason I don't its because I never seem to have time on acct. of people behind me being in a hurry.

But these accessorys which I am going to tell you about is some which I never heard of them being on the market and if any of them are I apologize to the inventor of same and no harm done.

No. 1 is a invention of Octavus Roy Cohen, of Birmingham, Alabama. This invention is a human being and should either ought to be a pastor or a lay reader.

If he is also a golfer himself so much the better as you can probably get him to go along with you just for the pleasure of playing but anyway the idear is that every time you start to shoot, he starts to pray and the result is that you have to keep your head down.

No. 2 is a simple contrivance namely a empty bbl. and is recommended to golfers like Irvin S. Cobb and James J. Montague who ain't no sooner than hit the ball than they are off down the field after it like it was a punt and they was ends.

The bbl. is placed side ways right ahead of their left ft. and as soon as they have swang and start their dash they fall over the bbl. and more than likely light on their nose and hurt themselfs. About a wk. of the bbl. cure will make a new man out of these kinds of boys.

No. 3 is another simple device namely a extra direction flag which the caddy carrys along and places it where it will do the most good. Like for inst. the golfers has got the sliceing habit and they ain't nobody can cure him of same. Well he comes to a blind hole and they's a regular direction flag right out in the middle of the course but if our hero was to aim at it he would land way over in the ruffles at the right.

So before he shoots the caddy takes this extra direction flag and sticks it in the ground on the edge of the rough on the left. Then the caddy hollers here is the direction flag and the man aims at it and the ball lands in the middle of the fair ways. In the case of he who hooks the direction flag is placed on the opp. or right side of the fair ways.

No. 4 is the common smoke screens used dureing what I have dubbed the great war. The screen is made by a kind of a bomb which you set fire to it and nothing happens only great big clouds of smoke comes out of the bomb and you can't see through them. As a golf accessory these bombs would be carried by the caddy till the golfer come to a place where he had to shoot over a mound or a valley or a water hazard.

The caddy would set off one of the bombs about 10 ft. ahead of where the player was going to make his shot and when the smoke was so thick that the player couldn't see what would happen to him if he topped his shot, why he could then go ahead and shoot without no nervous break down.

No. 5 is a pocket compass and is used in connections with putting. Like suppose for inst. you land on the green about 10 ft. from the cup, why the next thing is to find out what direction the hole is at and this can't be done and done right without a compass.

At lease I have seen a whole lot of golfers try and putt without no compass and their ball has went from 10 to 45 ft. degrees to the right or left of where the hole is actually located. This is because they was just guessing where as with a compass they's no guess work about it. If you miss a putt with a compass to tell you just where a hole is at, why it's because you can't putt so good.

No. 6 and last is like No. 1 namely it's a human being only this time it's a man who is in the sand and gravel business and he goes along with you around the course driveing a empty sand wagon till your ball lands in a sand trap and then you make a deal with him that he can have all the sand in the trap provided he removes it off the premises. You would be surprised how much easier it is to shoot out of a sand trap after the wagon has drove off with the sand.

The undersigned is now prepared to answer any questions my readers may wish to ask in regards to golf.

A Yacht Race

DISASTER

The first heat went to the Shamrock, but they's many a slipton between the cup and the Lipton. I don't know if that gag's been used before, but it's my own idear.

As I couldn't stand the excitement of continuously watching the 2 catboats as they sped forwards in the teeth of a 3 mile carm, I happened to be down in Lieut. Annotoyn's room when the Resolute done a Willard. Word was rushed in that the rest of the race would be a monologue as the Resolute's sails had flopped and I couldn't help from feeling sorry for her as I was to a evening dress suit dance one night and broke a suspender.

I went out on the porch and asked one of the newspaper boys how it could of happened and he said she had broke a gaff. You know how a woman feels these days when she breaks a gaff at the present price of gaffs. But anyway I went and seen Capt. Norton of our destroyer that use to play football at the navy in Annapolis and made All American but treated us fine, and he said he didn't think it was a broken gaff, but he thought it was a broken throat halyard and maybe she had died of tonsilitis.

Well I would of been satisfied with the broken throat diagnosis only Lieut. Comm. Dewes said he thought it was a combination of broken gaff jaw and a busted spinnaker. Per—only I come to the conclusions that I might as well use my own judgments as I once rowed a rowboat out on Lake Mich.

So I borrowed a pair of opera glasses off of a bum cartoonist and took a look at the Irresolute and it looked to me like she had croaked from a barnacle on her binnacle. Whatever it was, the boys on board of her all but perspired trying not to fix it. She was toed to a marine hospital and now they say that the second leg will be ran off Saturday if she can stand the gaff.

Maybe some of you boys has never seen a international yacht race so I will try and tell you a few of our experiences. In the first place we had to get up in the middle of the night so as we could be down to the battery in time to catch the press boats which was to leave at 8 A.M. but didn't.

Well along about half past eight we fell into a tug and was dragged out to the middle of the river where two destroyers was waiting for us though some of the boys looked like they had been destroyed the night before.

We reached the paddock along about 10 o'clock and the 2 yawls was already there warming up. The Shamrock was painted green for some reason another. We set there on the porch rocking till noon which was starting time. By that time the grounds was really too wet to play on, but they started the game anyway and the 2 scows got away to a pretty even start.

I will let the experts tell you about the technical side of it. Personly I wished we was at a 6-day bicycle race where you get about the same thrills only you don't half to set in a rocker.

As for old Tom's victory, I say why not leave him have the cup as he has got tea to pour into it, and what have we got? Nothing.

LOST LEGS

In the evening by the moonlight you could hear those experts wondering who had won. The Resolute was 5 miles ahead, but that don't mean nothing on acct. of the time allowance. Whatever you see wrote by the experts don't believe it. A little thing like a 5 mile lead combined with a handicap of six minutes and some seconds is no proof that the defender has beat the challenger or vice versa and personly I don't know which is which.

As me and my Destroyer go to press, the vote stands 546 electoral votes for Resie and 467 votes for Shimmy. But the complete returns from Ohio and California are still uncomplete. The latest returns was as follows:

California—456 precincts out of 604 gives the Resolute 4,517 and the Shamrock 2,809.

Ohio—516 precincts out of 607 gives Shamrock 4,517 and the Resolute 2,809.

Governor Hughes has evidently won Nevada.

At latest reports it looks like each sloop had lost a leg in the race, but I have seen one-legged men go faster than them two catboats and don't think for a minute that Tuesday's race will be slowed up by the loss of a leg apiece. You couldn't slow these birds any more than you could slow up a detective on the Elwell case. They're stopped before they start.

Somebody must of shot an albatross between Thursday and Saturday noon. Anyhow when it was time for the 2 fishing smacks to make their getaway, the sea and wind was both in what they call a dead calm, which just about agrees with my sentiments in regards to this here race. If they want the fans to go out there and see them again next Tuesday, they better put on a double header for one admission.

At high noon the wind was blowing a 2 inch gale backwards and neither scow would move, so the starter postponed it till along come a breath of fresh air, which was a 1/4 to 2. Then away went the 2 sloops like a snail with paralysis.

"It's a long, sleepy swell," said the Captain of the Destroyer on which we was on.

"Don't get personal," I said. "If you had to get up at 5 o'clock in the morning to see a race that don't start till 1:45 in the P.M. and when it's started you don't know if it's started or hasn't started, you would be a long, sleepy swell, too, provided you was long and sleepy and a swell."

"Shamrock's got the advantage today," said the captain after a wile. "They's 3 legs in the stead of 2 and the first leg is a beat wile the other 2 is reaches and Shamrock is supposed to be good on reaches."

"That's all right," I said, "but I was down to Toledo last 4 of July a yr. ago and by the time Dempsey got in the first beat, Willard's reaches didn't do him no good."

So the captain asked me what happened to Willard down there.

"Well," I said, "it looked to me like his throat halyard parted at the winch, and his gaff busted all to pieces.

Finely I asked the captain why he didn't challenge for the cup, as his destroyer could go along at a speed of 35 nuts per hr, as against nothing per hr. for the 2 slops that was out there supposed to be racing.

"Listen," he said, "you underestimate the speed of my ship. It didn't only take us 2 hrs. to get out here this morning with 150 nuts to say nothing about cartoonists."

A DELAYED START

Capt. Burton was officially canned off the good ship Shamrock before yesterday's race started, but when it started Capt. Burton was at the helm hard aport. In the other two days' races the experts had criticised Cap Burton severely for not taking advantage of his opportunities, and he was supplanted according to the newspapers by one Capt. Turner. So when it come time for the race Capt. Burton was still the skipper of the Shamrock and if he was made a monkey out of in the first two races, why somebody else was made a monkey out of yesterday.

But the boys say it isn't ethical to use the words The Shamrock and The Resolute. In order to be perfectly nautical the definite

article must be left out. So here and after we will try and do that
same.

So leave us give you a chronological acct. of the race.

The two slops was supposed to start at 12 noon, but neither them
or the breeze was ready, so they waited a ¼ of a hr. and away they
went like a mole crawling acrost the yard. At one o'clock sharp
Shamrock raised her fiddler's jib and Resolute countered by hoisting
her cello A string. Discords followed.

At 1:45 we turned on the electric fan in our destroyer in the hopes
it would stir up a little breeze. Nothing happened.

At 1:51 Shamrock hauled down her jib topsail and substituted a
gobboon. That is what really win the race as heretofore the sailors
was too busy looking out to sea to pay a tension to the sloop.

At 2:14 everybody was taking their siesta and I will say one thing
for the cup races that they's no nicer places to sleep than watching
them.

At 2:15 it was officially announced that Shamrock had rounded
the first boy which meant she had went 10 miles. The tidings was
greeted with a raspberry siren from all the vessels therabouts. Ten
miles in two hours is going some, even if you do it with a wheel
barrow. I know if I was wheeling my 1 yr. old child in his go cart
at that rate of speed he would turn around and say "Daddy what's
your hurry?" And I couldn't tell him.

At 2:34 Capt. Norton of our Destroyer announced that the wind
wasn't from the west. Nobody had said it was so they wasn't no argument. At this point Lt. W. P. O. Clark asked me to look out for an
attack of pyorreahhea wile in New York. At this point Shamrock
raised her club mainsail but Resolute come back at her by raising
her club sandwich.

The invading visiting boat was nicknamed Shamrock, but they
was no sham about the rocking on our little destroyer. In these connections I would like to say to Mr. Lipton and whoever owns the
other scow that if they really want to get somewheres they could get
there a whole lot quicker in a taxi or even a lawn mower. I personly
havent never seen nothing slower than these 2 dingheys unless it was
possibly a national convention.

At 3:45 Shamrock hoisted her skirts and put on a fresh pair of stockings. A master of salesmanship told me at this juncture that the race was practically over.

The crowning feature of the day was that one of the newspaper boys brought his golf clubs along on our destroyer, but wouldn't play on the grounds that they was too much salt water.

A PERFECT DAY

This would be a very enjoyable event if they would keep the 2 sloops out of it. The way they got things fixed now a person has to get up every little while and go up on the porch and look at the 2 contenders which between you and I can't neither of them go fast enough to get up a prespiration.

The only people that is sweating on this assignment is the newspaper boys, and speaking about them, I wished you could of seen the bunch on board of our destroyer Friday. Of course a person can't say that they was a lot of strange faces, because the reporters themselfs has got that kind, but these was birds that we never seen before and I asked somebody who they was and they said they was advertiseing mgrs. and I don't know what they was doing out there, but if thats their idear of a perfect day they are welcome. Personally I would or had rather stay in the store.

Friday's race was another 3-legged affair. 1 leg vs. the wind which they call a beat and the other 2 retches. The beat was about an even break, but when it come to the 2 retches the Shamrock was a whole lot the most retched. If Sir Thomas will take a suggestion from a bird that knows nothing about yachts and cares a whole lot more, why if I was him I would take down my club jib and put in a gasoline engine which they say you can get pretty reasonable if you go to the right place. In this race whoever was skipping the Shamrock kept changeing sails and the more they changed the slower they went. I wouldn't be surprised to find out that the Shamrock had a bet on the Resolute.

The official story of the race may be told in the following words by one who didn't see it. They started at 1 o'clock because starting time was high noon and they got away about even with neither slop making any headway. In fact they both looked like they was in reverse. I don't know if they have emergency brakes on yachts or no, but if they have they was certainly both useing them. In about two hours they rounded the first stake and the boats that was watching give a resounding cheer on their sirens.

Well Resolute was ahead at the first stake and the second stake and the last stake, and it looks now like the defender had a even chance of winning, but personly its a race between a hearse and a snail and may the slowest team win.

THE END OF IT

As far as us boys are concerned, the Shamrock and Resolute can have our riparian rights to Sandy Hook and environs.

In the first place, if the Shamrock was as good as old Tom claims it is, why don't he ride on it instead of on his steam yacht. It looks fishy to me.

At 11:45 yesterday the Shamrock hoisted the signal "V," which means in the nautical language that they's too much salt in the water for a race to-day. The Resolute countered with the signal "M," the significance of which is that they's too much sugar in Mr. Lipton's tea. But, as Grantland Rice says, Mr. Lipton's last off the "tea," last on the green. What could be sweeter?

Speaking of skippers, nobody knew why they called that skipper till everybody found out that it was because they skipped so many days when they might be sailing.

Don't leave anybody forget that the Shamrock had a handicap of six minutes and forty seconds on acct. of her sail acreage or something. It's just like putting Dempsey into the ring with Carpentier and saying to the last named:

"Now lookheré, Georges, yous must keep both votre hand behind votre back and extend the chin in a prominent place in the foreground."

Which means in the English language:

"George, keep your hands behind your back and your chin up front where he can get a crack at it."

Well boys the library of the Destroyer Semmes was exhausted yesterday and if the race had of went one more day we boys wouldn't of knew what to read to go to sleep by and probably would of had to take a sedative. All they was left was a Zane Grey novel and Damon Runyon was hanging to that.

Technically, when the race started both scows went on the carpet tack and the consensus at the finish was that the Philadelphia Athletics could of beat either team for the title, which is an awful thing to say about the two sloops.

YEARS LATER

So far as the undersigned knows, Sir Thomas Lipton is a man of honor whose word is as good as his bond and better than his catboats. Just the same business is business, and it seems to me that before the recent, hair-raising yachting contests off Newport are forgotten, it would be a sensible thing to get the old tea-taster to put in writing his verbal promise never to challenge for the Cup again. Otherwise there is a chance that he will send another mash note to the Vanderbilts ten years from now and if they remind him that he had given his word to let us alone, he will say: "Yes, but that was when I was just a kiddie and hadn't learned the facts of life."

Bill Rogers' scheme won't satisfy the old man or me either. Bill suggested that everybody chip in $1.00 apiece and send it to Mayor Walker, whose duty it would be to use the proceeds in the purchase of a consolation cup for Sir Thomas. In the first place, Mr. Lipton lives in a country where you don't have to pour your consolation into a cup even in the main dining-room. In the second place, suppose everyone but Bill Rogers did send a $1.00 to Mayor Walker; that would only make something like $120,000,000 and the Mayor would face the alternative of being called a cheap skater or paying for the saucer out of his own pocket. In the third place, I understand that Bill is already sorry he conceived the idea; its publication brought him back into the limelight and tore away the blanket of obscurity he has been trying to hide behind for the past fourteen years.

My objections to the Lipton Cup races are several. Chief among them is that they invariably cast a pall of gloom over the American people, gloom so contagious that even I, ordinarily equipped with an irresistible smile of good-fellowship for everybody, feel like hell from the moment a new Shamrock's barnacle is sighted off Muscle Shoals until at least a month after someone has called up the garage and had it towed back to Edinburgh. This depression of soul is generally attributed to our spirit of sportsmanship; we hate to see such a good fellow lose when he is so anxious to triumph, and so game. (His sorrowful words brokenly uttered during the last day at Newport—"I cannot win! I cannot win!"—left hardly a dry eye in any American speakeasy and will go down in history along with such famous slogans as Gridley's "Don't fire till you are damn good and ready!" and Admiral Schley's "I can't get them to go home!") The facts are, I think, that about ten Americans are acquainted with Sir Thomas and only six or seven are well enough acquainted with him to know whether he is a good fellow. As for his anxiety to triumph, I believe if that were on the level he would either have Gar Wood build him a boat or challenge the Philadelphia National League baseball team.

It seems to me the actual cause of gloom is that the defence of the Cup is in the hands of an exclusive yacht club and everybody hates an exclusive yacht club. What makes it exclusive is that you have to have a yacht to belong to it. Around New York and other cities, even cities where there is no water except the lavatory, you can find plenty of yacht clubs with members who would rather jump out of a twelfth-story window than look at a picture of the Europa. But a yacht club that bars you unless you own at least a canoe is a snooty organization which a large majority of us would love to see humiliated even by a Greek.

And then I object to the way our newspapers treat these feverish events. They spread them all over the front page and crowd out things you want to read, that are really news, such as the natural death of somebody in New Jersey. The lead stories are written by experts who carry along a pocket dictionary to refer to in case they forget the difference between a yawl and a squall. From the front page, the stories are jumped, for some whimsical reason, to the sporting section, where they are illustrated by photographs of the challenger and the defender (you can instantly tell which is which by reading the captions), and accompanied by several columns of sidelights under the signatures of special writers who wish, before the first limb of the course is covered, that they had been sent to the morgue, and will soon get their wish. The experts, or their managing editors, receive poison-pen letters from members of the yacht club because they made some technical error, like saying the winning boat lost, and the special writers are never again worth a damn and spend the balance of their lives meeting doctors.

I do not claim (except when I am all by myself in a room) that I was worth a damn to begin with, but I do know that the Lipton Club "race" of 1920 is what is the matter with my stomach today. I was assigned to sidelights and accepted the assignment with pleasure, as I really love dat ole davil sea and thought the job would cure me of the effects of the Democratic Convention in San Francisco, which was something of a strain on the abdomen.

Well, the newspaper boys were conveyed to and from the scene each day on U. S. destroyers, and the schedule was like this: You showed up at a certain pier in North River at five in the A.M. and got on a tug. The tug took you out to within eight feet of the destroyer (ours was the Semmes) and you covered the eight feet from the tug to the destroyer by walking a tight rope. When I am in the best of health and have had a good night's sleep, it is all I can do to keep from falling off the Boardwalk at Atlantic City. So when it was necessary to stay up till five o'clock so I would be up at five o'clock and then start the day with an eight-foot stroll on a piece of wire, I was all primed to turn out a column of sidelights that would keep readers in gales of silence.

As you will recall, the event was held off Sandy Hook that year. It started in August in a .02-mile wind and ended in February with the Shamrock defeated but still ahead. The Semmes had to stay in reverse to keep up with the flying contestants. I watched the entire orgy from a sleeping position in the lieutenant's bunk after leaving a call for 4:30 P.M. which was the usual time that the official statement, "No race," was given out.

When it became necessary for Sir Thomas to start back home and participate in the St. Patrick's Day pep meetings, we special writers gradually resumed contact with the world and discovered that many changes had taken place. Harding had been elected president, the European War was over, Herman Rosenthal had eaten some bad oysters, and my family had moved from Garden City to Great Neck.

Proponents of international cup racing point out that that race, held a decade ago, accomplished some good in a scientific way. They claim that the photographs taken of the two yachts in action were the origin of slow-motion pictures. But I would gladly trade that discovery for my good old digestive apparatus. And I say again that

Sir Thomas should be made to put his promise in writing. Or else that the 1940 race be started in the Niagara River, just above those old Falls.

A World's Serious

ADVANCE NOTICE

Sept. 30.—All though they have been world serious practally every yr. for the last 20 yrs. this next world serious which is supposed to open up Wed. p.m. at the Polo grounds is the most important world serious in history as far as I and my family are conserned and even more important to us than the famous world serious of 1919 which was win by the Cincinnati Reds greatly to their surprise.

Maybe I would better exclaim myself before going any further. Well, a few days previous to the serious of 1919 I was approached by a young lady who I soon recognized as my wife, and any way this woman says would I buy her a fur coat as the winter was comeing on and we was going to spend it in Connecticut which is not genally considered one of the tropics.

"But don't do it," she says, "unless you have got the money to spare because of course I can get along without it. In fact," she added bursting into teers, "I am so used to getting along without this, that and the other thing that maybe it would be best for you not to buy me that coat after all as the sight of a luxury of any kind might prove my undoing."

"Listen," was my reply, "as far as I am concerned you don't half to prove your undoing. But listen you are in a position to know that I can't spare the money to buy you one stoat leave alone enough of the little codgers skins to make a coat for a growed up girl like you. But if I can get a hold of any body that is sucker enough to bet on Cincinnati in this world serious, why I will borrow from some good pal and cover their bet and will try and make the bet big enough so as the winnings will buy you the handsomest muleskin coat in New England."

Well friends I found the sucker and got a hold of enough money to cover his bet and not only that but give him odds of 6 to 5 and that is why we did not go out much in Greenwich that winter and not for lack of invitations as certain smart Alex has let fall.

I might also mention at this junction that they was a similar agreement at that serious between Eddie Collins the capt. of the White Sox and his Mrs. only of course Eddie did not make no bet, but if his team win, why he should buy the madam a personal sedan whereas if his team lost, why she would half to walk all winter. Luckily the Collinses live in Lansdowne, Pa., where you can't walk far.

Well friends I do not know what is the automobile situation in the Collins family at the present writeing as have not saw them of late but the fur coat situation in my family is practically the same like it was in 1919 only as I hinted in the opening paragraph of this intimate article, it is a d-a-m sight worse.

Because this yr. they won't be no chance for the little woman to offset her paucity of outdoor raps by spending the winter in the house. She is going to need furs even there.

Therefore as I say this comeing serious is the most important of all as far as we are conserned for Mother ain't the same gal when she is cold and after all is said and done what is home with mother in her tantrums?

So I and my little ones is hopeing and praying that the boys on who I have staked my winters happiness this yr. will not have no meetings in no hotel rooms between now and Wednesday but will go into this serious determined to do their best which I once said was the best anybody could do and the man who heard me say it said "You are dead right Lardner" and if these boys do their best, why it looks to me like as if the serious should ought to be well over by Sunday night and the little woman's new fur coat delivered to our little home some time Monday and maybe we will get invited out somewheres that night and they will be a blizzard.

THE FIRST DAY

Oct. 5.—Well friends you can imagine my surprise and horror when I found out last night that the impression had got around some way another that as soon as this serious was over I was planning to buy a expensive fur coat for my Mrs. and put a lot of money into same and buy a coat that would probably run up into hundreds and hundreds of dollars.

Well I did not mean to give no such kind of a impression and I certainly hope that my little article was not read that way by everybody a specially around my little home because in the first place I am not a sucker enough to invest hundreds and hundreds of dollars in a garment which the chances are that the Mrs. will not wear it more than a couple times all winter as the way it looks now we are libel to have the most openest winter in history and if women folks should walk along the st. in expensive fur coats in the kind of weather which it looks like we are going to have why they would only be laughed at and any way I believe a couple can have a whole lot better time in winter staying home and reading a good book or maybe have a few friends to play bridge.

Further and more I met a man at supper last night that has been in the fur business all his life and aint did nothing you might say only deal in furs and this man says that they are a great many furs in this world which is reasonable priced that has got as much warmth in them as high price furs and looks a great deal better. For inst. he says that a man is a sucker to invest thousands and thousands of dollars in expensive furs like Erminie, Muleskin, squirrel skin and kerensky when for a hundred dollars or not even that much, why a man can buy a owl skin or horse skin or weasel skin garment that looks like big dough and practically prostrates people with the heat when they wear them.

So I hope my readers will put a quietus on the silly rumor that I am planning to plunge in the fur market. I will see that my Mrs. is dressed in as warm a style as she has been accustomed to but neither her or I is the kind that likes to make a big show and go up and down 5th ave sweltering in a $700 hogskin garment in order so as people will turn around and gap at us. Live and let live is my slocum.

So much for the fur coat episode and let us hear no more about it and will now go on with my article which I must apologize for it not being very good and the reason is on account of being very nervous after our little ride from the polo grounds to park row. It was my intentions to make this trip in the subway but while walking across the field after the game I run into Izzy Kaplan the photographer and he says would I like to ride down in a car which him and his friends had hired so I and Grantland Rice got in and we hadn't no sooner than started when one of our fellow passengers says that we ought to been with them coming up.

"We made the trip from park row in 24 minutes," he says, "and our driver said he was going to beat that record on the return trip."

So we asked what had held them back comeing up and one of them said that the driver had kept peeling and eating bananas all the way and that he did not drive so good when both his hands was off the wheel. Besides that, they had ran into a guy and had to wait till the ambulance come and picked him up.

Well friends I will not try and describe our flight only to say that we did not beat the record but tied it and the lack of bananas didn't prevent our hero from driving with his hands off the wheel as he used the last named to shake his fists at pedestrians and other riff raff that don't know enough to keep off the public highways during the rush hour.

Most of the things I was going to mention in this article was scared out of me during our little jaunt. One of them however was the man from Toronto that stood in line with his wife from 8 pm Tuesday night till the gates opened Wednesday morning so as to be sure of good seats. According to officials of the club, they could of got the same seats if they had not showed up till a couple hours before the game, but if they had of done that, why the lady would not of had no chance to brag when she got back home. The way it is, why she can say to her friends, "Charley may not be much for looks, but he certainly showed me the night life of New York."

Dividing interest with this couple was a couple of heel and toe pedestrians that done their base circling stunt just before the start of the game. One of them was the same guy that done it before the first game last fall, but this time he was accompanied by a lady hoofer and it is not too much to say that the lady was dressed practically as though for her bath. Casey Stengel expressed the general sentiment in the following words, "If that is just her walking costume I would hate to see her made up for tennis."

THE SECOND DAY

Oct. 6.—No doubt my readers has been tipped off by this time that the 2d game of the big serious was called on acct. of darkness but a great many of them may not know that the umpires and club owners was called a lot of different names which I will not repeat here but suffice it to say that none of them was honey, dearie and etc.

The boys that had paid $5.50 and up to see a ball game did not seem to think it was dark enough for the umps to step in and stop it. Personly I will not express no opinion as some of my best friends is umpires, but will merely state that I started out of the press box the instant it was over and by the aid of a powerful candle which I generally always carry to world serious games when Shawkey and Barnes is scheduled to pitch, why I was able to find my way down to the field where I run plum into A. D. Lasker who had forgot to light his headlights. Will further state that nobody who I passed on the way out to 8th avenue had yet put on their pajamas or made any other preparations that would indicate the fall of night and even when I got down to park's row, pretty near a hr. after the game's untimely end, I was still able to grope my way to the office by feeling along the sides of buildings and was seated right here at my typewriter writing this article before the hoot owls and nightin-gales begun to emit their nocturnal squawk.

However, one of our fellow passengers on the bus down town was Billy Evans, an umpire himself, and while he admitted that he had not saw none of the outfielders signalling to each other with flares, still and all he says the polo grounds is a terrible hard place for the athletes, and a specially the batters, to see a ball when they's the slightest twinge of darkness. As far as that is concerned there is 2 or 3 of the boys on each of the contending clubs that dont seem able to see the ball any too good even at high noon.

Anyway it means we are going to have a extra ball game to play over and some of we boys who predicted a short serious is being made to look like a monkey. Personly I was never so ashamed of myself since I picked Willard.

The general opinion amongst the writing boys tonight was that the game being a tie is a big help to one of the two teams but I forget which. It certainly aint no help to me and the only thing I liked about the day was the weather, which it would make a person sick to even talk about a fur coat in such weather, and it goes to show what a sucker a man would be to squander thousands and thousands of dollars in a costly fur garment and then may be have a whole winter of just such days like yesterday.

Personly I seen a girlie on the street last night wearing a linen duster and you have no idear how good they look on some people and keep you plenty warm too if you move around and dont stand still.

Well friends, I prophesied in these columns earlier in the week that Bob Shawkey would be a whole lot better this fall than he was last fall and that prophecy certainly come true, but the boy has still got the habit of pitching bad in the first innings and if I was running the Yank ball club here is what I would do. When it was Bob's turn to pitch, why just before the game started I would call Bob to one side and I would say, "well Bob it's the second innings all ready." If he believed it, why they would be nothing to prevent him from stepping right in and pitching his best from the start.

Jess Barnes pitched better than Bob at the start and not so good at finish. The way Jess pitched to Ruth did not seem to rouse unanimous enthusiasm amongst the bugs in the grandstand. Slow balls is what Jess feeds the Babe and the reason for same is because Bab dont hit slow balls out of the ball park. If Jess did not feed the Babe slow balls when he knows he cant hit slow balls so good, why that would make Jess a ½ wit and when he does feed the Babe slow balls, why it shows he is thinking. That is why the crowd hoots him for pitching slow balls, because the average baseball bug hates to see anybody think. It makes them jealous.

Well friends today is another day and may the best team win as I often say to Mother which is what I call the little woman when I am in a hurry and cant think of her name.

THE THIRD DAY

Oct. 7.—Amongst the inmates of our heavily mortgaged home in Great Neck is 3 members of what is sometimes referred to as the feline tribe born the 11th day of last April and christened respectully Barney, Blackie and Ringer.

These 3 little ones is motherless, as the lady cat who bore them, aptly named Robin Hood, took sick one June day and was give away by Fred to a friend to whom he kindly refrained from mentioning her illness.

These 3 little members of the feline tribe is the cutest and best behaved kitties in all catdom, their conduct having always been above reproaches outside of a tendency on the part of Ringer to bite strangers knuckles. Nowhere on Long Island is a more loveable trio of grimalkins and how it pierces my old heart to think that some day next week these 3 little fellows must be shot down like a dog so as their fur can be fashioned into a warm winter coat for she who their antics has so often caused to screek with laughter. Yes boys the 3 little kittens is practically doomed you might say and all because today's game at the polo grounds was not called on account of darkness long before it started though they was no time during the afternoon when the Yanks could see.

I probably never would of heard of a cat skin coat was it not for an accidental introduction last night to a man who has did nothing all his life but sell and wear fur coats and who told me that no finer or more warmer garment can be fashioned than is made from the skin of a milk fed kitty.

"Listen," was the way he put it. "You would be a even worse sucker than you are if you was to squander thousands on thousands of dollars on the fur of a muskrat or a mule when you have right in your own asylum the makings of the most satisfactory and handsome coat that money can buy."

"Yes," was my reply, "but the fur of 3 kittens would make a mighty small coat."

"Small coats is the rage," was his reply, "and I personally seen some of the best dressed women in New York strolling up and down 10th avenue during the last cold snap with cat skin garments no bigger than a guest towl."

So while I said a few paragraphs ago that the result of this ball game spelled the doom of our little kitties, why as a matter of fact I have just about made up my mind to not buy no costly furs even if the Yankees does come through and bring me out on the right side of the public ledger. Whatever I win in bets on this serious I will freely give to charity.

I would try and describe the game to you in intimate detail was it not played in such darkness that I was only able to see a few incidence. Of these few occured in the 3rd innings and consisted of Whitey Witt getting caught asleep off of first base by a snap throw from one of the Smith brothers.

The dean of Cleveland baseball experts explained this incidence by saying that Whitey thought he was still with the Athletics. It is more likely however that Whitey was deceived by the darkness into believing it was his bedtime.

The next incidence come in the innings when the Babe tried to go from first to third on a wallop by Bob Meusel that got away from Frisch. Frankie pegged the ball to Heine Groh who stood in Babe's path to third but it was so dark that Babe crashed right smack into him and secured a rolling fall. For a minute it looked like they would be fisticuffs between the 2 famous athletes but Heine suddenly remembered the advice given him by his first school teacher, "never be a bully," and the fight was over before it begun.

Fifteen minutes before the start of the game the official announcer come up to the press box and said that McQuillan was going to pitch for the Giants. A minute later he come around again and said to make it Scott instead of McQuillan. McQuillan thus broke Fred Toney's record for the length of time spent in a world series ball game.

I will close this article by making a apology to the boys to who I have give tickets for games no 1 and 3 and whose seats is in section 24 which is as far north as you can get without falling out of the grandstand. The gents who sold me these seats thought I was a close friend of the Meusel boys and might want to set out there myself and kid with them.

THE END

Oct. 9.—Well boys it looks like it was all over and the only complaint I have got to make is that the traffic regulations was not handled right.

The next time the Yankees takes part in world serious they should ought to have a traffic policeman stationed between 1st and 2nd base and another traffic policeman stationed between home and 1st.

The former should tell the boys when it is ok to run to 2nd. And the latter must inform them that when a ground ball is hit to the infield in a world serious the general theory which has never been disapproved is to run on high speed to 1st base which is the base towards the right field from the home plate.

The lack of a adequate stop and go system is what lost this serious on the part of the Yanks. The final game of the serious was marked by the only incedence of brains exhibited by the Yanks during the whole serious.

In the 2nd innings with two boys on the bases and one out Joe Bush passed Arthur Nehf to 1st base so as to get the head of the batting order up and not confuse the official scorers. This bit of thinking probably was responsible for nothing.

I will not try and dilate on the rest of the serious only to say that Charles A. Hughes and Eddie Batchelor of Detroit spent this a.m. at the Bronx Soo to try and see more animals. It is hard to satisfy the boys from Detroit.

All as I know what to write about on a occasion like this kind is little incedence that come off. The 1st incedence that calls to mine is in regards to Tommy Rice of the Brooklyn Eagle. Tommy wrote 7,000 words in regards to the 1st game of the serious and page by page it blew out of the window in the costly appartment building in which Brooklyn experts lives, there is no telling what the loss to the world is on account of not being able to read Tommy's story to say nothing about the readers of the Eagle.

Now boys I suppose they is a few interested in whether the little woman is going to get a costly fur coat. The other day I wrote a story to the general effects that we was going to kill our cats and use their fur to make the costly garment. This story was not appreciated in the heavily mortgaged home. After a long argument the master of the house compromised and decided to not doom the little members of the finny tribe to death. Instead of that we are going to use a idea furnished by the same Eddie Batchelor, of Detroit, mentioned a few thousand words ago. Eddie's idears is to start a chain letter to all our friends and readers asking them to look around the old homestead and find their family albums and take the plush off of the covers and send it to the undersigned and make a plush coat which everybody tells me is the most fashionable fur on the green footstool. The little woman can wear plush and a specially the red pigment but black and tan plush covers will be welcomed and this man tells me theys nothing more attractive than a black and red and tan blocked coat made out of plush albums.

I was going to say further in regards to the plush albums but Harry Frazee has just butted in with the story of his life. It seems like when Harry was a young man in Peoria his father said to him if you don't be wild and go into the theatrical business and stay around Peoria you will be as big a man as your uncle. So Harry looked at his uncle who was getting $125 per month staring at books.

"Well," says Harry, "I can get more than that catching runaway horses." So he is now catching runaway horses and selling them to the New York club.

As I now sit here and write I am surrounded by a corpse of experts just as ignorant as me and they don't seem to be none of them able to tell who is going to pitch tomorrow. Personally I think it will be Col. Ruppert and Huston.

Night and Day

Do Not Disturb, N. Y.

Nearly a year ago this department was expressing its admiration for the line "Let come what may" in the refrain of Allie Wrubel's nursery rhyme, "As You Desire Me." It struck me as perfect when it first came over the air, but in order to make sure of its perfection, I tried to improve it and asked my four spawn to do the same. Our efforts, including "Leave come what may," "Let may what come," "How come leave may," etc., were cast aside as inferior to the original, and the latter was ranked high gun (a high-gun expression) in our love nest until we heard an anthem entitled "It's Just a Little Street," or "Where Old Friends Meet," or both.

As in Mr. Wrubel's number, the stand-out line of this one occurred in the midst of the proceedings. It was, as I recall it, "Although I'm rich or poor, I still feel sure I'm welcome as the flow'rs in May." Once more I summoned the whippersnappers and conferred with them on a possible substitute for "Although" which would convey a similar meaning and add to the sublimity of the lyric. My own candidate, "What ho," was voted down as too risqué, but before that defect was discovered by a prowling helpmeet, the boys thought old daddy had again come through in a pinch, and

John, the eldest, was about to lead the famous victory yell—"Old Daddy! Old Daddy!" (All respire.)

Consideration was given to "Except," suggested by James (Jake the Barber) Lardner, and to "Suppose," which David (Winnie-the-Pooh) Lardner submitted. Both were discarded for not being in modern usage as conjunctions. Bill (Jake the Barber) Lardner was in one of his ribald moods and would offer nothing but "Hotcha," which didn't even scan. John (Winnie-the-Pooh) Lardner finally hit on a couple of likely ones—"Unless" and "Until"—and now, when the five of us get together for a sing, we frequently employ one or the other, preferably the other, as a replacement for "Although." Thus: "Unless I'm rich or poor, I still feel sure," and so on. But we do this merely for variety, not because we think we have improved on "Although."

The "Little Street" enjoyed a long radio life, a fact that ought to silence those pessimists who argue that a song can't last unless it's got something. However, it is seldom heard now, and the foregoing discussion was just a prelude to some stuff about the song "Night and Day," which continues to thrive on its own merits and because Freddie Astaire refused to believe the obituary notices of "Gay Divorce," the show in which it is featured.

You must know that Mr. Cole Porter, lyricist of "Night and Day," shares the mantle of W. S. Gilbert with Ira Gershwin, Lorenz Hart, Irving Caesar, Irving Berlin, Joseph V. McKee, Howard Dietz, Bert Kalmar, George M. Cohan, Gus Kahn, Primo Carnera, and George Herman (Columbia Lou) Gehrig. Well, it seems to me that in this number, Mr. Porter not only makes a monkey of his contemporaries but shows up Gilbert himself as a seventh-rate Gertrude Stein, and he does it all with one couplet, held back till late in the refrain and then delivered as a final, convincing sock in the ear, an ear already flopping from the sheer magnificence of the lines that have preceded. I reprint the couplet:

> Night and day under the hide of me
> There's an Oh, such a hungry yearning, burning inside of me.

So what? Well, I have heard the song only by radio, and those whom I have heard repeat the refrain have sung that immortal couplet the same both times. Fortunate friends who have seen "Gay Divorce" report that the number is generously encored and reprised, and as a matter of course, most of the encores are pedal, not vocal. When they are vocal, the words are not changed.

Again, so what? Well, just as the apparently perfect lines in the Wrubel song and the "Little Street" courted an attempt at improvement, so did this superb couplet of Mr. Porter's, and though the attempt is as much of a failure as the others, the fact that the song is still being sung on stage and air encourages me to publish a few modifications to which Freddie and the radio artists are welcome if ever they tire of the original.

This time my own kiddies were left out of the conference, most of them being away at school, taking a course in cuts. A little niece of mine, Miss Ann (Jake the Barber) Tobin of Niles, Mich., was the only party consulted. We agreed that there must be no needless trifling with the impeccable five words—"There's an Oh, such a"— which begin the second line; they should stand as written except where our rhythm made changes imperative.

Well, then, here is the first variant from Little Ann's pen, with spelling corrected by uncle:

Night and day under the rind of me
There's an Oh, such a zeal for spooning, ru'ning the mind of me.

And another, wherein she lapses into the patois:

Night and day under the peel o' me
There's a hert that will dree if ye think aucht but a' weel o' me.

And now a few by uncle himself:

1. Night and day under the fleece of me
   There's an Oh, such a flaming furneth burneth the grease of me.
2. Night and day under the bark of me
   There's an Oh, such a mob of microbes making a park of me.
3. Night and day under my dermis, dear,
   There's a spot just as hot as coffee kept in a thermos, dear.
4. Night and day under my cuticle
   There's a love all for you so true it never would do to kill.
5. Night and day under my tegument
   There's a voice telling me I'm he, the good little egg you meant.

As usual, the space is nearly all gone before I have said anything. There may be enough left to admit that Jack Benny was recently very funny in a Jekyll and Hyde sketch; to express the opinion that Joe Cook, in two trial heats, has convinced me that he is as valuable a radio comic as any sponsor is likely to find; and to report that Mr. John Underwood of Buffalo listened-in on the Washington baseball opening and heard Ted Husing speak of Maxie Bishop, Joey Kuhel, and Lukey Sewell, and is indignant because he didn't state that Pressy Roosevelt had thrown out the first ballie.

Sane Olympics

The eyes of the athaletic world is centered every four years in the place where ladies and gents from all the countries that is left are participating in what is aptly termed the Olympic games. These games was began pretty near 800 years B.C. for the purpose of developing and strengthening the Greeks and look at them now, those that ain't shining shoes is running restaurants in partnership with flies.

The first Olympic games was held at a place called Olympia and consisted of one event which was a footrace and the encyclopædia says it was win by a athalete named Corœbus in 776 B.C. but they's no way of telling if that was good time or not as the distance ain't stated. In later years they kept adding other events till they had a long run, a footrace for men in armor, a four horse chariot race and a contest for trumpeters and heralds, to say nothing about a combination boxing and wrestling match in which the contestants was allowed to tape their hands with andirons. It was understood that after a guy had win the all around championship he should live at public expense like one of our present day congressmen.

This all around championship was awarded to the party that got the most points in what they called the pentathlon from the Greek words pen meaning five and athlon meaning oof. The five events in the pentathlon or five-oof was running, jumping, discus and javelin throwing and wrestling.

Well finely people begun to realize that the most of the contests was not only silly but it was almost impossible to stage them, like for inst. the four horse chariot race, even if you did happen to have a chariot around the house where was you going to get a hold of four horses. All the heralds was newspapers and the trumpeters was charged with professionalism on acct. of holding positions with George Olsen or Paul Whiteman.

So one by one they weeded out what they considered obsolete and substituted contests which was considered up to date and are still clinging to same, which is the reason why I am writing this little article, namely to try and show that it is high time for another general reform. If the purpose of athaletics and especially the Olympic games is to benefit the contestants and make them more valuable citizens and better boys and gals, and husbands and wifes, then why not arrange a programme of events that will tend to same instead of running off a serious of contests that don't get nobody nowheres or prove nothing except that the entrants has wasted a lot of time practising?

For example suppose a man gets so as he throw a javelin 189 ft. 4¼ inches, will somebody kindly tell me how that is going to buy spare tires for his first baby's go-cart? And did you ever hear of a gal's mother saying to her suitor, "Why, certainly you can have Kate. I know you will make her a good husband because you have did 57 ft. 11½ inches in the running hop, step and jump." And in these days of the long distance telephone to say nothing of motorcycles, how many men is going to get a job as a Western Union messenger boy because they can run 26 miles in 2 hrs. 55 min. 20 sec. Even a man that can clear 6 ft. 5 in the running high jump ain't going to be no use hanging pictures because he don't stay up there long enough to be sure he is getting them straight.

I will leave it to the Olympic committees to figure out decent substitutes for the silly events now on the regular programme and will content myself with suggesting a new pentathlon consisting of contests which will show if a man or woman will make a good or a bad husband or wife or vice versa and when I say good I mean the kind that can sail what I have nicknamed the matrimonial seas without stubbing their toe on the rocks of petty annoyance.

1. *Appreciation.* For this event they must be provided a house and a woman which the contestants pretends is their house and their

wife. The contestants examine the house and then leave. During their absence, the pseudo-wife changes the furniture all around and hangs new curtains in all the windows. The contestants return and each enters the home separately. First prize goes to the contestant noticing the most improvements and making the most laudatory comments in regards to same. Booby prize to the contestant that don't know they's been any improvements.

2. *Punctuality*. This contest should take place on a Saturday or Sunday noon. The contestants each calls up the pseudo-wife and tells her they are going to play golf but will be home at 6:30. The winner is the one that gets there on or before eight o'clock.

3. *Immutability*. The pseudo-wife appears in a new hat or new dress. The contestants all tell her it looks great. The winner is the one that don't change his mind the second or third time she wears it and tell her it looks terrible.

4. *Tolerance*. The contestants and the mock wife go out on a drinking party. The contestants drink 20 cocktails apiece and get pie eyed. The winner is the contestant that lets the wife finish her 2d cocktail without telling her she has had enough.

5. *Versatility*. This event will require some time. Each contestant, in conjunction with the mock wife, entertains different friends at dinner every evening for a week. During every evening, the contestants must tell three anecdotes, personal experiences. The winner is the contestant that don't tell the same anecdote more than five times during the week.

The way they have got the Olympic games now, why the women folks ain't entered in nothing but swimming and tennis and I ain't never heard of a woman that win a good home because she was a human fish, wile as far as tennis is concerned, the best woman tennis player that ever lived is still playing singles in life's game. So in place of these two useless sports I have figured out the following:

1. *Patience*. Each contestant is required to set at a table in a scofflaw cabaret with her pretended husband. The winner is the one that don't say let's go home.

2. *Endurance*. The contestants is required to spend an afternoon and evening talking. The winner is the one that don't mention bobbed hair.

3. *Poise*. The contestants all sets around a room and a telephone

bell rings. The winner is the one that can keep from jumping out of her chair.

4. *Penetration.* Each contestant is given a railroad time table and required to find out what time a train leaves somewheres and gets somewheres else. The winner is the one who finds out within two hours without asking a man.

5. *Expert Accounting.* Each contestant is given a checking account of $1,000. The winner is the one who can tell how much of it is left at the end of a week without calling up the bank.

PART SIX

Native Dada

Thompson's Vacation
Play in Two Acts

CHARACTERS

THOMPSON, *a plain citizen.*
HAINES, *another.*
DILLON, *another.*

ACT I

August 28. The smoking car of a city-bound suburban train. Thompson is sitting alone. Haines comes in, recognizes him and takes the seat beside him.

HAINES Hello there, Thompson.
THOMPSON Hello, Mr. Haines.
HAINES What's the good word!
THOMPSON Well——
HAINES How's business?
THOMPSON I don't know. I've been on a vacation for two weeks.
HAINES Where was you?
THOMPSON Atlantic City.
HAINES Where did you stop?
THOMPSON At the Edgar.
HAINES The Edgar! Who steered you to that joint?
THOMPSON I liked it all right.
HAINES Why didn't you go to the Wallace? Same prices and everything up to date. How did you happen to pick out a dirty old joint like the Edgar?
THOMPSON I thought it was all right.

HAINES What did you do to kill time down there?

THOMPSON Oh, I swam and went to a couple of shows and laid around!

HAINES Didn't you go up in the air?

THOMPSON No.

HAINES That's the only thing they is to do in Atlantic City, is go up in the air. If you didn't do that, you didn't do nothing.

THOMPSON I never been up.

HAINES That's all they is to do down there, especially in August, when it's so hot.

THOMPSON They was generally always a breeze.

HAINES Yes, I know what that breeze is in August. It's like a blast out of a furnace. Did you go in any of them cabarets?

THOMPSON Yes, I was in the Mecca and the Garden.

HAINES Wasn't you in the La Marne?

THOMPSON No.

HAINES If you wasn't in the La Marne, you didn't see nothing.

THOMPSON I had some real beer in the Mecca.

HAINES Say, that stuff they give you in the Mecca is dishwater. They's only one place in Atlantic City to get real beer. That's the Wonderland. Didn't you make the Wonderland?

THOMPSON No.

HAINES Then you didn't have no real beer. Did you meet many dames?

THOMPSON Only a couple of them. But they was pips!

HAINES Pips! You don't see no real pips down there in August. The time to catch the pips down there is—well, June, July, September, May, or any time in the fall or winter or spring. You don't see them there in August. Did you go fishing?

THOMPSON No.

HAINES Oh, they's great fishing around there! If you didn't go fishing, you didn't do nothing.

THOMPSON (*rising*) Well, here we are.

HAINES I think you're a sucker to pick out August for a vacation. May or June or September, that's the time for a vacation.

THOMPSON Well, see you again.

ACT II

Four minutes later. A downtown subway express. Thompson is hanging on a strap. Dillon enters and hangs on the next strap.

DILLON Hello there, Thompson.
THOMPSON Hello.
DILLON How's everything?
THOMPSON All right, I guess.
DILLON Ain't you been on a vacation?
THOMPSON Yeah.
DILLON What kind of a time did you have?
THOMPSON Rotten.
DILLON Where was you?
THOMPSON Nowhere.

Clemo Uti—"The Water Lilies"

CHARACTERS

PADRE *a Priest.*
SETHSO
GETHSO } *Both Twins.*
WAYSHATTEN *a Shepherd's Boy.*
TWO CAPITALISTS.*
WAMA TAMMISCH *her daughter.*
KLEMA *a Janitor's third daughter.*
KEVELA *their mother, afterwards their aunt.*
[TRANSLATOR'S NOTE: *This show was written as if people were there to see it.*]

* NOTE: *The two Capitalists don't appear in this show.*

ACT I

(*The Outskirts of a Parchesi Board. People are wondering what has become of the discs. They quit wondering and sit up and sing the following song.*)

CHORUS

What has become of the discs?
What has become of the discs?
We took them at our own risks,
But what has become of the discs?

(*Wama enters from an exclusive waffle parlor. She exits as if she had had waffles.*)

ACTS II & III

(*These two acts were thrown out because nothing seemed to happen.*)

ACT IV

(*A silo. Two rats have got in there by mistake. One of them seems diseased. The other looks at him. They go out. Both rats come in again and wait for a laugh. They don't get it, and go out. Wama enters from an offstage barn. She is made up to represent the Homecoming of Casanova. She has a fainting spell. She goes out.*)

KEVELA Where was you born?
PADRE In Adrian, Michigan.
KEVELA Yes, but I thought I was confessing to you.

(*The Padre goes out on an old-fashioned high-wheel bicycle. He acts as if he had never ridden many of them. He falls off and is brought back. He is in pretty bad shape.*)

ACT V

(*A Couple of Salesmen enter. They are trying to sell Portable Houses. The rest of the cast don't want Portable Houses.*)

REST OF THE CAST

We don't want Portable Houses.
(*The Salesmen become hysterical and walk off-stage left.*)

KEVELA What a man!

WAYSHATTEN (*the Shepherd's Boy*) Why wasn't you out there this morning to help me look after my sheep?

CHORUS OF ASSISTANT SHEPHERDS

Why did you lay there asleep
When you should of looked after his sheep?
Why did you send telegrams
When you should of looked after his lambs?
Why did you sleep there, so old,
When you should of looked after his fold?

SETHSO Who is our father?

GETHSO What of it? We're twins, ain't we?

WAMA Hush, clemo uti (*the Water Lilies*) .

(*Two queels enter, overcome with water lilies. They both make fools of themselves. They don't seem to have any self-control. They quiver. They want to play the show over again, but it looks useless.*)

SHADES

I. Gaspiri

(*The Upholsterers*)

A DRAMA IN THREE ACTS

Adapted from the Bukovinan of Casper Redmonda

CHARACTERS

IAN OBRI, *a Blotter Salesman.*
JOHAN WASPER, *his wife.*
GRETA, *their daughter.*
HERBERT SWOPE, *a nonentity.*
FFENA, *their daughter, later their wife.*
EGSO, *a Pencil Guster.*
TONO, *a Typical Wastebasket.*

ACT I

(*A public street in a bathroom. A man named Tupper has evidently just taken a bath. A man named Brindle is now taking a bath. A man named Newburn comes out of the faucet which has been left running. He exits through the exhaust. Two strangers to each other meet on the bath mat.*)

FIRST STRANGER Where was you born?

SECOND STRANGER Out of wedlock.

FIRST STRANGER That's a mighty pretty country around there.

SECOND STRANGER Are you married?

FIRST STRANGER I don't know. There's a woman living with me, but I can't place her.

(*Three outsiders named Klein go across the stage three times. They think they are in a public library. A woman's cough is heard off-stage left.*)

A NEW CHARACTER Who is that cough?

TWO MOORS That is my cousin. She died a little while ago in a haphazard way.

A GREEK And what a woman she was!

(*The curtain is lowered for seven days to denote the lapse of a week.*)

ACT III

(*The Lincoln Highway. Two bearded glue lifters are seated at one side of the road.*)

(TRANSLATOR'S NOTE: *The principal industry in Phlace is hoarding hay. Peasants sit alongside of a road on which hay wagons are likely to pass. When a hay wagon does pass, the hay hoarders leap from their points of vantage and help themselves to a wisp of hay. On an average a hay hoarder accumulates a ton of hay every four years. This is called Mah Jong.*)

FIRST GLUE LIFTER Well, my man, how goes it?

SECOND GLUE LIFTER (Sings "My Man," to show how it goes.)

(*Eight realtors cross the stage in a friendly way. They are out of place.*)

CURTAIN

Quadroon

A PLAY IN FOUR PELTS WHICH MAY ALL BE ATTENDED
IN ONE DAY OR MISSED IN A GROUP

(Author's Note: The characters were all born synonymously; that is, in the "S'uth," they are known as halfcastes. The only time the play, or series of plays, was performed with a whole-cast, it was stopped by a swarm of little black flies, which don't bite, but are annoying. One time, in Charlotte, Utah, I forget what did happen.

At this point, a word or two concerning the actors may not embarrass you. Thomas Chalmers and Alice Brady are one and the same person. I owned some Alice-Chalmers before the crush in the market and had to give Kimbley & Co. twelve dollars hush money. I asked Mr. Nymeyer one of the partners to get me out of Wall Street and he said he had already moved me as far as Nassau. That is the kind of a friend to have in the stock market. He says one of the men in the firm paid $195,000 for a seat. Imagine, when you can get one for $22.00 to a Ziegfeld opening if you know Goldie or Alice. I can generally most always get one for nothing if he invites me to Boston or Pittsburgh to look at one of his shows and see whether I can improve it. Those kind, as Percy Hammond would say, are usually so good that they can't be improved and after I have heard the second comic's first wow, I wish I had stayed in the hospital, where men are orderlies.

Speaking of hospitals, I turned the last one I visited into a pretty good roadhouse. Harland Dixon came up and tap-danced, Vince Youmans and Paul Lanin dropped in twice and played, and Vic Arden made the piano speak a language with which it was entirely unfamiliar. Phil Ohman would have been there, too, if the doctor had given me a little more nerve tonic and Mrs. Bechlinger, the housekeeper, had had two pianos. Our gracious hostess told me, *con expressione,* that she had never heard of Messrs. Youmans, Lanin, Arden, and Dixon, but had read my stuff ever since she arrived in this country, ten years ago. This gave me a superiority complexion over all musicians and tap-dancers until, at parting, she called me Mr. Gardner. And dropping the subject of roadhouses entirely for the moment, Miss Claudette Colbert came up to call one day and almost instantly, piling in like interferers for Marchmont Schwartz, appeared fifteen internes, to take my temperature. Previously they had treated my room as vacant.

This play, as hinted in the subtitle, is actually four separate plays with four separate titles: "Hic," "Haec," "Hoc," and "Hujus." It can be seen that the original author was a born H lover. He was the first Manny O'Neill and a great friend to William A. Brady. He promised the latter, "If you ever have a daughter, I will provide her with a vehicle." Well, Bill had a daughter, but Manny passed on without leaving her even a roller-coaster. However, he had a great grandson, Eugene (("Greasy")) O'Neill, who acquired a fine sense of after-dinner speaking by playing the outfield for Cincinnati and coaching football at W. and J. He took up the work where the old man had left off, at the top of a blank sheet of fools cap paper, and I kind of monkeyed with it until now it begins at ten in the morning and lasts until Walter Winchell goes to bed.

Remarks have been brandied back and forth concerning the difference in the number of lines given the male and female characters in the piece. The women have a great deal many more lines to speak than the men. There is, of course, a two-fold purpose in this arrangement. The first fold is that it pleases the women. The second fold is that it promotes harmony in the cast. During the intermissions, the ladies, God use his own judgment, have said so much that they are out of lewd words. End of notatum.)

HIC

Part One of "The Quadroon"

CAST

(In Order to Confuse)

Christine, *his sister, played by Alla Nazimova*
Lavinia, *her daughter, played by Alice Brady*
Casey Jones, *a midwife, played by William A. Brady*

SCENE: *A Park Avenue Push-Wagon, Armistice Day, 1860.*

Luncheon Intermission of Half an Hour

The Roth Lunch
127 West Fifty-second Street
November 22, 1931

Special Luncheon, 65 Cents.

Chopped Tenderloin Steak
or Calves' Liver and Bacon.
Carrots Shoestring Potatoes String Beans
Choice of Desserts
Rice Pudding   Strawberry Tart
Tea, Coffee or Milk.

HAEC

Part Two of "The Quadroon"

CAST

CHRISTINE, *his sister, played by Alice Brady*
LAVINIA, *her daughter, played by Alla Nazimova*
FRANKIE AND JOHNNIE, *played by A. H. Woods*

SCENE: *Department of Plant and Structures. An evening in 1850.*

[CHRISTINE *and* LAVINIA *meet off-stage, dancing.*]
LAVINIA Did you-all evah see me-all in "Hedda Gabler"?
CHRISTINE Does yo'all mean "Hedda Gabler" by William Anthony McGuire?
LAVINIA Yo'all done said zac'ly wot Ah'm drivin' at. How did yo'all lak me?

CHRISTINE Well, Ah seen Mrs. Fiske.
FRANKIE AND JOHNNIE Let's you and I run up to Elizabeth Arden's
and free ourselves from fatigue with an Ardena Bath.

Dinner Intermission of One Hour and a Half*

Typical Dinner, $1.50

Medaillon of lobster au caviar
Grapefruit
Supreme of fresh fruit, Maraschino
Blue Point oyster cocktail
Fresh shrimp cocktail
or
Cream of lettuce, Parmentier
Clear green turtle, Amontillado

(*Choice*)
Filet of sole, Farci Isabella
Broiled Boston scrod, Maître d'Hôtel
Tartelette of Fresh mushrooms,
Lucullus
Country sausages, apple sauce
Breaded spring lamb chop
with Bacon, tomato sauce
Chicken hash au Gratin
Roast sugar cured ham, cider sauce
Omelette Glacé aux Confitures
Cold—Fresh calf's tongue
with chow chow

Stewed celery or fresh string beans
Mashed or French fried potatoes

* It will doubtless promote good fellowship and good service if, when entering
the hotel's dining-room, you say to the man in charge: "Hello, Maitre d'Hotel."

(*Choice*)
Pudding Creole   Coffee éclair
Assorted cakes
Vanilla, raspberry or chocolate
ice cream and cake

———

Delicious apple   Apple pie
French pastry   Coffee, Tea or Milk

*Make the Plaza Central
your New York Home During the
Entire Performance. Ask Arnold.*

HOC

Part Three of "The Quadroon"

CAST

LYNN FONTANNE, *a Mrs. Lunt, played by Grace George*
CASEY JONES, *a midwife, played by Bert Lahr*
FRANK CASE, *proprietor of the Algonquin, played by Alice Brady*

SCENE: *Jimmy Walker's Wardrobe Trunk.*

[*The Mayor and the Prince of Wales meet outside the stage door, dancing.*]
THE MAYOR New York is the richest market in the world.
THE PRINCE Not only that, but the New York Theatre Market is an unrivalled concentration of spending power.
THE MAYOR The New York Magazine Program reaches that market exclusively.
FRANK CASE Pardon me, Officer, but can either of you boys play a cellophane?

*Passengers will Please not Linger in Washrooms until
Other Passengers Have Completed Their Toilets.*

HUJUS

Part Four of "The Quadroon"

CAST

CHRISTINE, *her sister, played by Alla Nazimova*
LAVINIA, *their little one, played by Alice Brady*
FRED ASTAIRE, *a hoofer, played by Morris Gest*

SCENE: *An ambuscade in the Astor lobby.*

[FRED *and* LAVINIA *dance.*]

LAVINIA The minute you try Pebeco Tooth Paste you know by its "bitey" tang that here is a tooth paste that really "gets somewheres."

FRED Will you love me always?

LAVINIA As long as you keep kissable.

[*She kills him with an oyster fork.*]

(*Leave your ticket check with an usher and your car will come right to your seat.*)

Dinner Bridge

CHARACTERS

CROWLEY, *the foreman*
AMOROSI, *an Italian laborer*
TAYLOR, *a Negro laborer*
CHAMALES, *a Greek laborer*
HANSEN, *a Scandinavian laborer*
LLANUZA, *a Mexican laborer*
THE INQUISITIVE WAITER
THE DUMB WAITER

PROGRAM NOTE

This playlet is an adaptation from the Wallachian of Willie Stevens. For a great many years, Long Islanders and Manhattanites have been wondering why the Fifty-ninth Street Bridge was always torn up at one or more points. Mr. Stevens heard the following legend: that Alexander Woollcott, chief engineer in charge of the construction of the bridge, was something of a practical joker; that on the day preceding the completion of the bridge, he was invited to dinner by his wife's brother; that he bought a loaded cigar to give his brother-in-law after the meal, and that the cigar dropped out of his pocket and rolled under the unfinished surface planking. Ever since, gangs of men have been ripping up the surface of the bridge in search of the cigar, but an article the shape of a cigar is apt to roll in any and all directions. This is what has made it so difficult to find the lost article, and the (so far) vain search is the theme of Mr. Stevens' playlet.—*Adapter.*

SCENE: An area under repair on the Fifty-ninth Street Bridge. Part of the surface has been torn up, and, at the curtain's rise, three of the men are tearing up the rest of it with picks. Shovels, axes and other tools are scattered around the scene. Two men are fussing with a concrete mixer. Crowley is bossing the job. Crowley and the laborers are dressed in dirty working clothes. In the foreground is a flat-topped truck or wagon. The two waiters, dressed in waiters' jackets, dickies, etc., enter the scene, one of them carrying a tray with cocktails and the other a tray with caviar, etc. The laborers cease their work and consume these appetizers. The noon whistle blows. The waiters bring in a white table cloth and spread it over the truck or wagon. They also distribute six place cards and six chairs, or camp stools, around the truck, but the "table" is left bare of eating implements.

FIRST WAITER, *to* CROWLEY Dinner is served.

(CROWLEY *and the laborers move toward the table.*)

TAYLOR, *to* AMOROSI I believe I am to take you in.

(AMOROSI *gives* TAYLOR *his arm and* TAYLOR *escorts him to the table. The laborers all pick up the place cards to find out where they are to sit.*)

CROWLEY, *to* AMOROSI Here is your place, Mr. Amorosi. And Taylor is right beside you.

(*Note to producer: Inasmuch as* TAYLOR *and* AMOROSI *do most of the talking, they ought to face the audience. In spite of their nationalities, the laborers are to talk in correct Crowninshield dinner English, except that occasionally, say every fourth or fifth speech, whoever is talking suddenly bursts into dialect, either his own or Jewish or Chinese or what you will.*

All find their places and sit down. The two waiters now reënter, each carrying one dinner pail. One serves CROWLEY *and the other serves* AMOROSI. *The serving is done by the waiters' removing the cover of the pail and holding it in front of the diner. The latter looks into the pail and takes out some viand with his fingers. First he takes out, say, a sandwich. The waiter then replaces the cover on the pail and exits with it. All the laborers are served in this manner, two at a time, from their own dinner pails. As soon as one of them has completed the sandwich course, the waiter brings him the pail again and he helps himself to a piece of pie or an apple or orange. But the contents of all the pails should be different, according to the diner's taste. The serving goes on all through the scene, toward the end of which everyone is served with coffee from the cups on top of the pails.*)

CROWLEY, *to* AMOROSI Well, Mr. Amorosi, welcome to the Fifty-ninth Street Bridge.

AMOROSI Thank you, I really feel as if this was where I belonged.

HANSON, *politely* How is that?

AMOROSI On account of my father. He was among the pioneer Fifty-ninth Street Bridge destroyers. He had the sobriquet of Giacomo "Rip-Up-the-Bridge" Amorosi.

TAYLOR, *sotto voce, aside to* HANSEN This fellow seems to be quite a card!

LLANUZA I wonder if you could tell me the approximate date when your father worked here.

AMOROSI Why, yes. The bridge was completed on the fifth day of August, 1909. So that would make it the sixth day of August, 1909, when father started ripping it up.

TAYLOR, *aside to* HANSEN, *in marked Negro dialect* I repeats my assertation that this baby is quite a card!

AMOROSI, *in Jewish dialect* But I guess it must be a lot more fun nowadays, with so much motor traffic to pester.

TAYLOR And all the funerals. I sure does have fun with the funerals.

CROWLEY, *in Irish brogue* Taylor has a great time with the funerals.

HANSEN, CHAMALES *and* LLANUZA, *in unison* Taylor has a great time with the funerals.

AMOROSI, *to* TAYLOR How do you do it?

TAYLOR, *in dialect* Well, you see, I'm flagman for this outfit. When I get out and wave my flag, whatever is coming, it's got to stop. When I see a funeral coming, I let the hearse go by and stop the rest of the parade. Then when I see another funeral coming, I stop their hearse and let the rest of *their* procession go on. I keep doing this all morning to different funerals and by the time they get to Forest Hills, the wrong set of mourners is following the wrong hearse. It generally always winds up with the friends and relatives of the late Mr. Cohen attending the final obsequies of Mrs. Levinsky.

CROWLEY, HANSEN, CHAMALES *and* LLANUZA, *in unison* Taylor has a great time with the funerals.

AMOROSI I'm a *trumpet* medium myself.

TAYLOR, *aside to* HANSEN This boy will turn out to be quite a card!

LLANUZA Why do you always have to keep repairing it?

CROWLEY What do you mean, what's the matter?

LLANUZA Why do they always have to keep repairing it?

AMOROSI Perhaps Mr. Crowley has the repairian rights.

TAYLOR, *guffawing and slapping* HANSEN *or* CHAMALES *on the back* What did I tell you?

LLANUZA, *in dialect* But down in Mexico, where I come from, they don't keep repairing the same bridge.

AMOROSI, *to* LLANUZA If you'll pardon a newcomer. Mr.——, I don't believe I got your name.

LLANUZA Llanuza.

AMOROSI If you'll pardon a newcomer, Mr. Keeler, I want to say that if the United States isn't good enough for you, I'd be glad to start a subscription to send you back to where you came from.

LLANUZA I was beginning to like you, Mr. Amorosi.

ORT AMOROSI You get that right out of your mind, Mr. Barrows. I'm married; been married twice. My first wife died.

HANSEN How long were you married to her?

AMOROSI Right up to the time she died.

CHAMALES, *interrupting* Mr. Amorosi, you said you had been married twice.

AMOROSI Yes, sir. My second wife is a Swiss girl.

HANSEN Is she here with you?

AMOROSI No, she's in Switzerland, in jail. She turned out to be a murderer.

CROWLEY When it's a woman, you call her a murderess.

TAYLOR And when it's a Swiss woman, you call her a Swiss-ess.

(*One of the waiters is now engaged in serving* AMOROSI *with his dinner pail.*)

WAITER, *to* AMOROSI Whom did she murder?

(WAITER *exits hurriedly without seeming to care to hear the answer.*)

AMOROSI, *after looking wonderingly at the disappearing* WAITER What's the matter with *him?*

TAYLOR He's been that way for years—a born questioner but he hates answers.

CROWLEY Just the same, the rest of us would like to know whom your wife murdered.

TAYLOR, HANSEN, CHAMALES and LLANUZA, *to* CROWLEY Speak for yourself. We don't want to know.

CROWLEY Remember, boys, I'm foreman of this outfit. (*Aside to* AMOROSI) Who was it?

AMOROSI (*Whispers name in his ear.*)

CROWLEY I don't believe I knew him.

AMOROSI Neither did my wife.

CROWLEY Why did she kill him?

AMOROSI Well, you see, over in Italy and Switzerland, it's different from, say, Chicago. When they find a man murdered over in those places, they generally try to learn who it is and put his name in the papers. So my wife was curious about this fellow's identity and she figured that the easiest way to get the information was to pop him.

TAYLOR I'm a *trumpet* medium myself.

(WAITER *enters and serves one of the laborers from his dinner pail.*)
WAITER How long is she in for?
(WAITER *exits hurriedly without waiting for the answer.* AMOROSI *again looks after him wonderingly.*)
HANSEN, *to* AMOROSI Did you quarrel much?
AMOROSI Only when we were together.
TAYLOR I was a newspaper man once myself.
LLANUZA, *skeptically* You! What paper did you work on?
TAYLOR It was a tabloid—The Porno-graphic.
(WAITER *enters to serve somebody.*)
WAITER, *to* TAYLOR Newspaper men must have lots of interesting experiences. (*Exits without waiting for a response.*)
AMOROSI I suppose you've all heard this story——
THE OTHER LABORERS, *in unison* Is it a golf story?
AMOROSI No.
THE OTHERS, *resignedly* Tell it.
AMOROSI, *in dialect* It seems there was a woman went into a photographer's and asked the photographer if he took pictures of children.
(WAITER *enters to serve somebody.*)
WAITER How does it end? (WAITER *exits hurriedly.*)
AMOROSI She asked the photographer if he took pictures of children. "Why, yes, madam," replied the photographer——
TAYLOR He called her "madam."
AMOROSI The photographer told her yes, that he did take pictures of children. "And how much do you charge?" inquired the madam, and the photographer replied, "Three dollars a dozen." "Well," said the woman, "I guess I'll have to come back later. I've only got eleven."
(*The other laborers act just as if no story had been told.*)
LLANUZA Down in Mexico, where I come from, they don't keep repairing the same bridge.
TAYLOR, *to* HANSEN Can you imitate birds?
HANSEN No.
TAYLOR, *to* CHAMALES Can you imitate birds?
CHAMALES No.
TAYLOR Can anybody here imitate birds?

THE OTHER LABORERS, *in unison* No.

TAYLOR *I* can do it. Long before I got a job on this bridge, while I was helping tear up the crosstown streets, I used to entertain the boys all day, imitating birds.

AMOROSI What kind of birds can you imitate?

TAYLOR All kinds.

AMOROSI Well, what do you say we play some other game?

CROWLEY, *rising* Gentlemen, we are drawing near to the end of this dinner and I feel we should not leave the table until some one has spoken a few words of welcome to our newcomer, Mr. Amorosi. Myself, I am not much of a talker. (*Pauses for a denial.*)

TAYLOR You said a full quart.

CROWLEY Therefore, I will call on the man who is second to me in length of service on the Fifty-ninth Street Bridge, Mr. Harvey Taylor. (*Sits down.*)

TAYLOR, *rising amid a dead silence* Mr. Foreman, Mr. Amorosi and gentlemen: Welcoming Mr. Amorosi to our little group recalls vividly to my mind an experience of my own on the levee at New Orleans before Prohibition. (*He bursts suddenly into Negro dialect, mingled with Jewish.*) In those days my job was to load and unload those great big bales of cotton and my old mammy used to always be there at the dock to take me in her lap and croon me to sleep.

(WAITER *enters, serves somebody with coffee.*)

WAITER What was the experience you was going to tell? (*Exits hurriedly.*)

TAYLOR It was in those days that I studied bird life and learned to imitate the different bird calls. (*Before they can stop him, he gives a bird call.*) The finch. (*The others pay no attention. He gives another call.*) A Dowager. (TAYLOR *is pushed forcibly into his seat.*)

AMOROSI, *rising to respond* Mr. Foreman and gentlemen: I judge from Mr. Taylor's performance that the practice of imitating birds is quite popular in America. Over where I come from, we often engage in the pastime of mimicking public buildings. For example (*he gives a cry.*) The American Express Company's office at Rome. (*He gives another cry.*) The Vatican. (*He gives another cry.*) Hotel McAlpin. (*A whistle blows, denoting that the dinner hour is over.*)

CROWLEY, *rising* Shall we join the ladies?

(*All rise and resume the work of tearing up the bridge. The waiters enter to remove the table cloth and chairs.*)

WAITER (*the more talkative one*) How many Mack trucks would you guess had crossed this bridge in the last half hour? (*He exits without waiting for a reply.*)

(CURTAIN)

Cora, or Fun at a Spa
An Expressionist Drama of Love and Death and Sex—

CHARACTERS
(*In the order in which I admire them*)

A FRIEND OF THE PRESIDENT.
PLAGUE BENNETT, *an Embryo Steeplejack.*
ELSA, *their Ward.*
MANAGER OF THE PUMP ROOM.
A MAN WHO LOOKS A GOOD DEAL LIKE HEYWOOD BROUN
MRS. TYLER.*
CORA.
POULTRY, GAME IN SEASON, ETC.

ACT I

A Pharmacy at a Spa. The Proprietor is at present out of the city and Mrs. Tyler is taking his place. She is a woman who seems to have been obliged to leave school while in the eighth grade. Plague Bennett enters. His mother named him Plague as tribute to her husband, who died of it. As Plague enters, Mrs. Tyler is seen replacing a small vial in a case behind the counter.

* Mrs. Tyler appears only when one of the other characters is out of the city.

PLAGUE Well, Mrs. T.

MRS. TYLER "Mrs. T." indeed! I see you're still the same old Plague!

PLAGUE What are you doing?

MRS. TYLER What do I look like I was doing, spearing eels? I'm just putting this bottle of germs back in its place. The little fellows were trying to escape. They said they didn't like it here. I said, "Don't bacilli!"

(A Friend of the President enters)

PLAGUE Hello, Doctor.

(He calls him Doctor)

FRIEND OF THE PRESIDENT *(As if to himself)* That old devil sea!

PLAGUE Well, Doctor, I'm going to Washington tomorrow.

(He repeatedly calls him Doctor)

FRIEND OF THE PRESIDENT What of it?

PLAGUE Well, they tell me you and the President are pretty close.

FRIEND OF THE PRESIDENT *He* is.

(END OF FIRST ACT)

ACT II

A poultry yard at a Spa. The chairs and tables are in disarray as if a blotter salesman had been making his rounds. The Manager of the Pump Room is out of the city and the poultry are being fed by Mrs. Tyler. A Dead Ringer for David Belasco enters, crosses stage.

MRS. TYLER You old master you! *(Aside)* I can never tell whether he's in first speed or reverse.

(Dead Ringer for David Belasco exits. Manager of the Pump Room returns to the city unexpectedly and Mrs. Tyler goes into pictures. Manager of the Pump Room stands in center stage as if he had been everywhere)

MANAGER OF THE PUMP ROOM *(Aside)* I wonder what is keeping Elsa. *(Looks right)* Ah! There she comes now, dancing as usual! *(Elsa enters left, fooling him completely. She is not even dancing. She looks as if she had taken a bath)*

ELSA Well——

MANAGER OF THE PUMP ROOM *(Turns and sees her)* Elsa! I was just thinking about you. I was wondering what was keeping you.

ELSA I presume you mean who.

(*The curtain is lowered and raised to see if it will work*)

MANAGER OF THE PUMP ROOM What's the difference between that curtain and Ziegfeld?

ELSA It works. And that reminds me that I just met a man who looks something like Heywood Broun. Here he comes now, dancing as usual.

(*A Man Who Looks A Good Deal Like Heywood Broun enters*)

MANAGER OF THE PUMP ROOM (*Aside*) I'll say so!

MAN WHO LOOKS A GOOD DEAL LIKE HEYWOOD BROUN What's that?

MANAGER OF THE PUMP ROOM Why, this young lady was just saying she thought you looked something like Heywood Broun.

MAN WHO ETC. (*Throwing confetti in all directions*) She's conservative.

(END OF SECOND ACT)

ACT III

A Mixed Grill at a Spa. Two Milch Cows sit at a table in one corner, playing draughts. In another corner is seated a gigantic zebu.

FIRST MILCH COW Don't you feel a draught?

SECOND MILCH COW No. But we'd better be going. That gigantic zebu is trying to make us.

FIRST MILCH COW He thinks he is a cow catcher.

SECOND MILCH COW (*As they rise*) They say there are still a great many buffaloes in Yellowstone Park.

FIRST MILCH COW So I herd.

(*The Milch Cows go out, followed at a distance by the Zebu. Cora enters. She is dressed in the cat's pajamas. She looks as if she had once gone on an excursion to the Delaware Water Gap*)

CORA (*Aside*) I wonder if it could be!

(*Plague Bennett and A Friend of the President enter in time to overhear her remark*)

PLAGUE (*To Friend of the President*) Go on without me, Doctor.

(*He still calls him Doctor. Friend of the President exits and Plague turns to Cora*) You wonder if it could be who?

CORA Why, I just met a man who looks a little like Heywood Broun. Here he comes now, dancing as usual.

(*A Man Who Looks A Good Deal Like Heywood Broun enters*)

PLAGUE (*Aside*) He does, at that!

MAN WHO ETC. At what?

PLAGUE This little lady was just saying she thought you looked a little like Heywood Broun.

MAN WHO ETC. A little! She's putting it mildly!

(*Finds he is out of confetti and exits. A poisoned rat dashes into the open air, seeking water*)

PLAGUE That rat acts like he was poisoned.

CORA God! You ought to saw me last night!

(END OF THIRD ACT)

Abend Di Anni Nouveau
A Play in Five Acts

CHARACTERS

ST. JOHN ERVINE, *an immigrant.*

WALTER WINCHELL, *a nun.*

HEYWOOD BROUN, *an usher at Roxy's.*

DOROTHY THOMPSON, *a tackle.*

THEODORE DREISER, *a former Follies girl.*

H. L. MENCKEN, *a kleagle in the Moose.*

MABEL WILLEBRANDT, *secretary of the League of American Wheelman.*

BEN HECHT, *a taxi starter.*

JOHN ROACH STRATON, *a tap dancer.*

CARL LAEMMLE, *toys and games, sporting goods, outing flannels.*

ANNE NICHOLS, *a six-day bicyclist.*

ACT 1

(A hired hall. It is twenty-five minutes of nine on New Year's Eve. A party, to which all the members of the cast were invited, is supposed to have begun at thirty-four minutes after eight. A waiter enters on a horse and finds all the guests dead, their bodies riddled with bullets and frightfully garbled. He goes to the telephone)

WAITER *(telephoning)* I want a policeman. I want to report a fire. I want an ambulance.

(He tethers his mount and lies down on the hors d'oeuvres. The curtain is lowered and partially destroyed to denote the passage of four days. Two policemen enter, neither having had any idea that the other would come. They find the waiter asleep and shake him. He wakes and smilingly points at the havoc)

WAITER Look at the havoc.

FIRST POLICEMAN This is the first time I ever seen a havoc.

SECOND POLICEMAN It's an inside job, I think.

FIRST POLICEMAN You WHAT?

WAITER The trouble now is that we'll have to recast the entire play. Every member of the cast is dead.

FIRST POLICEMAN Is that unusual?

SECOND POLICEMAN When did it happen?

WAITER When did what happen?

SECOND POLICEMAN I've forgotten.

(END OF ACT 1)

ACT 2

(The interior of an ambulance. Three men named Louie Breese are playing bridge with an interne. The interne is Louie Breese's partner. Louie leads a club. The interne trumps it)

BREESE Kindly play interne.

INTERNE I get you men confused.

BREESE I'm not confused.

THE OTHER TWO BREESES Neither of us is confused.

(They throw the interne onto Seventh Avenue. An East Side gangster, who was being used as a card table, gets up and stretches)

GANGSTER Where are we at?

BREESE Was you the stretcher we was playing on?

GANGSTER Yes.

BREESE There's only three of us now. Will you make a fourt'?

GANGSTER There's no snow.

(END OF ACT 2)

ACTS 3, 4 AND 5

(*A one-way street in Jeopardy. Two snail-gunders enter from the right, riding a tricycle. They shout their wares*)

FIRST SNAIL-GUNDER Wares! Wares!

A NEWSBOY Wares who?

FIRST SNAIL-GUNDER Anybody. That is, anybody who wants their snails gunded.

(*Three men suddenly begin to giggle. It is a secret, but they give the impression that one of them's mother runs a waffle parlor. They go off the stage still giggling. Two Broadway theatrical producers, riding pelicans, enter almost nude*)

FIRST PRODUCER Have you got a dime?

SECOND PRODUCER What do you think I am, a stage hand?

FIRST PRODUCER Have you seen my new farce?

SECOND PRODUCER No. I was out of town that night.

(END OF ACTS 3, 4 AND 5)

Taxidea Americana
A Play in Six Acts

Translated from the Mastoid by
Ring W. Lardner

CHARACTERS

FRED RULLMAN, *an acorn huckster.*
OLD CHLOE, *their colored mammy.*
THOMAS GREGORY, *a poltroon.*
MRS. GREGORY, *his mother, afterward his wife.*
PHOEBE, *engaged to* CHLOE.
PROF. SCHWARTZ, *instructor in Swiss at Wisconsin.*
BUDDY, *their daughter.*
STUDENTS, *policemen, members of the faculty, sailors, etc.*
TIME—*The present.*
PLACE—*Madison, Wisconsin.*

ACT I.

(*In front of the library. Two students in the agricultural college creep across the stage with a seed in their hands. They are silent, as they cannot place one another. Durand and Von Tilzer come down the library steps and stand with their backs to the audience as if in a quandary.*)

DURAND Any news from home?

(*They go off stage left. Senator LaFollette enters from right and practises sliding to base for a few moments. Ruby Barron comes down the library steps.*)

RUBY Hello, Senator. What are you practising, sliding to base?

(*The Senator goes out left. Ruby does some tricks with cards and re-enters the library completely baffled. Two students in the pharmacy college, Pat and Mike, crawl on stage from left and fill more than one prescription. On the second refrain Pat takes the obbligato.*)

PAT I certainly feel sorry for people on the ocean to-night.

MIKE What makes you think so?

PAT You can call me whatever you like as long as you don't call me down.

(*They laugh.*)

CURTAIN

(*Note: Acts 2, 3, and 4 are left out through an oversight.*)

ACT 5.

(*Camp Randall. It is just before the annual game between Wisconsin and the Wilmerding School for the Blind. The Wisconsin band has come on the field and the cheer leaders are leading the Wisconsin battle hymn.*)

CHORUS

Far above Cayuga's waters with its waves of blue,
On Wisconsin, Minnesota and Bully for old Purdue.
Notre Dame, we yield to thee! Ohio State, hurrah!
We'll drink a cup o' kindness yet in praise of auld Nassau!

(*The Wilmerding rooters applaud and then sing their own song.*)

CHORUS

We are always there on time!
We are the Wilmerding School for the Blind!
Better backfield, better line!
We are the Wilmerding School for the Blind!
Yea!

(*Coach Ryan of Wisconsin appears on the field fully dressed and announces that the game is postponed to permit Referee Birch to take his turn in the barber's chair. The crowd remains seated till the following Tuesday, when there is a general tendency to go home.*)

CURTAIN

ACT 3.

(*Note: The coaches suddenly decide to send in Act 3 in place of Act 6. A livery barn in Stoughton. Slam Anderson, a former Wis-*

consin end, is making faces at the horses and they are laughing themselves sick. Slam goes home. Enter Dr. Boniface, the landlord of a
switch engine on the Soo lines. From the other direction, Farmer
Hookle enters on a pogo stick.)

DR. BONIFACE Hello, there, Hookle! I hear you are specializing in
hogs.
HOOKLE I don't know where you heard it, but it's the absolute truth.
DR. BONIFACE Well, do you have much luck with your hogs?
HOOKLE Oh, we never play for money.
CURTAIN

How to Tell a True Princess

Well my little boys and gals this is the case of a prince who his father had told him he must get married but the gal he married must be a true princess. So he says to the old man how do you tell if a princess is a true princess or a phony princess. So the old man says why if she is a true princess she must be delicate.

Yes said the prince but what is the true test of delicate.

Why said the old man who was probably the king if she is delicate why she probably can't sleep over 49 eiderdown quilts and 28 mattresses provided they's a pea parked under same which might disturb her. So they made her bed this day in these regards. They put a single green pea annext the spring and then piled 28 mattresses and 49 eider quilts on top of same and says if she can sleep on this quantity of bed clothing and not feel disturbed, why she can't possibly be delicate and is therefore not a princess.

Well the princess went to bed at 10 o'clock on acct. of having called up everybody and nobody would come over and play double Canfield with her and finely she give up and went to bed and hadn't been asleep more than 3 hrs. when she woke up and says I am very uncomfortable, they must be a pea under all these quilts. So they looked it up and sure enough they was a green pea under the quilts and mattresses. It made her miserable. She was practally helpless.

But the next day when she woke up they didn't know if she was a princess or the reverse. Because lots of people had slept under those conditions and maybe it was the mattress or the springs that had made them miserable. So finely the king suggested why not give her a modern trial.

So the next evening but one they sent her to bed under these conditions:

The counterpane was concrete and right under it was 30 layers of tin plate and then come 4 bales of cotton and beneath that 50 ft. of solid rock and under the entire layout a canary's feather.

"Now Princess," they said to her in a friendly way, "if you can tell us the name of the bird which you are sleeping on under all these condiments, why then we will know you are a true princess and worthy to marry the prince."

"Prince!" she said. "Is that the name of a dog?"

They all laughed at her in a friendly way.

"Why yes," she said, "I can tell you the name of that bird. His name is Dickie."

This turned the laugh on them and at the same time proved she was a true princess.

To-morrow night I will try to tell you the story of how 6 men travelled through the wide world and the story will begin at 6:30 and I hope it won't keep nobody up.

Cinderella

Once upon a time they was a prominent clubman that killed his wife after a party where she doubled a bid of four diamonds and the other side made four odd, giving them game and a $26.00 rubber. Well, she left him a daughter who was beginning to run absolutely hog wild and he couldn't do nothing with her, so he married again, this time drawing a widow with two gals of her own, Patricia and Micaela.

These two gals was terrible. Pat had a wen, besides which they couldn't nobody tell where her chin started and her neck left off. The other one, Mike, got into a brawl the night she come out and several of her teeth had came out with her. These two gals was impossible.

Well, the guy's own daughter was a pip, so both her stepmother and the two stepsisters hated her and made her sleep in the ashcan. Her name was Zelda, but they called her Cinderella on account of how the ashes and clinkers clang to her when she got up noons.

Well, they was a young fella in the town that to see him throw his money around, you would of thought he was the Red Sox infield trying to make a double play. So everybody called him a Prince. Finally he sent out invitations to a dance for just people that had dress suits. Pat and Mike was invited, but not Cinderella, as her best clothes looked like they worked in a garage. The other two gals made her help them doll up and they kidded her about not going, but she got partly even by garnisheeing their hair with eau de garlic.

Well, Pat and Mike started for Webster Hall in a bonded taxi and they hadn't much sooner than went when a little bit of an old dame stepped out of the kitchen sink and stood in front of Cinderella and says she was her fairy godmother.

"Listen," says Cinderella: "don't mention mother to me! I've tried two different kinds and they've both been a flop!"

"Yes, but listen yourself," says the godmother: "wouldn't you like to go to this here dance?"

"Who and the h—l wouldn't!" says Cinderella.

"Well, then," says the godmother, "go out in the garden and pick me a pumpkin."

"You're pie-eyed," was Cinderella's criticism, but anyway she went out and got a pumpkin and give it to the old dame and the last named touched it with her wand and it turned into a big, black touring car like murderers rides in.

Then the old lady made Cinderella go to the mouse-trap and fetch her six mice and she prodded them with her wand and they each became a cylinder. Next she had her bring a rat from the rat trap and she turned him into a big city chauffeur, which wasn't hardly any trouble.

"Now," says the godmother, "fetch me a couple lizards."

So Cinderella says, "What do you think this is, the zoo?" But she went in the living-room and choose a couple lizards off the lounge and the old lady turned them into footmen.

The next thing the old godmother done was tag Cinderella herself with the wand and all of a sudden the gal's rags had become a silk evening gown and her feet was wrapped up in a pair of plate-glass slippers.

"How do you like them slippers?" asked the old dame.

"Great!" says Cinderella. "I wished you had of made the rest of my garments of the same material."

"Now, listen," says the godmother: "don't stay no later than midnight because just as soon as the clock strikes twelve, your dress will fall off and your chauffeur and so forth will change back into vermin."

Well, Cinderella clumb in the car and they was about to start when the chauffeur got out and went around back of the tonneau.

"What's the matter?" says Cinderella.

"I wanted to be sure my tail-light was on," says the rat.

Finally they come to Webster Hall and when Cinderella entered the ballroom everybody stopped dancing and looked at her pop-eyed. The Prince went nuts and wouldn't dance with nobody else and when it come time for supper he got her two helpings of stewed rhubarb and liver and he also had her laughing herself sick at the different wows he pulled. Like for instance they was one occasion when he looked at her feet and asked her what was her shoes made of.

"Plate glass," says Cinderella.

"Don't you feel no pane?" asked the Prince.

Other guests heard this one and the laughter was general.

But finally it got to be pretty near twelve o'clock and Cinderella went home in her car and pretty soon Pat and Mike blowed in and found her in the ashcan and told her about the ball and how the strange gal had come and stole the show.

"We may see her again to-morrow night," says Pat.

"Oh," says Cinderella, "is they going to be another ball?"

"Why, no, you poor sap!" says Mike. "It's a Marathon."

"I wished I could go," says Cinderella. "I could if you would leave me take your yellow dress."

The two stepsisters both razzed her, little wreaking that it was all as she could do to help from laughing outright.

Anyway they both went back to the dance the next night and Cinderella followed them again, but this time the gin made her drowsy and before she realized it, the clock was striking twelve. So in her hurry to get out she threw a shoe and everybody scrambled for it, but the Prince got it. Meanw'ile on account of it being after midnight, the touring car had disappeared and Cindy had to walk home and her former chauffeur kept nibbling at her exposed foot and annoying her in many other ways.

Well, the Prince run a display ad the next morning that he would marry the gal who could wear the shoe and he sent a trumpeter and a shoe clerk to make a house to house canvass of Greater New York and try the shoe on all the dames they could find and finally they come to the clubman's house and the trumpeter woke up the two stepsisters for a fitting. Well, Pat took one look at the shoe and seen they was no use. Mike was game and tried her best to squeeze into it, but flopped, as her dogs was also mastiffs. She got sore and asked the trumpeter why hadn't he broughten a shoe horn instead of that bugle. He just laughed.

All of a sudden him and the shoe clerk catched a glimpse of Cinderella and seen that she had small feet and sure enough, the slipper fitted her and they run back to the Prince's apartment to tell him the news.

"Listen, Scott," they says, for that was the Prince's name: "we have found the gal!"

So Cinderella and the Prince got married and Cinderella forgive her two stepsisters for how they had treated her and she paid a high-priced dentist to fix Mike up with a removable bridge and staked Pat to a surgeon that advertised a new, safe method of exterminating wens.

That is all of the story, but it strikes me like the plot—with the poor, ragged little gal finally getting all the best of it—could be changed around and fixed up so as it would make a good idear for a play.

Red Riding Hood

Well, children, here is the story of little Red Riding Hood like I tell it to my little ones when they wake up in the morning with a headache after a tough night.

Well, one or two times they was a little gal that lived in the suburbs who they called her little Red Riding Hood because she always wore a red riding hood in the hopes that sometime a fresh guy in a high power roadster would pick her up and take her riding. But the rumor had spread the neighborhood that she was a perfectly nice gal, so she had to walk.

Red had a grandmother that lived over near the golf course and got in on most of the parties and one noon she got up and found that they wasn't no gin in the house for her breakfast so she called up her daughter and told her to send Red over with a bottle of gin as she was dying.

So Red starts out with a quart under her arm but had not went far when she met a police dog. A good many people has police dogs, and brags about them and how nice they are for children and etc. but personly I would just as leaf have my kids spend their week-end swimming in the State Shark Hatchery.

Well, this special police dog was like the most of them and hated everybody. When he seen Red he spoke to her and she answered him. Even a dog was better than nothing. She told him where she was going and he pretended like he wasn't paying no tension but no sooner had not she left him when he beat it up a alley and got to her grandmother's joint ahead of her.

Well the old lady heard him knock at the door and told him to come in, as she thought he must either be Red or a bootlegger. So he went in and the old lady was in bed with this hangover and the dog eat her alive.

Then he put on some pajamas and laid down in the bed and pertended like he was her, so pretty soon Red come along and knocked at the door and the dog told her to come in and she went up to the bed to hand him the quart. She thought of course it would be her grandmother laying in the bed and even when she seen the dog she still figured it was her grandmother and something she had drank the night before must of disagreed with her and made her look different.

"Well, grandmother," she says, "you must of hit the old hair tonic last night. Your arms looks like Luis Firpo."

"I will Firpo you in a minute," says the dog.

"But listen grandmother," says Red, "don't you think you ought to have your ears bobbed?"

"I will ear you in a minute," says the dog.

"But listen grandmother," says Red, "you are cock-eyed."

"Listen," says the dog, "if you had of had ½ of what I had last night you would of been stone blind."

"But listen grandmother," says Red, "where did you get the new store teeth?"

"I heard you was a tough egg," says the dog, "so I bought them to eat you with."

So then the dog jumped out of bed and went after Red and she screamed.

In the meanw'ile Red's father had been playing golf for a quarter a hole with a couple of guys that conceded themselfs all putts under 12 ft. and he was $.75 looser coming to the 10th. tee.

The 10th. hole is kind of tough as your drive has to have a carry of 50 yards or it will fall in a garbage incinerating plant. You can either lift out with a penalty of two strokes or else play it with a penalty of suffocation. Red's old man topped his drive and the ball rolled into the garbage. He elected to play it and made what looked like a beautiful shot, but when they got up on the green they found that he had hit a white radish instead of a golf ball.

A long argument followed during which the gallery went home to get his supper. The hole was finely conceded.

The 11th. hole on the course is probably the sportiest hole in golfdom. The tee and green are synonymous and the first shot is a putt, but the rules signify that the putt must be played off a high tee with a driver. Red's father was on in two and off in three more and finely sunk his approach for a birdie eight, squaring the match.

Thus the match was all square coming to the home hole which is right close to grandmother's cottage. Red's father hooked his drive through an open window in his mother-in-law's house and forced his caddy to lend him a niblick. He entered the cottage just as the dog was beginning to eat Red.

"What hole are you playing father?" asked Red.

"The eighteenth," says her father, "and it is a dog's leg."

Where-at he hit the police dog in the leg with his niblick and the dog was so surprised that he even give up the grandmother.

"I win, one up," says Red's father and he went out to tell the news to his two opponents. But they had quit and went home to dress for the Kiwanis Club dance.

Bluebeard

Well children it seems they was a gal married to a man named Bluebeard on acct. of he being rich. That was why she married him and not why they called him Bluebeard, the last-named being on acct. of him not having had time to shave for several days.

So on this day he come into his wife's boudoir whiskers and all and says he was going on the road for 6 wks. to sell tooth brushes with no bristles and might half to make a couple speeches at different Rotary Clubs.

"But listen dearie," he says before departing, "you have got a charge acct. at Haynes the butcher and the great Atlantic and Pacific Tea store so you should worry. And here is my keys," he says, "and this here key opens the rm. where I got my dough and this here key is the key to the rm. where the extra dishes is locked up in case you should have a whole lot of Co. and I hope you entertain all your friends w'ile I am gone so as we can get that much over with. And you can use all of these here keys except this little key which opens the closet at the end of the drawing rm. which I forbid you to enter same."

"Yes, but what is in this closet?" asked the little woman thinking to herself that it must be the place where he kept his Scotch and corkscrew which he had been drinking unbeknownest to her or why would he of went so many days without shaving.

"That is none of your business," was his husbandly reply. "But I am just telling you to lay off that little closet."

He hadn't no sooner than got out of the house when Co. begin to show up as they will when lease desired and amongst the Co. was 2 of her brothers and 1 sister and a couple guys that was stuck on her long before she married Bluebeard.

So they set around all evening and told stories and tried to sing but nothing to sustain them and the little woman wouldn't open the closet door where everybody thought the hootch was for the simple reason that she had got the key in the door and it wouldn't fit and finely they all went home and said they would come back the next day and hoped she would not be so stingy with the drinks.

So they beat it all but her sister, and the 2 gals hadn't no sooner went to bed when the doorbell ring and a Jap answered and who should it be but Bluebeard. And he come up to the rm. and asked her for the keys and she give them all to him except the key to what she thought was the wine cellar.

"Listen," he says, "I will give you 7 minutes to produce that one key which is the most important key in the house."

"Sure," she says, "because that key opens the closet where you are storing the hootch."

"If you think it's hootch, look it over," was his criticism.

So she went up and opened the door to this closet and instead of finding hootch, she found the skeleton forms of former wives and some of them looked like vintage.

"Now," says Bluebeard, "you are going to occupy a clothes hanger along with the rest of these gals."

"Just wait a minute," she says, "till I can go out and get cleaned and pressed."

So she pretended like she was sending herself out to the tailor's but in the meantime she was asking her sister to look out of the window and see was they any help coming and finely her 2 brothers and the guys that was stuck on her showed up and stuck a safety razor into Bluebeard's whiskers and the shock of getting shaved killed him and the little woman and her relatives divided the spoils and believe me spoils is right. The moral of this story is if your husband don't get shaved for 3 days, somebody should ought to step in and do their duty.

A Bedtime Story

Some of the boys in the radio company has been pestering me to death to come to the broadcasting station and tell a couple bedtime stories as they received numerable request from mothers all over the country asking for something that would put their children to sleep and the rumor had got out some way another that whenever I tell a story, why whoever is within hearing distance dozes right off.

Well friends I ain't got the voice necessary to carry over the radio

but will write out a fairy story like I told it to my own kiddies the
other night and it acted like cloroform and parents is welcome to
read it out loud to their children if they wish and the story is Little
Snow-White and I can't remember how it goes in the book so am
obliged to tell it in my own wds.

Well once at a time they was a Queen and she cut herself shaveing
and 3 drops of blood fell in the snow and it looked so pretty that
the Queen wished she could have a red and white kid and pretty
soon she gave birth to a little gal that soon learned to fix herself up
in the above color scheme and her mother nicknamed her Snow-
White and that winter the mother died of home made gin and the
King without needless delay married a chorus girl as he loved
beautiful baritone voices.

The new bride had once been elected Miss America at Atlantic
City and if you seen her at certain times in the day she was not ½
bad though the King gave her a mirror for a wedding present and
told her to get some of that stuff out of her eyelashes.

Well the new Queen was a woman at heart and could not help
from talking even when alone and one day she stood up in front of
the mirror and said:

> *"Mirror, mirror on the wall,*
> *Who is the dame for whom you'd fall?"*

And the mirror replied:

> *"I will half to hand it to you, O Queen,*
> *You are best I ever seen."*

Well this kept up till little Snow-White was a 7 year old flapper
and one day the Queen says to the mirror:

> *"Mirror, mirror on my dresser,*
> *Do I still lead? No sir or yes sir?"*

And the mirror replied:

> *"You use to top the list, O Queen,*
> *Now Snow-White has got you beat, old bean."*

Well this made no hit with the Queen as she could not stomach
the position of runner up so she said a word that is always spelt with

a capital letter and took a smash at the mirror and then give a boy from the East Side $15.00 to take Snow-White out to the park and bump her off and he was to bring back some of the little gal's giblets to show he had not missed.

But the gun man was noble at heart and could not bear to kill Snow-White and turned her loose near the zoo and then spent a very small portion of the $15.00 on some chicken livers en brochette which he took back to the Queen as evidence.

Well Snow-White was scared at being left alone and she run until she couldn't run no more on acct. of how her dogs fret her so she finely set down on the steps of a apt. bldg. along about midnight and pretty soon the 6 Green Brothers who had a musical act come home to this bldg. in which they had a apt. and they took Snow-White in and made her their house keeper.

She told them her story and they warned her to never let nobody in the apt. unless she knew who it was as the Queen would find out sooner or later that she was still alive and would try and get her.

Mean while the Queen eat the chicken livers and then visited the mirror and says:

> "Mirror, mirror upside down,
> Who is the prettiest gal in town?"

And the mirror replied in a cracked voice:

> "You still run second, O you Queen,
> To Snow-White who is working for the Brothers Green."

Well to make it a short story the Queen tried 3 different times to get rid of Snow-White and the first time she made up like a corset salesman and Snow-White was sucker enough to let her in and the Queen sold her a corset that was too small and the poor gal was chokeing to death when the Green boys come home and released her. On another occasion the Queen sold the gal a poison comb which she stuck in her hair and the Green boys got there just in time to prevent total baldness.

On the last occasion the Queen posed as a fruit peddler and Snow-White ast her did she have any apples and the Queen says yes I have some apples today but Snow-White said she was scared to eat one as it might be poisoned so the Queen says that to prove they was no danger, she would eat the corpse of the apple herself while Snow-White eat the outside.

Well the outside was the part that was poisoned and when Snow-White eat it she fell dead.

Now the way the Queen found out that the corset gag and the poisoned comb had flopped was by consulting with her mirror, like for inst. after the poisoned comb episode she says to the mirror:

> *"Mirror, mirror gift of the King,*
> *Who leads the Looks League now, old thing?"*

And the mirror was obliged to answer:

> *"You use to be fairer than all the others,*
> *But Snow-White is still rooming with the Six Green Brothers."*

But after the apple episode the mirror said in reply to a query:

> *"You lead the league once more, old head,*
> *For Snow-White seems to be practically dead."*

However when the Green Brothers arrived home and found Snow-White lying on the floor with her neck kind of bulged out like it was a cyst or something they called in a Xray expert and he soon located the apple in her throat and a man from the garage got it out with a applejack, whereupon Snow-White jumped up as good as new.

To celebrate the occasion the Greens took her along that night to the Supper Club where they was employed and there she met a wealthy bond thief who liked them young and merrily rang the bells. So the same day they was married, the Queen put the usual query to her mirror and the last named replied:

> *"I'd like to say you, but I've got to hand it*
> *To Snow-White, the wife of a well to do bandit."*

This made the Queen so sore that she drunk a qt. of $55.00 Scotch which she had been saveing for company and the next day her widower married the gal who had been sent to Atlantic City that year as Miss Seattle.

Preface to:
How to Write Short Stories (1924)

A glimpse at the advertising columns of our leading magazines shows that whatever else this country may be shy of, there is certainly no lack of correspondence schools that learns you the art of short-story writing. The most notorious of these schools makes the boast that one of their pupils cleaned up $5000.00 and no hundreds dollars writing short stories according to the system learnt in their course, though it don't say if that amount was cleaned up in one year or fifty.

However, for some reason another when you skin through the pages of high class periodicals, you don't very often find them cluttered up with stories that was written by boys or gals who had win their phy beta skeleton keys at this or that story-writing college. In fact, the most of the successful authors of the short fiction of to-day never went to no kind of a college, or if they did, they studied piano tuning or the barber trade. They could of got just as far in what I call the literary game if they had of stayed home those four years and helped mother carry out the empty bottles.

The answer is that you can't find no school in operation up to date, whether it be a general institution of learning or a school that specializes in story writing, which can make a great author out of a born druggist.

But a little group of our deeper drinkers has suggested that maybe boys and gals who wants to take up writing as their life work would be benefited if some person like I was to give them a few hints in regards to the technic of the short story, how to go about planning it and writing it, when and where to plant the love interest and climax, and finally how to market the finished product without leaving no bad taste in the mouth.

Well, then, it seems to me like the best method to use in giving out these hints is to try and describe my own personal procedure from the time I get inspired till the time the manuscript is loaded on to the trucks.

The first thing I generally always do is try and get hold of a catchy title, like for instance, "Basil Hargrave's Vermifuge," or "Fun at the Incinerating Plant." Then I set down to a desk or flat table of any kind and lay out 3 or 4 sheets of paper with as many different colored pencils and look at them cock-eyed a few moments before making a selection.

How to begin—or, as we professionals would say, "how to commence"—is the next question. It must be admitted that the method of approach ("L'approchement") differs even among first class fictionists. For example, Blasco Ibañez usually starts his stories with a Spanish word, Jack Dempsey with an "I" and Charley Peterson with a couple of simple declarative sentences about his leading character, such as "Hazel Gooftree had just gone mah jong. She felt faint."

Personally it has been my observation that the reading public prefers short dialogue to any other kind of writing and I always aim to open my tale with two or three lines of conversation between characters—or, as I call them, my puppets—who are to play important rôles. I have often found that something one of these characters says, words I have perhaps unconsciously put into his or her mouth, directs my plot into channels deeper than I had planned and changes, for the better, the entire sense of my story.

To illustrate this, let us pretend that I have laid out a plot as follows: Two girls, Dorothy Abbott and Edith Quaver, are spending the heated term at a famous resort. The Prince of Wales visits the resort, but leaves on the next train. A day or two later, a Mexican reaches the place and looks for accommodations, but is unable to find a room without a bath. The two girls meet him at the public filling station and ask him for a contribution to their autograph album. To their amazement, he utters a terrible oath, spits in their general direction and hurries out of town. It is not until years later that the two girls learn he is a notorious forger and realize how lucky they were after all.

Let us pretend that the above is the original plot. Then let us begin the writing with haphazard dialogue and see whither it leads:

"Where was you?" asked Edith Quaver.

"To the taxidermist's," replied Dorothy Abbott.

The two girls were spending the heated term at a famous watering trough. They had just been bathing and were now engaged in sorting dental floss.

"I am getting sick in tired of this place," went on Miss Quaver.

"It is mutual," said Miss Abbott, shying a cucumber at a passing paper-hanger.

There was a rap at their door and the maid's voice announced that company was awaiting them downstairs. The two girls went down and entered the music room. Garnett Whaledriver was at the piano and the girls tiptoed to the lounge.

The big Nordic, oblivious to their presence, allowed his fingers to form weird, fantastic minors before they strayed unconsciously into the first tones of Chopin's 121st Fugue for the Bass Drum.

From this beginning, a skilled writer could go most anywheres, but it would be my tendency to drop these three characters and take up the life of a mule in the Grand Canyon. The mule watches the trains come in from the east, he watches the trains come in from the west, and keeps wondering who is going to ride him. But she never finds out.

The love interest and climax would come when a man and a lady, both strangers, got to talking together on the train going back east.

"Well," said Mrs. Croot, for it was she, "what did you think of the Canyon?"

"Some cave," replied her escort.

"What a funny way to put it!" replied Mrs. Croot. "And now play me something."

Without a word, Warren took his place on the piano bench and at first allowed his fingers to form weird, fantastic chords on the black keys. Suddenly and with no seeming intention, he was in the midst of the second movement of Chopin's Twelfth Sonata for Flute and Cuspidor. Mrs. Croot felt faint.

That will give young writers an idea of how an apparently trivial thing such as a line of dialogue will upset an entire plot and lead an author far from the path he had pointed for himself. It will also serve as a model for beginners to follow in regards to style and technic. I will not insult my readers by going on with the story to its obvious conclusion. That simple task they can do for themselves, and it will be good practice.

So much for the planning and writing. Now for the marketing of the completed work. A good many young writers make the mistake of enclosing a stamped, self-addressed envelope, big enough for the manuscript to come back in. This is too much of a temptation to the editor.

Personally I have found it a good scheme to not even sign my name to the story, and when I have got it sealed up in its envelope and stamped and addressed, I take it to some town where I don't live and mail it from there. The editor has no idea who wrote the story, so how can he send it back? He is in a quandry.

In conclusion let me warn my pupils never to write their stories —or, as we professionals call them, "yarns"—on used paper. And never to write them on a post-card. And never to send them by telegraph (Morse code).

Stories ("yarns") of mine which have appeared in various publications—one of them having been accepted and published by the first editor that got it—are reprinted in the following pages and will illustrate in a half-hearted way what I am trying to get at.

RING LARDNER.

"THE MANGE,"
Great Neck, Long Island, 1924.

Preface to: The Love Nest (1926)

by Sarah E. Spooldripper*

It is hoped that a careful reading of the stories collected in this book will dispel the general illusion that in his later years Ring Lardner was just a tiresome old man induced by financial calamity and a fondness for narcotics to harp constantly on the futility of life on a branch line of the Long Island Railroad. In these tales we see the old fellow as perhaps not lovable, but certainly irresistible. There was an impishness in him that fascinated. It was part of his charm.

I know it for truth that from fifty on he indulged to an alarming extent in the lesser opiates, eating aspirin as if it were so much mud and seldom laying aside the all-day sucker which he plopped into his mouth the instant he had finished his breakfast. Lardner always bolted his food. He was afraid the rats would get it. It was part of his charm.

Appearance of "The Love Nest," the short story from which the book takes its name, in Cosmopolitan Magazine, created a furore on the east bank of the Hudson, commuters of that neighborhood nearly coming to blows in arguments over the identity, in real life, of the tale's principal characters. Two old cronies who had played halma together night after night for nearly a week suddenly began making faces at one another, hiding each other's gloves, pinching each other's forearms, and altogether making a fiasco of the entire relationship. The author heard rumors of this feud and others and knew their cause, but kept his own counsel till the last day of his earthly career, when he confided to me that the Lou Gregg of the story was President Fillmore and the Mrs. Gregg, Mary Lewis.

It was in the middle of this work that the rivalry between Lardner, Scott Fitzgerald, and Opie Reade for the love of Lily Langtry reached it height. During a dinner party at which the then raging beauty and her raging suitors were all present, the toastmaster, Gerald Chapman, asked Miss Langtry to rise and drink to "her

---

* Miss Spooldripper lived with the Lardners for years and took care of their wolf. She knew all there was to know about Lardner, and her mind was virtually blank. It was part of her charm.

favorite." The muscles of Fitzgerald and Reade were taut; Lardner's were very flabby.

After a pause that seemed to endure all night but really lasted only half that long, Miss Langtry got up, raised her glass and said: "I drink to Red Grange. Heston may have been his superior on defense and Coy, Thorpe, Eckersall, and Mahan more versatile, but as a common carrier I take off my hat to the Wheaton iceman."

Miss Langtry was deeply interested in college athletics and it was she who christened a certain New Jersey town Rahway because it was enroute to Rutgers, Princeton, and the University of Pennsylvania.

Her response to the toastmaster's request affected her three swains variously. Reade arose and told the story of the two half-breeds, Seminole and Deminole. Lardner and Fitzgerald took up rotation pool, and weighed themselves once a week. Every so often they became maudlin, or, better still, inaudible.

An insight into Lardner's true character may be obtained from the correspondence which passed between him and Mrs. Patrick Campbell while he was writing the story "Haircut" at Atlantic City.

"Dear Ringlets," wrote Mrs. Campbell (it was a name she had for him), "don't forget 'Miss England' while playing around with 'Miss America.'"

"Dear Pat," was Lardner's reply, "am having a 'swill' time, but I do 'Miss England' and indeed I would walk a mile for a Campbell."

On the back of the card was a picture of Young's Million Dollar Pier.*

"Haircut" was written under a severe strain, the writer having just engaged in a violent quarrel with John N. Wheeler, then editor of Liberty.

"Why didn't you lead me a spade?" demanded Wheeler.

"I was out of them," was the infuriating reply, and in a moment the two were rolling on the floor, with Wheeler's dice.

The character of the doctor in "Haircut" was a composite "photograph" of Mrs. Campbell and the Shuberts. It was Lardner's favorite

* This correspondence and other mash notes written by Lardner and his admirers were obtained from the street cleaners of East Shore Road, Great Neck, where the author threw all his mail, and are printed with the permission of Judge Landis.

among all his fictional characters, or, as he called them, "my puppets."

"Which is your favorite among all your 'puppets'?" I once asked him as we jointly gave the wolf a sitzbath.

"The doctor," he said.

The wolf was really the chief interest in Lardner's life. I have never elsewhere seen such a whole-souled comradeship as existed between the Master and this sinister pet. He was always hoping it would have a baby which he would have christened the Wolverine as a memorial to his native state.

Lardner's adoption of the beast was characteristic of the man. One afternoon in October while Mrs. Lardner (he always called her Junior as she was two or more years younger than he) was making out the May checks, she suddenly looked up from her work, sobbing, and said:

"Husband!"

"Yes, Junior. What is it?"

"I am overdrawn."

"You stay indoors and brood too much," replied Lardner. "A little exercise and a few pleasures would restore the bloom to both those cheeks."

"I am not referring to anything physical," said the little woman. "I mean there is less than no money in the bank."

At that moment there was a scratching outside that could not have been the children, as they had all had their baths.

"What is that noise, Junior?" inquired the Master.

"I will go and see," said the Madam, sliding headforemost to the front door, as she was a great admirer of Frankie Frisch.

She returned in a moment, sobbing louder than ever, with the news that the wolf was at the door.

This was the beginning of a friendship that the less said about it the better. But I suppose I ought not to complain, for the wolf's advent into the home was responsible for mine, and it is not every spinster who spends the latter days of her life under such pleasant conditions as existed in the household of Ring Lardner, God bless him!

The story "Reunion" followed a visit paid the Lardners by the little woman's sisters and their husbands, all strict Swedenborgians and innately opposed to meat-eating and outdoor sports. Lardner was, of course, a devotee of golf and considered days spent indoors as days wasted. So it was torture to him, this prolonged sojourn of his in-laws, and "Reunion" was penned in a spirit of bitterness. The character of Mrs. Stu Johnston's brother is a composite of G. P. Torrence of Indianapolis, Robin Hendry of Detroit, H. W. Kitchell of Evanston, and F. R. Kitchell of Hingham, Mass., all of whom married sisters of Junior.

In re Lardner's golf, the following amusing anecdote is recounted:

Lardner was playing a mixed twosome with Mayor Walker of New York. They were both playing a Spalding mesh ball, which is how they got mixed. Coming to the fifteenth tee, they had halved the preceding three holes and Lardner could not remember whose turn it was to drive first.

"Your honor?" he said to the Mayor.

"Yes?" the Mayor replied. "What can I do for you?"

It is incidents like this that paint the man in his true colors. He was forever blowing bubbles. It amounted to a whim.

The romance of "Mr. and Mrs. Fix-It," without ranking with Lardner's best or with his most popular compositions, and betraying here and there a less persistent hold on character than is usual with him, is still a fascinating story, full of his peculiar sensuousness and pathos, with striking scenes vividly portrayed, and an advance on his previous farces as respects his constantly growing power of imaginative description.

Publication of this story in Liberty caused an estrangement between the Master and the Grantland Rices, who were unmistakably the parties inspiring it. So accurately were their characters and idiosyncrasies depicted that they recognized themselves and did not speak to Lardner for a week. This was considered a triumph by the Master.

"But the lesson was all lost," he told me afterwards, when a reconciliation had been effected. "They knew I was writing about them, and now they are right up to their old tricks again, dictating where we shall buy our shirts, how to discipline our kiddies, what road to take South, what to order for breakfast, when to bathe in what kind of bath salts, and even how often to visit the chiropodist. It is an intolerable example of maniacal Southern hospitality."

He proceeded to a fresh attack, turning out "Who Dealt?" Mrs. Rice is unquestionably the first person in this story, the one who tells it; either she or Ruth Hale or perhaps Mrs. S. B. Thorne.

There is an interesting fact connected with the story "Zone of Quiet." It was written outdoors during the equinoctial gales. Nearly every other sheet of copy was blown away or destroyed by stray dogs, and when the manuscript finally reached Ray Long, editor of Cosmopolitan, over two-thirds of it was missing. Mr. Long thought this all for the best as he was crowded that month. Mr. Long is related by marriage to Mr. O. O. McIntyre, which is considered a horse on both of them.*

Most of the stories making up this volume are noticeably shorter than those Lardner wrote in the early days of his tepid career. This is due to the invention and perfection of radio. Not content with purchasing one of the standard radios on the market, the Master, who, like Jane Cowl, was something of a mechanical genius, made his own set and installed it in the suit of pajamas which he habitually wore nights. At first he was unable to get any station at all, and this condition held good up to the day of his death. But he was always trying to tune in on Glens Falls, N. Y., and it was only in his last illness that he found out there was no broadcasting station at that place. His sense of humor came to his rescue in this dilemma.

"Junior," he said to his wife, "they tell me there is no broadcasting station at Glens Falls."

"Am I to blame for that?" retorted the little Nordic, quick to take umbrage.**

"No," he answered. "It's Glens Falls."

Those of the tales in this book which have not already been mentioned were dashed off after the Master had contracted the cold that resulted in the fatal attack of conchoid, a disease which is superinduced by a rush of seashells to the auricle or outer ear. Present

---

* Strangely enough, Mr. Long's favorite amusement is horseback riding, so the innuendo is not so far out of the way. He is known as a keen whip around Greenwich and, during the winters, when he lives in town, can be seen in Times Square almost any morning astride his imported hunter, "Black Oxen," directing the traffic and selling tickets to the Field Day at Jamaica.

** Junior was an inveterate umbrage taker and frequently took more than was good for her.

during the last hours were only myself and the wolf, Junior having chosen this time to get a shampoo and wave in preparation for the series of dinner dances that were bound to follow.

"Edna," whispered the Master as he lay there idly watching the doctor change a tire, "to-morrow I will be all right again and you and I will get in a taxi and be ourselves."

He called me Edna only when he was up to some devilment. It was his way.

The Master is gone* and the next question is who will succeed him? Perhaps some writer still unborn. Perhaps one who will never be born. That is what I hope.

Preface to:
The Story of a Wonder Man (1927)

by Sarah E. Spooldripper

The publication of this autobiography is entirely without the late Master's sanction. He wrote it as a pastime and burnt up each chapter as soon as it was written; the salvaging was accomplished by ghouls who haunted the Lardners' ash bbl. during my whole tenure of office as night nurse to their dromedary.

Some of the copy was so badly charred as to be illegible. The ghouls took the liberty of filling in these hiatuses with "stuff" of their own, which can be readily distinguished from the Master's as it is not nearly as good. Readers and critics are therefore asked to bear in mind that those portions of the book which they find entertaining are the work of the Master himself; those which bore them or sound forced are interpolations by milksops.

---

* The joke is on Miss Spooldripper, for she is gone too. Two months ago she was found dead in the garage, her body covered with wolf bites left there by her former ward, who has probably forgotten where he left them.

Another request which I know the Master would have wished me to make is that neither reader nor critic read the book through at one sitting (Cries of "Fat chance!" and "Hold 'em, Stanford!"). It was written a chapter at a time and should be perused the same way with, say, a rest of from seven weeks to two months between chapters. It might even be advisable to read one chapter and then take the book back to the exchange desk, saying you had made a mistake.

Mr. Lardner's friends will regret that he omitted from these memoirs reference to his encounter with Mussolini, the Tiger of France and Italy. The two happened to be occupying the same compartment on "The Dixie Flyer" between Cannes and Mentone.

"Great golf weather," remarked the Tiger.

"I beg your pardon," replied the writer. "Je ne parle pas le Wop."

I forget what else happened.

A Close-Up of Domba Splew

Not since the tardy, posthumous death of Agera Cholera has the American literati been so baffled toward a rising genius of letters than has been demonstrated in regards to the Italian poet, Domba Splew, who, just a year ago, sprang into world-wide indifference by the publication, in The Bookman, of his verse, "La battia fella inna base tuba." (The weasel fell into the bathtub).

It is a matter of history that in the month in which this poem appeared, the circulation of the magazine in which it was printed increased two copies. And the fame of the author on this side of the old pond, as I call it, spread as far west as North Attleboro, Mass. You could not wake up in the morning or any other time without either wife or kiddies yelping, "Sweet papa, did you see this poem of Domba Splew's, 'La battia fella inna base tuba' (The weasel fell into the bathtub)?"

It got so finely a person could not sleep at home at all and I for one rented one of the big New York hotels and slept outdoors, not being able to get a room. Everybody wondered what was the matter, but I laughed at them. Finely the editor of Rickets Weekly caught me in an upright position in the gutter and made me the unheard-of offer of $5.00 and no hundreds dollars to go and interview this America-Italio sensation and find out something about his home life.

To locate a man as famous as him is what Ex-Attorney-General Daugherty would call "les arbeit tough" (a hard job). But the writer, an experienced interviewer, looked upon it as child's play and went to the nearest city ticket office where luckily I found a clerk who had not returned from lunch.

"Listen," I said, "where would a man be apt to run acrost a foreign literary genius, discovered only a year ago?"

647

"Listen," replied the clerk, "have you tried the artistic and bohemian mecca of American letters?"

"Where is that?" I coughed.

"Scranton, Pa.," was the clerk's reply.

So the writer bought a ticket to Scranton and arrived there only a half hour late.

To make a short story out of a risqué story, I found our hero living on the top floor of a six-story bungalow.

"If," he said, "I am away from the smoke and chimbley, I am at a lost. In other words, I am a gone gosling.

"Listen," he said: "I don't think you know much about Italy, but I will tell you. In the first place there is a military rule which provides that when a native born reaches the age of seven, they must spend the next three years in jail, or, as Oscar Wilde aptly named it, Reading Gaol. The reason I came over to America was on acct. of the fact that there is more words here. I need words."

In a little while he was supine.

"Now listen," I said: "I have been sent over here to Scranton to find out about your home life. Tell me what you do all day."

He went scarlet.

"I have got a set of rules," he said, pulling a fresh cucumber off the hatrack. "In the morning I get up and talk to my dromedaries. Oh, those dromedaries! I would walk a mile for one of them! I have got a collection of eighty of them and each one more laughable than the first one. Every morning somebody sends me a dromedary. After talking to my dromedaries, I sit down and read the telephone book from cover to cover charge. But now leave me go out and show you my garden."

The two of us strolled haltingly through his garden, which was an Italian garden with all the Italian dishes in bloom—ravioli, spaghetti, garlic, Aida, and citrous fruits.

"Is this your diversion?" I asked him.

"Yes," he said, toppling over a govvel sprig and breaking his ankle in two places.

"Tell me about your home life," I said with a sneer.

"I presume," he said, taking a pair of suspenders out of the nearest waste basket, "I presume you want to know my daily calendar.

Well, I always make it a point to get up at six in the morning and eat my breakfast food."

I found out later that his breakfast food was ground-up quail feathers, the rest of the carcass being thrown outdoors.

"I," he continued, "'spend my next ten minutes with my dromedaries. It is just a romp. Then I return to my own room, where an ostrich shaves me. Not too close.

"Then I sit down on a milk stool and begin my day's work. I aim to never write lest than one poem a day. For instance, look at this one I turned out this morning, just after the ostrich had shaved me."

And he read me the verse that was published by mistake in last month's Applejack—

> "Hail to thee, blithe owl!
> Bird thou never wantest to been.
> Queenly and efflorien,
> How did thou ever begin?"

"That," I said, "sounds like a steal on Kipling."

"Kipling yourself!" said the poet, and I loped over the nearest hedge.

"But listen," he said: "Have you heard my Goseflesh, after the style of Alfred Geese?"

There was no use saying no:

> "Quiescent, a person sits heart and soul,
> Thinking of daytime and Amy Lowell.
>
> A couple came walking along the street;
> Neither of them had ever met."

"That," said Mr. Splew, "is the verse I have worked on all winter."

"It's been a hard winter," I said. "We didn't have enough coal either."

With that, he climbed up on top of the pigeon house.

"I want to tell you about my wife," he said. "She has got what is called chronic paralysis. She has a stroke every day, but it is never quite enough."

With that, he led me into the beehive, where he and the dromedaries eat all their meals.

"Now, Mr. Splew," I said, "my editor wanted me to ask you how you got the name 'Domba.' He thought it might be a contraction of Dumbbell."

"Your editor is both wrong," said Mr. Splew. "I was named for my father, who gave the money to found the Kalter Aufschnitt (Cold High School) in Rome. And the children that attended the school said it must have been dumbfounded. Would you like to go into the pool?"

Don't Be a Drudge

I won't surprise nobody by saying that people gets along a whole lot better in this life if they have got some specialty or something which they can do which they ain't many other people can do it.

Every yr. they's more and more demand for specialists in some line another and as the number of novelties and new inventions increases, why the need of people that knows how to make them and fix them and monkey with them increases just as fast.

A man or woman that has got a nag along certain lines or is educated along same, why he or she can command a great deal more money than a man or woman that is too dumb for anything except empty the ash can and wash the windows though heavens knows these two professions is high paid enough at the present writing.

But any way the facts as I have stated is so well known that all the good schools and colleges has kept adding and adding to their special branches and besides that, dozens of correspondence schools has sprang up all over the country which the tuitions in same is so reasonable that pretty near everybody can borrow or save enough to fit themselfs for some lucrative trade or profession.

However technical education is still in its infancy you might say and right now to-day they's plenty of room for a great big university that won't teach nothing only specialties that ain't taught nowheres else. And that the graduates from this university would not have no trouble going right to work in their chosen profession can be showed by a study of the advertising columns of any big city daily where the help wanted dept. is filled day in and day out with unsatisfied appeals for men and gals fitted for these jobs.

Leave us take for example the classified section of one of last Sunday's papers and one of the ads that meets the eye under the heading of jewelry is a ad offering a steady position to "a good man on finding rings."

Now good men on finding rings is made and not born, and at the proposed university they would be a thorough course in the science of finding rings which the person getting a degree as bachelor of ring finding would half to know all they is to know in regards to this intricate profession.

First the students of the university both male and female would all be encouraged to wear rings. Every morning after classes had started up, the class in ring finding would visit the different dormitories and lodging houses and inspect the wash rooms of same and pick up all the rings left along side of wash bowls wile the owners was washing.

Then the class would pace back and 4th. acrost the campus examining the ground for rings that may of been dropped. As a rule boys and gals that goes to college don't eat as much as they use to at home and the result is that they loose flesh and when their fingers gets thin their rings falls off.

Ring finding is pleasant work, keeping you out in the open air a good deal of the time and the fact that the ad which I have quoted has appeared in the paper several times in succession is evidence that the field ain't overcrowded.

Under pianos we come acrost the following: "wanted piano varnisher and fly finisher." Now it don't take much of a technical education to varnish a piano and it don't take much of a technical education to finish flies, but a whole lot of close study and hard practice is necessary before a person can be both at the same time.

In my university I would have a laboratory in which they was about a equal number of pianos and windows and on the window sills I would place saucers full of sugar and other condiments which flies considers a treat.

Then I would arm the students with a varnishing brush in one hand and a fly swatter in the other and I would offer attractive little weekly prizes like a toy piano or a dozen sheets of fly paper, for the student varnishing the most pianos and finishing the most flies and vice versa.

Another ad in the piano dept. says "Wanted—Expert rough piano tuner." I figure that a one yr. intensive course, including plenty of gymnasium work, would fit a man so as he could tune the roughest kind of pianos and handle them in such a way that they would think a long time before getting out of tune again.

Under winders the following ad appears: "Wanted—Winders experienced on bottle bobbin artificial silk. Call all week." I suppose, though I don't know for sure, that they's plenty of winders that is experienced on bottle bobbin real silk, but artificial silk is a different problem and to cap the climax, how many people can call all week a specially in a poker game? Students in the winder dept. of my schools would spend their forenoon bobbin for bottles and devote their afternoons and evenings to calling.

The paper also contains two ads from different concerns in need of a mica splitter and I would insist that my university be provided with a thorough training in splitting mica as I feel like it would be a very popular profession as I can't imagine nothing more romantic then to be asked what you done for a living and be able to answer truthfully that you was a mica splitter.

Other courses suggested by the ads would be a course for "mangle girls, feeders and folders," "automatic men," "bushelmen" and "bonnaz stampers, able to spool."

I hope that some day one of my sons can brag that he graduated with high honors in bonnaz stamping and was considered one of the best spoolers in the university. And finely I would have a course where girls would be taught to be "All around girls," for which they seems to be a never ending demand and no wonder, as they are certainly a scarce article.

As soon as science has learned how to control people's height and gen. size I would also introduce courses teaching pupils how to be short or tall or large or small, according to which size was in special demand at the time.

Just now it seems like tall girls and small girls is equally desirable.

At lease I find one ad asking for a tall girl to assist in hooking up models and another ad asking for a small girl for office work in a doctor's office. The doctor probably wants somebody around who he can beat up at the end of a perfect day.

Segregate the Fats

One of the saddest things about life is that so few people is satisfied with themselfs and wish they was some one else and etc. and you can't get on intimate turns with no family without finding out that the wife is too fat and trying to get thin like Irene Castle or the husband is too skinny and trying to be a big man like Arbuckle or vice versa.

Some men are so short that you keep tripping over them on the st. and on the other hand a good many gals is tall enough so as they always got to be on their guard for the fear that linemen will come along and string wires on them. In either and all cases the situation is embarrassing to the parties and their relatives and Congress don't seem to take no interest in it.

Of the people that ain't right in one way another, the big majority belongs to the class that is over weight. In spite of the fact that prices of food is double and treble what they was 10 and 20 yrs. ago why it seems like they's twice as many cases now as they was then of people that is too fat or afraid they will get too fat and when you go to a dinner party where the guests is suppose to be having a good time, why 80 or 90 per cent of them, men and women alike, wishes they could eat more or realize they are eating too much and they look so miserable that neither them or their friends can't enjoy themselfs. The ailment has become so widespread that a person can't tell a story about a fat man or mention the word fat without two-thirds of the audience thinks you are taking a dig at them.

Well the magazines and newspapers is full of ads in regards to how to get thin which reads a whole lot better than they work, so

I don't want nobody to think that in this article I am trying to sell systems of diet or pills or belts that will bring you back to normalcy.

But what I am trying to do is to set forth what I believe is the only common sense solution of the problem and as I am making the suggestion free and without no personal interest only to be of benefit to red-blooded fat people and mankind in general, why you can either take it or leave it alone.

Like radio and airships and all other great inventions, my idear may at first sound kind of silly but when you think it over, it turns out to be worse than simple. In a word the scheme calls for a general redistribution of citizens or a segregation of same so that people of one shape would all live together in one place. That is, they would be towns in every state set aside for the exclusive use of fat folks only, where it would be vs. the law for a skinny person to set their ft.

The idear being of course that what makes fat people unhappy is the sight of thin people around them and that if a fat person was just one fat person amongst a population of fat persons, why they wouldn't be no hardship about being fat. Further and more, matters could be so arranged that the fatter a person was, why all the better as I will exclaim in a few moments together with a few other details of the plan which I have only space to state them briefly.

1. It would not be necessary to build new towns but it would be necessary to make alterations in towns which exists. Like for inst. we will suppose that Cincinnati is one of the towns that has been picked out for a fat colony and renamed Obes-city.

Well the present population of Cincinnati is around 450,000 which we will presume is all the town has got room for. Well this means that if all the people was fat, they wouldn't only be room for about one-third of 450,000 or 150,000. But to offset this we would select some city about the size of Cincinnati, say for inst. Milwaukee, and make it a colony for skinny folks only and whereas Milwaukee new houses about 450,000, why if they was all thin, they would be accommodations for 3 times 450,000 or 1,350,000.

In addition, the doors, sidewalks, streets, beds, chairs, and etc. in Cincinnati could all be widened so as to take care of the fats wile the same articles could be shrank in Milwaukee to fit the leans.

2. A fat town would be equipped with a public hay scales where

everybody would half to report once a wk. and get weighed. The citizen gaining the most weight in a wk. would be given a coupon and the one receiving the most coupons in a year would be awarded the championship emblem, a 100 lb. box of candy.

A citizen who showed a loss of weight would be warned the first wk. and if he or she showed another loss the following wk. they would be rode out of town on a truck. This scheme would make it worth your wile to fatten up and therefore the fatter you got the happier you would be instead of going around with a long face the way like now.

3. Suffrage would be granted to all male citizens over 21 that tipped the beam at 200 lbs. or better and all adult females weighing over 179.

4. Grocery stores and markets would be prohibited from selling any foods except starches, fats and sweets.

Those is just a few of the details of the scheme and the rest of them could be worked out as need arose and might state in conclusion how I come to think of the idear.

Well I happened to be setting in a card game the other night with 5 others of whom 2 besides myself was gents and at first I kept wondering to myself why was it I felt so happy as I am generally always miserable in a card game on acct. of not having no luck. Well my luck wasn't no better than usual so I had to look for another reason and it finely come to me like a flash. The other 2 gents in the game was also loosing their hair.

What of It?

I was telling this to a friend of mine that's in the furniture game; travels out of Grand Rapids for the Phillips people. And he says I ought to tell it to other friends of mine that's on the road a good deal so as they'll know how to protect themself when they bump into one of these here broadcasters like Lacey.

Well, it seems they was a fella named Dexter Cosset and in his spare time he wrote a play and mailed it to a friend of his in New York that was personally acquainted with Joe Morris, the producer. So he give it to Morris and somebody in Morris' office that could read told Morris the play was good, so Morris got somebody that could write to wire a telegram to Cosset. It says in the telegram:

"Accept your play ghosts but must change title as it seems man named Ibsen has a farce that title come New York at once as we want to go right into rehearsal have renamed play Carlotta's corns which will be permanent title unless you can think of better one."

Well, it seems Cosset lived in South Bend and clerked in Ellsworth's, and his gal clerked there, too, and when he wrote this play he named the heroine Carlotta because that was his gal's name if you get what I mean. He thought it would kind of tickle her to have the heroine of a play named after her, do you understand me?

But as I say, Carlotta clerked in Ellsworth's, too, and she was on her feet all day and had a good deal of trouble with them, and if she ever got word that Cosset had wrote a play and used her name in connections with the chiropody game, she would of give him the air and submitted to the caresses of Orville Pleat that was in the automobile game on Vistula Avenue.

And besides they wasn't no place in the play where any reference was made to anybody's corns let alone the heroine's, so if it was produced under the title suggested by Mr. Morris, why unless the author wrote in a new scene devoted to pedal disorders which he had no personal experience, why the critics would say what the hell.

So anyway Cosset got on this train this night determined to think up a decent title for his play before he clumb into Mrs. Pullman's spare bed, but Cosset, like a good many other South Bend boys, could not even start to think unless they was a live cigarette in his mush. So the first thing he done when he got on this train this night was look up a porter he knew personally named George something, a colored man. He asked George was they a buffet on the train.

"Why, no, massa," replied George in his laughable darky dialect. "We dinna run no buffet car on this train since ze railroads quit selling what you call ze liquor. But if you got something on ze hip," he added, rolling those big eyes and doing the double shuffle, "I get you ze ice and ze water."

Cosset then exclaimed that what he wanted was a place where he could sit and smoke and think without interruptions and the best the clever darky could suggest was the washroom in his own car. It seems the washrooms in the other cars was jammed with members of the Grand Forks Well-Kept Lawn Association, bound for the annual Get-Together Dinner at Saratoga, with a one-day stopover at Troy to get their collar cleaned.

As Cosset entered the washroom of his own Pullman—"Gastritis" —he noted that the only occupant was a man in the late twenties or forties who he remembered having seen once or twice walking up and down Michigan Street with such a big sample case that a great many people thought he must be selling warships. He was a travelling man named Ben Lacey; lived in Chicago and was married to a Kenosha woman who had luckily lost her hearing. The misery left Lacey's face when he seen Cosset come in. Here was an audience.

"Well," he said, as the young clerk-playwright seated himself, "according to my watch we are twelve minutes late leaving the Bend. And I'm pretty sure the watch is right. I've had this old watch eight years and only paid twenty smackers for it, and it runs just as true now like when I got it. How is that for a twenty dollar watch?"

"Pretty good," replied Cosset.

"I'll say it's pretty good," said Lacey. "They don't make watches no more like this here. I got a friend of mine that's in the watch game and he knows watches. That's his game. And he says they don't make no more watches like this here. His name's Fox, from Lafayette. Maybe you know him."

"No," replied Cosset, "I don't know him."

"He's in the watch game," said Lacey. "I just happened to meet him, and I thought you might maybe know him. He gives me a ring every time he hits Chi. He's a card. Keep you up all night telling gags and stories. And original, too. I remember one morning I met him on the train going from Chi to Benton Harbor. No, it was Niles. Well, he had a morning paper and they was a big story on the front page about the Cragin murder out in Los Angeles. You remember —Cragin, the picture director. They found him dead in his apartment, and it come out that they'd been a big party the night before where pretty near everybody there was a hophead. So this Fox, this friend of mine, he says had I saw the news in the paper and I says what news, and he says O, they's been another snowstorm in Hollywood. He's a card. Keeps everybody laughing. I thought maybe you might of ran across him."

"No," replied Cosset, "I don't know him."

"What game are you in?" asked Lacey.

"Dry goods," replied Cosset.

"I got a brother-in-law in that game," said Lacey. "He was in the insurance game, but now he's in the dry goods game. He's on the road for Smythe-Carter. He married my sister—that's my youngest sister, Bertha. She wouldn't of met him only for me. I got acquainted with him on a train coming from Racine to Chi. No, it was Janesville. He was living in a boarding-house and I felt kind of sorry for him, so I says when he didn't have nothing to do, to give me a ring. So he come out to the house one night to supper. The kid sister couldn't see him at first. They was a couple of his front teeth was discolored. But after you got used to him, you didn't notice it so much.

"So him and the kid got married. Now they got a home of their own out in Morgan Park. Built it cheap on account of one of his brothers being in the building game. They got two of the cutest kiddies you ever seen. The boy's named after me: Ben. That's my name. Little Ben's just two years old and he calls me plain Ben. He can't say uncle. So he just calls me Ben. Smart as a whip."

Cosset didn't deny this or make no comment of any kind as he hoped that absolute silence on his part might prove contagious. But he was too polite not to answer when Uncle Ben asked him a direct question, was he going to the Big Town. He said yes.

"Me, too," said Lacey. "I generally always take the Century, but I had to take this train this time on account of being tied up in Chi with a customer of mine. He's in the cement game. I'm in the elevator game myself; with the Trunkey people. Biggest elevator concern in the U.S. Well, this customer of mine got in town and give me a ring and I had to see him and after we was all through with our business I couldn't get away from him. Great talker. We got in a argument about Coolidge. He was panning Coolidge so I stepped in and told him where he was wrong. If a man says something I don't like, I tell him where he's wrong, customer or no customer. He admitted he was wrong after I'd talked to him. He says, 'I'm wrong, Lacey, and you're right.' So then we wound up telling stories. I thought he'd laugh himself sick when I told him the one about the Greek and the Spaniard. Have you heard that one?"

"No," replied Cosset.

"It's a good one if you ain't heard it," said Lacey. "It seems they was a Greek and a Spaniard and they was out with a couple of fly chorus dames——"

"Would you mind telling it to me after a while?" says Cosset. "Right now, before I forget it, I want to see if my grip's flied open. It don't catch right."

"Well, listen," said Lacey, "I got a friend of mine in the Big Town in the suitcase and trunk game and I'll give you a note to him and he'll sell you the best suitcase you ever seen, at cost."

"Well, I'm much obliged," said Cosset, and hurried out of the washroom and to his seat.

He sat there over an hour, trying and trying to think. But as I said a while ago, he couldn't even start to think unless they was a live cigarette in his mouth. And the car was half full of old women, bound for the annual banquet of the Little Rock Sorrel Growers' Association at Rutland, Vermont.

Well, finally the man that had the lower come in and sat down in the section. He was a man either forty-two or forty-six years old, named Harrison Quolt. He observed that Cosset was acting very nervous.

"You are acting very nervous," he said to Cosset. "What can be the matter?"

Cosset then told him all the circumstances and Quolt laughed softly.

"I've quit smoking myself," he says. "I quit on account of a bad stomach. So I don't have to travel in washrooms no more. But before I quit, I mastered the art of putting the quietus on these Pullman elocutionists. The last three or four trips I made with the cigarette habit, why I could share a washroom from morning till night with one of these here cross-country loud speakers and you'd never hear a word out of him; that is, after I'd give him the treatment."

"What was the treatment?" asked Cosset. "Did you just keep still and not answer nothing he said?"

"Oh, no," says Quolt. "Silence don't do no good. And it don't help none to pretend like you are reading. That just gives them something more to talk about—books and magazines and so forth. But if you are in earnest about the importance of this thinking you've got to do, why I'll go in there with you and fix this guy so's he'll have lockjaw all the rest of the way to New York."

Cosset gratefully accepted this proposition and the two gents went to the washroom where they found Lacey lighting a fresh cigar. He was on the long seat, next to the window. Quolt moved one of the chairs to a position facing Lacey, and seated himself. He begun staring at Lacey's right knee, like they was some item there that baffled or fascinated him. Lacey's eyes hastily followed the direction of Quolt's, but he couldn't detect nothing the matter and looked up again.

"Well," he said, "I was just reading in the paper about two more brokerage firms has failed in the Big Town. That must be a ticklish game. I was thinking once about going into that game myself. I was all set to go into it with another fella in Chi when a friend of mine that's with the Trunkey Elevator people give me a ring and asked me how would I like to go into the elevator game. I says I would try anything once, so I took the position and been with them ever since."

"What?" says Mr. Quolt, continuing to stare at Lacey's knee.

Lacey looked down again, but couldn't see nothing wrong.

"I was just saying," he repeated, "that I seen in this paper where they was two more brokerage houses in New York had took the big flop. I was saying it must be a mighty risky game. I'm tickled to death I stayed out of it. I pretty near got into it once with a fella in Chi. But just as we was making our plans, a friend of mine with the Trunkey Elevator people give me a ring and asked me would I like to go into the elevator game. Well, his proposition sounded reasonable so I took him up and been with them ever since."

"What of it?" said Mr. Quolt.

"Why," says Lacey, "it just shows how lucky a man can be sometimes and maybe don't appreciate just how lucky he was."

"What of it?" said Mr. Quolt, and kept staring at Lacey's knee.

Lacey's eyes followed Quolt's for the third time, but without results. The train was whistling for a station.

"That must be either Kendallville or Ligonier," said Lacey.

"What of it?" said Mr. Quolt.

For maybe a half an hour the three gents sat in silence. Quolt's eyes never left Lacey's knee and the owner of same looked at it nervously every little while. Once or twice he opened his mouth like he was going to say something, but thought better of it. Finally Cosset spoke up.

"That's plenty," he says to Quolt. "The treatment's worked grand and you don't have to stay in this stuffy hole no longer. I've got a swell name for my play already. It's going to be named 'What of It?' "

Mr. Quolt removed his glance from Lacey's knee and looked at Cosset.

"What did you say?" he asked him.

RING LARDNER: BIBLIOGRAPHY

As a popular journalist for over 25 years, Ring Lardner wrote many more articles, humorous columns, short stories, sports pieces and satires than have ever been collected in book form. The best complete bibliography is by Howard W. Webb, which is reproduced in part in Donald Elder's biography: *Ring Lardner*. A collection of Lardner's short stories originally appeared under the title *Round Up*. Two volumes of selected stories are now available: in hard cover *The Best Short Stories of Ring Lardner* and in paperback *Haircut and Other Stories*. *You know Me Al* was reissued in 1960, with an introduction by John Lardner; and in 1962 a selection of plays, articles and parodies was published under the title *Shut Up, He Explained*. The following bibliography includes these volumes along with Lardner's chief books and dates:

BIB BALLADS   *1915*

YOU KNOW ME AL   *1916*

GULLIBLE'S TRAVELS   *1917*

TREAT 'EM ROUGH   *1918*

OWN YOUR OWN HOME   *1919*

THE REAL DOPE   *1919*

THE YOUNG IMMIGRUNTS   *1920*

THE BIG TOWN   *1921*

SYMPTOMS OF BEING 35   *1921*

SAY IT WITH OIL   *1923*

HOW TO WRITE SHORT STORIES   *1924*

WHAT OF IT?   *1925*

THE LOVE NEST AND OTHER STORIES   *1926*

THE STORY OF A WONDER MAN   *1927*

ROUND UP   *1929*

JUNE MOON   *1930*
    (with George S. Kaufman)

LOSE WITH A SMILE   *1933*

FIRST AND LAST   *1934*
    Edited by Gilbert Seldes

THE COLLECTED SHORT STORIES OF RING LARDNER   *1941*
    (Modern Library edition)

THE PORTABLE RING LARDNER   *1946*
    Edited by Gilbert Seldes

RING LARDNER: A BIOGRAPHY   *1956*
    by Donald Elder

SHUT UP, HE EXPLAINED   *1962*
    Edited by Babette Rosmond and Henry Morgan

THE RING LARDNER READER   *1963*
    Edited by Maxwell Geismar